Some Physical Constants

Quantity	Symbol	Value[a]
Atomic mass unit	u	$1.660\ 538\ 86\ (28) \times 10^{-27}$ kg
		$931.494\ 043\ (80)$ MeV/c^2
Avogadro's number	N_A	$6.022\ 141\ 5\ (10) \times 10^{23}$ particles/mol
Bohr magneton	$\mu_B = \dfrac{e\hbar}{2m_e}$	$9.274\ 009\ 49\ (80) \times 10^{-24}$ J/T
Bohr radius	$a_0 = \dfrac{\hbar^2}{m_e e^2 k_e}$	$5.291\ 772\ 108\ (18) \times 10^{-11}$ m
Boltzmann's constant	$k_B = \dfrac{R}{N_A}$	$1.380\ 650\ 5\ (24) \times 10^{-23}$ J/K
Compton wavelength	$\lambda_C = \dfrac{h}{m_e c}$	$2.426\ 310\ 238\ (16) \times 10^{-12}$ m
Coulomb constant	$k_e = \dfrac{1}{4\pi\epsilon_0}$	$8.987\ 551\ 788 \ldots \times 10^9$ N$\cdot$m^2/C^2 (exact)
Deuteron mass	m_d	$3.343\ 583\ 35\ (57) \times 10^{-27}$ kg
		$2.013\ 553\ 212\ 70\ (35)$ u
Electron mass	m_e	$9.109\ 382\ 6\ (16) \times 10^{-31}$ kg
		$5.485\ 799\ 094\ 5\ (24) \times 10^{-4}$ u
		$0.510\ 998\ 918\ (44)$ MeV/c^2
Electron volt	eV	$1.602\ 176\ 53\ (14) \times 10^{-19}$ J
Elementary charge	e	$1.602\ 176\ 53\ (14) \times 10^{-19}$ C
Gas constant	R	$8.314\ 472\ (15)$ J/mol$\cdot$K
Gravitational constant	G	$6.674\ 2\ (10) \times 10^{-11}$ N$\cdot$m^2/kg^2
Josephson frequency–voltage ratio	$\dfrac{2e}{h}$	$4.835\ 978\ 79\ (41) \times 10^{14}$ Hz/V
Magnetic flux quantum	$\Phi_0 = \dfrac{h}{2e}$	$2.067\ 833\ 72\ (18) \times 10^{-15}$ T$\cdot$m^2
Neutron mass	m_n	$1.674\ 927\ 28\ (29) \times 10^{-27}$ kg
		$1.008\ 664\ 915\ 60\ (55)$ u
		$939.565\ 360\ (81)$ MeV/c^2
Nuclear magneton	$\mu_n = \dfrac{e\hbar}{2m_p}$	$5.050\ 783\ 43\ (43) \times 10^{-27}$ J/T
Permeability of free space	μ_0	$4\pi \times 10^{-7}$ T$\cdot$m/A (exact)
Permittivity of free space	$\epsilon_0 = \dfrac{1}{\mu_0 c^2}$	$8.854\ 187\ 817 \ldots \times 10^{-12}$ C^2/N$\cdot$m^2 (exact)
Planck's constant	h	$6.626\ 069\ 3\ (11) \times 10^{-34}$ J$\cdot$s
	$\hbar = \dfrac{h}{2\pi}$	$1.054\ 571\ 68\ (18) \times 10^{-34}$ J$\cdot$s
Proton mass	m_p	$1.672\ 621\ 71\ (29) \times 10^{-27}$ kg
		$1.007\ 276\ 466\ 88\ (13)$ u
		$938.272\ 029\ (80)$ MeV/c^2
Rydberg constant	R_H	$1.097\ 373\ 156\ 852\ 5\ (73) \times 10^7$ m^{-1}
Speed of light in vacuum	c	$2.997\ 924\ 58 \times 10^8$ m/s (exact)

Note: These constants are the values recommended in 2002 by CODATA, based on a least-squares adjustment of data from different measurements. For a more complete list, see P. J. Mohr and B. N. Taylor, "CODATA Recommended Values of the Fundamental Physical Constants: 2002." *Rev. Mod. Phys.* **77**:1, 2005.

[a] The numbers in parentheses for the values represent the uncertainties of the last two digits.

Solar System Data

Body	Mass (kg)	Mean Radius (m)	Period (s)	Distance from the Sun (m)
Mercury	3.18×10^{23}	2.43×10^6	7.60×10^6	5.79×10^{10}
Venus	4.88×10^{24}	6.06×10^6	1.94×10^7	1.08×10^{11}
Earth	5.98×10^{24}	6.37×10^6	3.156×10^7	1.496×10^{11}
Mars	6.42×10^{23}	3.37×10^6	5.94×10^7	2.28×10^{11}
Jupiter	1.90×10^{27}	6.99×10^7	3.74×10^8	7.78×10^{11}
Saturn	5.68×10^{26}	5.85×10^7	9.35×10^8	1.43×10^{12}
Uranus	8.68×10^{25}	2.33×10^7	2.64×10^9	2.87×10^{12}
Neptune	1.03×10^{26}	2.21×10^7	5.22×10^9	4.50×10^{12}
Pluto[a]	$\approx 1.4 \times 10^{22}$	$\approx 1.5 \times 10^6$	7.82×10^9	5.91×10^{12}
Moon	7.36×10^{22}	1.74×10^6	—	—
Sun	1.991×10^{30}	6.96×10^8	—	—

[a] In August 2006, the International Astronomical Union adopted a definition of a planet that separates Pluto from the other eight planets. Pluto is now defined as a "dwarf planet" (like the asteroid Ceres).

Physical Data Often Used

Average Earth–Moon distance	3.84×10^8 m
Average Earth–Sun distance	1.496×10^{11} m
Average radius of the Earth	6.37×10^6 m
Density of air (20°C and 1 atm)	1.20 kg/m^3
Density of water (20°C and 1 atm)	1.00×10^3 kg/m^3
Free-fall acceleration	9.80 m/s^2
Mass of the Earth	5.98×10^{24} kg
Mass of the Moon	7.36×10^{22} kg
Mass of the Sun	1.99×10^{30} kg
Standard atmospheric pressure	1.013×10^5 Pa

Note: These values are the ones used in the text.

Some Prefixes for Powers of Ten

Power	Prefix	Abbreviation	Power	Prefix	Abbreviation
10^{-24}	yocto	y	10^1	deka	da
10^{-21}	zepto	z	10^2	hecto	h
10^{-18}	atto	a	10^3	kilo	k
10^{-15}	femto	f	10^6	mega	M
10^{-12}	pico	p	10^9	giga	G
10^{-9}	nano	n	10^{12}	tera	T
10^{-6}	micro	μ	10^{15}	peta	P
10^{-3}	milli	m	10^{18}	exa	E
10^{-2}	centi	c	10^{21}	zetta	Z
10^{-1}	deci	d	10^{24}	yotta	Y

PHYSICS
for Scientists and Engineers

PHYSICS

for Scientists and Engineers

2 Chapters 15–22

Seventh Edition

Raymond A. Serway

Emeritus, James Madison University

John W. Jewett, Jr.

California State Polytechnic University, Pomona

THOMSON

BROOKS/COLE

Australia • Brazil • Canada • Mexico • Singapore • Spain • United Kingdom • United States

THOMSON

BROOKS/COLE

Physics for Scientists and Engineers, Chapters 15–22, Seventh Edition
Raymond A. Serway and John W. Jewett, Jr.

Physics Acquisition Editor: Chris Hall
Publisher: David Harris
Vice President, Editor-in-Chief, Sciences: Michelle Julet
Development Editor: Ed Dodd
Assistant Editor: Brandi Kirksey
Editorial Assistant: Shawn Vasquez
Technology Project Manager: Sam Subity
Marketing Manager: Mark Santee
Marketing Assistant: Melissa Wong
Managing Marketing Communications Manager: Bryan Vann
Project Manager, Editorial Production: Teri Hyde
Creative Director: Rob Hugel
Art Director: Lee Friedman
Print Buyers: Barbara Britton, Karen Hunt

Permissions Editors: Joohee Lee, Bob Kauser
Production Service: Lachina Publishing Services
Text Designer: Patrick Devine Design
Photo Researcher: Jane Sanders Miller
Copy Editor: Kathleen Lafferty
Illustrator: Rolin Graphics, Progressive Information
  Technologies, Lachina Publishing Services
Cover Designer: Patrick Devine Design
Cover Image: Front: © 2005 Tony Dunn; Back: © 2005 Kurt
  Hoffmann, Abra Marketing
Cover Printer: R.R. Donnelley/Willard
Compositor: Lachina Publishing Services
Printer: R.R. Donnelley/Willard

Printed in the United States of America
1 2 3 4 5 6 7 11 10 09 08 07

Library of Congress Control Number: 2006936870

ISBN-13: 978-0-495-11235-8
ISBN-10: 0-495-11235-6

Thomson Higher Education
10 Davis Drive
Belmont, CA 94002-3098
USA

For more information about our products, contact us at:

Thomson Learning Academic Resource Center
(+1) 1-800-423-0563

For permission to use material from this text or product,
submit a request online at
http://www.thomsonrights.com.

Any additional questions about permissions can be
submitted by e-mail to **thomsonrights@thomson.com.**

John W. Jewett, Jr.

Courtesy of NASA

© Thomson Learning/Charles D. Winters

Courtesy of Henry Leap and Jim Lehman

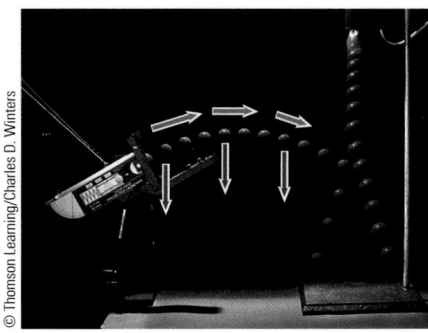

© Thomson Learning/Charles D. Winters

ix

NASA

© Thomson Learning/George Sample

© Thomson Learning/Charles D. Winters

© Thomson Learning/Charles D. Winters

We dedicate this book to our wives
Elizabeth and Lisa and all our children
and grandchildren for their loving
understanding when we spent time on
writing instead of being with them.

Raymond A. Serway received his doctorate at Illinois Institute of Technology and is Professor Emeritus at James Madison University. In 1990, he received the Madison Scholar Award at James Madison University, where he taught for 17 years. Dr. Serway began his teaching career at Clarkson University, where he conducted research and taught from 1967 to 1980. He was the recipient of the Distinguished Teaching Award at Clarkson University in 1977 and of the Alumni Achievement Award from Utica College in 1985. As Guest Scientist at the IBM Research Laboratory in Zurich, Switzerland, he worked with K. Alex Müller, 1987 Nobel Prize recipient. Dr. Serway also was a visiting scientist at Argonne National Laboratory, where he collaborated with his mentor and friend, Sam Marshall. In addition to earlier editions of this textbook, Dr. Serway is the coauthor of *Principles of Physics,* fourth edition; *College Physics,* seventh edition; *Essentials of College Physics;* and *Modern Physics,* third edition. He also is the coauthor of the high school textbook *Physics,* published by Holt, Rinehart, & Winston. In addition, Dr. Serway has published more than 40 research papers in the field of condensed matter physics and has given more than 70 presentations at professional meetings. Dr. Serway and his wife, Elizabeth, enjoy traveling, golf, singing in a church choir, and spending quality time with their four children and eight grandchildren.

John W. Jewett, Jr., earned his doctorate at Ohio State University, specializing in optical and magnetic properties of condensed matter. Dr. Jewett began his academic career at Richard Stockton College of New Jersey, where he taught from 1974 to 1984. He is currently Professor of Physics at California State Polytechnic University, Pomona. Throughout his teaching career, Dr. Jewett has been active in promoting science education. In addition to receiving four National Science Foundation grants, he helped found and direct the Southern California Area Modern Physics Institute. He also directed Science IMPACT (Institute for Modern Pedagogy and Creative Teaching), which works with teachers and schools to develop effective science curricula. Dr. Jewett's honors include the Stockton Merit Award at Richard Stockton College in 1980, the Outstanding Professor Award at California State Polytechnic University for 1991–1992, and the Excellence in Undergraduate Physics Teaching Award from the American Association of Physics Teachers in 1998. He has given more than 80 presentations at professional meetings, including presentations at international conferences in China and Japan. In addition to his work on this textbook, he is coauthor of *Principles of Physics,* fourth edition, with Dr. Serway and author of *The World of Physics . . . Mysteries, Magic, and Myth.* Dr. Jewett enjoys playing keyboard with his all-physicist band, traveling, and collecting antiques that can be used as demonstration apparatus in physics lectures. Most importantly, he relishes spending time with his wife, Lisa, and their children and grandchildren.

In writing this seventh edition of *Physics for Scientists and Engineers*, we continue our ongoing efforts to improve the clarity of presentation and include new pedagogical features that help support the learning and teaching processes. Drawing on positive feedback from users of the sixth edition and reviewers' suggestions, we have refined the text to better meet the needs of students and teachers.

This textbook is intended for a course in introductory physics for students majoring in science or engineering. The entire contents of the book in its extended version could be covered in a three-semester course, but it is possible to use the material in shorter sequences with the omission of selected chapters and sections. The mathematical background of the student taking this course should ideally include one semester of calculus. If that is not possible, the student should be enrolled in a concurrent course in introductory calculus.

Objectives

This introductory physics textbook has two main objectives: to provide the student with a clear and logical presentation of the basic concepts and principles of physics and to strengthen an understanding of the concepts and principles through a broad range of interesting applications to the real world. To meet these objectives, we have placed emphasis on sound physical arguments and problem-solving methodology. At the same time, we have attempted to motivate the student through practical examples that demonstrate the role of physics in other disciplines, including engineering, chemistry, and medicine.

Changes in the Seventh Edition

A large number of changes and improvements have been made in preparing the seventh edition of this text. Some of the new features are based on our experiences and on current trends in science education. Other changes have been incorporated in response to comments and suggestions offered by users of the sixth edition and by reviewers of the manuscript. The features listed here represent the major changes in the seventh edition.

QUESTIONS AND PROBLEMS A substantial revision to the end-of-chapter questions and problems was made in an effort to improve their variety, interest, and pedagogical value, while maintaining their clarity and quality. Approximately 23% of the questions and problems are new or substantially changed. Several of the questions for each chapter are in objective format. Several problems in each chapter explicitly ask for qualitative reasoning in some parts as well as for quantitative answers in other parts:

> 19. ● Assume a parcel of air in a straight tube moves with a constant acceleration of -4.00 m/s^2 and has a velocity of 13.0 m/s at 10:05:00 a.m. on a certain date. (a) What is its velocity at 10:05:01 a.m.? (b) At 10:05:02 a.m.? (c) At 10:05:02.5 a.m.? (d) At 10:05:04 a.m.? (e) At 10:04:59 a.m.? (f) Describe the shape of a graph of velocity versus time for this parcel of air. (g) Argue for or against the statement, "Knowing the single value of an object's constant acceleration is like knowing a whole list of values for its velocity."

© Thomson Learning/ Charles D. Winters

WORKED EXAMPLES All in-text worked examples have been recast and are now presented in a two-column format to better reinforce physical concepts. The left column shows textual information that describes the steps for solving the problem. The right column shows the mathematical manipulations and results of taking these steps. This layout facilitates matching the concept with its mathematical execution and helps students organize their work. These reconstituted examples closely follow a General Problem-Solving Strategy introduced in Chapter 2 to reinforce effective problem-solving habits. A sample of a worked example can be found on the next page.

Each solution has been reconstituted to more closely follow the General Problem-Solving Strategy as outlined in Chapter 2, to reinforce good problem-solving habits.

Each step of the solution is detailed in a two-column format. The left column provides an explanation for each mathematical step in the right column, to better reinforce the physical concepts.

EXAMPLE 3.2 | A Vacation Trip

A car travels 20.0 km due north and then 35.0 km in a direction 60.0° west of north as shown in Figure 3.11a. Find the magnitude and direction of the car's resultant displacement.

SOLUTION

Conceptualize The vectors $\vec{A}$ and $\vec{B}$ drawn in Figure 3.11a help us conceptualize the problem.

Categorize We can categorize this example as a simple analysis problem in vector addition. The displacement $\vec{R}$ is the resultant when the two individual displacements $\vec{A}$ and $\vec{B}$ are added. We can further categorize it as a problem about the analysis of triangles, so we appeal to our expertise in geometry and trigonometry.

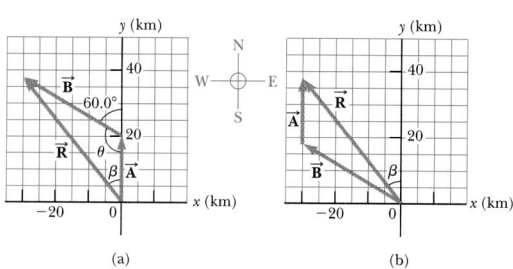

Figure 3.11 (Example 3.2) (a) Graphical method for finding the resultant displacement vector $\vec{R} = \vec{A} + \vec{B}$. (b) Adding the vectors in reverse order ($\vec{B} + \vec{A}$) gives the same result for $\vec{R}$.

Analyze In this example, we show two ways to analyze the problem of finding the resultant of two vectors. The first way is to solve the problem geometrically, using graph paper and a protractor to measure the magnitude of $\vec{R}$ and its direction in Figure 3.11a. (In fact, even when you know you are going to be carrying out a calculation, you should sketch the vectors to check your results.) With an ordinary ruler and protractor, a large diagram typically gives answers to two-digit but not to three-digit precision.

The second way to solve the problem is to analyze it algebraically. The magnitude of $\vec{R}$ can be obtained from the law of cosines as applied to the triangle (see Appendix B.4).

Use $R^2 = A^2 + B^2 - 2AB \cos \theta$ from the law of cosines to find R:

$$R = \sqrt{A^2 + B^2 - 2AB \cos \theta}$$

Substitute numerical values, noting that $\theta = 180° - 60° = 120°$:

$$R = \sqrt{(20.0 \text{ km})^2 + (35.0 \text{ km})^2 - 2(20.0 \text{ km})(35.0 \text{ km}) \cos 120°}$$

$$= \boxed{48.2 \text{ km}}$$

Use the law of sines (Appendix B.4) to find the direction of $\vec{R}$ measured from the northerly direction:

$$\frac{\sin \beta}{B} = \frac{\sin \theta}{R}$$

$$\sin \beta = \frac{B}{R} \sin \theta = \frac{35.0 \text{ km}}{48.2 \text{ km}} \sin 120° = 0.629$$

$$\beta = \boxed{38.9°}$$

The resultant displacement of the car is 48.2 km in a direction 38.9° west of north.

Finalize Does the angle β that we calculated agree with an estimate made by looking at Figure 3.11a or with an actual angle measured from the diagram using the graphical method? Is it reasonable that the magnitude of $\vec{R}$ is larger than that of both $\vec{A}$ and $\vec{B}$? Are the units of $\vec{R}$ correct?

Although the graphical method of adding vectors works well, it suffers from two disadvantages. First, some people find using the laws of cosines and sines to be awkward. Second, a triangle only results if you are adding two vectors. If you are adding three or more vectors, the resulting geometric shape is usually not a triangle. In Section 3.4, we explore a new method of adding vectors that will address both of these disadvantages.

What If? Suppose the trip were taken with the two vectors in reverse order: 35.0 km at 60.0° west of north first and then 20.0 km due north. How would the magnitude and the direction of the resultant vector change?

Answer They would not change. The commutative law for vector addition tells us that the order of vectors in an addition is irrelevant. Graphically, Figure 3.11b shows that the vectors added in the reverse order give us the same resultant vector.

What If? statements appear in about 1/3 of the worked examples and offer a variation on the situation posed in the text of the example. For instance, this feature might explore the effects of changing the conditions of the situation, determine what happens when a quantity is taken to a particular limiting value, or question whether additional information can be determined about the problem situation. This feature encourages students to think about the results of the example and assists in conceptual understanding of the principles.

All worked examples are also available to be assigned as interactive examples in the Enhanced WebAssign homework management system (visit **www.pse7.com** for more details).

ONLINE HOMEWORK It is now easier to assign online homework with Serway and Jewett and Enhanced WebAssign. All worked examples, end-of-chapter problems, active figures, quick quizzes, and most questions are available in WebAssign. Most problems include hints and feedback to provide instantaneous reinforcement or direction for that problem. In addition to the text content, we have also added math remediation tools to help students get up to speed in algebra, trigonometry, and calculus.

SUMMARIES Each chapter contains a summary that reviews the important concepts and equations discussed in that chapter. A marginal note next to each chapter summary directs students to additional quizzes, animations, and interactive exercises for that chapter on the book's companion Web site. The format of the end-of-chapter summary has been completely revised for this edition. The summary is divided into three sections: Definitions, Concepts and Principles, and Analysis Models for Problem-Solving. In each section, flashcard-type boxes focus on each separate definition, concept, principle, or analysis model.

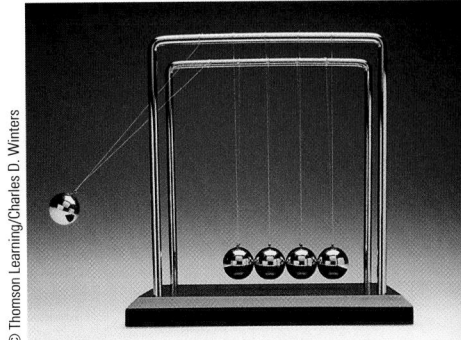

© Thomson Learning/Charles D. Winters

MATH APPENDIX The math appendix, a valuable tool for students, has been updated to show the math tools in a physics context. This resource is ideal for students who need a quick review on topics such as algebra, trigonometry, and calculus.

CONTENT CHANGES The content and organization of the textbook are essentially the same as in the sixth edition. Many sections in various chapters have been streamlined, deleted, or combined with other sections to allow for a more balanced presentation. Vectors are now denoted in boldface with an arrow over them (for example, $\vec{v}$), making them easier to recognize. Chapters 7 and 8 have been completely reorganized to prepare students for a unified approach to energy that is used throughout the text. A new section in Chapter 9 teaches students how to analyze deformable systems with the conservation of energy equation and the impulse-momentum theorem. Chapter 34 is longer than in the sixth edition because of the movement into that chapter of the material on displacement current from Chapter 30 and Maxwell's equations from Chapter 31. A more detailed list of content changes can be found on the instructor's companion Web site.

Content

The material in this book covers fundamental topics in classical physics and provides an introduction to modern physics. The book is divided into six parts. Part 1 (Chapters 1 to 14) deals with the fundamentals of Newtonian mechanics and the physics of fluids; Part 2 (Chapters 15 to 18) covers oscillations, mechanical waves, and sound; Part 3 (Chapters 19 to 22) addresses heat and thermodynamics; Part 4 (Chapters 23 to 34) treats electricity and magnetism; Part 5 (Chapters 35 to 38) covers light and optics; and Part 6 (Chapters 39 to 46) deals with relativity and modern physics.

Text Features

Most instructors believe that the textbook selected for a course should be the student's primary guide for understanding and learning the subject matter. Furthermore, the textbook should be easily accessible and should be styled and written to facilitate instruction and learning. With these points in mind, we have included many pedagogical features, listed below, that are intended to enhance its usefulness to both students and instructors.

Problem Solving and Conceptual Understanding

GENERAL PROBLEM-SOLVING STRATEGY A general strategy outlined at the end of Chapter 2 provides students with a structured process for solving problems. In all remaining chapters, the strategy is employed explicitly in every example so that students learn how it is applied. Students are encouraged to follow this strategy when working end-of-chapter problems.

MODELING   Although students are faced with hundreds of problems during their physics courses, instructors realize that a relatively small number of physical situations form the basis of these problems. When faced with a new problem, a physicist forms a *model* of the problem that can be solved in a simple way by identifying the common physical situation that occurs in the problem. For example, many problems involve particles under constant acceleration, isolated systems, or waves under refraction. Because the physicist has studied these situations extensively and understands the associated behavior, he or she can apply this knowledge as a model for solving a new problem. In certain chapters, this edition identifies Analysis Models, which are physical situations (such as the particle under constant acceleration, the isolated system, or the wave under refraction) that occur so often that they can be used as a model for solving an unfamiliar problem. These models are discussed in the chapter text, and the student is reminded of them in the end-of-chapter summary under the heading "Analysis Models for Problem-Solving."

PROBLEMS   An extensive set of problems is included at the end of each chapter; in all, the text contains approximately three thousand problems. Answers to odd-numbered problems are provided at the end of the book. For the convenience of both the student and the instructor, about two-thirds of the problems are keyed to specific sections of the chapter. The remaining problems, labeled "Additional Problems," are not keyed to specific sections. The problem numbers for straightforward problems are printed in black, intermediate-level problems are in blue, and challenging problems are in magenta.

- **"Not-just-a-number" problems** Each chapter includes several marked problems that require students to think qualitatively in some parts and quantitatively in others. Instructors can assign such problems to guide students to display deeper understanding, practice good problem-solving techniques, and prepare for exams.
- **Problems for developing symbolic reasoning** Each chapter contains problems that ask for solutions in symbolic form as well as many problems asking for numerical answers. To help students develop skill in symbolic reasoning, each chapter contains a pair of otherwise identical problems, one asking for a numerical solution and one asking for a symbolic derivation. In this edition, each chapter also contains a problem giving a numerical value for every datum but one so that the answer displays how the unknown depends on the datum represented symbolically. The answer to such a problem has the form of a function of one variable. Reasoning about the behavior of this function puts emphasis on the *Finalize* step of the General Problem-Solving Strategy. All problems developing symbolic reasoning are identified by a tan background screen:

> 53. ● A light spring has an unstressed length of 15.5 cm. It is described by Hooke's law with spring constant 4.30 N/m. One end of the horizontal spring is held on a fixed vertical axle, and the other end is attached to a puck of mass *m* that can move without friction over a horizontal surface. The puck is set into motion in a circle with a period of 1.30 s. (a) Find the extension of the spring *x* as it depends on *m*. Evaluate *x* for (b) *m* = 0.070 0 kg, (c) *m* = 0.140 kg, (d) *m* = 0.180 kg, and (e) *m* = 0.190 kg. (f) Describe the pattern of variation of *x* as it depends on *m*.

- **Review problems** Many chapters include review problems requiring the student to combine concepts covered in the chapter with those discussed in previous chapters. These problems reflect the cohesive nature of the principles in the text and verify that physics is not a scattered set of ideas. When facing a real-world issue such as global warming or nuclear weapons, it may be necessary to call on ideas in physics from several parts of a textbook such as this one.
- **"Fermi problems"** As in previous editions, at least one problem in each chapter asks the student to reason in order-of-magnitude terms.

- **Design problems** Several chapters contain problems that ask the student to determine design parameters for a practical device so that it can function as required.
- **"*Jeopardy!*" problems** Some chapters give students practice in changing between different representations by stating equations and asking for a description of a situation to which they apply as well as for a numerical answer.
- **Calculus-based problems** Every chapter contains at least one problem applying ideas and methods from differential calculus and one problem using integral calculus.

The instructor's Web site, **www.thomsonedu.com/physics/serway,** provides lists of problems using calculus, problems encouraging or requiring computer use, problems with "What If?" parts, problems referred to in the chapter text, problems based on experimental data, order-of-magnitude problems, problems about biological applications, design problems, *Jeopardy!* problems, review problems, problems reflecting historical reasoning about confusing ideas, problems developing symbolic reasoning skill, problems with qualitative parts, ranking questions, and other objective questions.

QUESTIONS The questions section at the end of each chapter has been significantly revised. Multiple-choice, ranking, and true–false questions have been added. The instructor may select items to assign as homework or use in the classroom, possibly with "peer instruction" methods and possibly with "clicker" systems. More than eight hundred questions are included in this edition. Answers to selected questions are included in the *Student Solutions Manual/Study Guide*, and answers to all questions are found in the *Instructor's Solutions Manual*.

---

19. **O (i)** Rank the gravitational accelerations you would measure for (a) a 2-kg object 5 cm above the floor, (b) a 2-kg object 120 cm above the floor, (c) a 3-kg object 120 cm above the floor, and (d) a 3-kg object 80 cm above the floor. List the one with the largest-magnitude acceleration first. If two are equal, show their equality in your list. **(ii)** Rank the gravitational forces on the same four objects, largest magnitude first. **(iii)** Rank the gravitational potential energies (of the object–Earth system) for the same four objects, largest first, taking $y = 0$ at the floor.

23. **O** An ice cube has been given a push and slides without friction on a level table. Which is correct? (a) It is in stable equilibrium. (b) It is in unstable equilibrium. (c) It is in neutral equilibrium (d) It is not in equilibrium.

WORKED EXAMPLES Two types of worked examples are presented to aid student comprehension. All worked examples in the text may be assigned for homework in WebAssign.

The first example type presents a problem and numerical answer. As discussed earlier, solutions to these examples have been altered in this edition to feature a two-column layout to explain the physical concepts and the mathematical steps side by side. Every example follows the explicit steps of the General Problem-Solving Strategy outlined in Chapter 2.

The second type of example is conceptual in nature. To accommodate increased emphasis on understanding physical concepts, the many conceptual examples are labeled as such, set off in boxes, and designed to focus students on the physical situation in the problem.

WHAT IF? Approximately one-third of the worked examples in the text contain a **What If?** feature. At the completion of the example solution, a **What If?** question offers a variation on the situation posed in the text of the example. For instance, this feature might explore the effects of changing the conditions of the situation, determine what happens when a quantity is taken to a particular limiting value, or question whether additional information can be determined about the situation. This feature encourages students to think about the results of the example, and it also assists in conceptual understanding of the principles. **What If?** questions also prepare students to encounter novel problems that may be included on exams. Some of the end-of-chapter problems also include this feature.

QUICK QUIZZES   Quick Quizzes provide students an opportunity to test their understanding of the physical concepts presented. The questions require students to make decisions on the basis of sound reasoning, and some of the questions have been written to help students overcome common misconceptions. Quick Quizzes have been cast in an objective format, including multiple-choice, true–false, and ranking. Answers to all Quick Quiz questions are found at the end of each chapter. Additional Quick Quizzes that can be used in classroom teaching are available on the instructor's companion Web site. Many instructors choose to use such questions in a "peer instruction" teaching style or with the use of personal response system "clickers," but they can be used in standard quiz format as well. Quick Quizzes are set off from the text by horizontal lines:

Quick Quiz 7.5   A dart is loaded into a spring-loaded toy dart gun by pushing the spring in by a distance x. For the next loading, the spring is compressed a distance $2x$. How much faster does the second dart leave the gun compared with the first? (a) four times as fast   (b) two times as fast   (c) the same   (d) half as fast   (e) one-fourth as fast

---

PITFALL PREVENTION 16.2
Two Kinds of Speed/Velocity

Do not confuse v, the speed of the wave as it propagates along the string, with v_y, the transverse velocity of a point on the string. The speed v is constant for a uniform medium, whereas v_y varies sinusoidally.

PITFALL PREVENTIONS   More than two hundred Pitfall Preventions (such as the one to the left) are provided to help students avoid common mistakes and misunderstandings. These features, which are placed in the margins of the text, address both common student misconceptions and situations in which students often follow unproductive paths.

Helpful Features

STYLE   To facilitate rapid comprehension, we have written the book in a clear, logical, and engaging style. We have chosen a writing style that is somewhat informal and relaxed so that students will find the text appealing and enjoyable to read. New terms are carefully defined, and we have avoided the use of jargon.

IMPORTANT STATEMENTS AND EQUATIONS   Most important statements and definitions are set in **boldface** or are highlighted with a background screen for added emphasis and ease of review. Similarly, important equations are highlighted with a background screen to facilitate location.

MARGINAL NOTES   Comments and notes appearing in the margin with a ▶ icon can be used to locate important statements, equations, and concepts in the text.

PEDAGOGICAL USE OF COLOR   Readers should consult the **pedagogical color chart** (inside the front cover) for a listing of the color-coded symbols used in the text diagrams. This system is followed consistently throughout the text.

MATHEMATICAL LEVEL   We have introduced calculus gradually, keeping in mind that students often take introductory courses in calculus and physics concurrently. Most steps are shown when basic equations are developed, and reference is often made to mathematical appendices near the end of the textbook. Vector products are introduced later in the text, where they are needed in physical applications. The dot product is introduced in Chapter 7, which addresses energy of a system; the cross product is introduced in Chapter 11, which deals with angular momentum.

SIGNIFICANT FIGURES   Significant figures in both worked examples and end-of-chapter problems have been handled with care. Most numerical examples are worked to either two or three significant figures, depending on the precision of the data provided. End-of-chapter problems regularly state data and answers to three-digit precision.

UNITS The international system of units (SI) is used throughout the text. The U.S. customary system of units is used only to a limited extent in the chapters on mechanics and thermodynamics.

APPENDICES AND ENDPAPERS Several appendices are provided near the end of the textbook. Most of the appendix material represents a review of mathematical concepts and techniques used in the text, including scientific notation, algebra, geometry, trigonometry, differential calculus, and integral calculus. Reference to these appendices is made throughout the text. Most mathematical review sections in the appendices include worked examples and exercises with answers. In addition to the mathematical reviews, the appendices contain tables of physical data, conversion factors, and the SI units of physical quantities as well as a periodic table of the elements. Other useful information—fundamental constants and physical data, planetary data, a list of standard prefixes, mathematical symbols, the Greek alphabet, and standard abbreviations of units of measure—appears on the endpapers.

Course Solutions That Fit Your Teaching Goals and Your Students' Learning Needs

Recent advances in educational technology have made homework management systems and audience response systems powerful and affordable tools to enhance the way you teach your course. Whether you offer a more traditional text-based course, are interested in using or are currently using an online homework management system such as WebAssign, or are ready to turn your lecture into an interactive learning environment with JoinIn on TurningPoint, you can be confident that the text's proven content provides the foundation for each and every component of our technology and ancillary package.

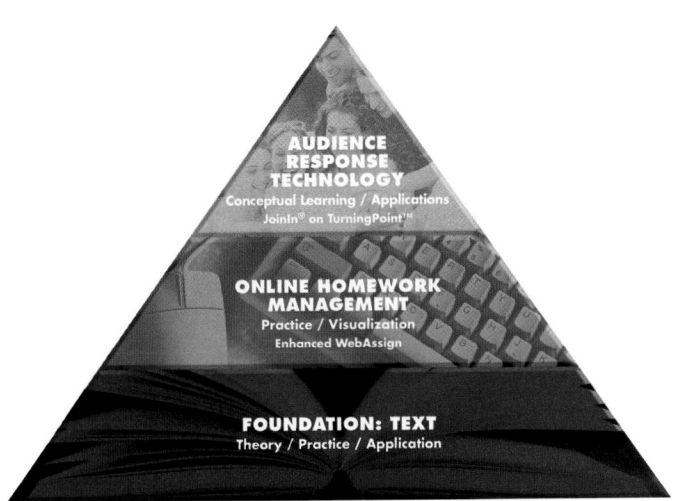

Homework Management Systems

Enhanced WebAssign Whether you're an experienced veteran or a beginner, Enhanced WebAssign is the perfect solution to fit your homework management needs. Designed by physicists for physicists, this system is a reliable and user-friendly teaching companion. Enhanced WebAssign is available for *Physics for Scientists and Engineers*, giving you the freedom to assign

- every end-of-chapter Problem and Question, enhanced with hints and feedback
- every worked example, enhanced with hints and feedback, to help strengthen students' problem-solving skills
- every Quick Quiz, giving your students ample opportunity to test their conceptual understanding.

- animated Active Figures, enhanced with hints and feedback, to help students develop their visualization skills
- a math review to help students brush up on key quantitative concepts

Please visit **www.thomsonedu.com/physics/serway** to view a live demonstration of Enhanced WebAssign.

The text also supports the following Homework Management Systems:

LON-CAPA: A Computer-Assisted Personalized Approach
    http://www.lon-capa.org/

The University of Texas Homework Service
    contact **moore@physics.utexas.edu**

Personal Response Systems

JoinIn on TurningPoint Pose book-specific questions and display students' answers seamlessly within the Microsoft® PowerPoint slides of your own lecture in conjunction with the "clicker" hardware of your choice. JoinIn on TurningPoint works with most infrared or radio frequency keypad systems, including Responsecard, EduCue, H-ITT, and even laptops. Contact your local sales representative to learn more about our personal response software and hardware.

Personal Response System Content Regardless of the response system you are using, we provide the tested content to support it. Our ready-to-go content includes all the questions from the Quick Quizzes, test questions, and a selection of end-of-chapter questions to provide helpful conceptual checkpoints to drop into your lecture. Our series of Active Figure animations have also been enhanced with multiple-choice questions to help test students' observational skills.

We also feature the Assessing to Learn in the Classroom content from the University of Massachusetts at Amherst. This collection of 250 advanced conceptual questions has been tested in the classroom for more than ten years and takes peer learning to a new level.

Visit **www.thomsonedu.com/physics/serway** to download samples of our personal response system content.

Lecture Presentation Resources

The following resources provide support for your presentations in lecture.

MULTIMEDIA MANAGER INSTRUCTOR'S RESOURCE CD   An easy-to-use multimedia lecture tool, the Multimedia Manager Instructor's Resource CD allows you to quickly assemble art, animations, digital video, and database files with notes to create fluid lectures. The two-volume set (Volume 1: Chapters 1–22; Volume 2: Chapters 23–46) includes prebuilt PowerPoint lectures, a database of animations, video clips, and digital art from the text as well as editable electronic files of the *Instructor's Solutions Manual* and *Test Bank*.

TRANSPARENCY ACETATES   Each volume contains approximately one hundred transparency acetates featuring art from the text. Volume 1 contains Chapters 1 through 22, and Volume 2 contains Chapters 23 through 46.

Assessment and Course Preparation Resources

A number of resources listed below will assist with your assessment and preparation processes.

INSTRUCTOR'S SOLUTIONS MANUAL by Ralph McGrew. This two-volume manual contains complete worked solutions to all end-of-chapter problems in the textbook as well as answers to the even-numbered problems and all the questions. The solutions to problems new to the seventh edition are marked for easy identification. Volume 1 contains

Chapters 1 through 22, and Volume 2 contains Chapters 23 through 46. Electronic files of the Instructor's Solutions are available on the Multimedia Manager CD as well.

PRINTED TEST BANK by Edward Adelson. This two-volume test bank contains approximately 2 200 multiple-choice questions. These questions are also available in electronic format with complete answers and solutions in the ExamView test software and as editable Word® files on the Multimedia Manager CD. Volume 1 contains Chapters 1 through 22, and Volume 2 contains Chapters 23 through 46.

EXAMVIEW This easy-to-use test generator CD features all of the questions from the printed test bank in an editable format.

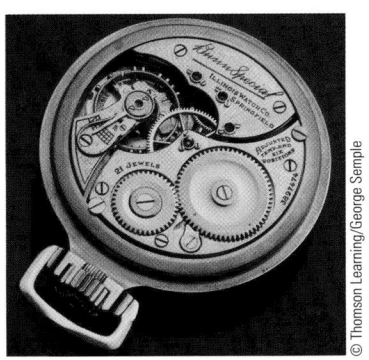

WEBCT AND BLACKBOARD CONTENT For users of either course management system, we provide our test bank questions in the proper format for easy upload into your online course. In addition, you can integrate the ThomsonNOW for Physics student tutorial content into your WebCT or Blackboard course, providing your students a single sign-on to all their Web-based learning resources. Contact your local sales representative to learn more about our WebCT and Blackboard resources.

INSTRUCTOR'S COMPANION WEB SITE Consult the instructor's site by pointing your browser to **www.thomsonedu.com/physics/serway** for additional Quick Quiz questions, a detailed list of content changes since the sixth edition, a problem correlation guide, images from the text, and sample PowerPoint lectures. Instructors adopting the seventh edition of *Physics for Scientists and Engineers* may download these materials after securing the appropriate password from their local Thomson•Brooks/Cole sales representative.

Student Resources

STUDENT SOLUTIONS MANUAL/STUDY GUIDE by John R. Gordon, Ralph McGrew, Raymond Serway, and John W. Jewett, Jr. This two-volume manual features detailed solutions to 20% of the end-of-chapter problems from the text. The manual also features a list of important equations, concepts, and notes from key sections of the text in addition to answers to selected end-of-chapter questions. Volume 1 contains Chapters 1 through 22, and Volume 2 contains Chapters 23 through 46.

THOMSONNOW PERSONAL STUDY This assessment-based student tutorial system provides students with a personalized learning plan based on their performance on a series of diagnostic pre-tests. Rich interactive content, including Active Figures, Coached Problems, and Interactive Examples, helps students prepare for tests and exams.

Teaching Options

The topics in this textbook are presented in the following sequence: classical mechanics, oscillations and mechanical waves, and heat and thermodynamics followed by electricity and magnetism, electromagnetic waves, optics, relativity, and modern physics. This presentation represents a traditional sequence, with the subject of mechanical waves being presented before electricity and magnetism. Some instructors may prefer to discuss both mechanical and electromagnetic waves together after completing electricity and magnetism. In this case, Chapters 16 through 18 could be covered along with Chapter 34. The chapter on relativity is placed near the end of the text because this topic often is treated as an introduction to the era of "modern physics." If time permits, instructors may choose to cover Chapter 39 after completing Chapter 13 as a conclusion to the material on Newtonian mechanics.

For those instructors teaching a two-semester sequence, some sections and chapters could be deleted without any loss of continuity. The following sections can be considered optional for this purpose:

Acknowledgments

This seventh edition of *Physics for Scientists and Engineers* was prepared with the guidance and assistance of many professors who reviewed selections of the manuscript, the prerevision text, or both. We wish to acknowledge the following scholars and express our sincere appreciation for their suggestions, criticisms, and encouragement:

David P. Balogh, *Fresno City College*
Leonard X. Finegold, *Drexel University*
Raymond Hall, *California State University, Fresno*
Bob Jacobsen, *University of California, Berkeley*
Robin Jordan, *Florida Atlantic University*
Rafael Lopez-Mobilia, *University of Texas at San Antonio*
Diana Lininger Markham, *City College of San Francisco*
Steven Morris, *Los Angeles Harbor City College*
Taha Mzoughi, *Kennesaw State University*
Nobel Sanjay Rebello, *Kansas State University*
John Rosendahl, *University of California, Irvine*
Mikolaj Sawicki, *John A. Logan College*

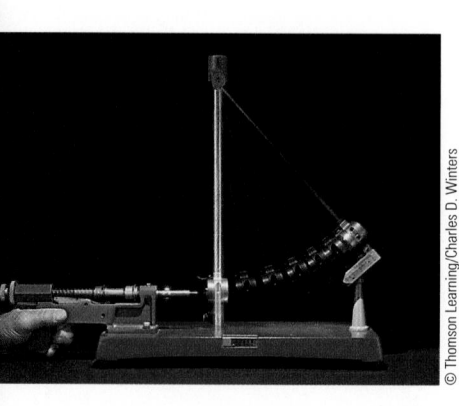

Glenn B. Stracher, *East Georgia College*
Som Tyagi, *Drexel University*
Robert Weidman, *Michigan Technological University*
Edward A. Whittaker, *Stevens Institute of Technology*

This title was carefully checked for accuracy by Zinoviy Akkerman, *City College of New York;* Grant Hart, *Brigham Young University;* Michael Kotlarchyk, *Rochester Institute of Technology;* Andres LaRosa, *Portland State University;* Bruce Mason, *University of Oklahoma at Norman;* Peter Moeck, *Portland State University;* Brian A. Raue, *Florida International University;* James E. Rutledge, *University of California at Irvine;* Bjoern Seipel, *Portland State University;* Z. M. Stadnick, *University of Ottawa;* and Harry W. K. Tom, *University of California at Riverside.* We thank them for their diligent efforts under schedule pressure.

We are grateful to Ralph McGrew for organizing the end-of-chapter problems, writing many new problems, and suggesting improvements in the content of the textbook. Problems and questions new to this edition were written by Duane Deardorff, Thomas Grace, Francisco Izaguirre, John Jewett, Robert Forsythe, Randall Jones, Ralph McGrew, Kurt Vandervoort, and Jerzy Wrobel. Help was very kindly given by Dwight Neuenschwander, Michael Kinney, Amy Smith, Will Mackin, and the Sewer Department of Grand Forks, North Dakota. Daniel Kim, Jennifer Hoffman, Ed Oberhofer, Richard Webb, Wesley Smith, Kevin Kilty, Zinoviy Akkerman, Michael Rudmin, Paul Cox, Robert LaMontagne, Ken Menningen, and Chris Church made corrections to problems taken from previous editions. We are grateful to authors John R. Gordon and Ralph McGrew for preparing the *Student Solutions Manual/Study Guide.* Author Ralph McGrew has prepared an excellent *Instructor's Solutions Manual.* Edward Adelson has carefully edited and improved the test bank. Kurt Vandervoort prepared extra Quick Quiz questions for the instructor's companion Web site.

Special thanks and recognition go to the professional staff at the Brooks/Cole Publishing Company—in particular, Ed Dodd, Brandi Kirksey (who managed the ancillary program and so much more), Shawn Vasquez, Sam Subity, Teri Hyde, Michelle Julet, David Harris, and Chris Hall—for their fine work during the development and production of this textbook. Mark Santee is our seasoned marketing manager, and Bryan Vann coordinates our marketing communications. We recognize the skilled production service and excellent artwork provided by the staff at Lachina Publishing Services, and the dedicated photo research efforts of Jane Sanders Miller.

Finally, we are deeply indebted to our wives, children, and grandchildren for their love, support, and long-term sacrifices.

Raymond A. Serway
St. Petersburg, Florida

John W. Jewett, Jr.
Pomona, California

It is appropriate to offer some words of advice that should be of benefit to you, the student. Before doing so, we assume you have read the Preface, which describes the various features of the text and support materials that will help you through the course.

How to Study

Instructors are often asked, "How should I study physics and prepare for examinations?" There is no simple answer to this question, but we can offer some suggestions based on our own experiences in learning and teaching over the years.

First and foremost, maintain a positive attitude toward the subject matter, keeping in mind that physics is the most fundamental of all natural sciences. Other science courses that follow will use the same physical principles, so it is important that you understand and are able to apply the various concepts and theories discussed in the text.

Concepts and Principles

It is essential that you understand the basic concepts and principles before attempting to solve assigned problems. You can best accomplish this goal by carefully reading the textbook before you attend your lecture on the covered material. When reading the text, you should jot down those points that are not clear to you. Also be sure to make a diligent attempt at answering the questions in the Quick Quizzes as you come to them in your reading. We have worked hard to prepare questions that help you judge for yourself how well you understand the material. Study the **What If?** features that appear in many of the worked examples carefully. They will help you extend your understanding beyond the simple act of arriving at a numerical result. The Pitfall Preventions will also help guide you away from common misunderstandings about physics. During class, take careful notes and ask questions about those ideas that are unclear to you. Keep in mind that few people are able to absorb the full meaning of scientific material after only one reading; several readings of the text and your notes may be necessary. Your lectures and laboratory work supplement the textbook and should clarify some of the more difficult material. You should minimize your memorization of material. Successful memorization of passages from the text, equations, and derivations does not necessarily indicate that you understand the material. Your understanding of the material will be enhanced through a combination of efficient study habits, discussions with other students and with instructors, and your ability to solve the problems presented in the textbook. Ask questions whenever you believe that clarification of a concept is necessary.

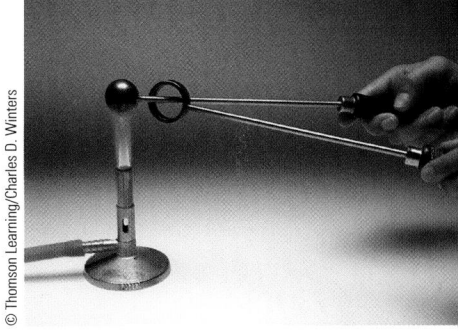
© Thomson Learning/Charles D. Winters

Study Schedule

It is important that you set up a regular study schedule, preferably a daily one. Make sure that you read the syllabus for the course and adhere to the schedule set by your instructor. The lectures will make much more sense if you read the corresponding text material *before* attending them. As a general rule, you should devote about two hours of study time for each hour you are in class. If you are having trouble with the course, seek the advice of the instructor or other students who have taken the course. You may find it necessary to seek further instruction from experienced students. Very often, instructors offer review sessions in addition to regular class periods. Avoid the practice of delaying study until a day or two before an exam. More often than not, this approach has disastrous results. Rather than undertake an all-night study session before a test, briefly review the basic concepts and equations, and then get a good night's rest. If you believe that you need additional help in understanding the concepts, in preparing for exams, or in problem solving, we suggest that you acquire a copy of the *Student Solutions Manual/Study Guide* that accompanies this textbook; this manual should be available at your college bookstore or through the publisher.

Use the Features

You should make full use of the various features of the text discussed in the Preface. For example, marginal notes are useful for locating and describing important equations and concepts, and **boldface** indicates important statements and definitions. Many useful tables are contained in the appendices, but most are incorporated in the text where they are most often referenced. Appendix B is a convenient review of mathematical tools used in the text.

Answers to odd-numbered problems are given at the end of the textbook, answers to Quick Quizzes are located at the end of each chapter, and solutions to selected end-of-chapter questions and problems are provided in the *Student Solutions Manual/Study Guide*. The table of contents provides an overview of the entire text, and the index enables you to locate specific material quickly. Footnotes are sometimes used to supplement the text or to cite other references on the subject discussed.

After reading a chapter, you should be able to define any new quantities introduced in that chapter and discuss the principles and assumptions that were used to arrive at certain key relations. The chapter summaries and the review sections of the *Student Solutions Manual/Study Guide* should help you in this regard. In some cases, you may find it necessary to refer to the textbook's index to locate certain topics. You should be able to associate with each physical quantity the correct symbol used to represent that quantity and the unit in which the quantity is specified. Furthermore, you should be able to express each important equation in concise and accurate prose.

Problem Solving

R. P. Feynman, Nobel laureate in physics, once said, "You do not know anything until you have practiced." In keeping with this statement, we strongly advise you to develop the skills necessary to solve a wide range of problems. Your ability to solve problems will be one of the main tests of your knowledge of physics; therefore, you should try to solve as many problems as possible. It is essential that you understand basic concepts and principles before attempting to solve problems. It is good practice to try to find alternate solutions to the same problem. For example, you can solve problems in mechanics using Newton's laws, but very often an alternative method that draws on energy considerations is more direct. You should not deceive yourself into thinking that you understand a problem merely because you have seen it solved in class. You must be able to solve the problem and similar problems on your own.

The approach to solving problems should be carefully planned. A systematic plan is especially important when a problem involves several concepts. First, read the problem several times until you are confident you understand what is being asked. Look for any key words that will help you interpret the problem and perhaps allow you to make certain assumptions. Your ability to interpret a question properly is an integral part of problem solving. Second, you should acquire the habit of writing down the information given in a problem and those quantities that need to be found; for example, you might construct a table listing both the quantities given and the quantities to be found. This procedure is sometimes used in the worked examples of the textbook. Finally, after you have decided on the method you believe is appropriate for a given problem, proceed with your solution. The General Problem-Solving Strategy will guide you through complex problems. If you follow the steps of this procedure *(Conceptualize, Categorize, Analyze, Finalize),* you will find it easier to come up with a solution and gain more from your efforts. This Strategy, located at the end of Chapter 2, is used in all worked examples in the remaining chapters so that you can learn how to apply it. Specific problem-solving strategies for certain types of situations are included in the text and appear with a blue heading. These specific strategies follow the outline of the General Problem-Solving Strategy.

Often, students fail to recognize the limitations of certain equations or physical laws in a particular situation. It is very important that you understand and remember the assumptions that underlie a particular theory or formalism. For example, certain equations in kinematics apply only to a particle moving with constant acceleration. These equations are not valid for describing motion whose acceleration is not constant such as the motion of an object connected to a spring or the motion of an object through a fluid. Study the Analysis Models for Problem-Solving in the chapter summaries carefully so that you know how each model can be applied to a specific situation.

Experiments

Physics is a science based on experimental observations. Therefore, we recommend that you try to supplement the text by performing various types of "hands-on" experiments either at home or in the laboratory. These experiments can be used to test ideas and models discussed in class or in the textbook. For example, the common Slinky toy is excellent for studying traveling waves, a ball swinging on the end of a long string can be used to investigate pendulum motion, various masses attached to the end of a vertical spring or rubber band can be used to determine their elastic nature, an old pair of Polaroid sunglasses and some discarded lenses and a magnifying glass are the components of various experiments in optics, and an approximate measure of the free-fall acceleration can be determined simply by measuring with a stopwatch the time it takes for a ball to drop from a known height. The list of such experiments is endless. When physical models are not available, be imaginative and try to develop models of your own.

New Media

We strongly encourage you to use the **ThomsonNOW** Web-based learning system that accompanies this textbook. It is far easier to understand physics if you see it in action, and these new materials will enable you to become a part of that action. **Thomson-NOW** media described in the Preface and accessed at **www.thomsonedu.com/physics/serway** feature a three-step learning process consisting of a pre-test, a personalized learning plan, and a post-test.

It is our sincere hope that you will find physics an exciting and enjoyable experience and that you will benefit from this experience, regardless of your chosen profession. Welcome to the exciting world of physics!

The scientist does not study nature because it is useful; he studies it because he delights in it, and he delights in it because it is beautiful. If nature were not beautiful, it would not be worth knowing, and if nature were not worth knowing, life would not be worth living.

—Henri Poincaré

Oscillations and Mechanical Waves

We begin this new part of the text by studying a special type of motion called *periodic* **motion, the repeating** motion of an object in which it continues to return to a given position after a fixed time interval. The repetitive movements of such an object are called *oscillations*. We will focus our attention on a special case of periodic motion called *simple harmonic motion*. All periodic motions can be modeled as combinations of simple harmonic motions.

Simple harmonic motion also forms the basis for our understanding of *mechanical waves*. Sound waves, seismic waves, waves on stretched strings, and water waves are all produced by some source of oscillation. As a sound wave travels through the air, elements of the air oscillate back and forth; as a water wave travels across a pond, elements of the water oscillate up and down and backward and forward. The motion of the elements of the medium bears a strong resemblance to the periodic motion of an oscillating pendulum or an object attached to a spring.

To explain many other phenomena in nature, we must understand the concepts of oscillations and waves. For instance, although skyscrapers and bridges appear to be rigid, they actually oscillate, something the architects and engineers who design and build them must take into account. To understand how radio and television work, we must understand the origin and nature of electromagnetic waves and how they propagate through space. Finally, much of what scientists have learned about atomic structure has come from information carried by waves. Therefore, we must first study oscillations and waves if we are to understand the concepts and theories of atomic physics.

Drops of water fall from a leaf into a pond. The disturbance caused by the falling water causes the water surface to oscillate. These oscillations are associated with waves moving away from the point at which the water fell. In Part 2 of the text, we will explore the principles related to oscillations and waves. (Don Bonsey/Getty Images)

To reduce swaying in tall buildings because of the wind, tuned dampers are placed near the top of the building. These mechanisms include an object of large mass that oscillates under computer control at the same frequency as the building, reducing the swaying. The large sphere in the photograph on the left is part of the tuned damper system of the building in the photograph on the right, called Taipei 101, in Taiwan. The building, also called the Taipei Financial Center, was completed in 2004, at which time it held the record as the world's tallest building. (left, Courtesy of Motioneering, Inc.; right, © Simon Kwang/Reuters/CORBIS)

15 Oscillatory Motion

Periodic motion **is motion of an object that regularly returns to a given position** after a fixed time interval. With a little thought, we can identify several types of periodic motion in everyday life. Your car returns to the driveway each afternoon. You return to the dinner table each night to eat. A bumped chandelier swings back and forth, returning to the same position at a regular rate. The Earth returns to the same position in its orbit around the Sun each year, resulting in the variation among the four seasons.

In addition to these everyday examples, numerous other systems exhibit periodic motion. The molecules in a solid oscillate about their equilibrium positions; electromagnetic waves, such as light waves, radar, and radio waves, are characterized by oscillating electric and magnetic field vectors; and in alternating-current electrical circuits, voltage, current, and electric charge vary periodically with time.

A special kind of periodic motion occurs in mechanical systems when the force acting on an object is proportional to the position of the object relative to some equilibrium position. If this force is always directed toward the equilibrium position, the motion is called *simple harmonic motion*, which is the primary focus of this chapter.

15.1   Motion of an Object Attached to a Spring

As a model for simple harmonic motion, consider a block of mass m attached to the end of a spring, with the block free to move on a horizontal, frictionless surface (Active Fig. 15.1). When the spring is neither stretched nor compressed, the block is at rest at the position called the **equilibrium position** of the system, which we identify as $x = 0$. We know from experience that such a system oscillates back and forth if disturbed from its equilibrium position.

We can understand the oscillating motion of the block in Active Figure 15.1 qualitatively by first recalling that when the block is displaced to a position x, the spring exerts on the block a force that is proportional to the position and given by **Hooke's law** (see Section 7.4):

$$F_s = -kx \qquad (15.1)$$

◀ Hooke's law

We call F_s a **restoring force** because it is always directed toward the equilibrium position and therefore *opposite* the displacement of the block from equilibrium. That is, when the block is displaced to the right of $x = 0$ in Active Figure 15.1a, the position is positive and the restoring force is directed to the left. Figure 15.1b shows the block at $x = 0$, where the force on the block is zero. When the block is displaced to the left of $x = 0$ as in Figure 15.1c, the position is negative and the restoring force is directed to the right.

Applying Newton's second law to the motion of the block, with Equation 15.1 providing the net force in the x direction, we obtain

$$-kx = ma_x$$

$$a_x = -\frac{k}{m}x \qquad (15.2)$$

That is, the acceleration of the block is proportional to its position, and the direction of the acceleration is opposite the direction of the displacement of the block from equilibrium. Systems that behave in this way are said to exhibit **simple harmonic motion.** An object moves with simple harmonic motion whenever its acceleration is proportional to its position and is oppositely directed to the displacement from equilibrium.

If the block in Active Figure 15.1 is displaced to a position $x = A$ and released from rest, its *initial* acceleration is $-kA/m$. When the block passes through the equilibrium position $x = 0$, its acceleration is zero. At this instant, its speed is a maximum because the acceleration changes sign. The block then continues to travel to the left of equilibrium with a positive acceleration and finally reaches $x = -A$, at which time its acceleration is $+kA/m$ and its speed is again zero as discussed in Sections 7.4 and 7.9. The block completes a full cycle of its motion by returning to the original position, again passing through $x = 0$ with maximum speed. Therefore,

PITFALL PREVENTION 15.1
The Orientation of the Spring

Active Figure 15.1 shows a *horizontal* spring, with an attached block sliding on a frictionless surface. Another possibility is a block hanging from a *vertical* spring. All the results we discuss for the horizontal spring are the same for the vertical spring with one exception: when the block is placed on the vertical spring, its weight causes the spring to extend. If the resting position of the block is defined as $x = 0$, the results of this chapter also apply to this vertical system.

ACTIVE FIGURE 15.1

A block attached to a spring moving on a frictionless surface. (a) When the block is displaced to the right of equilibrium ($x > 0$), the force exerted by the spring acts to the left. (b) When the block is at its equilibrium position ($x = 0$), the force exerted by the spring is zero. (c) When the block is displaced to the left of equilibrium ($x < 0$), the force exerted by the spring acts to the right.

Sign in at www.thomsonedu.com and go to ThomsonNOW to choose the spring constant and the initial position and velocity of the block and see the resulting simple harmonic motion.

the block oscillates between the turning points $x = \pm A$. In the absence of friction, this idealized motion will continue forever because the force exerted by the spring is conservative. Real systems are generally subject to friction, so they do not oscillate forever. We shall explore the details of the situation with friction in Section 15.6.

Quick Quiz 15.1 A block on the end of a spring is pulled to position $x = A$ and released from rest. In one full cycle of its motion, through what total distance does it travel? (a) $A/2$ (b) A (c) $2A$ (d) $4A$

15.2 The Particle in Simple Harmonic Motion

The motion described in the preceding section occurs so often that we identify the **particle in simple harmonic motion** model to represent such situations. To develop a mathematical representation for this model, first recognize that the block is a particle under a net force as described in Equation 15.1. We will generally choose x as the axis along which the oscillation occurs; hence, we will drop the subscript-x notation in this discussion. Recall that, by definition, $a = dv/dt = d^2x/dt^2$, and so we can express Equation 15.2 as

$$\frac{d^2x}{dt^2} = -\frac{k}{m}x \tag{15.3}$$

If we denote the ratio k/m with the symbol ω^2 (we choose ω^2 rather than ω so as to make the solution we develop below simpler in form), then

$$\omega^2 = \frac{k}{m} \tag{15.4}$$

and Equation 15.3 can be written in the form

$$\frac{d^2x}{dt^2} = -\omega^2 x \tag{15.5}$$

Let's now find a mathematical solution to Equation 15.5, that is, a function $x(t)$ that satisfies this second-order differential equation and is a mathematical representation of the position of the particle as a function of time. We seek a function whose second derivative is the same as the original function with a negative sign and multiplied by ω^2. The trigonometric functions sine and cosine exhibit this behavior, so we can build a solution around one or both of them. The following cosine function is a solution to the differential equation:

▶ Position versus time for an object in simple harmonic motion

$$x(t) = A \cos{(\omega t + \phi)} \tag{15.6}$$

where A, ω, and ϕ are constants. To show explicitly that this solution satisfies Equation 15.5, notice that

$$\frac{dx}{dt} = A \frac{d}{dt} \cos{(\omega t + \phi)} = -\omega A \sin{(\omega t + \phi)} \tag{15.7}$$

$$\frac{d^2x}{dt^2} = -\omega A \frac{d}{dt} \sin{(\omega t + \phi)} = -\omega^2 A \cos{(\omega t + \phi)} \tag{15.8}$$

Comparing Equations 15.6 and 15.8, we see that $d^2x/dt^2 = -\omega^2 x$ and Equation 15.5 is satisfied.

The parameters A, ω, and ϕ are constants of the motion. To give physical significance to these constants, it is convenient to form a graphical representation of the motion by plotting x as a function of t as in Active Figure 15.2a. First, A, called the **amplitude** of the motion, is simply **the maximum value of the position of the particle in either the positive or negative x direction.** The constant ω is called the

angular frequency, and it has units[1] of rad/s. It is a measure of how rapidly the oscillations are occurring; the more oscillations per unit time, the higher the value of ω. From Equation 15.4, the angular frequency is

$$\omega = \sqrt{\frac{k}{m}} \qquad (15.9)$$

The constant angle ϕ is called the **phase constant** (or initial phase angle) and, along with the amplitude A, is determined uniquely by the position and velocity of the particle at $t = 0$. If the particle is at its maximum position $x = A$ at $t = 0$, the phase constant is $\phi = 0$ and the graphical representation of the motion is as shown in Active Figure 15.2b. The quantity $(\omega t + \phi)$ is called the **phase** of the motion. Notice that the function $x(t)$ is periodic and its value is the same each time ωt increases by 2π radians.

Equations 15.1, 15.5, and 15.6 form the basis of the mathematical representation of the particle in simple harmonic motion model. If you are analyzing a situation and find that the force on a particle is of the mathematical form of Equation 15.1, you know the motion is that of a simple harmonic oscillator and the position of the particle is described by Equation 15.6. If you analyze a system and find that it is described by a differential equation of the form of Equation 15.5, the motion is that of a simple harmonic oscillator. If you analyze a situation and find that the position of a particle is described by Equation 15.6, you know the particle undergoes simple harmonic motion.

Quick Quiz 15.2   Consider a graphical representation (Fig. 15.3) of simple harmonic motion as described mathematically in Equation 15.6. When the object is at point Ⓐ on the graph, what can you say about its position and velocity? (a) The position and velocity are both positive. (b) The position and velocity are both negative. (c) The position is positive, and its velocity is zero. (d) The position is negative, and its velocity is zero. (e) The position is positive, and its velocity is negative. (f) The position is negative, and its velocity is positive.

Quick Quiz 15.3   Figure 15.4 shows two curves representing objects undergoing simple harmonic motion. The correct description of these two motions is that the simple harmonic motion of object B is (a) of larger angular frequency and larger amplitude than that of object A, (b) of larger angular frequency and smaller amplitude than that of object A, (c) of smaller angular frequency and larger amplitude than that of object A, or (d) of smaller angular frequency and smaller amplitude than that of object A.

Let us investigate further the mathematical description of simple harmonic motion. The **period** T of the motion is the time interval required for the particle to go through one full cycle of its motion (Active Fig. 15.2a). That is, the values of x and v for the particle at time t equal the values of x and v at time $t + T$. Because the phase increases by 2π radians in a time interval of T,

$$[\omega(t + T) + \phi] - (\omega t + \phi) = 2\pi$$

Simplifying this expression gives $\omega T = 2\pi$, or

$$T = \frac{2\pi}{\omega} \qquad (15.10)$$

---

[1] We have seen many examples in earlier chapters in which we evaluate a trigonometric function of an angle. The argument of a trigonometric function, such as sine or cosine, *must* be a pure number. The radian is a pure number because it is a ratio of lengths. Angles in degrees are pure numbers because the degree is an artificial "unit"; it is not related to measurements of lengths. The argument of the trigonometric function in Equation 15.6 must be a pure number. Therefore, ω *must* be expressed in rad/s (and not, for example, in revolutions per second) if t is expressed in seconds. Furthermore, other types of functions such as logarithms and exponential functions require arguments that are pure numbers.

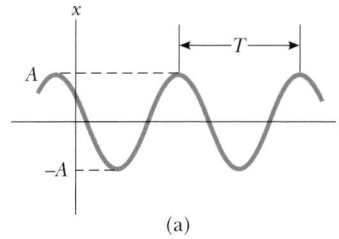

(a)

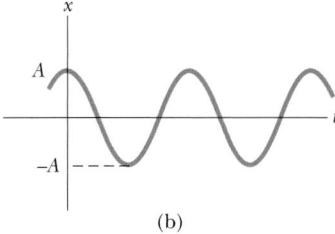

(b)

ACTIVE FIGURE 15.2

(a) An x–t graph for an object undergoing simple harmonic motion. The amplitude of the motion is A, the period (defined in Eq. 15.10) is T. (b) The x–t graph in the special case in which $x = A$ at $t = 0$ and hence $\phi = 0$.

Sign in at www.thomsonedu.com and go to ThomsonNOW to adjust the graphical representation and see the resulting simple harmonic motion of the block in Active Figure 15.1.

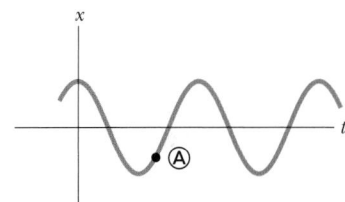

Figure 15.3   (Quick Quiz 15.2) An x–t graph for an object undergoing simple harmonic motion. At a particular time, the object's position is indicated by Ⓐ in the graph.

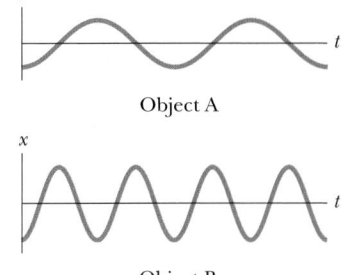

Object A

Object B

Figure 15.4   (Quick Quiz 15.3) Two x–t graphs for objects undergoing simple harmonic motion. The amplitudes and frequencies are different for the two objects.

PITFALL PREVENTION 15.4
Two Kinds of Frequency

We identify two kinds of frequency for a simple harmonic oscillator: f, called simply the *frequency*, is measured in hertz, and ω, the *angular frequency*, is measured in radians per second. Be sure you are clear about which frequency is being discussed or requested in a given problem. Equations 15.11 and 15.12 show the relationship between the two frequencies.

The inverse of the period is called the **frequency** f of the motion. Whereas the period is the time interval per oscillation, the frequency represents the **number of oscillations the particle undergoes per unit time interval:**

$$f = \frac{1}{T} = \frac{\omega}{2\pi} \tag{15.11}$$

The units of f are cycles per second, or **hertz** (Hz). Rearranging Equation 15.11 gives

$$\omega = 2\pi f = \frac{2\pi}{T} \tag{15.12}$$

Equations 15.9, 15.10, and 15.11 can be used to express the period and frequency of the motion for the particle in simple harmonic motion in terms of the characteristics m and k of the system as

Period ▶

$$T = \frac{2\pi}{\omega} = 2\pi\sqrt{\frac{m}{k}} \tag{15.13}$$

Frequency ▶

$$f = \frac{1}{T} = \frac{1}{2\pi}\sqrt{\frac{k}{m}} \tag{15.14}$$

That is, the period and frequency depend *only* on the mass of the particle and the force constant of the spring and *not* on the parameters of the motion, such as A or ϕ. As we might expect, the frequency is larger for a stiffer spring (larger value of k) and decreases with increasing mass of the particle.

We can obtain the velocity and acceleration[2] of a particle undergoing simple harmonic motion from Equations 15.7 and 15.8:

Velocity of an object in ▶
simple harmonic motion

$$v = \frac{dx}{dt} = -\omega A \sin(\omega t + \phi) \tag{15.15}$$

Acceleration of an object ▶
in simple harmonic motion

$$a = \frac{d^2x}{dt^2} = -\omega^2 A \cos(\omega t + \phi) \tag{15.16}$$

From Equation 15.15 we see that, because the sine and cosine functions oscillate between ±1, the extreme values of the velocity v are $\pm\omega A$. Likewise, Equation 15.16 shows that the extreme values of the acceleration a are $\pm\omega^2 A$. Therefore, the *maximum* values of the magnitudes of the velocity and acceleration are

Maximum magnitudes of ▶
velocity and acceleration in
simple harmonic motion

$$v_{\text{max}} = \omega A = \sqrt{\frac{k}{m}}\, A \tag{15.17}$$

$$a_{\text{max}} = \omega^2 A = \frac{k}{m}\, A \tag{15.18}$$

Figure 15.5a plots position versus time for an arbitrary value of the phase constant. The associated velocity–time and acceleration–time curves are illustrated in Figures 15.5b and 15.5c. They show that the phase of the velocity differs from the phase of the position by $\pi/2$ rad, or 90°. That is, when x is a maximum or a minimum, the velocity is zero. Likewise, when x is zero, the speed is a maximum. Furthermore, notice that the phase of the acceleration differs from the phase of the position by π radians, or 180°. For example, when x is a maximum, a has a maximum magnitude in the opposite direction.

Quick Quiz 15.4 An object of mass m is hung from a spring and set into oscillation. The period of the oscillation is measured and recorded as T. The object of

---

[2] Because the motion of a simple harmonic oscillator takes place in one dimension, we denote velocity as v and acceleration as a, with the direction indicated by a positive or negative sign as in Chapter 2.

mass m is removed and replaced with an object of mass $2m$. When this object is set into oscillation, what is the period of the motion? (a) $2T$ (b) $\sqrt{2}T$ (c) T (d) $T/\sqrt{2}$ (e) $T/2$

Equation 15.6 describes simple harmonic motion of a particle in general. Let's now see how to evaluate the constants of the motion. The angular frequency ω is evaluated using Equation 15.9. The constants A and ϕ are evaluated from the initial conditions, that is, the state of the oscillator at $t = 0$.

Suppose the particle is set into motion by pulling it from equilibrium by a distance A and releasing it from rest at $t = 0$ as in Active Figure 15.6. We must then require our solutions for $x(t)$ and $v(t)$ (Eqs. 15.6 and 15.15) to obey the initial conditions that $x(0) = A$ and $v(0) = 0$:

$$x(0) = A \cos \phi = A$$

$$v(0) = -\omega A \sin \phi = 0$$

These conditions are met if $\phi = 0$, giving $x = A \cos \omega t$ as our solution. To check this solution, notice that it satisfies the condition that $x(0) = A$ because $\cos 0 = 1$.

The position, velocity, and acceleration versus time are plotted in Figure 15.7a for this special case. The acceleration reaches extreme values of $\mp \omega^2 A$ when the position has extreme values of $\pm A$. Furthermore, the velocity has extreme values of $\pm \omega A$, which both occur at $x = 0$. Hence, the quantitative solution agrees with our qualitative description of this system.

Let's consider another possibility. Suppose the system is oscillating and we define $t = 0$ as the instant the particle passes through the unstretched position of the spring while moving to the right (Active Fig. 15.8). In this case, our solutions for $x(t)$ and $v(t)$ must obey the initial conditions that $x(0) = 0$ and $v(0) = v_i$:

$$x(0) = A \cos \phi = 0$$

$$v(0) = -\omega A \sin \phi = v_i$$

The first of these conditions tells us that $\phi = \pm \pi/2$. With these choices for ϕ, the second condition tells us that $A = \mp v_i/\omega$. Because the initial velocity is positive and the amplitude must be positive, we must have $\phi = -\pi/2$. Hence, the solution is

$$x = \frac{v_i}{\omega} \cos \left(\omega t - \frac{\pi}{2} \right)$$

The graphs of position, velocity, and acceleration versus time for this choice of $t = 0$ are shown in Figure 15.7b. Notice that these curves are the same as those in Figure 15.7a, but shifted to the right by one fourth of a cycle. This shift is described mathematically by the phase constant $\phi = -\pi/2$, which is one fourth of a full cycle of 2π.

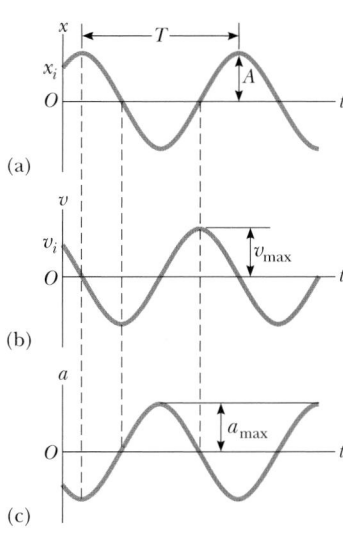

Figure 15.5 Graphical representation of simple harmonic motion. (a) Position versus time. (b) Velocity versus time. (c) Acceleration versus time. Notice that at any specified time the velocity is 90° out of phase with the position and the acceleration is 180° out of phase with the position.

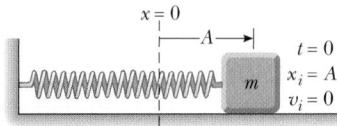

ACTIVE FIGURE 15.6

A block-spring system that begins its motion from rest with the block at $x = A$ at $t = 0$. In this case, $\phi = 0$; therefore, $x = A \cos \omega t$.

Sign in at www.thomsonedu.com and go to ThomsonNOW to compare the oscillations of two blocks starting from different initial positions and see that the frequency is independent of the amplitude.

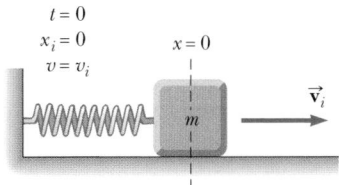

ACTIVE FIGURE 15.8

The block–spring system is undergoing oscillation, and $t = 0$ is defined at an instant when the block passes through the equilibrium position $x = 0$ and is moving to the right with speed v_i.

Sign in at www.thomsonedu.com and go to ThomsonNOW to compare the oscillations of two blocks with different velocities at $t = 0$ and see that the frequency is independent of the amplitude.

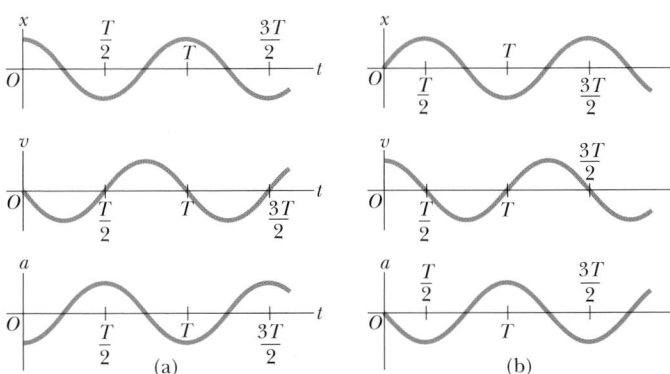

Figure 15.7 (a) Position, velocity, and acceleration versus time for a block undergoing simple harmonic motion under the initial conditions that at $t = 0$, $x(0) = A$ and $v(0) = 0$. (b) Position, velocity, and acceleration versus time for a block undergoing simple harmonic motion under the initial conditions that at $t = 0$, $x(0) = 0$ and $v(0) = v_i$.

EXAMPLE 15.1 **A Block-Spring System**

A 200-g block connected to a light spring for which the force constant is 5.00 N/m is free to oscillate on a horizontal, frictionless surface. The block is displaced 5.00 cm from equilibrium and released from rest as in Active Figure 15.6.

(A) Find the period of its motion.

SOLUTION

Conceptualize Study Active Figure 15.6 and imagine the block moving back and forth in simple harmonic motion once it is released. Set up an experimental model in the vertical direction by hanging a heavy object such as a stapler from a strong rubber band.

Categorize The block is modeled as a particle in simple harmonic motion. We find values from equations developed in this section for the particle in simple harmonic motion model, so we categorize this example as a substitution problem.

Use Equation 15.9 to find the angular frequency of the block-spring system:

$$\omega = \sqrt{\frac{k}{m}} = \sqrt{\frac{5.00 \text{ N/m}}{200 \times 10^{-3} \text{ kg}}} = 5.00 \text{ rad/s}$$

Use Equation 15.13 to find the period of the system:

$$T = \frac{2\pi}{\omega} = \frac{2\pi}{5.00 \text{ rad/s}} = \boxed{1.26 \text{ s}}$$

(B) Determine the maximum speed of the block.

SOLUTION

Use Equation 15.17 to find v_{max}:

$$v_{max} = \omega A = (5.00 \text{ rad/s})(5.00 \times 10^{-2} \text{ m}) = \boxed{0.250 \text{ m/s}}$$

(C) What is the maximum acceleration of the block?

SOLUTION

Use Equation 15.18 to find a_{max}:

$$a_{max} = \omega^2 A = (5.00 \text{ rad/s})^2(5.00 \times 10^{-2} \text{ m}) = \boxed{1.25 \text{ m/s}^2}$$

(D) Express the position, velocity, and acceleration as functions of time.

SOLUTION

Find the phase constant from the initial condition that $x = A$ at $t = 0$:

$$x(0) = A \cos \phi = A \quad \rightarrow \quad \phi = 0$$

Use Equation 15.6 to write an expression for $x(t)$:

$$x = A \cos (\omega t + \phi) = \boxed{(0.050\,0 \text{ m}) \cos 5.00t}$$

Use Equation 15.15 to write an expression for $v(t)$:

$$v = -\omega A \sin (\omega t + \phi) = \boxed{-(0.250 \text{ m/s}) \sin 5.00t}$$

Use Equation 15.16 to write an expression for $a(t)$:

$$a = -\omega^2 A \cos (\omega t + \phi) = \boxed{-(1.25 \text{ m/s}^2) \cos 5.00t}$$

What If? What if the block were released from the same initial position, $x_i = 5.00$ cm, but with an initial velocity of $v_i = -0.100$ m/s? Which parts of the solution change and what are the new answers for those that do change?

Answers Part (A) does not change because the period is independent of how the oscillator is set into motion. Parts (B), (C), and (D) will change.

Write position and velocity expressions for the initial conditions:

$$(1) \quad x(0) = A \cos \phi = x_i$$

$$(2) \quad v(0) = -\omega A \sin \phi = v_i$$

Divide Equation (2) by Equation (1) to find the phase constant:

$$\frac{-\omega A \sin \phi}{A \cos \phi} = \frac{v_i}{x_i}$$

$$\tan \phi = -\frac{v_i}{\omega x_i} = -\frac{-0.100 \text{ m/s}}{(5.00 \text{ rad/s})(0.050 \, 0 \text{ m})} = 0.400$$

$$\phi = 0.127\pi$$

Use Equation (1) to find A:

$$A = \frac{x_i}{\cos \phi} = \frac{0.050 \, 0 \text{ m}}{\cos (0.127\pi)} = 0.054 \, 3 \text{ m}$$

Find the new maximum speed:

$$v_{max} = \omega A = (5.00 \text{ rad/s})(5.43 \times 10^{-2} \text{ m}) = 0.271 \text{ m/s}$$

Find the new magnitude of the maximum acceleration:

$$a_{max} = \omega^2 A = (5.00 \text{ rad/s})^2 (5.43 \times 10^{-2} \text{ m}) = 1.36 \text{ m/s}^2$$

Find new expressions for position, velocity, and acceleration:

$$x = (0.054 \, 3 \text{ m}) \cos (5.00t + 0.127\pi)$$

$$v = -(0.271 \text{ m/s}) \sin (5.00t + 0.127\pi)$$

$$a = -(1.36 \text{ m/s}^2) \cos (5.00t + 0.127\pi)$$

As we saw in Chapters 7 and 8, many problems are easier to solve using an energy approach rather than one based on variables of motion. This particular **What If?** is easier to solve from an energy approach. Therefore, we shall investigate the energy of the simple harmonic oscillator in the next section.

EXAMPLE 15.2   **Watch Out for Potholes!**

A car with a mass of 1 300 kg is constructed so that its frame is supported by four springs. Each spring has a force constant of 20 000 N/m. Two people riding in the car have a combined mass of 160 kg. Find the frequency of vibration of the car after it is driven over a pothole in the road.

SOLUTION

Conceptualize   Think about your experiences with automobiles. When you sit in a car, it moves downward a small distance because your weight is compressing the springs further. If you push down on the front bumper and release it, the front of the car oscillates a few times.

Categorize   We imagine the car as being supported by a single spring and model the car as a particle in simple harmonic motion.

Analyze   First, let's determine the effective spring constant of the four springs combined. For a given extension x of the springs, the combined force on the car is the sum of the forces from the individual springs.

Find an expression for the total force on the car:

$$F_{total} = \sum (-kx) = -\left(\sum k\right)x$$

In this expression, x has been factored from the sum because it is the same for all four springs. The effective spring constant for the combined springs is the sum of the individual spring constants.

Evaluate the effective spring constant:

$$k_{eff} = \sum k = 4 \times 20 \, 000 \text{ N/m} = 80 \, 000 \text{ N/m}$$

Use Equation 15.14 to find the frequency of vibration:

$$f = \frac{1}{2\pi} \sqrt{\frac{k_{eff}}{m}} = \frac{1}{2\pi} \sqrt{\frac{80 \, 000 \text{ N/m}}{1 \, 460 \text{ kg}}} = \boxed{1.18 \text{ Hz}}$$

Finalize   The mass we used here is that of the car plus the people because that is the total mass that is oscillating. Also notice that we have explored only up-and-down motion of the car. If an oscillation is established in which the car rocks back and forth such that the front end goes up when the back end goes down, the frequency will be different.

What If?   Suppose the car stops on the side of the road and the two people exit the car. One of them pushes downward on the car and releases it so that it oscillates vertically. Is the frequency of the oscillation the same as the value we just calculated?

Answer   The suspension system of the car is the same, but the mass that is oscillating is smaller: it no longer includes the mass of the two people. Therefore, the frequency should be higher. Let's calculate the new frequency taking the mass to be 1 300 kg:

$$f = \frac{1}{2\pi}\sqrt{\frac{k_{\text{eff}}}{m}} = \frac{1}{2\pi}\sqrt{\frac{80\ 000\ \text{N/m}}{1\ 300\ \text{kg}}} = 1.25\ \text{Hz}$$

As predicted, the new frequency is a bit higher.

15.3   Energy of the Simple Harmonic Oscillator

Let us examine the mechanical energy of the block-spring system illustrated in Active Figure 15.1. Because the surface is frictionless, the system is isolated and we expect the total mechanical energy of the system to be constant. We assume a massless spring, so the kinetic energy of the system corresponds only to that of the block. We can use Equation 15.15 to express the kinetic energy of the block as

◀ Kinetic energy of a simple harmonic oscillator

$$K = \tfrac{1}{2}mv^2 = \tfrac{1}{2}m\omega^2 A^2 \sin^2\left(\omega t + \phi\right) \tag{15.19}$$

The elastic potential energy stored in the spring for any elongation x is given by $\tfrac{1}{2}kx^2$ (see Eq. 7.22). Using Equation 15.6 gives

◀ Potential energy of a simple harmonic oscillator

$$U = \tfrac{1}{2}kx^2 = \tfrac{1}{2}kA^2 \cos^2\left(\omega t + \phi\right) \tag{15.20}$$

We see that K and U are *always* positive quantities or zero. Because $\omega^2 = k/m$, we can express the total mechanical energy of the simple harmonic oscillator as

$$E = K + U = \tfrac{1}{2}kA^2\left[\sin^2\left(\omega t + \phi\right) + \cos^2\left(\omega t + \phi\right)\right]$$

From the identity $\sin^2\theta + \cos^2\theta = 1$, we see that the quantity in square brackets is unity. Therefore, this equation reduces to

◀ Total energy of a simple harmonic oscillator

$$E = \tfrac{1}{2}kA^2 \tag{15.21}$$

That is, **the total mechanical energy of a simple harmonic oscillator is a constant of the motion and is proportional to the square of the amplitude.** The total mechanical energy is equal to the maximum potential energy stored in the spring when $x = \pm A$ because $v = 0$ at these points and there is no kinetic energy. At the equilibrium position, where $U = 0$ because $x = 0$, the total energy, all in the form of kinetic energy, is again $\tfrac{1}{2}kA^2$.

Plots of the kinetic and potential energies versus time appear in Active Figure 15.9a, where we have taken $\phi = 0$. At all times, the sum of the kinetic and potential energies is a constant equal to $\tfrac{1}{2}kA^2$, the total energy of the system.

The variations of K and U with the position x of the block are plotted in Active Figure 15.9b. Energy is continuously being transformed between potential energy stored in the spring and kinetic energy of the block.

Active Figure 15.10 illustrates the position, velocity, acceleration, kinetic energy, and potential energy of the block-spring system for one full period of the motion. Most of the ideas discussed so far are incorporated in this important figure. Study it carefully.

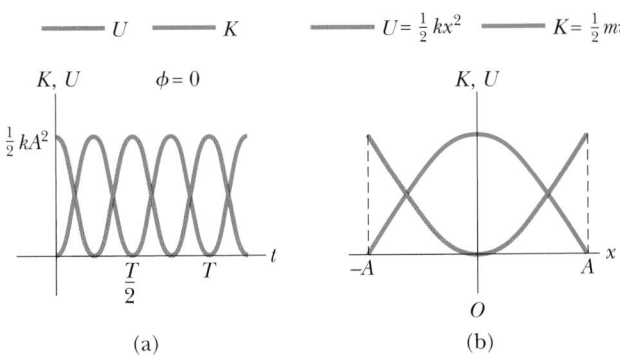

(a)

ACTIVE FIGURE 15.9

(a) Kinetic energy and potential energy versus time for a simple harmonic oscillator with $\phi = 0$. (b) Kinetic energy and potential energy versus position for a simple harmonic oscillator. In either plot, notice that $K + U = $ constant.

Sign in at **www.thomsonedu.com** and go to ThomsonNOW to compare the physical oscillation of a block with energy graphs in this figure as well as with energy bar graphs.

Finally, we can obtain the velocity of the block at an arbitrary position by expressing the total energy of the system at some arbitrary position x as

$$E = K + U = \tfrac{1}{2}mv^2 + \tfrac{1}{2}kx^2 = \tfrac{1}{2}kA^2$$

$$v = \pm\sqrt{\frac{k}{m}(A^2 - x^2)} = \pm\omega\sqrt{A^2 - x^2} \qquad \textbf{(15.22)}$$

◀ Velocity as a function of position for a simple harmonic oscillator

When you check Equation 15.22 to see whether it agrees with known cases, you find that it verifies that the speed is a maximum at $x = 0$ and is zero at the turning points $x = \pm A$.

You may wonder why we are spending so much time studying simple harmonic oscillators. We do so because they are good models of a wide variety of physical phenomena. For example, recall the Lennard–Jones potential discussed in Example 7.9. This complicated function describes the forces holding atoms together. Figure 15.11a (page 428) shows that for small displacements from the equilibrium position, the potential energy curve for this function approximates a parabola, which represents the potential energy function for a simple harmonic oscillator. Therefore, we can model the complex atomic binding forces as being due to tiny springs as depicted in Figure 15.11b.

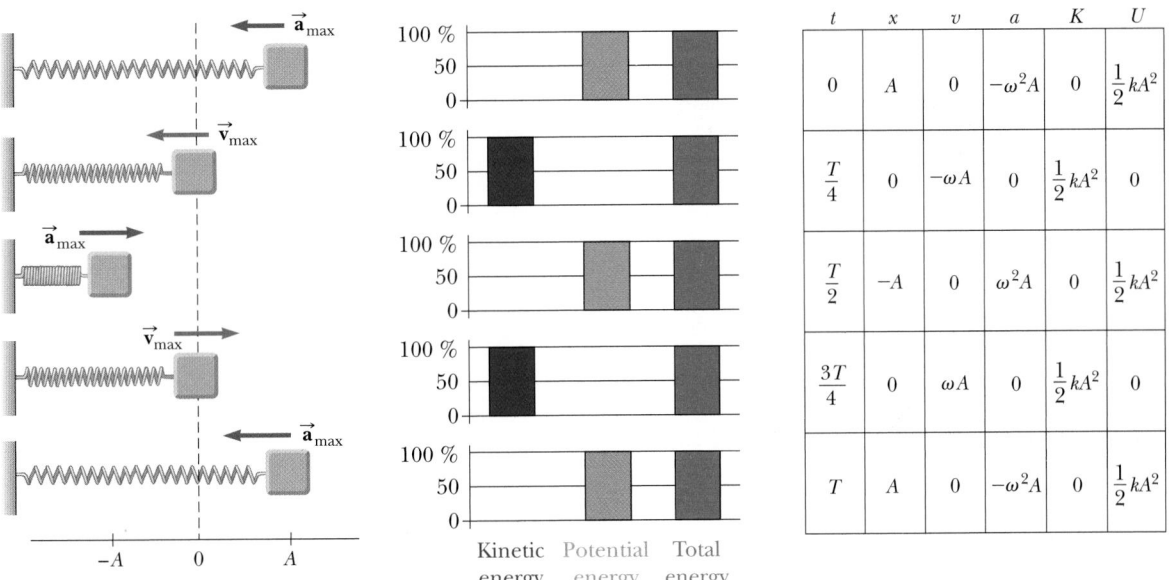

ACTIVE FIGURE 15.10

Several instants in the simple harmonic motion for a block–spring system. Energy bar graphs show the distribution of the energy of the system at each instant. The parameters in the table at the right refer to the block–spring system, assuming that at $t = 0$, $x = A$; hence, $x = A \cos \omega t$.

Sign in at **www.thomsonedu.com** and go to ThomsonNOW to set the initial position of the block and see the block–spring system and the analogous energy bar graphs.

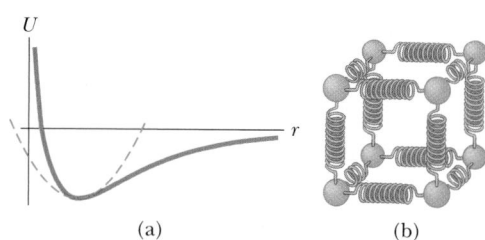

Figure 15.11 (a) If the atoms in a molecule do not move too far from their equilibrium positions, a graph of potential energy versus separation distance between atoms is similar to the graph of potential energy versus position for a simple harmonic oscillator (dashed blue curve). (b) The forces between atoms in a solid can be modeled by imagining springs between neighboring atoms.

The ideas presented in this chapter apply not only to block-spring systems and atoms, but also to a wide range of situations that include bungee jumping, tuning in a television station, and viewing the light emitted by a laser. You will see more examples of simple harmonic oscillators as you work through this book.

EXAMPLE 15.3 | **Oscillations on a Horizontal Surface**

A 0.500-kg cart connected to a light spring for which the force constant is 20.0 N/m oscillates on a horizontal, frictionless air track.

(A) Calculate the total energy of the system and the maximum speed of the cart if the amplitude of the motion is 3.00 cm.

SOLUTION

Conceptualize The system oscillates in exactly the same way as the block in Active Figure 15.10.

Categorize The cart is modeled as a particle in simple harmonic motion.

Analyze Use Equation 15.21 to find the energy of the oscillator:

$$E = \tfrac{1}{2}kA^2 = \tfrac{1}{2}(20.0 \text{ N/m})(3.00 \times 10^{-2} \text{ m})^2$$

$$= \boxed{9.00 \times 10^{-3} \text{ J}}$$

When the cart is at $x = 0$, the energy of the oscillator is entirely kinetic, so set $E = \tfrac{1}{2}mv_{\text{max}}^2$:

$$\tfrac{1}{2}mv_{\text{max}}^2 = 9.00 \times 10^{-3} \text{ J}$$

Solve for the maximum speed:

$$v_{\text{max}} = \sqrt{\frac{2(9.00 \times 10^{-3} \text{ J})}{0.500 \text{ kg}}} = \boxed{0.190 \text{ m/s}}$$

(B) What is the velocity of the cart when the position is 2.00 cm?

SOLUTION

Use Equation 15.22 to evaluate the velocity:

$$v = \pm\sqrt{\frac{k}{m}(A^2 - x^2)}$$

$$= \pm\sqrt{\frac{20.0 \text{ N/m}}{0.500 \text{ kg}}[(0.030\ 0 \text{ m})^2 - (0.020\ 0 \text{ m})^2]}$$

$$= \boxed{\pm 0.141 \text{ m/s}}$$

The positive and negative signs indicate that the cart could be moving to either the right or the left at this instant.

(C) Compute the kinetic and potential energies of the system when the position is 2.00 cm.

SOLUTION

Use the result of part (B) to evaluate the kinetic energy at $x = 0.020\ 0$ m:

$$K = \tfrac{1}{2}mv^2 = \tfrac{1}{2}(0.500\ \text{kg})(0.141\ \text{m/s})^2 = \boxed{5.00 \times 10^{-3}\ \text{J}}$$

Evaluate the elastic potential energy at $x = 0.020\ 0$ m:

$$U = \tfrac{1}{2}kx^2 = \tfrac{1}{2}(20.0\ \text{N/m})(0.0200\ \text{m})^2 = \boxed{4.00 \times 10^{-3}\ \text{J}}$$

Finalize   Notice that the sum of the kinetic and potential energies in part (C) is equal to the total energy found in part (A). That must be true for *any* position of the cart.

What If?   The cart in this example could have been set into motion by releasing the cart from rest at $x = 3.00$ cm. What if the cart were released from the same position, but with an initial velocity of $v = -0.100$ m/s? What are the new amplitude and maximum speed of the cart?

Answer   This question is of the same type we asked at the end of Example 15.1, but here we apply an energy approach.

First calculate the total energy of the system at $t = 0$:

$$E = \tfrac{1}{2}mv^2 + \tfrac{1}{2}kx^2$$

$$= \tfrac{1}{2}(0.500\ \text{kg})(-0.100\ \text{m/s})^2 + \tfrac{1}{2}(20.0\ \text{N/m})(0.030\ 0\ \text{m})^2$$

$$= 1.15 \times 10^{-2}\ \text{J}$$

Equate this total energy to the potential energy when the cart is at the end point of the motion:

$$E = \tfrac{1}{2}kA^2$$

Solve for the amplitude A:

$$A = \sqrt{\frac{2E}{k}} = \sqrt{\frac{2(1.15 \times 10^{-2}\ \text{J})}{20.0\ \text{N/m}}} = 0.033\ 9\ \text{m}$$

Find the new maximum speed by equating the total energy to the kinetic energy when the cart is at the equilibrium position:

$$E = \tfrac{1}{2}mv_{\text{max}}^2$$

Solve for the maximum speed:

$$v_{\text{max}} = \sqrt{\frac{2E}{m}} = \sqrt{\frac{2(1.15 \times 10^{-2}\ \text{J})}{0.500\ \text{kg}}} = 0.214\ \text{m/s}$$

The amplitude and maximum velocity are larger than the previous values because the cart was given an initial velocity at $t = 0$.

15.4   Comparing Simple Harmonic Motion with Uniform Circular Motion

Some common devices in our everyday life exhibit a relationship between oscillatory motion and circular motion. For example, the pistons in an automobile engine (Fig. 15.12a, page 430) go up and down—oscillatory motion—yet the net result of this motion is circular motion of the wheels. In an old-fashioned locomotive (Fig. 15.12b), the drive shaft goes back and forth in oscillatory motion, causing a circular motion of the wheels. In this section, we explore this interesting relationship between these two types of motion.

   Active Figure 15.13 (page 430) is a view of an experimental arrangement that shows this relationship. A ball is attached to the rim of a turntable of radius A, which is illuminated from the side by a lamp. The ball casts a shadow on a screen. **As the turntable rotates with constant angular speed, the shadow of the ball moves back and forth in simple harmonic motion.**

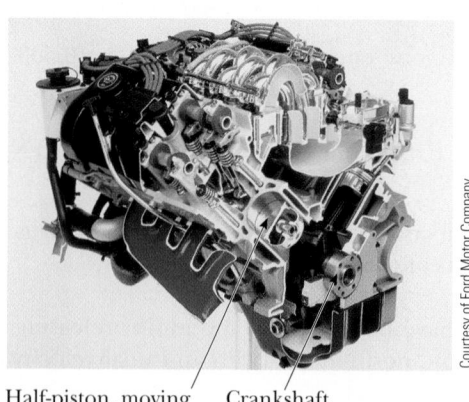

Half-piston, moving   Crankshaft
in a cutaway cylinder

Figure 15.12 (*Left*) The pistons of an automobile engine move in periodic motion along a single dimension as shown in this cutaway view of two of these pistons. This motion is converted to circular motion of the crankshaft, at the lower right, and ultimately of the wheels of the automobile. (*Right*) The back-and-forth motion of pistons (in the curved housing at the left) in an old-fashioned locomotive is converted to circular motion of the wheels.

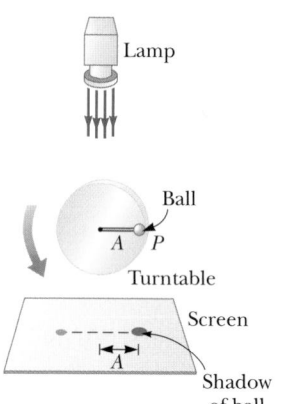

ACTIVE FIGURE 15.13

An experimental setup for demonstrating the connection between simple harmonic motion and uniform circular motion. As the ball rotates on the turntable with constant angular speed, its shadow on the screen moves back and forth in simple harmonic motion.

Sign in at www.thomsonedu.com and go to ThomsonNOW to adjust the frequency and radial position of the ball and see the resulting simple harmonic motion of the shadow.

Consider a particle located at point P on the circumference of a circle of radius A as in Figure 15.14a, with the line OP making an angle ϕ with the x axis at $t = 0$. We call this circle a *reference circle* for comparing simple harmonic motion with uniform circular motion, and we choose the position of P at $t = 0$ as our reference position. If the particle moves along the circle with constant angular speed ω until OP makes an angle θ with the x axis as in Figure 15.14b, at some time $t > 0$ the angle between OP and the x axis is $\theta = \omega t + \phi$. As the particle moves along the circle, the projection of P on the x axis, labeled point Q, moves back and forth along the x axis between the limits $x = \pm A$.

Notice that points P and Q always have the same x coordinate. From the right triangle OPQ, we see that this x coordinate is

$$x(t) = A \cos (\omega t + \phi) \tag{15.23}$$

This expression is the same as Equation 15.6 and shows that the point Q moves with simple harmonic motion along the x axis. Therefore, **simple harmonic motion along a straight line can be represented by the projection of uniform circular motion along a diameter of a reference circle.**

This geometric interpretation shows that the time interval for one complete revolution of the point P on the reference circle is equal to the period of motion T for simple harmonic motion between $x = \pm A$. That is, the angular speed ω of P is the same as the angular frequency ω of simple harmonic motion along the x axis

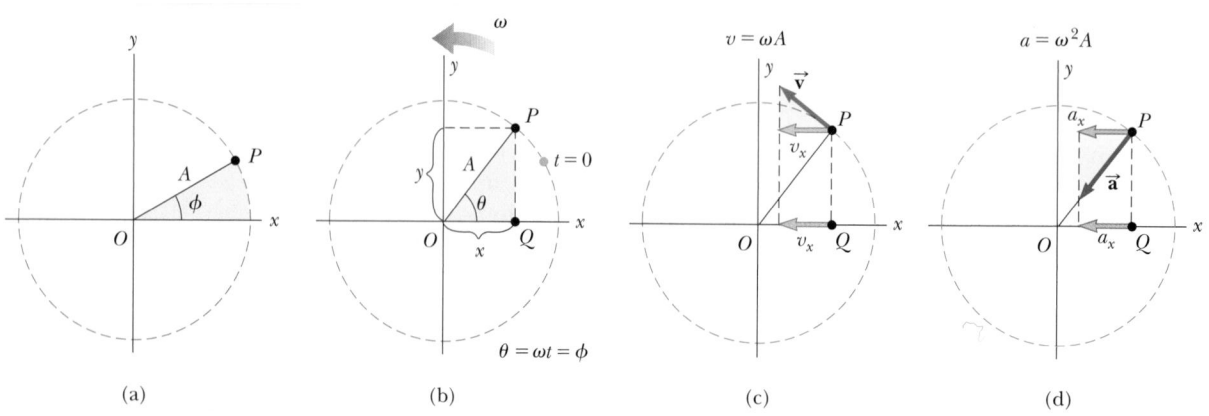

Figure 15.14 Relationship between the uniform circular motion of a point P and the simple harmonic motion of a point Q. A particle at P moves in a circle of radius A with constant angular speed ω. (a) A reference circle showing the position of P at $t = 0$. (b) The x coordinates of points P and Q are equal and vary in time according to the expression $x = A \cos (\omega t + \phi)$. (c) The x component of the velocity of P equals the velocity of Q. (d) The x component of the acceleration of P equals the acceleration of Q.

(which is why we use the same symbol). The phase constant ϕ for simple harmonic motion corresponds to the initial angle OP makes with the x axis. The radius A of the reference circle equals the amplitude of the simple harmonic motion.

Because the relationship between linear and angular speed for circular motion is $v = r\omega$ (see Eq. 10.10), the particle moving on the reference circle of radius A has a velocity of magnitude ωA. From the geometry in Figure 15.14c, we see that the x component of this velocity is $-\omega A \sin (\omega t + \phi)$. By definition, point Q has a velocity given by dx/dt. Differentiating Equation 15.23 with respect to time, we find that the velocity of Q is the same as the x component of the velocity of P.

The acceleration of P on the reference circle is directed radially inward toward O and has a magnitude $v^2/A = \omega^2 A$. From the geometry in Figure 15.14d, we see that the x component of this acceleration is $-\omega^2 A \cos (\omega t + \phi)$. This value is also the acceleration of the projected point Q along the x axis, as you can verify by taking the second derivative of Equation 15.23.

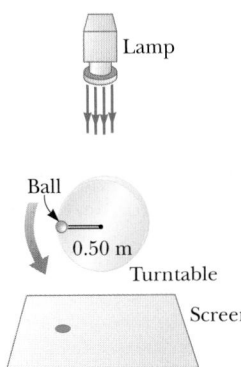

Quick Quiz 15.5   Figure 15.15 shows the position of an object in uniform circular motion at $t = 0$. A light shines from above and projects a shadow of the object on a screen below the circular motion. What are the correct values for the *amplitude* and *phase constant* (relative to an x axis to the right) of the simple harmonic motion of the shadow? (a) 0.50 m and 0   (b) 1.00 m and 0   (c) 0.50 m and π (d) 1.00 m and π

Figure 15.15   (Quick Quiz 15.5) An object moves in circular motion, casting a shadow on the screen below. Its position at an instant of time is shown.

| EXAMPLE 15.4 | **Circular Motion with Constant Angular Speed** |

A particle rotates counterclockwise in a circle of radius 3.00 m with a constant angular speed of 8.00 rad/s. At $t = 0$, the particle has an x coordinate of 2.00 m and is moving to the right.

(A) Determine the x coordinate of the particle as a function of time.

SOLUTION

Conceptualize   Be sure you understand the relationship between circular motion of a particle and simple harmonic motion of its shadow as described in Active Figure 15.13.

Categorize   The particle on the circle is a particle under constant angular speed. The shadow is a particle in simple harmonic motion.

Analyze   Use Equation 15.23 to write an expression for the x coordinate of the rotating particle with $\omega = 8.00$ rad/s:

$$x = A \cos (\omega t + \phi) = (3.00 \text{ m}) \cos (8.00t + \phi)$$

Evaluate ϕ by using the initial condition $x = 2.00$ m at $t = 0$:

$$2.00 \text{ m} = (3.00 \text{ m}) \cos (0 + \phi)$$

Solve for ϕ:

$$\phi = \cos^{-1} \left(\frac{2.00 \text{ m}}{3.00 \text{ m}} \right) = \cos^{-1} (0.667) = \pm 48.2° = \pm 0.841 \text{ rad}$$

If we were to take $\phi = +0.841$ rad as our answer, the particle would be moving to the left at $t = 0$. Because the particle is moving to the right at $t = 0$, we must choose $\phi = -0.841$ rad.

Write the x coordinate as a function of time:

$$x = \boxed{(3.00 \text{ m}) \cos (8.00t - 0.841)}$$

(B) Find the x components of the particle's velocity and acceleration at any time t.

SOLUTION

Differentiate the x coordinate with respect to time to find the velocity at any time:

$$v_x = \frac{dx}{dt} = (-3.00 \text{ m})(8.00 \text{ rad/s}) \sin (8.00t - 0.841)$$

$$= -(24.0 \text{ m/s}) \sin (8.00t - 0.841)$$

Differentiate the velocity with respect to time to find the acceleration at any time:

$$a_x = \frac{dv_x}{dt} = (-24.0 \text{ m/s})(8.00 \text{ rad/s}) \cos (8.00t - 0.841)$$

$$= -(192 \text{ m/s}^2) \cos (8.00t - 0.841)$$

Finalize Although we have evaluated these results for the particle moving in the circle, remember that these same results apply to the shadow, which is moving in simple harmonic motion.

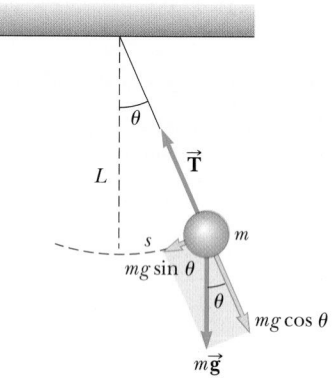

ACTIVE FIGURE 15.16

The restoring force is $-mg \sin \theta$, the component of the gravitational force tangent to the arc. When θ is small, a simple pendulum oscillates in simple harmonic motion about the equilibrium position $\theta = 0$.

Sign in at www.thomsonedu.com and go to ThomsonNOW to adjust the mass of the bob, the length of the string, and the initial angle and see the resulting oscillation of the pendulum.

PITFALL PREVENTION 15.5

Not True Simple Harmonic Motion

The pendulum *does not* exhibit true simple harmonic motion for *any* angle. If the angle is less than about 10°, the motion is close to and can be *modeled* as simple harmonic.

15.5 The Pendulum

The **simple pendulum** is another mechanical system that exhibits periodic motion. It consists of a particle-like bob of mass m suspended by a light string of length L that is fixed at the upper end as shown in Active Figure 15.16. The motion occurs in the vertical plane and is driven by the gravitational force. We shall show that, provided the angle θ is small (less than about 10°), the motion is very close to that of a simple harmonic oscillator.

The forces acting on the bob are the force $\vec{T}$ exerted by the string and the gravitational force $m\vec{g}$. The tangential component $mg \sin \theta$ of the gravitational force always acts toward $\theta = 0$, opposite the displacement of the bob from the lowest position. Therefore, the tangential component is a restoring force, and we can apply Newton's second law for motion in the tangential direction:

$$F_t = -mg \sin \theta = m \frac{d^2 s}{dt^2}$$

where s is the bob's position measured along the arc and the negative sign indicates that the tangential force acts toward the equilibrium (vertical) position. Because $s = L\theta$ (Eq. 10.1a) and L is constant, this equation reduces to

$$\frac{d^2\theta}{dt^2} = -\frac{g}{L} \sin \theta$$

Considering θ as the position, let us compare this equation to Equation 15.3. Does it have the same mathematical form? The right side is proportional to $\sin \theta$ rather than to θ; hence, we would not expect simple harmonic motion because this expression is not of the form of Equation 15.3. If we assume θ is *small* (less than about 10° or 0.2 rad), however, we can use the **small angle approximation**, in which $\sin \theta \approx \theta$, where θ is measured in radians. Table 15.1 shows angles in degrees and radians and the sines of these angles. As long as θ is less than approximately 10°, the angle in radians and its sine are the same to within an accuracy of less than 1.0%.

Therefore, for small angles, the equation of motion becomes

$$\frac{d^2\theta}{dt^2} = -\frac{g}{L} \theta \quad \text{(for small values of } \theta\text{)} \tag{15.24}$$

Equation 15.24 has the same form as Equation 15.3, so we conclude that the motion for small amplitudes of oscillation can be modeled as simple harmonic motion. Therefore, the solution of Equation 15.24 is $\theta = \theta_{\text{max}} \cos (\omega t + \phi)$, where θ_{max} is the *maximum angular position* and the angular frequency ω is

Angular frequency for ▶
a simple pendulum

$$\omega = \sqrt{\frac{g}{L}} \tag{15.25}$$

TABLE 15.1

Angles and Sines of Angles

Angle in Degrees	Angle in Radians	Sine of Angle	Percent Difference
0°	0.000 0	0.000 0	0.0%
1°	0.017 5	0.017 5	0.0%
2°	0.034 9	0.034 9	0.0%
3°	0.052 4	0.052 3	0.0%
5°	0.087 3	0.087 2	0.1%
10°	0.174 5	0.173 6	0.5%
15°	0.261 8	0.258 8	1.2%
20°	0.349 1	0.342 0	2.1%
30°	0.523 6	0.500 0	4.7%

The period of the motion is

$$T = \frac{2\pi}{\omega} = 2\pi\sqrt{\frac{L}{g}}$$

(15.26)   ◀ Period of a simple pendulum

In other words, **the period and frequency of a simple pendulum depend only on the length of the string and the acceleration due to gravity.** Because the period is independent of the mass, we conclude that all simple pendula that are of equal length and are at the same location (so that g is constant) oscillate with the same period.

The simple pendulum can be used as a timekeeper because its period depends only on its length and the local value of g. It is also a convenient device for making precise measurements of the free-fall acceleration. Such measurements are important because variations in local values of g can provide information on the location of oil and other valuable underground resources.

Quick Quiz 15.6 A grandfather clock depends on the period of a pendulum to keep correct time. **(i)** Suppose a grandfather clock is calibrated correctly and then a mischievous child slides the bob of the pendulum downward on the oscillating rod. Does the grandfather clock run (a) slow, (b) fast, or (c) correctly? **(ii)** Suppose a grandfather clock is calibrated correctly at sea level and is then taken to the top of a very tall mountain. Does the grandfather clock now run (a) slow, (b) fast, or (c) correctly?

EXAMPLE 15.5   **A Connection Between Length and Time**

Christian Huygens (1629–1695), the greatest clockmaker in history, suggested that an international unit of length could be defined as the length of a simple pendulum having a period of exactly 1 s. How much shorter would our length unit be if his suggestion had been followed?

SOLUTION

Conceptualize Imagine a pendulum that swings back and forth in exactly 1 second. Based on your experience in observing swinging objects, can you make an estimate of the required length? Hang a small object from a string and simulate the 1-s pendulum.

Categorize This example involves a simple pendulum, so we categorize it as an application of the concepts introduced in this section.

Analyze Solve Equation 15.26 for the length and substitute the known values:

$$L = \frac{T^2 g}{4\pi^2} = \frac{(1.00\text{ s})^2(9.80\text{ m/s}^2)}{4\pi^2} = 0.248\text{ m}$$

Finalize The meter's length would be slightly less than one-fourth of its current length. Also, the number of significant digits depends only on how precisely we know g because the time has been defined to be exactly 1 s.

What If? What if Huygens had been born on another planet? What would the value for g have to be on that planet such that the meter based on Huygens's pendulum would have the same value as our meter?

Answer Solve Equation 15.26 for g:

$$g = \frac{4\pi^2 L}{T^2} = \frac{4\pi^2 (1.00 \text{ m})}{(1.00 \text{ s})^2} = 4\pi^2 \text{ m/s}^2 = 39.5 \text{ m/s}^2$$

No planet in our solar system has an acceleration due to gravity that large.

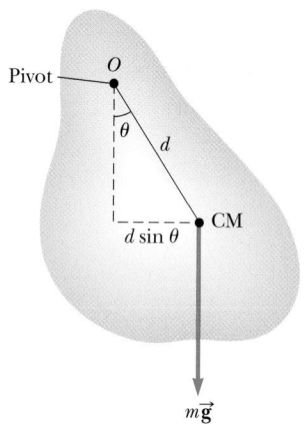

Figure 15.17 A physical pendulum pivoted at O.

Physical Pendulum

Suppose you balance a wire coat hanger so that the hook is supported by your extended index finger. When you give the hanger a small angular displacement (with your other hand) and then release it, it oscillates. If a hanging object oscillates about a fixed axis that does not pass through its center of mass and the object cannot be approximated as a point mass, we cannot treat the system as a simple pendulum. In this case, the system is called a **physical pendulum**.

Consider a rigid object pivoted at a point O that is a distance d from the center of mass (Fig. 15.17). The gravitational force provides a torque about an axis through O, and the magnitude of that torque is $mgd \sin \theta$, where θ is as shown in Figure 15.17. We model the object as a rigid object under a net torque and use the rotational form of Newton's second law, $\Sigma \tau = I\alpha$, where I is the moment of inertia of the object about the axis through O. The result is

$$-mgd \sin \theta = I \frac{d^2\theta}{dt^2}$$

The negative sign indicates that the torque about O tends to decrease θ. That is, the gravitational force produces a restoring torque. If we again assume θ is small, the approximation $\sin \theta \approx \theta$ is valid and the equation of motion reduces to

$$\frac{d^2\theta}{dt^2} = -\left(\frac{mgd}{I}\right)\theta = -\omega^2\theta \tag{15.27}$$

Because this equation is of the same form as Equation 15.3, its solution is that of the simple harmonic oscillator. That is, the solution of Equation 15.27 is given by $\theta = \theta_{\text{max}} \cos (\omega t + \phi)$, where θ_{max} is the maximum angular position and

$$\omega = \sqrt{\frac{mgd}{I}}$$

The period is

Period of a physical pendulum ▶

$$T = \frac{2\pi}{\omega} = 2\pi \sqrt{\frac{I}{mgd}} \tag{15.28}$$

This result can be used to measure the moment of inertia of a flat rigid object. If the location of the center of mass—and hence the value of d—is known, the moment of inertia can be obtained by measuring the period. Finally, notice that Equation 15.28 reduces to the period of a simple pendulum (Eq. 15.26) when $I = md^2$, that is, when all the mass is concentrated at the center of mass.

EXAMPLE 15.6	A Swinging Rod

A uniform rod of mass M and length L is pivoted about one end and oscillates in a vertical plane (Fig. 15.18). Find the period of oscillation if the amplitude of the motion is small.

SOLUTION

Conceptualize   Imagine a rod swinging back and forth when pivoted at one end. Try it with a meterstick or a scrap piece of wood.

Categorize   Because the rod is not a point particle, we categorize it as a physical pendulum.

Analyze   In Chapter 10, we found that the moment of inertia of a uniform rod about an axis through one end is $\frac{1}{3}ML^2$. The distance d from the pivot to the center of mass of the rod is $L/2$.

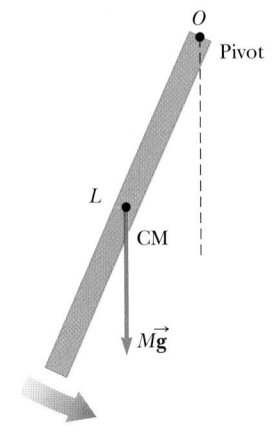

Figure 15.18   (Example 15.6) A rigid rod oscillating about a pivot through one end is a physical pendulum with $d = L/2$ and, from Table 10.2, $I = \frac{1}{3}ML^2$.

Substitute these quantities into Equation 15.28:

$$T = 2\pi\sqrt{\frac{\frac{1}{3}ML^2}{Mg(L/2)}} = 2\pi\sqrt{\frac{2L}{3g}}$$

Finalize   In one of the Moon landings, an astronaut walking on the Moon's surface had a belt hanging from his space suit, and the belt oscillated as a physical pendulum. A scientist on the Earth observed this motion on television and used it to estimate the free-fall acceleration on the Moon. How did the scientist make this calculation?

Torsional Pendulum

Figure 15.19 shows a rigid object suspended by a wire attached at the top to a fixed support. When the object is twisted through some angle θ, the twisted wire exerts on the object a restoring torque that is proportional to the angular position. That is,

$$\tau = -\kappa\theta$$

where κ (Greek letter kappa) is called the *torsion constant* of the support wire. The value of κ can be obtained by applying a known torque to twist the wire through a measurable angle θ. Applying Newton's second law for rotational motion, we find that

$$\tau = -\kappa\theta = I\frac{d^2\theta}{dt^2}$$

$$\frac{d^2\theta}{dt^2} = -\frac{\kappa}{I}\theta \tag{15.29}$$

Again, this result is the equation of motion for a simple harmonic oscillator, with $\omega = \sqrt{\kappa/I}$ and a period

$$T = 2\pi\sqrt{\frac{I}{\kappa}} \tag{15.30}$$

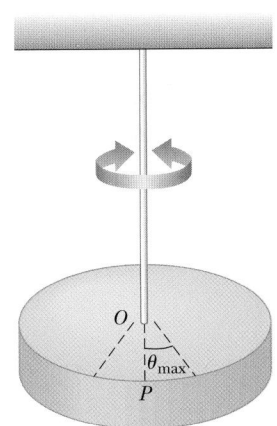

Figure 15.19   A torsional pendulum consists of a rigid object suspended by a wire attached to a rigid support. The object oscillates about the line OP with an amplitude θ_{max}.

◀ Period of a torsional pendulum

This system is called a *torsional pendulum*. There is no small-angle restriction in this situation as long as the elastic limit of the wire is not exceeded.

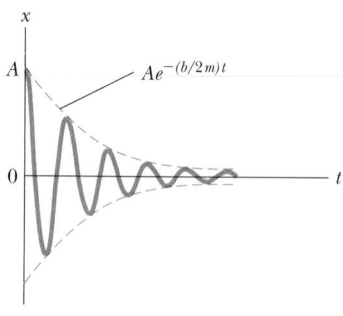

Figure 15.20 One example of a damped oscillator is an object attached to a spring and submersed in a viscous liquid.

15.6 Damped Oscillations

The oscillatory motions we have considered so far have been for ideal systems, that is, systems that oscillate indefinitely under the action of only one force, a linear restoring force. In many real systems, nonconservative forces such as friction retard the motion. Consequently, the mechanical energy of the system diminishes in time, and the motion is said to be *damped*. The lost mechanical energy is transformed into internal energy in the object and the retarding medium. Figure 15.20 depicts one such system: an object attached to a spring and submersed in a viscous liquid.

One common type of retarding force is that discussed in Section 6.4, where the force is proportional to the speed of the moving object and acts in the direction opposite the velocity of the object with respect to the medium. This retarding force is often observed when an object moves through air, for instance. Because the retarding force can be expressed as $\vec{R} = -b\vec{v}$ (where b is a constant called the *damping coefficient*) and the restoring force of the system is $-kx$, we can write Newton's second law as

$$\sum F_x = -kx - bv_x = ma_x$$

$$-kx - b\frac{dx}{dt} = m\frac{d^2x}{dt^2} \qquad (15.31)$$

The solution to this equation requires mathematics that may be unfamiliar to you; we simply state it here without proof. When the retarding force is small compared with the maximum restoring force—that is, when b is small—the solution to Equation 15.31 is

$$x = Ae^{-(b/2m)t}\cos(\omega t + \phi) \qquad (15.32)$$

where the angular frequency of oscillation is

$$\omega = \sqrt{\frac{k}{m} - \left(\frac{b}{2m}\right)^2} \qquad (15.33)$$

This result can be verified by substituting Equation 15.32 into Equation 15.31. It is convenient to express the angular frequency of a damped oscillator in the form

$$\omega = \sqrt{\omega_0^2 - \left(\frac{b}{2m}\right)^2}$$

where $\omega_0 = \sqrt{k/m}$ represents the angular frequency in the absence of a retarding force (the undamped oscillator) and is called the **natural frequency** of the system.

Active Figure 15.21 shows the position as a function of time for an object oscillating in the presence of a retarding force. **When the retarding force is small, the oscillatory character of the motion is preserved but the amplitude decreases in time, with the result that the motion ultimately ceases.** Any system that behaves in this way is known as a **damped oscillator.** The dashed blue lines in Active Figure 15.21, which define the *envelope* of the oscillatory curve, represent the exponential factor in Equation 15.32. This envelope shows that **the amplitude decays exponentially with time.** For motion with a given spring constant and object mass, the oscillations dampen more rapidly for larger values of the retarding force.

When the magnitude of the retarding force is small such that $b/2m < \omega_0$, the system is said to be **underdamped.** The resulting motion is represented by the blue curve in Figure 15.22. As the value of b increases, the amplitude of the oscillations decreases more and more rapidly. When b reaches a critical value b_c such that $b_c/2m = \omega_0$, the system does not oscillate and is said to be **critically damped.** In this case, the system, once released from rest at some nonequilibrium position, approaches but does not pass through the equilibrium position. The graph of position versus time for this case is the red curve in Figure 15.22.

ACTIVE FIGURE 15.21

Graph of position versus time for a damped oscillator. Notice the decrease in amplitude with time.

Sign in at www.thomsonedu.com and go to ThomsonNOW to adjust the spring constant, the mass of the object, and the damping constant and see the resulting damped oscillation of the object.

If the medium is so viscous that the retarding force is large compared to the restoring force—that is, if $b/2m > \omega_0$—the system is **overdamped.** Again, the displaced system, when free to move, does not oscillate but rather simply returns to its equilibrium position. As the damping increases, the time interval required for the system to approach equilibrium also increases as indicated by the black curve in Figure 15.22. For critically damped and overdamped systems, there is no angular frequency ω and the solution in Equation 15.32 is not valid.

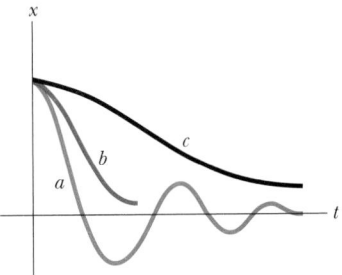

Figure 15.22 Graphs of position versus time for an underdamped oscillator (blue, curve a), a critically damped oscillator (red, curve b), and an overdamped oscillator (black, curve c).

15.7 Forced Oscillations

We have seen that the mechanical energy of a damped oscillator decreases in time as a result of the resistive force. It is possible to compensate for this energy decrease by applying an external force that does positive work on the system. At any instant, energy can be transferred into the system by an applied force that acts in the direction of motion of the oscillator. For example, a child on a swing can be kept in motion by appropriately timed "pushes." The amplitude of motion remains constant if the energy input per cycle of motion exactly equals the decrease in mechanical energy in each cycle that results from resistive forces.

A common example of a forced oscillator is a damped oscillator driven by an external force that varies periodically, such as $F(t) = F_0 \sin \omega t$, where F_0 is a constant and ω is the angular frequency of the driving force. In general, the frequency ω of the driving force is variable, whereas the natural frequency ω_0 of the oscillator is fixed by the values of k and m. Newton's second law in this situation gives

$$\sum F = ma \quad \rightarrow \quad F_0 \sin \omega t - b\frac{dx}{dt} - kx = m\frac{d^2x}{dt^2} \tag{15.34}$$

Again, the solution of this equation is rather lengthy and will not be presented. After the driving force on an initially stationary object begins to act, the amplitude of the oscillation will increase. After a sufficiently long period of time, when the energy input per cycle from the driving force equals the amount of mechanical energy transformed to internal energy for each cycle, a steady-state condition is reached in which the oscillations proceed with constant amplitude. In this situation, the solution of Equation 15.34 is

$$x = A \cos (\omega t + \phi) \tag{15.35}$$

where

$$A = \frac{F_0/m}{\sqrt{(\omega^2 - \omega_0^2)^2 + \left(\dfrac{b\omega}{m}\right)^2}} \tag{15.36}$$

◀ Amplitude of a driven oscillator

and where $\omega_0 = \sqrt{k/m}$ is the natural frequency of the undamped oscillator ($b = 0$).

Equations 15.35 and 15.36 show that the forced oscillator vibrates at the frequency of the driving force and that the amplitude of the oscillator is constant for a given driving force because it is being driven in steady-state by an external force. For small damping, the amplitude is large when the frequency of the driving force is near the natural frequency of oscillation, or when $\omega \approx \omega_0$. The dramatic increase in amplitude near the natural frequency is called **resonance,** and the natural frequency ω_0 is also called the **resonance frequency** of the system.

The reason for large-amplitude oscillations at the resonance frequency is that energy is being transferred to the system under the most favorable conditions. We can better understand this concept by taking the first time derivative of x in Equation 15.35, which gives an expression for the velocity of the oscillator. We find that v is proportional to $\sin (\omega t + \phi)$, which is the same trigonometric function as that describing the driving force. Therefore, the applied force $\vec{F}$ is in phase with the velocity. The rate at which work is done on the oscillator by $\vec{F}$ equals the dot product

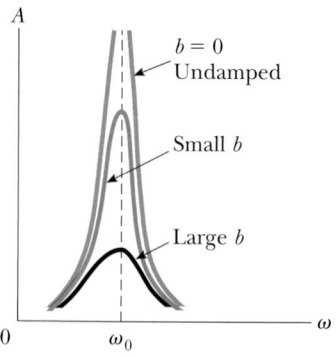

Figure 15.23 Graph of amplitude versus frequency for a damped oscillator when a periodic driving force is present. When the frequency ω of the driving force equals the natural frequency ω_0 of the oscillator, resonance occurs. Notice that the shape of the resonance curve depends on the size of the damping coefficient b.

$\vec{F} \cdot \vec{v}$; this rate is the power delivered to the oscillator. Because the product $\vec{F} \cdot \vec{v}$ is a maximum when $\vec{F}$ and $\vec{v}$ are in phase, we conclude that **at resonance, the applied force is in phase with the velocity and the power transferred to the oscillator is a maximum.**

Figure 15.23 is a graph of amplitude as a function of frequency for a forced oscillator with and without damping. Notice that the amplitude increases with decreasing damping ($b \to 0$) and that the resonance curve broadens as the damping increases. In the absence of a damping force ($b = 0$), we see from Equation 15.36 that the steady-state amplitude approaches infinity as ω approaches ω_0. In other words, if there are no losses in the system and we continue to drive an initially motionless oscillator with a periodic force that is in phase with the velocity, the amplitude of motion builds without limit (see the brown curve in Fig. 15.23). This limitless building does not occur in practice because some damping is always present in reality.

Later in this book we shall see that resonance appears in other areas of physics. For example, certain electric circuits have natural frequencies. A bridge has natural frequencies that can be set into resonance by an appropriate driving force. A dramatic example of such resonance occurred in 1940 when the Tacoma Narrows Bridge in the state of Washington was destroyed by resonant vibrations. Although the winds were not particularly strong on that occasion, the "flapping" of the wind across the roadway (think of the "flapping" of a flag in a strong wind) provided a periodic driving force whose frequency matched that of the bridge. The resulting oscillations of the bridge caused it to ultimately collapse (Fig. 15.24) because the bridge design had inadequate built-in safety features.

Many other examples of resonant vibrations can be cited. A resonant vibration you may have experienced is the "singing" of telephone wires in the wind. Machines often break if one vibrating part is in resonance with some other moving part. Soldiers marching in cadence across a bridge have been known to set up resonant vibrations in the structure and thereby cause it to collapse. Whenever any real physical system is driven near its resonance frequency, you can expect oscillations of very large amplitudes.

(a)   (b)

Figure 15.24 (a) In 1940, turbulent winds set up torsional vibrations in the Tacoma Narrows Bridge, causing it to oscillate at a frequency near one of the natural frequencies of the bridge structure. (b) Once established, this resonance condition led to the bridge's collapse. *(UPI/Bettmann Newsphotos)*

Summary

ThomsonNOW Sign in at **www.thomsonedu.com** and go to ThomsonNOW to take a practice test for this chapter.

CONCEPTS AND PRINCIPLES

The kinetic energy and potential energy for an object of mass m oscillating at the end of a spring of force constant k vary with time and are given by

$$K = \tfrac{1}{2}mv^2 = \tfrac{1}{2}m\omega^2 A^2 \sin^2(\omega t + \phi) \quad \textbf{(15.19)}$$

$$U = \tfrac{1}{2}kx^2 = \tfrac{1}{2}kA^2 \cos^2(\omega t + \phi) \quad \textbf{(15.20)}$$

The total energy of a simple harmonic oscillator is a constant of the motion and is given by

$$E = \tfrac{1}{2}kA^2 \quad \textbf{(15.21)}$$

A **simple pendulum** of length L moves in simple harmonic motion for small angular displacements from the vertical. Its period is

$$T = 2\pi\sqrt{\frac{L}{g}} \quad \textbf{(15.26)}$$

For small angular displacements from the vertical, a **physical pendulum** moves in simple harmonic motion about a pivot that does not go through the center of mass. The period of this motion is

$$T = 2\pi\sqrt{\frac{I}{mgd}} \quad \textbf{(15.28)}$$

where I is the moment of inertia about an axis through the pivot and d is the distance from the pivot to the center of mass.

If an oscillator experiences a damping force $\vec{R} = -b\vec{v}$, its position for small damping is described by

$$x = Ae^{-(b/2m)t}\cos(\omega t + \phi) \quad \textbf{(15.32)}$$

where

$$\omega = \sqrt{\frac{k}{m} - \left(\frac{b}{2m}\right)^2} \quad \textbf{(15.33)}$$

If an oscillator is subject to a sinusoidal driving force $F(t) = F_0 \sin \omega t$, it exhibits **resonance,** in which the amplitude is largest when the driving frequency ω matches the natural frequency $\omega_0 = \sqrt{k/m}$ of the oscillator.

ANALYSIS MODEL FOR PROBLEM SOLVING

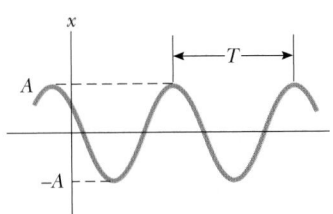

Particle in Simple Harmonic Motion If a particle is subject to a force of the form of Hooke's law $F = -kx$, the particle exhibits **simple harmonic motion**. Its position is described by

$$x(t) = A\cos(\omega t + \phi) \quad \textbf{(15.6)}$$

where A is the **amplitude** of the motion, ω is the **angular frequency,** and ϕ is the **phase constant.** The value of ϕ depends on the initial position and initial velocity of the oscillator.

The **period** of the oscillation is

$$T = \frac{2\pi}{\omega} = 2\pi\sqrt{\frac{m}{k}} \quad \textbf{(15.13)}$$

and the inverse of the period is the **frequency.**

Questions

□ denotes answer available in *Student Solutions Manual/Study Guide;* **O** denotes objective question

1. Is a bouncing ball an example of simple harmonic motion? Is the daily movement of a student from home to school and back simple harmonic motion? Why or why not?

2. **O** A particle on a spring moves in simple harmonic motion along the x axis between turning points at $x_1 = 100$ cm and $x_2 = 140$ cm. **(i)** At which of the following positions does the particle have maximum speed? (a) 100 cm (b) 110 cm (c) 120 cm (d) some other position (e) The same greatest value occurs at multiple points. **(ii)** At which position does it have maximum acceleration? Choose from the same possibilities. **(iii)** At which position is the greatest net force exerted on the particle? **(iv)** At which position does the particle have the greatest magnitude of momentum? **(v)** At which position does the particle have greatest kinetic energy? **(vi)** At which position does the particle-spring system have the greatest total energy?

3. If the coordinate of a particle varies as $x = -A \cos \omega t$, what is the phase constant in Equation 15.6? At what position is the particle at $t = 0$?

4. **O** Rank the periods of the following oscillating systems from the greatest to the smallest. If any periods are equal, show their equality in your ranking. Each system differs in only one way from system (a), which is a 0.1-kg glider on a horizontal, frictionless surface, oscillating with amplitude 0.1 m on a spring with force constant 10 N/m. In situation (b), the amplitude is 0.2 m. In situation (c), the mass is 0.2 kg. In situation (d), the spring has stiffness constant 20 N/m. Situation (e) is just like situation (a) except for being in a gravitational field of 4.9 m/s² instead of 9.8 m/s². Situation (f) is just like situation (a) except that the object bounces in simple harmonic motion on the bottom end of the spring hanging vertically. Situation (g) is just like situation (a) except that a small resistive force makes the motion underdamped.

5. **O** For a simple harmonic oscillator, the position is measured as the displacement from equilibrium. (a) Can the quantities position and velocity be in the same direction? (b) Can velocity and acceleration be in the same direction? (c) Can position and acceleration be in the same direction?

6. **O** The top end of a spring is held fixed. A block is hung on the bottom end and the frequency f of the oscillation of the system is measured. The block, a second identical block, and the spring are carried up in a space shuttle to Earth orbit. The two blocks are attached to the ends of the spring. The spring is compressed, without making adjacent coils touch, and the system is released to oscillate while floating within the shuttle cabin. What is the frequency of oscillation for this system in terms of f? (a) $f/4$ (b) $f/2$ (c) $f/\sqrt{2}$ (d) f (e) $\sqrt{2}f$ (f) $2f$ (g) $4f$

7. **O** You attach a block to the bottom end of a spring hanging vertically. You slowly let the block move down and find that it hangs at rest with the spring stretched by 15.0 cm. Next, you lift the block back up and release it from rest with the spring unstretched. What maximum distance does it move down? (a) 7.5 cm (b) 15.0 cm (c) 30.0 cm (d) 60.0 cm (e) The distance cannot be determined without knowing the mass and spring constant.

8. The equations listed in Table 2.2 give position as a function of time, velocity as a function of time, and velocity as function of position for an object moving in a straight line with constant acceleration. The quantity v_{xi} appears in every equation. Do any of these equations apply to an object moving in a straight line with simple harmonic motion? Using a similar format, make a table of equations describing simple harmonic motion. Include equations giving acceleration as a function of time and acceleration as a function of position. State the equations in such a form that they apply equally to a block-spring system, to a pendulum, and to other vibrating systems. What quantity appears in every equation?

9. **O** A simple pendulum has a period of 2.5 s. **(i)** What is its period if its length is made four times larger? (a) 0.625 s (b) 1.25 s (c) 2.5 s (d) 3.54 s (e) 5 s (f) 10 s **(ii)** What is its period if, instead of changing its length, the mass of the suspended bob is made four times larger? Choose from the same possibilities.

10. **O** A simple pendulum is suspended from the ceiling of a stationary elevator, and the period is determined. **(i)** When the elevator accelerates upward, is the period (a) greater, (b) smaller, or (c) unchanged? **(ii)** When the elevator has a downward acceleration, is the period (a) greater, (b) smaller, or (c) unchanged? **(iii)** When the elevator moves with constant upward velocity, is the period of the pendulum (a) greater, (b) smaller, or (c) unchanged?

11. Figure Q15.11 shows graphs of the potential energy of four different systems versus the position of a particle in each system. Each particle is set into motion with a push at an arbitrarily chosen location. Describe its subsequent motion in each case (a), (b), (c), and (d).

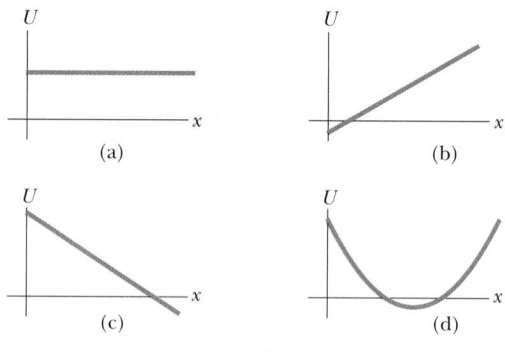

Figure Q15.11

12. A simple pendulum can be modeled as exhibiting simple harmonic motion when θ is small. Is the motion periodic when θ is large? How does the period of motion change as θ increases?

13. The mechanical energy of an undamped block-spring system is constant as kinetic energy transforms to elastic potential energy and vice versa. For comparison, explain

in the same terms what happens to the energy of a damped oscillator.

14. A student thinks that any real vibration must be damped. Is the student correct? If so, give convincing reasoning. If not, give an example of a real vibration that keeps constant amplitude forever if the system is isolated.

15. Will damped oscillations occur for any values of b and k? Explain.

16. Is it possible to have damped oscillations when a system is at resonance? Explain.

17. You stand on the end of a diving board and bounce to set it into oscillation. You find a maximum response, in terms of the amplitude of oscillation of the end of the board, when you bounce at frequency f. You now move to the middle of the board and repeat the experiment. Is the resonance frequency for forced oscillations at this point higher, lower, or the same as f? Why?

18. You are looking at a small, leafy tree. You do not notice any breeze, and most of the leaves on the tree are motionless. One leaf, however, is fluttering back and forth wildly. After a while, that leaf stops moving and you notice a different leaf moving much more than all the others. Explain what could cause the large motion of one particular leaf.

19. The bob of a certain pendulum is a sphere filled with water. What would happen to the frequency of vibration of this pendulum if there were a hole in the sphere that allowed the water to leak out slowly?

Problems

WebAssign The Problems from this chapter may be assigned online in WebAssign.

ThomsonNOW Sign in at **www.thomsonedu.com** and go to ThomsonNOW to assess your understanding of this chapter's topics with additional quizzing and conceptual questions.

1, 2, 3 denotes straightforward, intermediate, challenging;   ☐ denotes full solution available in *Student Solutions Manual/Study Guide;*   ▲ denotes coached solution with hints available at **www.thomsonedu.com;**   denotes developing symbolic reasoning;   ● denotes asking for qualitative reasoning;   ⬛ denotes computer useful in solving problem

> *Note:* Ignore the mass of every spring, except in Problems 62 and 64.

Section 15.1 Motion of an Object Attached to a Spring

> Problems 16, 17, 18, 26, and 60 in Chapter 7 can also be assigned with this section.

1. ● A ball dropped from a height of 4.00 m makes an elastic collision with the ground. Assuming no mechanical energy is lost due to air resistance, (a) show that the ensuing motion is periodic and (b) determine the period of the motion. (c) Is the motion simple harmonic? Explain.

Section 15.2 The Particle in Simple Harmonic Motion

2. In an engine, a piston oscillates with simple harmonic motion so that its position varies according to the expression

$$x = (5.00 \text{ cm}) \cos\left(2t + \frac{\pi}{6}\right)$$

where x is in centimeters and t is in seconds. At $t = 0$, find (a) the position of the particle, (b) its velocity, and (c) its acceleration. (d) Find the period and amplitude of the motion.

3. The position of a particle is given by the expression $x = (4.00 \text{ m}) \cos(3.00\pi t + \pi)$, where x is in meters and t is in seconds. Determine (a) the frequency and period of the motion, (b) the amplitude of the motion, (c) the phase constant, and (d) the position of the particle at $t = 0.250$ s.

4. ● (a) A hanging spring stretches by 35.0 cm when an object of mass 450 g is hung on it at rest. In this situation, we define its position as $x = 0$. The object is pulled down an additional 18.0 cm and released from rest to oscillate without friction. What is its position x at a moment 84.4 s later? (b) **What If?** Another hanging spring stretches by 35.5 cm when an object of mass 440 g is hung on it at rest. We define this new position as $x = 0$. This object is also pulled down an additional 18.0 cm and released from rest to oscillate without friction. Find its position 84.4 s later. (c) Why are the answers to parts (a) and (b) different by such a large percentage when the data are so similar? Does this circumstance reveal a fundamental difficulty in calculating the future? (d) Find the distance traveled by the vibrating object in part (a). (e) Find the distance traveled by the object in part (b).

5. ▲ A particle moving along the x axis in simple harmonic motion starts from its equilibrium position, the origin, at $t = 0$ and moves to the right. The amplitude of its motion is 2.00 cm, and the frequency is 1.50 Hz. (a) Show that the position of the particle is given by

$$x = (2.00 \text{ cm}) \sin (3.00\pi t)$$

Determine (b) the maximum speed and the earliest time ($t > 0$) at which the particle has this speed, (c) the maximum acceleration and the earliest time ($t > 0$) at which the particle has this acceleration, and (d) the total distance traveled between $t = 0$ and $t = 1.00$ s.

6. A simple harmonic oscillator takes 12.0 s to undergo five complete vibrations. Find (a) the period of its motion, (b) the frequency in hertz, and (c) the angular frequency in radians per second.

7. A 7.00-kg object is hung from the bottom end of a vertical spring fastened to an overhead beam. The object is set into vertical oscillations having a period of 2.60 s. Find the force constant of the spring.

8. **Review problem.** A particle moves along the x axis. It is initially at the position 0.270 m, moving with velocity

0.140 m/s and acceleration -0.320 m/s^2. Suppose it moves with constant acceleration for 4.50 s. Find (a) its position and (b) its velocity at the end of this time interval. Next, assume it moves with simple harmonic motion for 4.50 s and $x = 0$ is its equilibrium position. Find (c) its position and (d) its velocity at the end of this time interval.

9. A piston in a gasoline engine is in simple harmonic motion. Taking the extremes of its position relative to its center point as ± 5.00 cm, find the maximum velocity and acceleration of the piston when the engine is running at the rate of 3 600 rev/min.

10. A 1.00-kg glider attached to a spring with a force constant of 25.0 N/m oscillates on a horizontal, frictionless air track. At $t = 0$, the glider is released from rest at $x = -3.00$ cm. (That is, the spring is compressed by 3.00 cm.) Find (a) the period of its motion, (b) the maximum values of its speed and acceleration, and (c) the position, velocity, and acceleration as functions of time.

11. A 0.500-kg object attached to a spring with a force constant of 8.00 N/m vibrates in simple harmonic motion with an amplitude of 10.0 cm. Calculate (a) the maximum value of its speed and acceleration, (b) the speed and acceleration when the object is 6.00 cm from the equilibrium position, and (c) the time interval required for the object to move from $x = 0$ to $x = 8.00$ cm.

12. ● You attach an object to the bottom end of a hanging vertical spring. It hangs at rest after extending the spring 18.3 cm. You then set the object vibrating. Do you have enough information to find its period? Explain your answer and state whatever you can about its period.

13. A 1.00-kg object is attached to a horizontal spring. The spring is initially stretched by 0.100 m, and the object is released from rest there. It proceeds to move without friction. The next time the speed of the object is zero is 0.500 s later. What is the maximum speed of the object?

Section 15.3 Energy of the Simple Harmonic Oscillator

14. A 200-g block is attached to a horizontal spring and executes simple harmonic motion with a period of 0.250 s. The total energy of the system is 2.00 J. Find (a) the force constant of the spring and (b) the amplitude of the motion.

15. ▲ An automobile having a mass of 1 000 kg is driven into a brick wall in a safety test. The car's bumper behaves like a spring of constant 5.00×10^6 N/m and compresses 3.16 cm as the car is brought to rest. What was the speed of the car before impact, assuming that no mechanical energy is lost during impact with the wall?

16. A block-spring system oscillates with an amplitude of 3.50 cm. The spring constant is 250 N/m, and the mass of the block is 0.500 kg. Determine (a) the mechanical energy of the system, (b) the maximum speed of the block, and (c) the maximum acceleration.

17. A 50.0-g object connected to a spring with a force constant of 35.0 N/m oscillates on a horizontal, frictionless surface with an amplitude of 4.00 cm. Find (a) the total energy of the system and (b) the speed of the object when the position is 1.00 cm. Find (c) the kinetic energy and (d) the potential energy when the position is 3.00 cm.

18. A 2.00-kg object is attached to a spring and placed on a horizontal, smooth surface. A horizontal force of 20.0 N is required to hold the object at rest when it is pulled 0.200 m from its equilibrium position (the origin of the x axis). The object is now released from rest with an initial position of $x_i = 0.200$ m, and it subsequently undergoes simple harmonic oscillations. Find (a) the force constant of the spring, (b) the frequency of the oscillations, and (c) the maximum speed of the object. Where does this maximum speed occur? (d) Find the maximum acceleration of the object. Where does it occur? (e) Find the total energy of the oscillating system. Find (f) the speed and (g) the acceleration of the object when its position is equal to one-third of the maximum value.

19. A particle executes simple harmonic motion with an amplitude of 3.00 cm. At what position does its speed equal one half of its maximum speed?

20. A 65.0-kg bungee jumper steps off a bridge with a light bungee cord tied to her and to the bridge (Fig. P15.20). The unstretched length of the cord is 11.0 m. The jumper reaches the bottom of her motion 36.0 m below the bridge before bouncing back. Her motion can be separated into an 11.0-m free fall and a 25.0-m section of simple harmonic oscillation. (a) For what time interval is she in free fall? (b) Use the principle of conservation of energy to find the spring constant of the bungee cord. (c) What is the location of the equilibrium point where the spring force balances the gravitational force exerted on the jumper? This point is taken as the origin in our mathematical description of simple harmonic oscillation. (d) What is the angular frequency of the oscillation? (e) What time interval is required for the cord to stretch by 25.0 m? (f) What is the total time interval for the entire 36.0 m drop?

Figure P15.20   Problems 20 and 54.

21. A cart attached to a spring with constant 3.24 N/m vibrates such that its position is given by the function $x = (5.00 \text{ cm}) \cos (3.60t \text{ rad/s})$. (a) During the first cycle, for $0 < t < 1.75$ s, at what value of t is the system's potential energy changing most rapidly into kinetic energy? (b) What is the maximum rate of energy transformation?

Section 15.4 Comparing Simple Harmonic Motion with Uniform Circular Motion

22. ● Consider the simplified single-piston engine in Figure P15.22. Assuming the wheel rotates with constant angular speed, explain why the piston rod oscillates in simple harmonic motion.

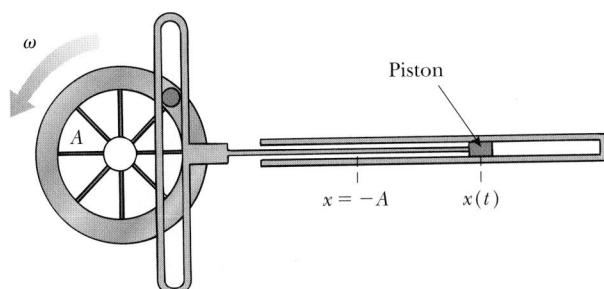

Figure P15.22

23. ● While riding behind a car traveling at 3.00 m/s, you notice that one of the car's tires has a small hemispherical bump on its rim as shown in Figure P15.23. (a) Explain why the bump, from your viewpoint behind the car, executes simple harmonic motion. (b) If the radii of the car's tires are 0.300 m, what is the bump's period of oscillation?

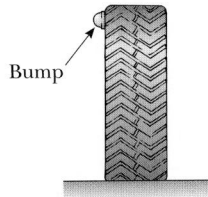

Figure P15.23

Section 15.5 The Pendulum

Problem 52 in Chapter 1 can also be assigned with this section.

24. A "seconds pendulum" is one that moves through its equilibrium position once each second. (The period of the pendulum is precisely 2 s.) The length of a seconds pendulum is 0.992 7 m at Tokyo, Japan, and 0.994 2 m at Cambridge, England. What is the ratio of the free-fall accelerations at these two locations?

25. ▲ ● A simple pendulum has a mass of 0.250 kg and a length of 1.00 m. It is displaced through an angle of 15.0° and then released. What are (a) the maximum speed, (b) the maximum angular acceleration, and (c) the maximum restoring force? **What If?** Solve this problem by using the simple harmonic motion model for the motion of the pendulum and then solve the problem by using more general principles. Compare the answers.

26. The angular position of a pendulum is represented by the equation $\theta = (0.032\ 0\ \text{rad}) \cos \omega t$, where θ is in radians and $\omega = 4.43$ rad/s. Determine the period and length of the pendulum.

27. A particle of mass m slides without friction inside a hemispherical bowl of radius R. Show that if the particle starts from rest with a small displacement from equilibrium, it moves in simple harmonic motion with an angular frequency equal to that of a simple pendulum of length R. That is, $\omega = \sqrt{g/R}$.

28. Review problem. A simple pendulum is 5.00 m long. (a) What is the period of small oscillations for this pendu-

lum if it is located in an elevator accelerating upward at 5.00 m/s²? (b) What is its period if the elevator is accelerating downward at 5.00 m/s²? (c) What is the period of this pendulum if it is placed in a truck that is accelerating horizontally at 5.00 m/s²?

29. A physical pendulum in the form of a planar object moves in simple harmonic motion with a frequency of 0.450 Hz. The pendulum has a mass of 2.20 kg, and the pivot is located 0.350 m from the center of mass. Determine the moment of inertia of the pendulum about the pivot point.

30. ▪ A small object is attached to the end of a string to form a simple pendulum. The period of its harmonic motion is measured for small angular displacements and three lengths. For each length, the time interval for 50 oscillations is measured with a stopwatch. For lengths of 1.000 m, 0.750 m, and 0.500 m, total time intervals of 99.8 s, 86.6 s, and 71.1 s are measured for 50 oscillations. (a) Determine the period of motion for each length. (b) Determine the mean value of g obtained from these three independent measurements and compare it with the accepted value. (c) Plot T^2 versus L and obtain a value for g from the slope of your best-fit straight-line graph. Compare this value with that obtained in part (b).

31. Consider the physical pendulum of Figure 15.17. (a) Represent its moment of inertia about an axis passing through its center of mass and parallel to the axis passing through its pivot point as I_{CM}. Show that its period is

$$T = 2\pi \sqrt{\frac{I_{CM} + md^2}{mgd}}$$

where d is the distance between the pivot point and center of mass. (b) Show that the period has a minimum value when d satisfies $md^2 = I_{CM}$.

32. A very light rigid rod with a length of 0.500 m extends straight out from one end of a meterstick. The meterstick is suspended from a pivot at the far end of the rod and is set into oscillation. (a) Determine the period of oscillation. *Suggestion:* Use the parallel-axis theorem from Section 10.5. (b) By what percentage does the period differ from the period of a simple pendulum 1.00 m long?

33. A clock balance wheel (Fig. P15.33) has a period of oscillation of 0.250 s. The wheel is constructed so that its mass of 20.0 g is concentrated around a rim of radius 0.500 cm. What are (a) the wheel's moment of inertia and (b) the torsion constant of the attached spring?

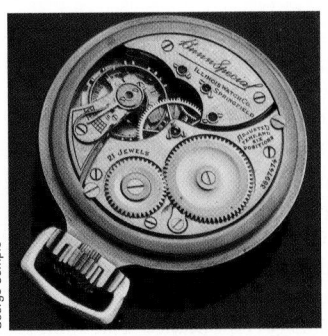

Figure P15.33

Section 15.6 Damped Oscillations

34. Show that the time rate of change of mechanical energy for a damped, undriven oscillator is given by $dE/dt = -bv^2$ and hence is always negative. To do so, differentiate the expression for the mechanical energy of an oscillator, $E = \frac{1}{2}mv^2 + \frac{1}{2}kx^2$, and use Equation 15.31.

35. A pendulum with a length of 1.00 m is released from an initial angle of 15.0°. After 1 000 s, its amplitude has been reduced by friction to 5.50°. What is the value of $b/2m$?

36. Show that Equation 15.32 is a solution of Equation 15.31 provided $b^2 < 4mk$.

37. A 10.6-kg object oscillates at the end of a vertical spring that has a spring constant of 2.05×10^4 N/m. The effect of air resistance is represented by the damping coefficient $b = 3.00$ N·s/m. (a) Calculate the frequency of the damped oscillation. (b) By what percentage does the amplitude of the oscillation decrease in each cycle? (c) Find the time interval that elapses while the energy of the system drops to 5.00% of its initial value.

Section 15.7 Forced Oscillations

38. The front of her sleeper wet from teething, a baby rejoices in the day by crowing and bouncing up and down in her crib. Her mass is 12.5 kg, and the crib mattress can be modeled as a light spring with force constant 4.30 kN/m. (a) The baby soon learns to bounce with maximum amplitude and minimum effort by bending her knees at what frequency? (b) She learns to use the mattress as a trampoline—losing contact with it for part of each cycle—when her amplitude exceeds what value?

39. A 2.00-kg object attached to a spring moves without friction and is driven by an external force given by $F = (3.00 \text{ N}) \sin (2\pi t)$. The force constant of the spring is 20.0 N/m. Determine (a) the period and (b) the amplitude of the motion.

40. Considering an undamped, forced oscillator ($b = 0$), show that Equation 15.35 is a solution of Equation 15.34, with an amplitude given by Equation 15.36.

41. A block weighing 40.0 N is suspended from a spring that has a force constant of 200 N/m. The system is undamped and is subjected to a harmonic driving force of frequency 10.0 Hz, resulting in a forced-motion amplitude of 2.00 cm. Determine the maximum value of the driving force.

42. Damping is negligible for a 0.150-kg object hanging from a light 6.30-N/m spring. A sinusoidal force with an amplitude of 1.70 N drives the system. At what frequency will the force make the object vibrate with an amplitude of 0.440 m?

43. You are a research biologist. Even though your emergency pager's batteries are getting low, you take the pager along to a fine restaurant. You switch the small pager to vibrate instead of beep, and you put it into a side pocket of your suit coat. The arm of your chair presses the light cloth against your body at one spot. Fabric with a length of 8.21 cm hangs freely below that spot, with the pager at the bottom. A coworker urgently needs instructions and pages you from the laboratory. The motion of the pager makes the hanging part of your coat swing back and forth with remarkably large amplitude. The waiter, maître d', wine steward, and nearby diners notice immediately and fall silent. Your daughter pipes up and says, accurately enough,

"Daddy, look! Your cockroaches must have gotten out again!" Find the frequency at which your pager vibrates.

Additional Problems

44. ● **Review problem.** The problem extends the reasoning of Problem 54 in Chapter 9. Two gliders are set in motion on an air track. Glider one has mass $m_1 = 0.240$ kg and velocity $0.740\hat{i}$ m/s. It will have a rear-end collision with glider number two, of mass $m_2 = 0.360$ kg, which has original velocity $0.120\hat{i}$ m/s. A light spring of force constant 45.0 N/m is attached to the back end of glider two as shown in Figure P9.54. When glider one touches the spring, superglue instantly and permanently makes it stick to its end of the spring. (a) Find the common velocity the two gliders have when the spring compression is a maximum. (b) Find the maximum spring compression distance. (c) Argue that the motion after the gliders become attached consists of the center of mass of the two-glider system moving with the constant velocity found in part (a) while both gliders oscillate in simple harmonic motion relative to the center of mass. (d) Find the energy of the center-of-mass motion. (e) Find the energy of the oscillation.

45. ● An object of mass m moves in simple harmonic motion with amplitude 12.0 cm on a light spring. Its maximum acceleration is 108 cm/s². Regard m as a variable. (a) Find the period T of the object. (b) Find its frequency f. (c) Find the maximum speed v_{max} of the object. (d) Find the energy E of the vibration. (e) Find the force constant k of the spring. (f) Describe the pattern of dependence of each of the quantities T, f, v_{max}, E, and k on m.

46. ● **Review problem.** A rock rests on a concrete sidewalk. An earthquake strikes, making the ground move vertically in harmonic motion with a constant frequency of 2.40 Hz and with gradually increasing amplitude. (a) With what amplitude does the ground vibrate when the rock begins to lose contact with the sidewalk? Another rock is sitting on the concrete bottom of a swimming pool full of water. The earthquake produces only vertical motion, so the water does not slosh from side to side. (b) Present a convincing argument that when the ground vibrates with the amplitude found in part (a), the submerged rock also barely loses contact with the floor of the swimming pool.

47. A small ball of mass M is attached to the end of a uniform rod of equal mass M and length L that is pivoted at the top (Fig. P15.47). (a) Determine the tensions in the rod at the pivot and at the point P when the system is stationary. (b) Calculate the period of oscillation for small displacements from equilibrium and determine this period for $L = 2.00$ m. *Suggestions:* Model the object at the end of the rod as a particle and use Eq. 15.28.

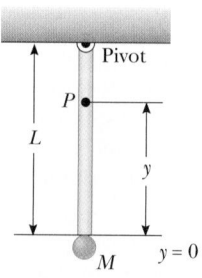

Figure P15.47

---

48. An object of mass $m_1 = 9.00$ kg is in equilibrium, connected to a light spring of constant $k = 100$ N/m that is fastened to a wall as shown in Figure P15.48a. A second object, $m_2 = 7.00$ kg, is slowly pushed up against m_1, compressing the spring by the amount $A = 0.200$ m (see Fig. P15.48b). The system is then released, and both objects start moving to the right on the frictionless surface. (a) When m_1 reaches the equilibrium point, m_2 loses contact with m_1 (see Fig. P15.48c) and moves to the right with speed v. Determine the value of v. (b) How far apart are the objects when the spring is fully stretched for the first time (D in Fig. P15.48d)? *Suggestion:* First determine the period of oscillation and the amplitude of the m_1–spring system after m_2 loses contact with m_1.

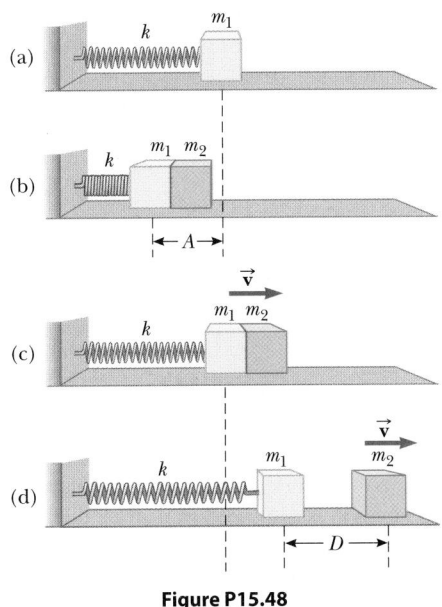

Figure P15.48

49. ▲ A large block P executes horizontal simple harmonic motion as it slides across a frictionless surface with a frequency $f = 1.50$ Hz. Block B rests on it as shown in Figure P15.49, and the coefficient of static friction between the two is $\mu_s = 0.600$. What maximum amplitude of oscillation can the system have if block B is not to slip?

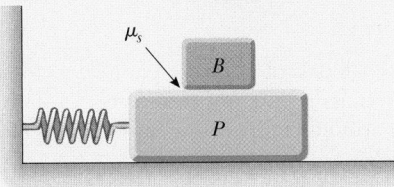

Figure P15.49 Problems 49 and 50.

50. A large block P executes horizontal simple harmonic motion as it slides across a frictionless surface with a frequency f. Block B rests on it as shown in Figure P15.49, and the coefficient of static friction between the two is μ_s. What maximum amplitude of oscillation can the system have if the upper block is not to slip?

51. The mass of the deuterium molecule (D_2) is twice that of the hydrogen molecule (H_2). If the vibrational frequency of H_2 is 1.30×10^{14} Hz, what is the vibrational frequency of D_2? Assume the "spring constant" of attracting forces is the same for the two molecules.

52. ● *You can now more completely analyze the situation in Problem 54 of Chapter 7.* Two steel balls, each of diameter 25.4 mm, move in opposite directions at 5.00 m/s. They collide head-on and bounce apart elastically. (a) Does their interaction last only for an instant or for a nonzero time interval? State your evidence. (b) One of the balls is squeezed in a vise while precise measurements are made of the resulting amount of compression. Assume Hooke's law is a good model of the ball's elastic behavior. For one datum, a force of 16.0 kN exerted by each jaw of the vise reduces the diameter by 0.200 mm. Modeling the ball as a spring, find its spring constant. (c) Assume the balls have the density of iron. Compute the kinetic energy of each ball before the balls collide. (d) Model each ball as a particle with a massless spring as its front bumper. Let the particle have the initial kinetic energy found in part (c) and the bumper have the spring constant found in part (b). Compute the maximum amount of compression each ball undergoes when the balls collide. (e) Model the motion of each ball, while the balls are in contact, as one half of a cycle of simple harmonic motion. Compute the time interval for which the balls are in contact.

53. A light, cubical container of volume a^3 is initially filled with a liquid of mass density ρ. The cube is initially supported by a light string to form a simple pendulum of length L_i, measured from the center of mass of the filled container, where $L_i \gg a$. The liquid is allowed to flow from the bottom of the container at a constant rate (dM/dt). At any time t, the level of the fluid in the container is h and the length of the pendulum is L (measured relative to the instantaneous center of mass). (a) Sketch the apparatus and label the dimensions a, h, L_i, and L. (b) Find the time rate of change of the period as a function of time t. (c) Find the period as a function of time.

54. After a thrilling plunge, bungee jumpers bounce freely on the bungee cord through many cycles (Fig. P15.20). After the first few cycles, the cord does not go slack. Your younger brother can make a pest of himself by figuring out the mass of each person, using a proportion that you set up by solving this problem: An object of mass m is oscillating freely on a vertical spring with a period T. Another object of unknown mass m' on the same spring oscillates with a period T'. Determine (a) the spring constant and (b) the unknown mass.

55. A pendulum of length L and mass M has a spring of force constant k connected to it at a distance h below its point of suspension (Fig. P15.55). Find the frequency of vibration

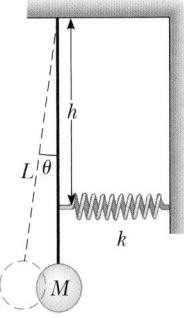

Figure P15.55

of the system for small values of the amplitude (small θ). Assume the vertical suspension rod of length L is rigid, but ignore its mass.

56. A particle with a mass of 0.500 kg is attached to a spring with a force constant of 50.0 N/m. At the moment $t = 0$, the particle has its maximum speed of 20.0 m/s and is moving to the left. (a) Determine the particle's equation of motion, specifying its position as a function of time. (b) Where in the motion is the potential energy three times the kinetic energy? (c) Find the length of a simple pendulum with the same period. (d) Find the minimum time interval required for the particle to move from $x = 0$ to $x = 1.00$ m.

57. A horizontal plank of mass m and length L is pivoted at one end. The plank's other end is supported by a spring of force constant k (Fig. P15.57). The moment of inertia of the plank about the pivot is $\frac{1}{3}mL^2$. The plank is displaced by a small angle θ from its horizontal equilibrium position and released. (a) Show that the plank moves with simple harmonic motion with an angular frequency $\omega = \sqrt{3k/m}$. (b) Evaluate the frequency, taking the mass as 5.00 kg and the spring force constant as 100 N/m.

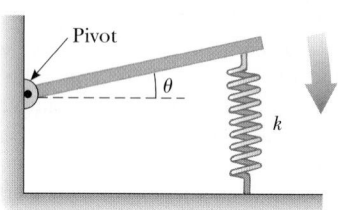

Figure P15.57

58. ● **Review problem.** A particle of mass 4.00 kg is attached to a spring with a force constant of 100 N/m. It is oscillating on a horizontal, frictionless surface with an amplitude of 2.00 m. A 6.00-kg object is dropped vertically on top of the 4.00-kg object as it passes through its equilibrium point. The two objects stick together. (a) By how much does the amplitude of the vibrating system change as a result of the collision? (b) By how much does the period change? (c) By how much does the energy change? (d) Account for the change in energy.

59. A simple pendulum with a length of 2.23 m and a mass of 6.74 kg is given an initial speed of 2.06 m/s at its equilibrium position. Assume it undergoes simple harmonic motion. Determine its (a) period, (b) total energy, and (c) maximum angular displacement.

60. **Review problem.** One end of a light spring with force constant 100 N/m is attached to a vertical wall. A light string is tied to the other end of the horizontal spring. The string changes from horizontal to vertical as it passes over a solid pulley of diameter 4.00 cm. The pulley is free to turn on a fixed, smooth axle. The vertical section of the string supports a 200-g object. The string does not slip at its contact with the pulley. Find the frequency of oscillation of the object, assuming the mass of the pulley is (a) negligible, (b) 250 g, and (c) 750 g.

61. ● People who ride motorcycles and bicycles learn to look out for bumps in the road and especially for *washboarding*, a condition in which many equally spaced ridges are worn into the road. What is so bad about washboarding? A motorcycle has several springs and shock absorbers in its suspension, but you can model it as a single spring supporting a block. You can estimate the force constant by thinking about how far the spring compresses when a heavy rider sits on the seat. A motorcyclist traveling at highway speed must be particularly careful of washboard bumps that are a certain distance apart. What is the order of magnitude of their separation distance? State the quantities you take as data and the values you measure or estimate for them.

62. A block of mass M is connected to a spring of mass m and oscillates in simple harmonic motion on a horizontal, frictionless track (Fig. P15.62). The force constant of the spring is k, and the equilibrium length is ℓ. Assume all portions of the spring oscillate in phase and the velocity of a segment dx is proportional to the distance x from the fixed end; that is, $v_x = (x/\ell)v$. Also, notice that the mass of a segment of the spring is $dm = (m/\ell)\,dx$. Find (a) the kinetic energy of the system when the block has a speed v and (b) the period of oscillation.

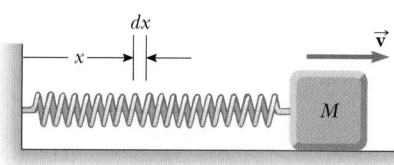

Figure P15.62

63. ▲ A ball of mass m is connected to two rubber bands of length L, each under tension T as shown in Figure P15.63. The ball is displaced by a small distance y perpendicular to the length of the rubber bands. Assuming the tension does not change, show that (a) the restoring force is $-(2T/L)y$ and (b) the system exhibits simple harmonic motion with an angular frequency $\omega = \sqrt{2T/mL}$.

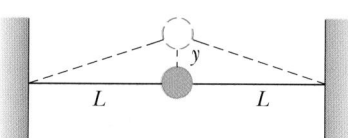

Figure P15.63

64. ♒ When a block of mass M, connected to the end of a spring of mass $m_s = 7.40$ g and force constant k, is set into simple harmonic motion, the period of its motion is

$$T = 2\pi\sqrt{\frac{M + (m_s/3)}{k}}$$

A two-part experiment is conducted with the use of blocks of various masses suspended vertically from the spring as shown in Figure P15.64. (a) Static extensions of 17.0, 29.3, 35.3, 41.3, 47.1, and 49.3 cm are measured for M values of 20.0, 40.0, 50.0, 60.0, 70.0, and 80.0 g, respectively. Construct a graph of Mg versus x and perform a linear least-squares fit to the data. From the slope of your graph, determine a value for k for this spring. (b) The system is now set into simple harmonic motion, and periods are measured with a stopwatch. With $M = 80.0$ g, the total

2 = intermediate;   3 = challenging;   □ = SSM/SG;   ▲ = ThomsonNOW;   ▨ = symbolic reasoning;   ● = qualitative reasoning

time interval required for ten oscillations is measured to be 13.41 s. The experiment is repeated with M values of 70.0, 60.0, 50.0, 40.0, and 20.0 g, with corresponding time intervals for ten oscillations of 12.52, 11.67, 10.67, 9.62, and 7.03 s. Compute the experimental value for T from each of these measurements. Plot a graph of T^2 versus M and determine a value for k from the slope of the linear least-squares fit through the data points. Compare this value of k with that obtained in part (a). (c) Obtain a value for m_s from your graph and compare it with the given value of 7.40 g.

Figure P15.64

65. A smaller disk of radius r and mass m is attached rigidly to the face of a second larger disk of radius R and mass M as shown in Figure P15.65. The center of the small disk is located at the edge of the large disk. The large disk is mounted at its center on a frictionless axle. The assembly is rotated through a small angle θ from its equilibrium position and released. (a) Show that the speed of the center of the small disk as it passes through the equilibrium position is

$$v = 2\left[\frac{Rg(1 - \cos\theta)}{(M/m) + (r/R)^2 + 2}\right]^{1/2}$$

(b) Show that the period of the motion is

$$T = 2\pi\left[\frac{(M + 2m)R^2 + mr^2}{2mgR}\right]^{1/2}$$

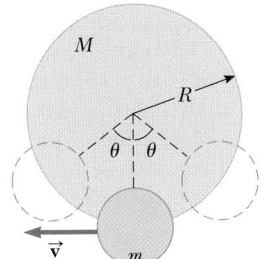

Figure P15.65

66. Consider a damped oscillator illustrated in Figures 15.20 and 15.21. The mass of the object is 375 g, the spring constant is 100 N/m, and $b = 0.100$ N·s/m. (a) Over what time interval does the amplitude drop to half its initial value? (b) **What If?** Over what time interval does the mechanical energy drop to half its initial value? (c) Show that, in general, the fractional rate at which the amplitude decreases in a damped harmonic oscillator is one-half the fractional rate at which the mechanical energy decreases.

67. A block of mass m is connected to two springs of force constants k_1 and k_2 in two ways as shown in Figures

P15.67a and P15.67b. In both cases, the block moves on a frictionless table after it is displaced from equilibrium and released. Show that in the two cases the block exhibits simple harmonic motion with periods

(a) $T = 2\pi\sqrt{\dfrac{m(k_1 + k_2)}{k_1 k_2}}$ and (b) $T = 2\pi\sqrt{\dfrac{m}{k_1 + k_2}}$

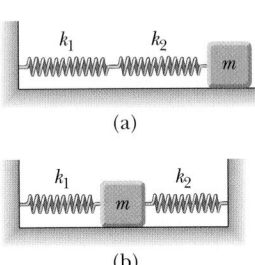

Figure P15.67

68. A lobsterman's buoy is a solid wooden cylinder of radius r and mass M. It is weighted at one end so that it floats upright in calm seawater, having density ρ. A passing shark tugs on the slack rope mooring the buoy to a lobster trap, pulling the buoy down a distance x from its equilibrium position and releasing it. Show that the buoy will execute simple harmonic motion if the resistive effects of the water are ignored and determine the period of the oscillations.

69. **Review problem.** Imagine that a hole is drilled through the center of the Earth to the other side. An object of mass m at a distance r from the center of the Earth is pulled toward the center of the Earth only by the mass within the sphere of radius r (the reddish region in Fig. P15.69). (a) Write Newton's law of gravitation for an object at the distance r from the center of the Earth and show that the force on it is of Hooke's law form, $F = -kr$, where the effective force constant is $k = \frac{4}{3}\pi\rho Gm$. Here ρ is the density of the Earth, assumed uniform, and G is the gravitational constant. (b) Show that a sack of mail dropped into the hole will execute simple harmonic motion if it moves without friction. When will it arrive at the other side of the Earth?

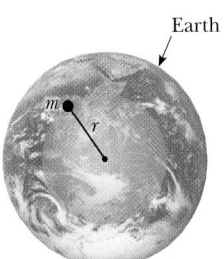

Figure P15.69

70. Your thumb squeaks on a plate you have just washed. Your sneakers squeak on the gym floor. Car tires squeal when you start or stop abruptly. Mortise joints groan in an old barn. The concertmaster's violin sings out over a full orchestra. You can make a goblet sing by wiping your moistened finger around its rim. As you slide it across the table, a Styrofoam cup may not make much sound, but it

makes the surface of some water inside it dance in a complicated resonance vibration. When chalk squeaks on a blackboard, you can see that it makes a row of regularly spaced dashes. As these examples suggest, vibration commonly results when friction acts on a moving elastic object. The oscillation is not simple harmonic motion, but is called *stick and slip*. This problem models stick-and-slip motion.

A block of mass m is attached to a fixed support by a horizontal spring with force constant k and negligible mass (Fig. P15.70). Hooke's law describes the spring both in extension and in compression. The block sits on a long horizontal board, with which it has coefficient of static friction μ_s and a smaller coefficient of kinetic friction μ_k. The board moves to the right at constant speed v. Assume the block spends most of its time sticking to the board and moving to the right, so the speed v is small in comparison to the average speed the block has as it slips back toward the left. (a) Show that the maximum extension of the spring from its unstressed position is very nearly given by $\mu_s mg/k$. (b) Show that the block oscillates around an equilibrium position at which the spring is stretched by $\mu_k mg/k$. (c) Graph the block's position versus time. (d) Show that the amplitude of the block's motion is

$$A = \frac{(\mu_s - \mu_k)mg}{k}$$

(e) Show that the period of the block's motion is

$$T = \frac{2(\mu_s - \mu_k)mg}{vk} + \pi\sqrt{\frac{m}{k}}$$

(f) Evaluate the frequency of the motion, taking $\mu_s = 0.400$, $\mu_k = 0.250$, $m = 0.300$ kg, $k = 12.0$ N/m, and $v = 2.40$ cm/s. (g) **What If?** What happens to the frequency if the mass increases? (h) If the spring constant increases? (i) If the speed of the board increases? (j) If the coefficient of static friction increases relative to the coefficient of kinetic friction? It is the excess of static over kinetic friction that is important for the vibration. "The squeaky wheel gets the grease" because even a viscous fluid cannot exert a force of static friction.

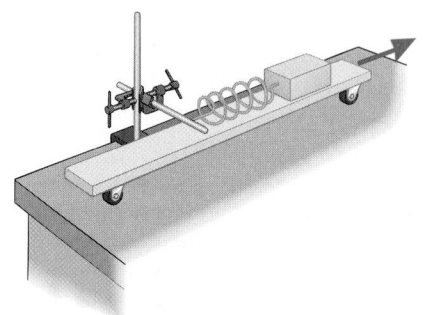

Figure P15.70

Answers to Quick Quizzes

15.1 (d). From its maximum positive position to the equilibrium position, the block travels a distance A. Next, it goes an equal distance past the equilibrium position to its maximum negative position. It then repeats these two motions in the reverse direction to return to its original position and complete one cycle.

15.2 (f). The object is in the region $x < 0$, so the position is negative. Because the object is moving back toward the origin in this region, the velocity is positive.

15.3 (a). The amplitude is larger because the curve for object B shows that the displacement from the origin (the vertical axis on the graph) is larger. The frequency is larger for object B because there are more oscillations per unit time interval.

15.4 (b). According to Equation 15.13, the period is proportional to the square root of the mass.

15.5 (c). The amplitude of the simple harmonic motion is the same as the radius of the circular motion. The initial position of the object in its circular motion is π radians from the positive x axis.

15.6 (i), (a). With a longer length, the period of the pendulum will increase. Therefore, it will take longer to execute each swing, so each second according to the clock will take longer than an actual second and the clock will run slow. (ii), (a). At the top of the mountain, the value of g is less than that at sea level. As a result, the period of the pendulum will increase and the clock will run slow.

Ocean waves combine properties of both transverse and longitudinal waves. With proper balance and timing, a surfer can capture a wave and take it for a ride. (© Rick Doyle/Corbis)

16 Wave Motion

Most of us experienced waves as children when we dropped a pebble into a pond. At the point the pebble hits the water's surface, waves are created. These waves move outward from the creation point in expanding circles until they reach the shore. If you were to examine carefully the motion of a small object floating on the disturbed water, you would see that the object moves vertically and horizontally about its original position but does not undergo any net displacement away from or toward the point the pebble hit the water. The small elements of water in contact with the object, as well as all the other water elements on the pond's surface, behave in the same way. That is, the water *wave* moves from the point of origin to the shore, but the water is not carried with it.

The world is full of waves, the two main types being *mechanical* waves and *electromagnetic* waves. In the case of mechanical waves, some physical medium is being disturbed; in our pebble example, elements of water are disturbed. Electromagnetic waves do not require a medium to propagate; some examples of electromagnetic waves are visible light, radio waves, television signals, and x-rays. Here, in this part of the book, we study only mechanical waves.

Consider again the small object floating on the water. We have caused the object to move at one point in the water by dropping a pebble at another location. The object has gained kinetic energy from our action, so energy must have trans-

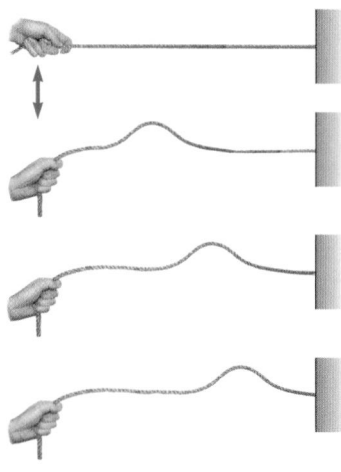

Figure 16.1 A pulse traveling down a stretched string. The shape of the pulse is approximately unchanged as it travels along the string.

ferred from the point at which the pebble is dropped to the position of the object. This feature is central to wave motion: *energy* is transferred over a distance, but *matter* is not.

16.1   Propagation of a Disturbance

The introduction to this chapter alluded to the essence of wave motion: the transfer of energy through space without the accompanying transfer of matter. In the list of energy transfer mechanisms in Chapter 8, two mechanisms—mechanical waves and electromagnetic radiation—depend on waves. By contrast, in another mechanism, matter transfer, the energy transfer is accompanied by a movement of matter through space.

All mechanical waves require (1) some source of disturbance, (2) a medium containing elements that can be disturbed, and (3) some physical mechanism through which elements of the medium can influence each other. One way to demonstrate wave motion is to flick one end of a long string that is under tension and has its opposite end fixed as shown in Figure 16.1. In this manner, a single bump (called a *pulse*) is formed and travels along the string with a definite speed. Figure 16.1 represents four consecutive "snapshots" of the creation and propagation of the traveling pulse. The string is the medium through which the pulse travels. The pulse has a definite height and a definite speed of propagation along the medium (the string). The shape of the pulse changes very little as it travels along the string.[1]

We shall first focus on a pulse traveling through a medium. Once we have explored the behavior of a pulse, we will then turn our attention to a *wave*, which is a *periodic* disturbance traveling through a medium. We create a pulse on our string by flicking the end of the string once as in Figure 16.1. If we were to move the end of the string up and down repeatedly, we would create a traveling wave, which has characteristics a pulse does not have. We shall explore these characteristics in Section 16.2.

As the pulse in Figure 16.1 travels, each disturbed element of the string moves in a direction *perpendicular* to the direction of propagation. Figure 16.2 illustrates this point for one particular element, labeled *P*. Notice that no part of the string ever moves in the direction of the propagation. A traveling wave or pulse that

Figure 16.2 A transverse pulse traveling on a stretched string. The direction of motion of any element *P* of the string (blue arrows) is perpendicular to the direction of propagation (red arrows).

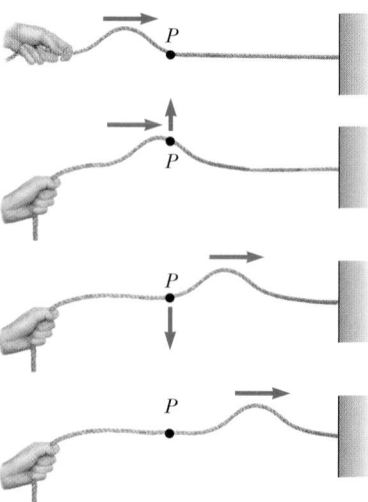

[1] In reality, the pulse changes shape and gradually spreads out during the motion. This effect, called *dispersion*, is common to many mechanical waves as well as to electromagnetic waves. We do not consider dispersion in this chapter.

Compressed

Figure 16.3   A longitudinal pulse along a stretched spring. The displacement of the coils is parallel to the direction of the propagation.

causes the elements of the disturbed medium to move perpendicular to the direction of propagation is called a **transverse wave.**

Compare this wave with another type of pulse, one moving down a long, stretched spring as shown in Figure 16.3. The left end of the spring is pushed briefly to the right and then pulled briefly to the left. This movement creates a sudden compression of a region of the coils. The compressed region travels along the spring (to the right in Fig. 16.3). Notice that the direction of the displacement of the coils is *parallel* to the direction of propagation of the compressed region. A traveling wave or pulse that causes the elements of the medium to move parallel to the direction of propagation is called a **longitudinal wave.**

Sound waves, which we shall discuss in Chapter 17, are another example of longitudinal waves. The disturbance in a sound wave is a series of high-pressure and low-pressure regions that travel through air.

Some waves in nature exhibit a combination of transverse and longitudinal displacements. Surface-water waves are a good example. When a water wave travels on the surface of deep water, elements of water at the surface move in nearly circular paths as shown in Active Figure 16.4. The disturbance has both transverse and longitudinal components. The transverse displacements seen in Active Figure 16.4 represent the variations in vertical position of the water elements. The longitudinal displacements represent elements of water moving back and forth in a horizontal direction.

The three-dimensional waves that travel out from a point under the Earth's surface at which an earthquake occurs are of both types, transverse and longitudinal. The longitudinal waves are the faster of the two, traveling at speeds in the range of 7 to 8 km/s near the surface. They are called **P waves,** with "P" standing for *primary,* because they travel faster than the transverse waves and arrive first at a seismograph (a device used to detect waves due to earthquakes). The slower transverse waves, called **S waves,** with "S" standing for *secondary,* travel through the Earth at 4 to 5 km/s near the surface. By recording the time interval between the arrivals of these two types of waves at a seismograph, the distance from the seismograph to the point of origin of the waves can be determined. A single measurement establishes an imaginary sphere centered on the seismograph, with the sphere's radius determined by the difference in arrival times of the P and S waves. The origin of the waves is located somewhere on that sphere. The imaginary spheres from three or more monitoring stations located far apart from one another intersect at one region of the Earth, and this region is where the earthquake occurred.

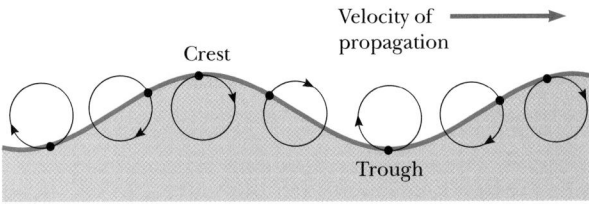

ACTIVE FIGURE 16.4

The motion of water elements on the surface of deep water in which a wave is propagating is a combination of transverse and longitudinal displacements. The result is that elements at the surface move in nearly circular paths. Each element is displaced both horizontally and vertically from its equilibrium position.

Sign in at www.thomsonedu.com and go to ThomsonNOW to observe the displacement of water elements at the surface of the moving waves.

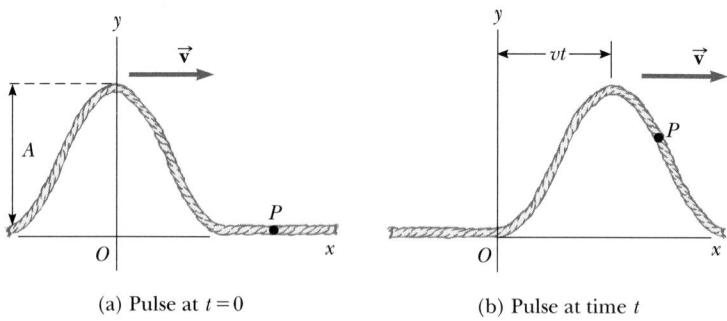

Figure 16.5   A one-dimensional pulse traveling to the right with a speed v. (a) At $t = 0$, the shape of the pulse is given by $y = f(x)$. (b) At some later time t, the shape remains unchanged and the vertical position of an element of the medium at any point P is given by $y = f(x - vt)$.

Consider a pulse traveling to the right on a long string as shown in Figure 16.5. Figure 16.5a represents the shape and position of the pulse at time $t = 0$. At this time, the shape of the pulse, whatever it may be, can be represented by some mathematical function that we will write as $y(x, 0) = f(x)$. This function describes the transverse position y of the element of the string located at each value of x at time $t = 0$. Because the speed of the pulse is v, the pulse has traveled to the right a distance vt at the time t (Fig. 16.5b). We assume the shape of the pulse does not change with time. Therefore, at time t, the shape of the pulse is the same as it was at time $t = 0$ as in Figure 16.5a. Consequently, an element of the string at x at this time has the same y position as an element located at $x - vt$ had at time $t = 0$:

$$y(x, t) = y(x - vt, 0)$$

In general, then, we can represent the transverse position y for all positions and times, measured in a stationary frame with the origin at O, as

Pulse traveling to the right ▶

$$y(x, t) = f(x - vt) \tag{16.1}$$

Similarly, if the pulse travels to the left, the transverse positions of elements of the string are described by

Pulse traveling to the left ▶

$$y(x, t) = f(x + vt) \tag{16.2}$$

The function y, sometimes called the **wave function,** depends on the two variables x and t. For this reason, it is often written $y(x, t)$, which is read "y as a function of x and t."

It is important to understand the meaning of y. Consider an element of the string at point P, identified by a particular value of its x coordinate. As the pulse passes through P, the y coordinate of this element increases, reaches a maximum, and then decreases to zero. **The wave function $y(x, t)$ represents the y coordinate— the transverse position—of any element located at position x at any time t.** Furthermore, if t is fixed (as, for example, in the case of taking a snapshot of the pulse), the wave function $y(x)$, sometimes called the **waveform,** defines a curve representing the geometric shape of the pulse at that time.

Quick Quiz 16.1   **(i)** In a long line of people waiting to buy tickets, the first person leaves and a pulse of motion occurs as people step forward to fill the gap. As each person steps forward, the gap moves through the line. Is the propagation of this gap (a) transverse or (b) longitudinal? **(ii)** Consider the "wave" at a baseball game: people stand up and raise their arms as the wave arrives at their location, and the resultant pulse moves around the stadium. Is this wave (a) transverse or (b) longitudinal?

EXAMPLE 16.1   **A Pulse Moving to the Right**

A pulse moving to the right along the x axis is represented by the wave function

$$y(x, t) = \frac{2}{(x - 3.0t)^2 + 1}$$

where x and y are measured in centimeters and t is measured in seconds. Find expressions for the wave function at $t = 0$, $t = 1.0$ s, and $t = 2.0$ s.

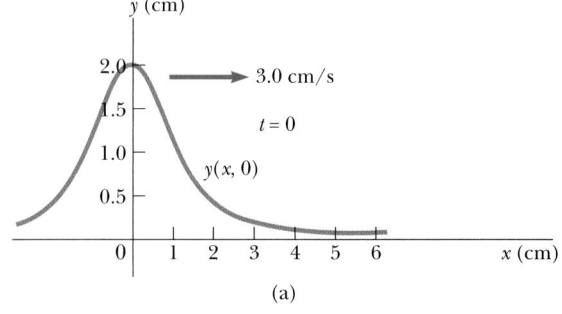

SOLUTION

Conceptualize Figure 16.6a shows the pulse represented by this wave function at $t = 0$. Imagine this pulse moving to the right and maintaining its shape as suggested by Figures 16.6b and 16.6c.

Categorize We categorize this example as a relatively simple analysis problem in which we interpret the mathematical representation of a pulse.

Analyze The wave function is of the form $y = f(x - vt)$. Inspection of the expression for $y(x, t)$ reveals that the wave speed is $v = 3.0$ cm/s. Furthermore, by letting $x - 3.0t = 0$, we find that the maximum value of y is given by $A = 2.0$ cm.

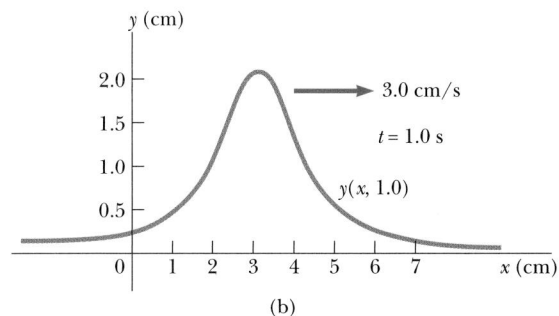

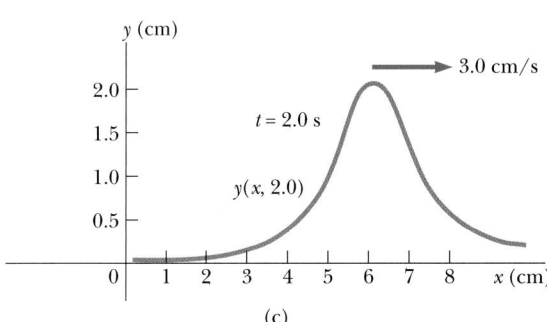

Figure 16.6   (Example 16.1) Graphs of the function $y(x, t) = 2/[(x - 3.0t)^2 + 1]$ at (a) $t = 0$, (b) $t = 1.0$ s, and (c) $t = 2.0$ s.

Write the wave function expression at $t = 0$:

$$y(x, 0) = \frac{2}{x^2 + 1}$$

Write the wave function expression at $t = 1.0$ s:

$$y(x, 1.0) = \frac{2}{(x - 3.0)^2 + 1}$$

Write the wave function expression at $t = 2.0$ s:

$$y(x, 2.0) = \frac{2}{(x - 6.0)^2 + 1}$$

For each of these expressions, we can substitute various values of x and plot the wave function. This procedure yields the wave functions shown in the three parts of Figure 16.6.

Finalize These snapshots show that the pulse moves to the right without changing its shape and that it has a constant speed of 3.0 cm/s.

What If?   What if the wave function were

$$y(x, t) = \frac{4}{(x + 3.0t)^2 + 1}$$

How would that change the situation?

Answer One new feature in this expression is the plus sign in the denominator rather than the minus sign. The new expression represents a pulse with the same shape as that in Figure 16.6, but moving to the left as time progresses. Another new feature here is the numerator of 4 rather than 2. Therefore, the new expression represents a pulse with twice the height of that in Figure 16.6.

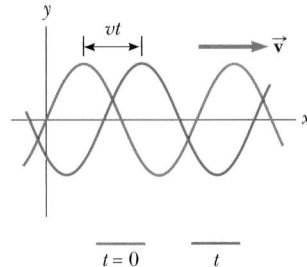

ACTIVE FIGURE 16.7

A one-dimensional sinusoidal wave traveling to the right with a speed v. The brown curve represents a snapshot of the wave at $t = 0$, and the blue curve represents a snapshot at some later time t.

Sign in at www.thomsonedu.com and go to ThomsonNOW to watch the wave move and take snapshots of it at various times.

PITFALL PREVENTION 16.1

What's the Difference Between Active Figures 16.8a and 16.8b?

Notice the visual similarity between Active Figures 16.8a and 16.8b. The shapes are the same, but (a) is a graph of vertical position versus horizontal position, whereas (b) is vertical position versus time. Active Figure 16.8a is a pictorial representation of the wave *for a series of particles of the medium;* it is what you would see at an instant of time. Active Figure 16.8b is a graphical representation of the position of *one element of the medium* as a function of time. That both figures have the identical shape represents Equation 16.1: a wave is the *same* function of both x and t.

16.2 The Traveling Wave Model

In this section, we introduce an important wave function whose shape is shown in Active Figure 16.7. The wave represented by this curve is called a **sinusoidal wave** because the curve is the same as that of the function $\sin \theta$ plotted against θ. A sinusoidal wave could be established on a rope by shaking the end of the rope up and down in simple harmonic motion.

The sinusoidal wave is the simplest example of a periodic continuous wave and can be used to build more complex waves (see Section 18.8). The brown curve in Active Figure 16.7 represents a snapshot of a traveling sinusoidal wave at $t = 0$, and the blue curve represents a snapshot of the wave at some later time t. Imagine two types of motion that can occur. First, the entire waveform in Active Figure 16.7 moves to the right so that the brown curve moves toward the right and eventually reaches the position of the blue curve. This movement is the motion of the *wave.* If we focus on one element of the medium, such as the element at $x = 0$, we see that each element moves up and down along the y axis in simple harmonic motion. This movement is the motion of the *elements of the medium.* It is important to differentiate between the motion of the wave and the motion of the elements of the medium.

In the early chapters of this book, we developed several analysis models based on the particle model. With our introduction to waves, we can develop a new simplification model, the **wave model,** that will allow us to explore more analysis models for solving problems. An ideal particle has zero size. We can build physical objects with nonzero size as combinations of particles. Therefore, the particle can be considered a basic building block. An ideal wave has a single frequency and is infinitely long; that is, the wave exists throughout the Universe. (An unbounded wave of finite length must necessarily have a mixture of frequencies.) When this concept is explored in Section 18.8, we will find that ideal waves can be combined, just as we combined particles.

In what follows, we will develop the principal features and mathematical representations of the analysis model of a **traveling wave.** This model is used in situations in which a wave moves through space without interacting with other waves or particles.

Active Figure 16.8a shows a snapshot of a wave moving through a medium. Active Figure 16.8b shows a graph of the position of one element of the medium as a function of time. A point in Active Figure 16.8a at which the displacement of the element from its normal position is highest is called the **crest** of the wave. The lowest point is called the **trough.** The distance from one crest to the next is called the **wavelength** λ (Greek letter lambda). More generally, **the wavelength is the minimum distance between any two identical points on adjacent waves** as shown in Active Figure 16.8a.

If you count the number of seconds between the arrivals of two adjacent crests at a given point in space, you measure the **period** T of the waves. In general, **the period is the time interval required for two identical points of adjacent waves to pass by a point** as shown in Active Figure 16.8b. The period of the wave is the same as the period of the simple harmonic oscillation of one element of the medium.

The same information is more often given by the inverse of the period, which is called the **frequency** f. In general, **the frequency of a periodic wave is the number of crests (or troughs, or any other point on the wave) that pass a given point in a unit time interval.** The frequency of a sinusoidal wave is related to the period by the expression

$$f = \frac{1}{T} \qquad \textbf{(16.3)}$$

The frequency of the wave is the same as the frequency of the simple harmonic oscillation of one element of the medium. The most common unit for frequency, as we learned in Chapter 15, is s^{-1}, or **hertz** (Hz). The corresponding unit for T is seconds.

The maximum position of an element of the medium relative to its equilibrium position is called the **amplitude** A of the wave.

Waves travel with a specific speed, and this speed depends on the properties of the medium being disturbed. For instance, sound waves travel through room-temperature air with a speed of about 343 m/s (781 mi/h), whereas they travel through most solids with a speed greater than 343 m/s.

Consider the sinusoidal wave in Active Figure 16.8a, which shows the position of the wave at $t = 0$. Because the wave is sinusoidal, we expect the wave function at this instant to be expressed as $y(x, 0) = A \sin ax$, where A is the amplitude and a is a constant to be determined. At $x = 0$, we see that $y(0, 0) = A \sin a(0) = 0$, consistent with Active Figure 16.8a. The next value of x for which y is zero is $x = \lambda/2$. Therefore,

$$y\left(\frac{\lambda}{2}, 0\right) = A \sin\left(a\frac{\lambda}{2}\right) = 0$$

For this equation to be true, we must have $a\lambda/2 = \pi$, or $a = 2\pi/\lambda$. Therefore, the function describing the positions of the elements of the medium through which the sinusoidal wave is traveling can be written

$$y(x, 0) = A \sin\left(\frac{2\pi}{\lambda}x\right) \qquad \textbf{(16.4)}$$

where the constant A represents the wave amplitude and the constant λ is the wavelength. Notice that the vertical position of an element of the medium is the same whenever x is increased by an integral multiple of λ. If the wave moves to the right with a speed v, the wave function at some later time t is

$$y(x, t) = A \sin\left[\frac{2\pi}{\lambda}(x - vt)\right] \qquad \textbf{(16.5)}$$

The wave function has the form $f(x - vt)$ (Eq. 16.1). If the wave were traveling to the left, the quantity $x - vt$ would be replaced by $x + vt$ as we learned when we developed Equations 16.1 and 16.2.

By definition, the wave travels through a displacement Δx equal to one wavelength λ in a time interval Δt of one period T. Therefore, the wave speed, wavelength, and period are related by the expression

$$v = \frac{\Delta x}{\Delta t} = \frac{\lambda}{T} \qquad \textbf{(16.6)}$$

Substituting this expression for v into Equation 16.5 gives

$$y = A \sin\left[2\pi\left(\frac{x}{\lambda} - \frac{t}{T}\right)\right] \qquad \textbf{(16.7)}$$

This form of the wave function shows the *periodic* nature of y. Note that we will often use y rather than $y(x, t)$ as a shorthand notation. At any given time t, y has the *same* value at the positions x, $x + \lambda$, $x + 2\lambda$, and so on. Furthermore, at any given position x, the value of y is the same at times t, $t + T$, $t + 2T$, and so on.

We can express the wave function in a convenient form by defining two other quantities, the **angular wave number** k (usually called simply the **wave number**) and the **angular frequency** ω:

$$k \equiv \frac{2\pi}{\lambda} \qquad \textbf{(16.8)}$$

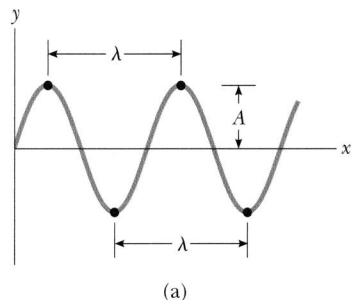
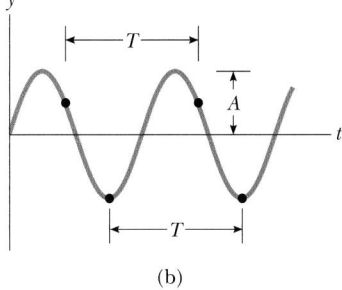

(a)

(b)

ACTIVE FIGURE 16.8

(a) A snapshot of a sinusoidal wave. The wavelength λ of a wave is the distance between adjacent crests or adjacent troughs. (b) The position of one element of the medium as a function of time. The period T of a wave is the time interval required for the element to complete one cycle of its oscillation and for the wave to travel one wavelength.

Sign in at www.thomsonedu.com and go to ThomsonNOW to change the parameters to see the effect on the wave function.

◀ Angular wave number

Angular frequency ▶

$$\omega \equiv \frac{2\pi}{T} = 2\pi f \qquad (16.9)$$

Using these definitions, Equation 16.7 can be written in the more compact form

Wave function for a ▶
sinusoidal wave

$$y = A \sin (kx - \omega t) \qquad (16.10)$$

Using Equations 16.3, 16.8, and 16.9, the wave speed v originally given in Equation 16.6 can be expressed in the following alternative forms:

$$v = \frac{\omega}{k} \qquad (16.11)$$

Speed of a sinusoidal wave ▶

$$v = \lambda f \qquad (16.12)$$

The wave function given by Equation 16.10 assumes the vertical position y of an element of the medium is zero at $x = 0$ and $t = 0$. That need not be the case. If it is not, we generally express the wave function in the form

General expression for a ▶
sinusoidal wave

$$y = A \sin (kx - \omega t + \phi) \qquad (16.13)$$

where ϕ is the **phase constant,** just as we learned in our study of periodic motion in Chapter 15. This constant can be determined from the initial conditions.

Quick Quiz 16.2   A sinusoidal wave of frequency f is traveling along a stretched string. The string is brought to rest, and a second traveling wave of frequency $2f$ is established on the string. **(i)** What is the wave speed of the second wave? (a) twice that of the first wave   (b) half that of the first wave   (c) the same as that of the first wave   (d) impossible to determine   **(ii)** From the same choices, describe the wavelength of the second wave. **(iii)** From the same choices, describe the amplitude of the second wave.

EXAMPLE 16.2   A Traveling Sinusoidal Wave

A sinusoidal wave traveling in the positive x direction has an amplitude of 15.0 cm, a wavelength of 40.0 cm, and a frequency of 8.00 Hz. The vertical position of an element of the medium at $t = 0$ and $x = 0$ is also 15.0 cm as shown in Figure 16.9.

(A) Find the wave number k, period T, angular frequency ω, and speed v of the wave.

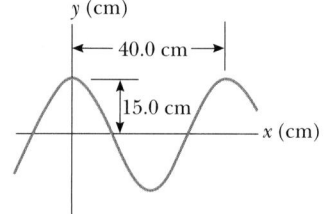

Figure 16.9 (Example 16.2) A sinusoidal wave of wavelength $\lambda = 40.0$ cm and amplitude $A = 15.0$ cm. The wave function can be written in the form $y = A \cos (kx - \omega t)$.

SOLUTION

Conceptualize Figure 16.9 shows the wave at $t = 0$. Imagine this wave moving to the right and maintaining its shape.

Categorize We will evaluate parameters of the wave using equations generated in the preceding discussion, so we categorize this example as a substitution problem.

Evaluate the wave number from Equation 16.8:

$$k = \frac{2\pi}{\lambda} = \frac{2\pi \text{ rad}}{40.0 \text{ cm}} = \boxed{0.157 \text{ rad/cm}}$$

Evaluate the period of the wave from Equation 16.3:

$$T = \frac{1}{f} = \frac{1}{8.00 \text{ s}^{-1}} = \boxed{0.125 \text{ s}}$$

Evaluate the angular frequency of the wave from Equation 16.9:

$$\omega = 2\pi f = 2\pi (8.00 \text{ s}^{-1}) = \boxed{50.3 \text{ rad/s}}$$

Evaluate the wave speed from Equation 16.12:

$$v = \lambda f = (40.0 \text{ cm})(8.00 \text{ s}^{-1}) = \boxed{320 \text{ cm/s}}$$

(B) Determine the phase constant ϕ and write a general expression for the wave function.

SOLUTION

Substitute $A = 15.0$ cm, $y = 15.0$ cm, $x = 0$, and $t = 0$ into Equation 16.13:

$$15.0 = (15.0) \sin \phi \quad \rightarrow \quad \sin \phi = 1 \quad \rightarrow \quad \phi = \frac{\pi}{2} \text{ rad}$$

Write the wave function:

$$y = A \sin \left(kx - \omega t + \frac{\pi}{2} \right) = A \cos (kx - \omega t)$$

Substitute the values for A, k, and ω into this expression:

$$y = (15.0 \text{ cm}) \cos (0.157x - 50.3t)$$

Sinusoidal Waves on Strings

In Figure 16.1, we demonstrated how to create a pulse by jerking a taut string up and down once. To create a series of such pulses—a wave—let's replace the hand with an oscillating blade vibrating in simple harmonic motion. Active Figure 16.10 represents snapshots of the wave created in this way at intervals of $T/4$. Because the end of the blade oscillates in simple harmonic motion, **each element of the string, such as that at *P*, also oscillates vertically with simple harmonic motion.** That must be the case because each element follows the simple harmonic motion of the blade. Therefore, every element of the string can be treated as a simple harmonic oscillator vibrating with a frequency equal to the frequency of oscillation of the blade.[2] Notice that although each element oscillates in the y direction, the wave travels in the x direction with a speed v. Of course, that is the definition of a transverse wave.

If the wave at $t = 0$ is as described in Active Figure 16.10b, the wave function can be written as

$$y = A \sin (kx - \omega t)$$

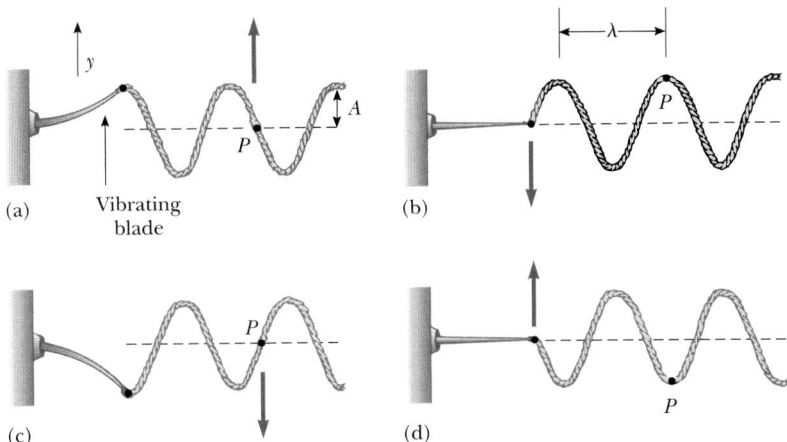

(a)   Vibrating blade   (b)

(c)   (d)

ACTIVE FIGURE 16.10

One method for producing a sinusoidal wave on a string. The left end of the string is connected to a blade that is set into oscillation. Every element of the string, such as that at point P, oscillates with simple harmonic motion in the vertical direction.

Sign in at www.thomsonedu.com and go to ThomsonNOW to adjust the frequency of the blade.

[2] In this arrangement, we are assuming that a string element always oscillates in a vertical line. The tension in the string would vary if an element were allowed to move sideways. Such motion would make the analysis very complex.

We can use this expression to describe the motion of any element of the string. An element at point P (or any other element of the string) moves only vertically, and so its x coordinate remains constant. Therefore, the **transverse speed** v_y (not to be confused with the wave speed v) and the **transverse acceleration** a_y of elements of the string are

$$v_y = \frac{dy}{dt}\bigg]_{x=\text{constant}} = \frac{\partial y}{\partial t} = -\omega A \cos (kx - \omega t) \qquad (16.14)$$

$$a_y = \frac{dv_y}{dt}\bigg]_{x=\text{constant}} = \frac{\partial v_y}{\partial t} = -\omega^2 A \sin (kx - \omega t) \qquad (16.15)$$

PITFALL PREVENTION 16.2
Two Kinds of Speed/Velocity

Do not confuse v, the speed of the wave as it propagates along the string, with v_y, the transverse velocity of a point on the string. The speed v is constant for a uniform medium, whereas v_y varies sinusoidally.

These expressions incorporate partial derivatives (see Section 7.8) because y depends on both x and t. In the operation $\partial y/\partial t$, for example, we take a derivative with respect to t while holding x constant. The maximum values of the transverse speed and transverse acceleration are simply the absolute values of the coefficients of the cosine and sine functions:

$$v_{y,\,\text{max}} = \omega A \qquad (16.16)$$

$$a_{y,\,\text{max}} = \omega^2 A \qquad (16.17)$$

The transverse speed and transverse acceleration of elements of the string do not reach their maximum values simultaneously. The transverse speed reaches its maximum value (ωA) when $y = 0$, whereas the magnitude of the transverse acceleration reaches its maximum value ($\omega^2 A$) when $y = \pm A$. Finally, Equations 16.16 and 16.17 are identical in mathematical form to the corresponding equations for simple harmonic motion, Equations 15.17 and 15.18.

Quick Quiz 16.3 The amplitude of a wave is doubled, with no other changes made to the wave. As a result of this doubling, which of the following statements is correct? (a) The speed of the wave changes. (b) The frequency of the wave changes. (c) The maximum transverse speed of an element of the medium changes. (d) Statements (a) through (c) are all true. (e) None of statements (a) through (c) is true.

16.3 The Speed of Waves on Strings

In this section, we determine the speed of a transverse pulse traveling on a taut string. Let's first conceptually predict the parameters that determine the speed. If a string under tension is pulled sideways and then released, the force of tension is responsible for accelerating a particular element of the string back toward its equilibrium position. According to Newton's second law, the acceleration of the element increases with increasing tension. If the element returns to equilibrium more rapidly due to this increased acceleration, we would intuitively argue that the wave speed is greater. Therefore, we expect the wave speed to increase with increasing tension.

Likewise, because it is more difficult to accelerate a massive element of the string than a light element, the wave speed should decrease as the mass per unit length of the string increases. If the tension in the string is T and its mass per unit length is μ (Greek letter mu), the wave speed, as we shall show, is

Speed of a wave on a ▶
stretched string

$$v = \sqrt{\frac{T}{\mu}} \qquad (16.18)$$

Let us use a mechanical analysis to derive Equation 16.18. Consider a pulse moving on a taut string to the right with a uniform speed v measured relative to a stationary frame of reference. Instead of staying in this reference frame, it is more convenient to choose a different inertial reference frame that moves along with the pulse with the same speed as the pulse so that the pulse is at rest within the frame. This change of reference frame is permitted because Newton's laws are valid in either a stationary frame or one that moves with constant velocity. In our new reference frame, all elements of the string move to the left: a given element of the string initially to the right of the pulse moves to the left, rises up and follows the shape of the pulse, and then continues to move to the left. Figure 16.11a shows such an element at the instant it is located at the top of the pulse.

The small element of the string of length Δs shown in Figure 16.11a, and magnified in Figure 16.11b, forms an approximate arc of a circle of radius R. In the moving frame of reference (which moves to the right at a speed v along with the pulse), the shaded element moves to the left with a speed v. This element has a centripetal acceleration equal to v^2/R, which is supplied by components of the force $\vec{\mathbf{T}}$ whose magnitude is the tension in the string. The force $\vec{\mathbf{T}}$ acts on both sides of the element and is tangent to the arc as shown in Figure 16.11b. The horizontal components of $\vec{\mathbf{T}}$ cancel, and each vertical component $T \sin \theta$ acts radially toward the arc's center. Hence, the total radial force on the element is $2T \sin \theta$. Because the element is small, θ is small, and we can therefore use the small-angle approximation $\sin \theta \approx \theta$. So, the total radial force is

$$F_r = 2T \sin \theta \ \approx \ 2T\theta$$

The element has a mass $m = \mu \Delta s$. Because the element forms part of a circle and subtends an angle 2θ at the center, $\Delta s = R(2\theta)$, and

$$m \ = \ \mu \Delta s \ = \ 2\mu R\theta$$

Applying Newton's second law to this element in the radial direction gives

$$F_r = ma = \frac{mv^2}{R}$$

$$2T\theta = \frac{2\mu R\theta v^2}{R} \ \rightarrow \ v = \sqrt{\frac{T}{\mu}}$$

This expression for v is Equation 16.18.

Notice that this derivation is based on the assumption that the pulse height is small relative to the length of the string. Using this assumption, we were able to use the approximation $\sin \theta \approx \theta$. Furthermore, the model assumes the tension T is not affected by the presence of the pulse; therefore, T is the same at all points on the string. Finally, this proof does *not* assume any particular shape for the pulse. Therefore, a pulse of *any shape* travels along the string with speed $v = \sqrt{T/\mu}$ without any change in pulse shape.

Quick Quiz 16.4 Suppose you create a pulse by moving the free end of a taut string up and down once with your hand beginning at $t = 0$. The string is attached at its other end to a distant wall. The pulse reaches the wall at time t. Which of the following actions, taken by itself, decreases the time interval required for the pulse to reach the wall? More than one choice may be correct. (a) moving your hand more quickly, but still only up and down once by the same amount   (b) moving your hand more slowly, but still only up and down once by the same amount (c) moving your hand a greater distance up and down in the same amount of time (d) moving your hand a lesser distance up and down in the same amount of time (e) using a heavier string of the same length and under the same tension   (f) using a lighter string of the same length and under the same tension   (g) using a string of the same linear mass density but under decreased tension   (h) using a string of the same linear mass density but under increased tension

PITFALL PREVENTION 16.3
Multiple Ts

Do not confuse the T in Equation 16.18 for the tension with the symbol T used in this chapter for the period of a wave. The context of the equation should help you identify which quantity is meant. There simply aren't enough letters in the alphabet to assign a unique letter to each variable!

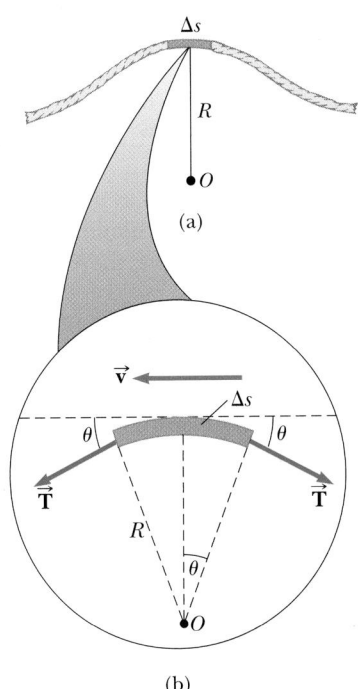

Figure 16.11 (a) To obtain the speed v of a wave on a stretched string, it is convenient to describe the motion of a small element of the string in a moving frame of reference. (b) In the moving frame of reference, the small element of length Δs moves to the left with speed v. The net force on the element is in the radial direction because the horizontal components of the tension force cancel.

The Speed of a Pulse on a Cord

A uniform string has a mass of 0.300 kg and a length of 6.00 m (Fig. 16.12). The string passes over a pulley and supports a 2.00-kg object. Find the speed of a pulse traveling along this string.

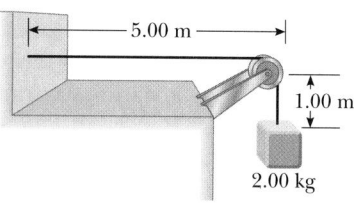

SOLUTION

Conceptualize In Figure 16.12, the hanging block establishes a tension in the horizontal string. This tension determines the speed with which waves move on the string.

Figure 16.12 (Example 16.3) The tension T in the cord is maintained by the suspended object. The speed of any wave traveling along the cord is given by $v = \sqrt{T/\mu}$.

Categorize To find the tension in the string, we model the hanging block as a particle in equilibrium. Then we use the tension to evaluate the wave speed on the string using Equation 16.18.

Analyze Apply the particle in equilibrium model to the block:

$$\sum F_y = T - m_{block}g = 0$$

Solve for the tension in the string:

$$T = m_{block}g$$

Use Equation 16.18 to find the wave speed, using $\mu = m_{string}/\ell$ for the linear mass density of the string:

$$v = \sqrt{\frac{T}{\mu}} = \sqrt{\frac{m_{block}g\ell}{m_{string}}}$$

Evaluate the wave speed:

$$v = \sqrt{\frac{(2.00\ kg)(9.80\ m/s^2)(6.00\ m)}{0.300\ kg}} = \boxed{19.8\ m/s}$$

Finalize The calculation of the tension neglects the small mass of the string. Strictly speaking, the string can never be exactly straight; therefore, the tension is not uniform.

What If? What if the block were swinging back and forth with respect to the vertical? How would that affect the wave speed on the string?

Answer The swinging block is categorized as a particle under a net force. The magnitude of one of the forces on the block is the tension in the string, which determines the wave speed. As the block swings, the tension changes, so the wave speed changes.

When the block is at the bottom of the swing, the string is vertical and the tension is larger than the weight of the block because the net force must be upward to provide the centripetal acceleration of the block. Therefore, the wave speed must be greater than 19.8 m/s.

When the block is at its highest point at the end of a swing, it is momentarily at rest, so there is no centripetal acceleration at that instant. The block is a particle in equilibrium in the radial direction. The tension is balanced by a component of the gravitational force on the block. Therefore, the tension is smaller than the weight and the wave speed is less than 19.8 m/s.

Rescuing the Hiker

An 80.0-kg hiker is trapped on a mountain ledge following a storm. A helicopter rescues the hiker by hovering above him and lowering a cable to him. The mass of the cable is 8.00 kg, and its length is 15.0 m. A sling of mass 70.0 kg is attached to the end of the cable. The hiker attaches himself to the sling, and the helicopter then accelerates upward. Terrified by hanging from the cable in midair, the hiker tries to signal the pilot by sending transverse pulses up the cable. A pulse takes 0.250 s to travel the length of the cable. What is the acceleration of the helicopter?

SOLUTION

Conceptualize Imagine the effect of the acceleration of the helicopter on the cable. The greater the upward acceleration, the larger the tension in the cable. In turn, the larger the tension, the higher the speed of pulses on the cable.

Categorize This problem is a combination of one involving the speed of pulses on a string and one in which the hiker and sling are modeled as a particle under a net force.

Analyze Use the time interval for the pulse to travel from the hiker to the helicopter to find the speed of the pulses on the cable:

$$v = \frac{\Delta x}{\Delta t} = \frac{15.0 \text{ m}}{0.250 \text{ s}} = 60.0 \text{ m/s}$$

Solve Equation 16.18 for the tension in the cable:

$$v = \sqrt{\frac{T}{\mu}} \quad \rightarrow \quad T = \mu v^2$$

Model the hiker and sling as a particle under a net force, noting that the acceleration of this particle of mass m is the same as the acceleration of the helicopter:

$$\sum F = ma \quad \rightarrow \quad T - mg = ma$$

Solve for the acceleration:

$$a = \frac{T}{m} - g = \frac{\mu v^2}{m} - g = \frac{m_{cable} v^2}{\ell_{cable} m} - g$$

Substitute numerical values:

$$a = \frac{(8.00 \text{ kg})(60.0 \text{ m/s})^2}{(15.0 \text{ m})(150.0 \text{ kg})} - 9.80 \text{ m/s}^2 = \boxed{3.00 \text{ m/s}^2}$$

Finalize A real cable has stiffness in addition to tension. Stiffness tends to return a wire to its original straight-line shape even when it is not under tension. For example, a piano wire straightens if released from a curved shape; package-wrapping string does not.

Stiffness represents a restoring force in addition to tension and increases the wave speed. Consequently, for a real cable, the speed of 60.0 m/s that we determined is most likely associated with a smaller acceleration of the helicopter.

16.4 Reflection and Transmission

The traveling wave model describes waves traveling through a uniform medium without interacting with anything along the way. We now consider how a traveling wave is affected when it encounters a change in the medium. For example, consider a pulse traveling on a string that is rigidly attached to a support at one end as in Active Figure 16.13. When the pulse reaches the support, a severe change in the medium occurs: the string ends. As a result, the pulse undergoes **reflection;** that is, the pulse moves back along the string in the opposite direction.

Notice that the reflected pulse is *inverted*. This inversion can be explained as follows. When the pulse reaches the fixed end of the string, the string produces an upward force on the support. By Newton's third law, the support must exert an equal-magnitude and oppositely directed (downward) reaction force on the string. This downward force causes the pulse to invert upon reflection.

Now consider another case. This time, the pulse arrives at the end of a string that is free to move vertically as in Active Figure 16.14 (page 462). The tension at the free end is maintained because the string is tied to a ring of negligible mass that is free to slide vertically on a smooth post without friction. Again, the pulse is reflected, but this time it is not inverted. When it reaches the post, the pulse exerts a force on the free end of the string, causing the ring to accelerate upward. The ring rises as high as the incoming pulse, and then the downward component of the tension force pulls the ring back down. This movement of the ring produces a reflected pulse that is not inverted and that has the same amplitude as the incoming pulse.

Finally, consider a situation in which the boundary is intermediate between these two extremes. In this case, part of the energy in the incident pulse is reflected and part undergoes **transmission;** that is, some of the energy passes through the boundary. For instance, suppose a light string is attached to a heavier

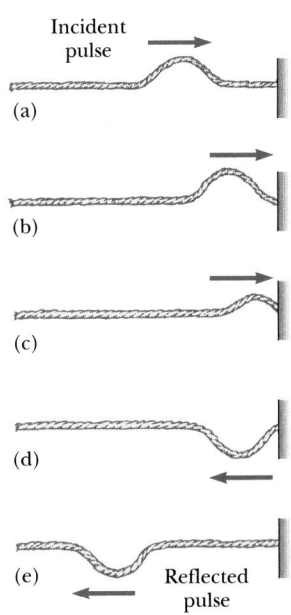

ACTIVE FIGURE 16.13

The reflection of a traveling pulse at the fixed end of a stretched string. The reflected pulse is inverted, but its shape is otherwise unchanged.

Sign in at www.thomsonedu.com and go to ThomsonNOW to adjust the linear mass density of the string and the transverse direction of the initial pulse.

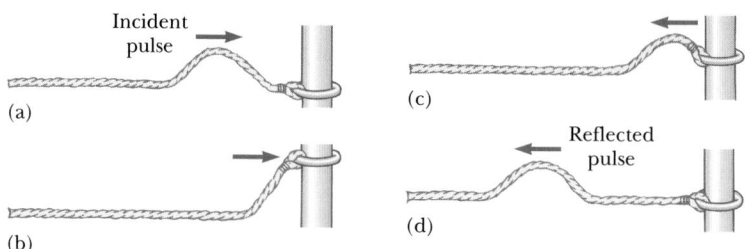

string as in Active Figure 16.15. When a pulse traveling on the light string reaches the boundary between the two strings, part of the pulse is reflected and inverted and part is transmitted to the heavier string. The reflected pulse is inverted for the same reasons described earlier in the case of the string rigidly attached to a support.

The reflected pulse has a smaller amplitude than the incident pulse. In Section 16.5, we show that the energy carried by a wave is related to its amplitude. According to the principle of the conservation of energy, when the pulse breaks up into a reflected pulse and a transmitted pulse at the boundary, the sum of the energies of these two pulses must equal the energy of the incident pulse. Because the reflected pulse contains only part of the energy of the incident pulse, its amplitude must be smaller.

When a pulse traveling on a heavy string strikes the boundary between the heavy string and a lighter one as in Active Figure 16.16, again part is reflected and part is transmitted. In this case, the reflected pulse is not inverted.

In either case, the relative heights of the reflected and transmitted pulses depend on the relative densities of the two strings. If the strings are identical, there is no discontinuity at the boundary and no reflection takes place.

According to Equation 16.18, the speed of a wave on a string increases as the mass per unit length of the string decreases. In other words, a wave travels more slowly on a heavy string than on a light string if both are under the same tension. The following general rules apply to reflected waves: **when a wave or pulse travels from medium A to medium B and $v_A > v_B$ (that is, when B is denser than A), it is inverted upon reflection. When a wave or pulse travels from medium A to medium B and $v_A < v_B$ (that is, when A is denser than B), it is not inverted upon reflection.**

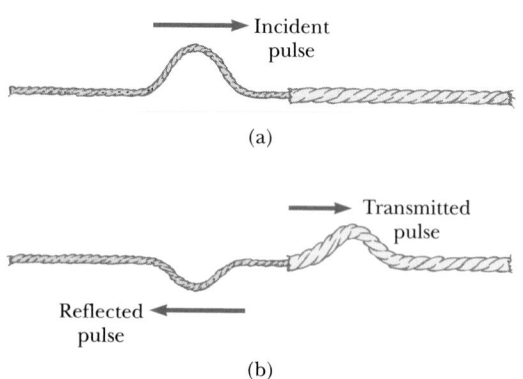

ACTIVE FIGURE 16.15

(a) A pulse traveling to the right on a light string attached to a heavier string. (b) Part of the incident pulse is reflected (and inverted), and part is transmitted to the heavier string.

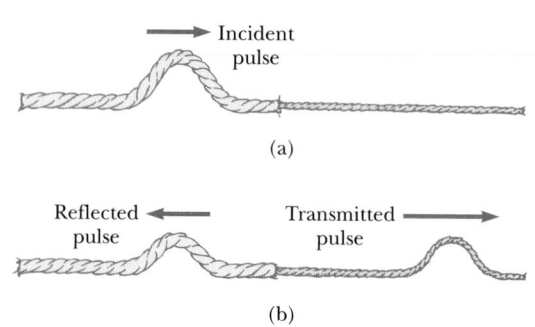

ACTIVE FIGURE 16.16

(a) A pulse traveling to the right on a heavy string attached to a lighter string. (b) The incident pulse is partially reflected and partially transmitted, and the reflected pulse is not inverted.

16.5 Rate of Energy Transfer by Sinusoidal Waves on Strings

Waves transport energy through a medium as they propagate. For example, suppose an object is hanging on a stretched string and a pulse is sent down the string as in Figure 16.17a. When the pulse meets the suspended object, the object is momentarily displaced upward as in Figure 16.17b. In the process, energy is transferred to the object and appears as an increase in the gravitational potential energy of the object–Earth system. This section examines the rate at which energy is transported along a string. We shall assume a one-dimensional sinusoidal wave in the calculation of the energy transferred.

Consider a sinusoidal wave traveling on a string (Fig. 16.18). The source of the energy is some external agent at the left end of the string, which does work in producing the oscillations. We can consider the string to be a nonisolated system. As the external agent performs work on the end of the string, moving it up and down, energy enters the system of the string and propagates along its length. Let's focus our attention on an infinitesimal element of the string of length dx and mass dm. Each such element moves vertically with simple harmonic motion. Therefore, we can model each element of the string as a simple harmonic oscillator, with the oscillation in the y direction. All elements have the same angular frequency ω and the same amplitude A. The kinetic energy K associated with a moving particle is $K = \frac{1}{2}mv^2$. If we apply this equation to the infinitesimal element, the kinetic energy dK of this element is

$$dK = \tfrac{1}{2}(dm)v_y^{\,2}$$

where v_y is the transverse speed of the element. If μ is the mass per unit length of the string, the mass dm of the element of length dx is equal to $\mu\,dx$. Hence, we can express the kinetic energy of an element of the string as

$$dK = \tfrac{1}{2}(\mu\,dx)v_y^{\,2} \qquad\qquad \textbf{(16.19)}$$

Substituting for the general transverse speed of a simple harmonic oscillator using Equation 16.14 gives

$$dK = \tfrac{1}{2}\mu\left[-\omega A \cos\left(kx - \omega t\right)\right]^2 dx = \tfrac{1}{2}\mu\omega^2 A^2 \cos^2\left(kx - \omega t\right) dx$$

If we take a snapshot of the wave at time $t = 0$, the kinetic energy of a given element is

$$dK = \tfrac{1}{2}\mu\omega^2 A^2 \cos^2\left(kx\right) dx$$

Integrating this expression over all the string elements in a wavelength of the wave gives the total kinetic energy K_λ in one wavelength:

$$K_\lambda = \int dK = \int_0^\lambda \tfrac{1}{2}\mu\omega^2 A^2 \cos^2\left(kx\right) dx = \tfrac{1}{2}\mu\omega^2 A^2 \int_0^\lambda \cos^2\left(kx\right) dx$$

$$= \tfrac{1}{2}\mu\omega^2 A^2 \left[\tfrac{1}{2}x + \frac{1}{4k}\sin 2kx\right]_0^\lambda = \tfrac{1}{2}\mu\omega^2 A^2\left[\tfrac{1}{2}\lambda\right] = \tfrac{1}{4}\mu\omega^2 A^2 \lambda$$

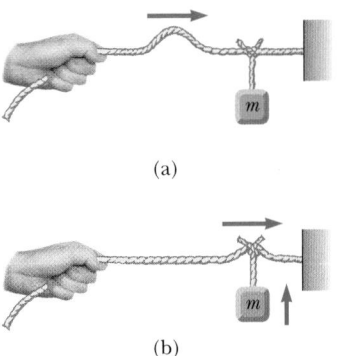

Figure 16.17 (a) A pulse traveling to the right on a stretched string that has an object suspended from it. (b) Energy is transmitted to the suspended object when the pulse arrives.

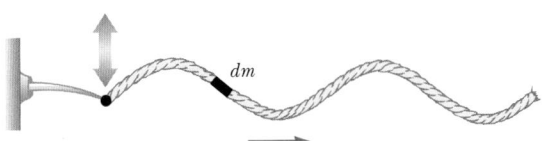

Figure 16.18 A sinusoidal wave traveling along the x axis on a stretched string. Every element of the string moves vertically, and every element has the same total energy.

In addition to kinetic energy, there is potential energy associated with each element of the string due to its displacement from the equilibrium position and the restoring forces from neighboring elements. A similar analysis to that above for the total potential energy U_λ in one wavelength gives exactly the same result:

$$U_\lambda = \tfrac{1}{4}\mu\omega^2 A^2 \lambda$$

The total energy in one wavelength of the wave is the sum of the potential and kinetic energies:

$$E_\lambda = U_\lambda + K_\lambda = \tfrac{1}{2}\mu\omega^2 A^2 \lambda \qquad (16.20)$$

As the wave moves along the string, this amount of energy passes by a given point on the string during a time interval of one period of the oscillation. Therefore, the power $\mathcal{P}$, or rate of energy transfer T_{MW} associated with the mechanical wave, is

$$\mathcal{P} = \frac{T_{MW}}{\Delta t} = \frac{E_\lambda}{T} = \frac{\tfrac{1}{2}\mu\omega^2 A^2 \lambda}{T} = \tfrac{1}{2}\mu\omega^2 A^2 \left(\frac{\lambda}{T}\right)$$

Power of a wave ▶

$$\mathcal{P} = \tfrac{1}{2}\mu\omega^2 A^2 v \qquad (16.21)$$

Equation 16.21 shows that the rate of energy transfer by a sinusoidal wave on a string is proportional to (a) the square of the frequency, (b) the square of the amplitude, and (c) the wave speed. In fact, **the rate of energy transfer in any sinusoidal wave is proportional to the square of the angular frequency and to the square of the amplitude.**

Quick Quiz 16.5 Which of the following, taken by itself, would be most effective in increasing the rate at which energy is transferred by a wave traveling along a string? (a) reducing the linear mass density of the string by one half (b) doubling the wavelength of the wave (c) doubling the tension in the string (d) doubling the amplitude of the wave

---

EXAMPLE 16.5 | **Power Supplied to a Vibrating String**

A taut string for which $\mu = 5.00 \times 10^{-2}$ kg/m is under a tension of 80.0 N. How much power must be supplied to the string to generate sinusoidal waves at a frequency of 60.0 Hz and an amplitude of 6.00 cm?

SOLUTION

Conceptualize Consider Active Figure 16.10 again and notice that the vibrating blade supplies energy to the string at a certain rate. This energy then propagates to the right along the string.

Categorize We evaluate quantities from equations developed in the chapter, so we categorize this example as a substitution problem.

Evaluate the wave speed on the string from Equation 16.18:

$$v = \sqrt{\frac{T}{\mu}} = \sqrt{\frac{80.0\ \text{N}}{5.00 \times 10^{-2}\ \text{kg/m}}} = 40.0\ \text{m/s}$$

Evaluate the angular frequency ω of the sinusoidal waves on the string from Equation 16.9:

$$\omega = 2\pi f = 2\pi(60.0\ \text{Hz}) = 377\ \text{s}^{-1}$$

Use these values and $A = 6.00 \times 10^{-2}$ m in Equation 16.21 to evaluate the power:

$$\mathcal{P} = \tfrac{1}{2}\mu\omega^2 A^2 v$$

$$= \tfrac{1}{2}(5.00 \times 10^{-2}\ \text{kg/m})(377\ \text{s}^{-1})^2 (6.00 \times 10^{-2}\ \text{m})^2 (40.0\ \text{m/s})$$

$$= \boxed{512\ \text{W}}$$

What If?   What if the string is to transfer energy at a rate of 1 000 W? What must be the required amplitude if all other parameters remain the same?

Answer Let us set up a ratio of the new and old power, reflecting only a change in the amplitude:

$$\frac{\mathcal{P}_{\text{new}}}{\mathcal{P}_{\text{old}}} = \frac{\frac{1}{2}\mu\omega^2 A_{\text{new}}^2 v}{\frac{1}{2}\mu\omega^2 A_{\text{old}}^2 v} = \frac{A_{\text{new}}^2}{A_{\text{old}}^2}$$

Solving for the new amplitude gives

$$A_{\text{new}} = A_{\text{old}}\sqrt{\frac{\mathcal{P}_{\text{new}}}{\mathcal{P}_{\text{old}}}} = (6.00 \text{ cm})\sqrt{\frac{1\,000 \text{ W}}{512 \text{ W}}} = 8.39 \text{ cm}$$

16.6   The Linear Wave Equation

In Section 16.1, we introduced the concept of the wave function to represent waves traveling on a string. All wave functions $y(x, t)$ represent solutions of an equation called the *linear wave equation*. This equation gives a complete description of the wave motion, and from it one can derive an expression for the wave speed. Furthermore, the linear wave equation is basic to many forms of wave motion. In this section, we derive this equation as applied to waves on strings.

Suppose a traveling wave is propagating along a string that is under a tension T. Let's consider one small string element of length Δx (Fig. 16.19). The ends of the element make small angles θ_A and θ_B with the x axis. The net force acting on the element in the vertical direction is

$$\sum F_y = T\sin\theta_B - T\sin\theta_A = T(\sin\theta_B - \sin\theta_A)$$

Because the angles are small, we can use the small-angle approximation $\sin\theta \approx \tan\theta$ to express the net force as

$$\sum F_y \approx T(\tan\theta_B - \tan\theta_A) \tag{16.22}$$

Imagine undergoing an infinitesimal displacement outward from the end of the rope element in Figure 16.19 along the blue line representing the force $\vec{\mathbf{T}}$. This displacement has infinitesimal x and y components and can be represented by the vector $dx\hat{\mathbf{i}} + dy\hat{\mathbf{j}}$. The tangent of the angle with respect to the x axis for this displacement is dy/dx. Because we evaluate this tangent at a particular instant of time, we must express it in partial form as $\partial y/\partial x$. Substituting for the tangents in Equation 16.22 gives

$$\sum F_y \approx T\left[\left(\frac{\partial y}{\partial x}\right)_B - \left(\frac{\partial y}{\partial x}\right)_A\right] \tag{16.23}$$

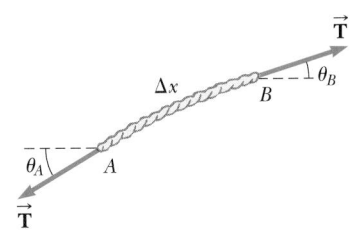

Figure 16.19   An element of a string under tension T.

Now let's apply Newton's second law to the element, with the mass of the element given by $m = \mu\,\Delta x$:

$$\sum F_y = ma_y = \mu\,\Delta x\left(\frac{\partial^2 y}{\partial t^2}\right) \tag{16.24}$$

Combining Equation 16.23 with Equation 16.24 gives

$$\mu\,\Delta x\left(\frac{\partial^2 y}{\partial t^2}\right) = T\left[\left(\frac{\partial y}{\partial x}\right)_B - \left(\frac{\partial y}{\partial x}\right)_A\right]$$

$$\frac{\mu}{T}\frac{\partial^2 y}{\partial t^2} = \frac{(\partial y/\partial x)_B - (\partial y/dx)_A}{\Delta x} \tag{16.25}$$

The right side of Equation 16.25 can be expressed in a different form if we note that the partial derivative of any function is defined as

$$\frac{\partial f}{\partial x} \equiv \lim_{\Delta x \to 0} \frac{f(x + \Delta x) - f(x)}{\Delta x}$$

Associating $f(x + \Delta x)$ with $(\partial y / \partial x)_B$ and $f(x)$ with $(\partial y / \partial x)_A$, we see that, in the limit $\Delta x \to 0$, Equation 16.25 becomes

Linear wave equation for a string ▶

$$\frac{\mu}{T} \frac{\partial^2 y}{\partial t^2} = \frac{\partial^2 y}{\partial x^2} \qquad (16.26)$$

This expression is the linear wave equation as it applies to waves on a string.

The linear wave equation (Eq. 16.26) is often written in the form

Linear wave equation in general ▶

$$\frac{\partial^2 y}{\partial x^2} = \frac{1}{v^2} \frac{\partial^2 y}{\partial t^2} \qquad (16.27)$$

Equation 16.27 applies in general to various types of traveling waves. For waves on strings, y represents the vertical position of elements of the string. For sound waves, y corresponds to longitudinal position of elements of air from equilibrium or variations in either the pressure or the density of the gas through which the sound waves are propagating. In the case of electromagnetic waves, y corresponds to electric or magnetic field components.

We have shown that the sinusoidal wave function (Eq. 16.10) is one solution of the linear wave equation (Eq. 16.27). Although we do not prove it here, the linear wave equation is satisfied by *any* wave function having the form $y = f(x \pm vt)$. Furthermore, we have seen that the linear wave equation is a direct consequence of Newton's second law applied to any element of a string carrying a traveling wave.

Summary

DEFINITIONS

A one-dimensional **sinusoidal wave** is one for which the positions of the elements of the medium vary sinusoidally. A sinusoidal wave traveling to the right can be expressed with a **wave function**

$$y(x, t) = A \sin \left[\frac{2\pi}{\lambda} (x - vt) \right] \qquad (16.5)$$

where A is the **amplitude**, λ is the **wavelength**, and v is the **wave speed**.

The **angular wave number** k and **angular frequency** ω of a wave are defined as follows:

$$k \equiv \frac{2\pi}{\lambda} \qquad (16.8)$$

$$\omega \equiv \frac{2\pi}{T} = 2\pi f \qquad (16.9)$$

where T is the **period** of the wave and f is its **frequency**.

A **transverse wave** is one in which the elements of the medium move in a direction *perpendicular* to the direction of propagation. A **longitudinal wave** is one in which the elements of the medium move in a direction *parallel* to the direction of propagation.

(*continued*)

CONCEPTS AND PRINCIPLES

Any one-dimensional wave traveling with a speed v in the x direction can be represented by a wave function of the form

$$y(x, t) = f(x \pm vt) \qquad \textbf{(16.1, 16.2)}$$

where the positive sign applies to a wave traveling in the negative x direction and the negative sign applies to a wave traveling in the positive x direction. The shape of the wave at any instant in time (a snapshot of the wave) is obtained by holding t constant.

The speed of a wave traveling on a taut string of mass per unit length μ and tension T is

$$v = \sqrt{\frac{T}{\mu}} \qquad \textbf{(16.18)}$$

A wave is totally or partially reflected when it reaches the end of the medium in which it propagates or when it reaches a boundary where its speed changes discontinuously. If a wave traveling on a string meets a fixed end, the wave is reflected and inverted. If the wave reaches a free end, it is reflected but not inverted.

The **power** transmitted by a sinusoidal wave on a stretched string is

$$\mathcal{P} = \tfrac{1}{2}\mu\omega^2 A^2 v \qquad \textbf{(16.21)}$$

Wave functions are solutions to a differential equation called the **linear wave equation:**

$$\frac{\partial^2 y}{\partial x^2} = \frac{1}{v^2}\frac{\partial^2 y}{\partial t^2} \qquad \textbf{(16.27)}$$

ANALYSIS MODEL FOR PROBLEM SOLVING

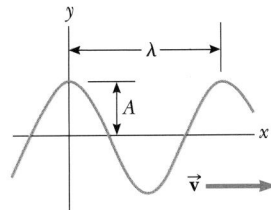

Traveling Wave. The wave speed of a sinusoidal wave is

$$v = \frac{\lambda}{T} = \lambda f \qquad \textbf{(16.6, 16.12)}$$

A sinusoidal wave can be expressed as

$$y = A \sin(kx - \omega t) \qquad \textbf{(16.10)}$$

Questions

☐ denotes answer available in *Student Solutions Manual/Study Guide;* **O** denotes objective question

1. Why is a pulse on a string considered to be transverse?

2. How would you create a longitudinal wave in a stretched spring? Would it be possible to create a transverse wave in a spring?

3. **O** (i) Rank the waves represented by the following functions according to their amplitudes from the largest to the smallest. If two waves have the same amplitude, show them as having equal rank.
   - (a) $y = 2 \sin(3x - 15t + 2)$
   - (b) $y = 4 \sin(3x - 15t)$
   - (c) $y = 6 \cos(3x + 15t - 2)$
   - (d) $y = 8 \sin(2x + 15t)$
   - (e) $y = 8 \cos(4x + 20t)$
   - (f) $y = 7 \sin(6x - 24t)$

(ii) Rank the same waves according to their wavelengths from largest to smallest. (iii) Rank the same waves according to their frequencies from largest to smallest. (iv) Rank the same waves according to their periods from largest to smallest. (v) Rank the same waves according to their speeds from largest to smallest.

4. **O** If the string does not stretch, by what factor would you have to multiply the tension in a taut string so as to double the wave speed? (a) 8 (b) 4 (c) 2 (d) 0.5 (e) You could not change the speed by a predictable factor by changing the tension.

5. O When all the strings on a guitar are stretched to the same tension, will the speed of a wave along the most massive bass string be (a) faster, (b) slower, or (c) the same as the speed of a wave on the lighter strings? Alternatively, (d) is the speed on the bass string not necessarily any of these answers?

6. O If you stretch a rubber hose and pluck it, you can observe a pulse traveling up and down the hose. **(i)** What happens to the speed of the pulse if you stretch the hose more tightly? (a) It increases. (b) It decreases. (c) It is constant. (d) It changes unpredictably. **(ii)** What happens to the speed if you fill the hose with water? Choose from the same possibilities.

7. When a pulse travels on a taut string, does it always invert upon reflection? Explain.

8. Does the vertical speed of a segment of a horizontal taut string, through which a wave is traveling, depend on the wave speed?

9. O (a) Can a wave on a string move with a wave speed that is greater than the maximum transverse speed $v_{y, \text{max}}$ of an element of the string? (b) Can the wave speed be much greater than the maximum element speed? (c) Can the wave speed be equal to the maximum element speed? (d) Can the wave speed be less than $v_{y, \text{max}}$?

10. If you shake one end of a taut rope steadily three times each second, what would be the period of the sinusoidal wave set up in the rope?

11. If a long rope is hung from a ceiling and waves are sent up the rope from its lower end, they do not ascend with constant speed. Explain.

12. O A source vibrating at constant frequency generates a sinusoidal wave on a string under constant tension. If the power delivered to the string is doubled, by what factor does the amplitude change? (a) 4 (b) 2 (c) $\sqrt{2}$ (d) 1 (e) 0.707 (f) cannot be predicted

13. O If one end of a heavy rope is attached to one end of a light rope, a wave can move from the heavy rope into the lighter one. **(i)** What happens to the speed of the wave? (a) It increases. (b) It decreases. (c) It is constant. (d) It changes unpredictably. **(ii)** What happens to the frequency? Choose from the same possibilities. **(iii)** What happens to the wavelength? Choose from the same possibilities.

14. A solid can transport both longitudinal waves and transverse waves, but a homogeneous fluid can transport only longitudinal waves. Why?

15. In an earthquake both S (transverse) and P (longitudinal) waves propagate from the focus of the earthquake. The focus is in the ground below the epicenter on the surface. Assume the waves move in straight lines through uniform material. The S waves travel through the Earth more slowly than the P waves (at about 5 km/s versus 8 km/s). By detecting the time of arrival of the waves, how can one determine the distance to the focus of the earthquake? How many detection stations are necessary to locate the focus unambiguously?

16. In mechanics, massless strings are often assumed. Why is that not a good assumption when discussing waves on strings?

Problems

WebAssign   The Problems from this chapter may be assigned online in WebAssign.

ThomsonNOW   Sign in at **www.thomsonedu.com** and go to ThomsonNOW to assess your understanding of this chapter's topics with additional quizzing and conceptual questions.

1, 2, 3 denotes straightforward, intermediate, challenging;   □ denotes full solution available in *Student Solutions Manual/Study Guide;*   ▲ denotes coached solution with hints available at **www.thomsonedu.com;**   denotes developing symbolic reasoning; ● denotes asking for qualitative reasoning;   ▪ denotes computer useful in solving problem

Section 16.1 Propagation of a Disturbance

1. At $t = 0$, a transverse pulse in a wire is described by the function

$$y = \frac{6}{x^2 + 3}$$

where x and y are in meters. Write the function $y(x, t)$ that describes this pulse if it is traveling in the positive x direction with a speed of 4.50 m/s.

2. ● Ocean waves with a crest-to-crest distance of 10.0 m can be described by the wave function

$$y(x, t) = (0.800 \text{ m}) \sin [0.628(x - vt)]$$

where $v = 1.20$ m/s. (a) Sketch $y(x, t)$ at $t = 0$. (b) Sketch $y(x, t)$ at $t = 2.00$ s. Compare this graph with that for part (a) and explain similarities and differences. What has the wave done between picture (a) and picture (b)?

3. Two points A and B on the surface of the Earth are at the same longitude and 60.0° apart in latitude. Suppose an earthquake at point A creates a P wave that reaches point B by traveling straight through the body of the Earth at a constant speed of 7.80 km/s. The earthquake also radiates a Rayleigh wave that travels along the surface of the Earth at 4.50 km/s. (a) Which of these two seismic waves arrives at B first? (b) What is the time difference between the arrivals of these two waves at B? Take the radius of the Earth to be 6 370 km.

4. A seismographic station receives S and P waves from an earthquake, 17.3 s apart. Assume the waves have traveled over the same path at speeds of 4.50 km/s and 7.80 km/s. Find the distance from the seismograph to the hypocenter of the earthquake.

Section 16.2 The Traveling Wave Model

5. ▲ The wave function for a traveling wave on a taut string is (in SI units)

$$y(x, t) = (0.350 \text{ m}) \sin \left(10\pi t - 3\pi x + \frac{\pi}{4} \right)$$

(a) What are the speed and direction of travel of the wave? (b) What is the vertical position of an element of the string at $t = 0$, $x = 0.100$ m? (c) What are the wavelength and frequency of the wave? (d) What is the maximum transverse speed of an element of the string?

6. ● A certain uniform string is held under constant tension. (a) Draw a side-view snapshot of a sinusoidal wave on a string as shown in diagrams in the text. (b) Immediately below diagram (a), draw the same wave at a moment later by one quarter of the period of the wave. (c) Then, draw a wave with an amplitude 1.5 times larger than the wave in diagram (a). (d) Next, draw a wave differing from the one in your diagram (a) just by having a wavelength 1.5 times larger. (e) Finally, draw a wave differing from that in diagram (a) just by having a frequency 1.5 times larger.

7. A sinusoidal wave is traveling along a rope. The oscillator that generates the wave completes 40.0 vibrations in 30.0 s. Also, a given maximum travels 425 cm along the rope in 10.0 s. What is the wavelength of the wave?

8. For a certain transverse wave, the distance between two successive crests is 1.20 m, and eight crests pass a given point along the direction of travel every 12.0 s. Calculate the wave speed.

9. A wave is described by $y = (2.00$ cm$)$ sin $(kx - \omega t)$, where $k = 2.11$ rad/m, $\omega = 3.62$ rad/s, x is in meters, and t is in seconds. Determine the amplitude, wavelength, frequency, and speed of the wave.

10. When a particular wire is vibrating with a frequency of 4.00 Hz, a transverse wave of wavelength 60.0 cm is produced. Determine the speed of waves along the wire.

11. The string shown in Active Figure 16.10 is driven at a frequency of 5.00 Hz. The amplitude of the motion is 12.0 cm, and the wave speed is 20.0 m/s. Furthermore, the wave is such that $y = 0$ at $x = 0$ and $t = 0$. Determine (a) the angular frequency and (b) wave number for this wave. (c) Write an expression for the wave function. Calculate (d) the maximum transverse speed and (e) the maximum transverse acceleration of a point on the string.

12. Consider the sinusoidal wave of Example 16.2 with the wave function

$$y = (15.0 \text{ cm}) \cos (0.157x - 50.3t)$$

At a certain instant, let point A be at the origin and point B be the first point along the x axis where the wave is 60.0° out of phase with A. What is the coordinate of B?

13. A sinusoidal wave is described by the wave function

$$y = (0.25 \text{ m}) \sin (0.30x - 40t)$$

where x and y are in meters and t is in seconds. Determine for this wave the (a) amplitude, (b) angular frequency, (c) angular wave number, (d) wavelength, (e) wave speed, and (f) direction of motion.

14. ● (a) Plot y versus t at $x = 0$ for a sinusoidal wave of the form $y = (15.0$ cm$)$ cos $(0.157x - 50.3t)$, where x and y are in centimeters and t is in seconds. (b) Determine the period of vibration from this plot. State how your result compares with the value found in Example 16.2.

15. ▲ (a) Write the expression for y as a function of x and t for a sinusoidal wave traveling along a rope in the *nega-*

tive x direction with the following characteristics: $A = 8.00$ cm, $\lambda = 80.0$ cm, $f = 3.00$ Hz, and $y(0, t) = 0$ at $t = 0$. (b) **What If?** Write the expression for y as a function of x and t for the wave in part (a) assuming that $y(x, 0) = 0$ at the point $x = 10.0$ cm.

16. A sinusoidal wave traveling in the $-x$ direction (to the left) has an amplitude of 20.0 cm, a wavelength of 35.0 cm, and a frequency of 12.0 Hz. The transverse position of an element of the medium at $t = 0$, $x = 0$ is $y = -3.00$ cm, and the element has a positive velocity here. (a) Sketch the wave at $t = 0$. (b) Find the angular wave number, period, angular frequency, and wave speed of the wave. (c) Write an expression for the wave function $y(x, t)$.

17. A transverse wave on a string is described by the wave function

$$y = (0.120 \text{ m}) \sin \left(\frac{\pi}{8} x + 4\pi t \right)$$

(a) Determine the transverse speed and acceleration of the string at $t = 0.200$ s for the point on the string located at $x = 1.60$ m. (b) What are the wavelength, period, and speed of propagation of this wave?

18. A transverse sinusoidal wave on a string has a period $T = 25.0$ ms and travels in the negative x direction with a speed of 30.0 m/s. At $t = 0$, an element of the string at $x = 0$ has a transverse position of 2.00 cm and is traveling downward with a speed of 2.00 m/s. (a) What is the amplitude of the wave? (b) What is the initial phase angle? (c) What is the maximum transverse speed of an element of the string? (d) Write the wave function for the wave.

19. A sinusoidal wave of wavelength 2.00 m and amplitude 0.100 m travels on a string with a speed of 1.00 m/s to the right. Initially, the left end of the string is at the origin. Find (a) the frequency and angular frequency, (b) the angular wave number, and (c) the wave function for this wave. Determine the equation of motion for (d) the left end of the string and (e) the point on the string at $x = 1.50$ m to the right of the left end. (f) What is the maximum speed of any point on the string?

20. A wave on a string is described by the wave function $y = (0.100$ m$)$ sin $(0.50x - 20t)$. (a) Show that an element of the string at $x = 2.00$ m executes harmonic motion. (b) Determine the frequency of oscillation of this particular point.

Section 16.3 The Speed of Waves on Strings

21. A telephone cord is 4.00 m long. The cord has a mass of 0.200 kg. A transverse pulse is produced by plucking one end of the taut cord. The pulse makes four trips down and back along the cord in 0.800 s. What is the tension in the cord?

22. A transverse traveling wave on a taut wire has an amplitude of 0.200 mm and a frequency of 500 Hz. It travels with a speed of 196 m/s. (a) Write an equation in SI units of the form $y = A$ sin $(kx - \omega t)$ for this wave. (b) The mass per unit length of this wire is 4.10 g/m. Find the tension in the wire.

23. A piano string having a mass per unit length equal to 5.00×10^{-3} kg/m is under a tension of 1 350 N. Find the speed with which a wave travels on this string.

2 = intermediate;   3 = challenging;   □ = SSM/SG;   ▲ = ThomsonNOW;   = symbolic reasoning;   ● = qualitative reasoning

24. Transverse pulses travel with a speed of 200 m/s along a taut copper wire whose diameter is 1.50 mm. What is the tension in the wire? (The density of copper is 8.92 g/cm³.)

25. An astronaut on the Moon wishes to measure the local value of the free-fall acceleration by timing pulses traveling down a wire that has an object of large mass suspended from it. Assume a wire has a mass of 4.00 g and a length of 1.60 m and assume a 3.00-kg object is suspended from it. A pulse requires 36.1 ms to traverse the length of the wire. Calculate g_{Moon} from these data. (You may ignore the mass of the wire when calculating the tension in it.)

26. A simple pendulum consists of a ball of mass M hanging from a uniform string of mass m and length L, with $m \ll M$. Let T represent the period of oscillations for the pendulum. Determine the speed of a transverse wave in the string when the pendulum hangs at rest.

27. Transverse waves travel with a speed of 20.0 m/s in a string under a tension of 6.00 N. What tension is required for a wave speed of 30.0 m/s in the same string?

28. **Review problem.** A light string with a mass per unit length of 8.00 g/m has its ends tied to two walls separated by a distance equal to three-fourths the length of the string (Fig. P16.28). An object of mass m is suspended from the center of the string, putting a tension in the string. (a) Find an expression for the transverse wave speed in the string as a function of the mass of the hanging object. (b) What should be the mass of the object suspended from the string if the wave speed is to be 60.0 m/s?

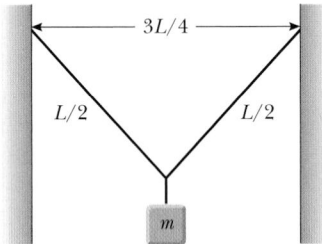

Figure P16.28

29. The elastic limit of a piece of steel wire is 2.70×10^8 Pa. What is the maximum speed at which transverse wave pulses can propagate along this wire without exceeding this stress? (The density of steel is 7.86×10^3 kg/m³.)

30. ● A student taking a quiz finds on a reference sheet the two equations

$$f = \frac{1}{T} \quad \text{and} \quad v = \sqrt{\frac{T}{\mu}}$$

She has forgotten what T represents in each equation. (a) Use dimensional analysis to determine the units required for T in each equation. (b) Explain how you can identify the physical quantity each T represents from the units.

31. ▲ A steel wire of length 30.0 m and a copper wire of length 20.0 m, both with 1.00-mm diameters, are connected end to end and stretched to a tension of 150 N. During what time interval will a transverse wave travel the entire length of the two wires?

Section 16.5 Rate of Energy Transfer by Sinusoidal Waves on Strings

32. A taut rope has a mass of 0.180 kg and a length of 3.60 m. What power must be supplied to the rope so as to generate sinusoidal waves having an amplitude of 0.100 m and a wavelength of 0.500 m and traveling with a speed of 30.0 m/s?

33. A two-dimensional water wave spreads in circular ripples. Show that the amplitude A at a distance r from the initial disturbance is proportional to $1/\sqrt{r}$. *Suggestion:* Consider the energy carried by one outward-moving ripple.

34. Transverse waves are being generated on a rope under constant tension. By what factor is the required power increased or decreased if (a) the length of the rope is doubled and the angular frequency remains constant, (b) the amplitude is doubled and the angular frequency is halved, (c) both the wavelength and the amplitude are doubled, and (d) both the length of the rope and the wavelength are halved?

35. ▲ Sinusoidal waves 5.00 cm in amplitude are to be transmitted along a string that has a linear mass density of 4.00×10^{-2} kg/m. The source can deliver a maximum power of 300 W and the string is under a tension of 100 N. What is the highest frequency at which the source can operate?

36. A 6.00-m segment of a long string contains four complete waves and has a mass of 180 g. The string vibrates sinusoidally with a frequency of 50.0 Hz and a peak-to-valley displacement of 15.0 cm. (The "peak-to-valley" distance is the vertical distance from the farthest positive position to the farthest negative position.) (a) Write the function that describes this wave traveling in the positive x direction. (b) Determine the power being supplied to the string.

37. A sinusoidal wave on a string is described by the wave function

$$y = (0.15 \text{ m}) \sin (0.80x - 50t)$$

where x and y are in meters and t is in seconds. The mass per unit length of this string is 12.0 g/m. Determine (a) the speed of the wave, (b) the wavelength, (c) the frequency, and (d) the power transmitted to the wave.

38. The wave function for a wave on a taut string is

$$y(x, t) = (0.350 \text{ m}) \sin \left(10\pi t - 3\pi x + \frac{\pi}{4} \right)$$

where x is in meters and t is in seconds. (a) What is the average rate at which energy is transmitted along the string if the linear mass density is 75.0 g/m? (b) What is the energy contained in each cycle of the wave?

39. A horizontal string can transmit a maximum power $\mathcal{P}_0$ (without breaking) if a wave with amplitude A and angular frequency ω is traveling along it. To increase this maximum power, a student folds the string and uses this "double string" as a medium. Determine the maximum power that can be transmitted along the "double string," assuming that the tension in the two strands together is the same as the original tension in the single string.

40. ● In a region far from the epicenter of an earthquake, a seismic wave can be modeled as transporting energy in a single direction without absorption, just as a string wave

does. Suppose the seismic wave moves from granite into mudfill with similar density but with a much smaller bulk modulus. Assume the speed of the wave gradually drops by a factor of 25.0, with negligible reflection of the wave. Explain whether the amplitude of the ground shaking will increase or decrease. Does it change by a predictable factor? This phenomenon led to the collapse of part of the Nimitz Freeway in Oakland, California, during the Loma Prieta earthquake of 1989.

Section 16.6 The Linear Wave Equation

41. ● (a) Evaluate A in the scalar equality $(7 + 3)4 = A$. (b) Evaluate A, B, and C in the vector equality $7.00\hat{\mathbf{i}} + 3.00\hat{\mathbf{k}} = A\hat{\mathbf{i}} + B\hat{\mathbf{j}} + C\hat{\mathbf{k}}$. Explain how you arrive at the answers to convince a student who thinks that you cannot solve a single equation for three different unknowns. (c) **What If?** The functional equality or identity

$$A + B\cos(Cx + Dt + E) = (7.00 \text{ mm})\cos(3x + 4t + 2)$$

is true for all values of the variables x and t, measured in meters and in seconds, respectively. Evaluate the constants A, B, C, D, and E. Explain how you arrive at the answers.

42. Show that the wave function $y = e^{b(x-vt)}$ is a solution of the linear wave equation (Eq. 16.27), where b is a constant.

43. Show that the wave function $y = \ln[b(x - vt)]$ is a solution to Equation 16.27, where b is a constant.

44. (a) Show that the function $y(x, t) = x^2 + v^2t^2$ is a solution to the wave equation. (b) Show that the function in part (a) can be written as $f(x + vt) + g(x - vt)$ and determine the functional forms for f and g. (c) **What If?** Repeat parts (a) and (b) for the function $y(x, t) = \sin(x)\cos(vt)$.

Additional Problems

45. The "wave" is a particular type of pulse that can propagate through a large crowd gathered at a sports arena (Fig. P16.45). The elements of the medium are the spectators, with zero position corresponding to their being seated and maximum position corresponding to their standing and raising their arms. When a large fraction of the spectators participate in the wave motion, a somewhat stable pulse shape can develop. The wave speed depends on people's reaction time, which is typically on the order of 0.1 s. Estimate the order of magnitude, in minutes, of the time interval required for such a pulse to make one circuit around a large sports stadium. State the quantities you measure or estimate and their values.

Figure P16.45

46. ● A sinusoidal wave in a string is described by the wave function

$$y = (0.150 \text{ m})\sin(0.800x - 50.0t)$$

where x is in meters and t is in seconds. The mass per length of the string is 12.0 g/m. (a) Find the maximum transverse acceleration of an element on this string. (b) Determine the maximum transverse force on a 1.00-cm segment of the string. State how this force compares with the tension in the string.

47. Motion picture film is projected at 24.0 frames per second. Each frame is a photograph 19.0 mm high. At what constant speed does the film pass into the projector?

48. A transverse wave on a string is described by the wave function

$$y(x, t) = (0.350 \text{ m})\sin[(1.25 \text{ rad/m})x + (99.6 \text{ rad/s})t]$$

Consider the element of the string at $x = 0$. (a) What is the time interval between the first two instants when this element has a position of $y = 0.175$ m? (b) What distance does the wave travel during this time interval?

49. **Review problem.** A 2.00-kg block hangs from a rubber cord, being supported so that the cord is not stretched. The unstretched length of the cord is 0.500 m, and its mass is 5.00 g. The "spring constant" for the cord is 100 N/m. The block is released and stops at the lowest point. (a) Determine the tension in the cord when the block is at this lowest point. (b) What is the length of the cord in this "stretched" position? (c) Find the speed of a transverse wave in the cord if the block is held in this lowest position.

50. **Review problem.** A block of mass M hangs from a rubber cord. The block is supported so that the cord is not stretched. The unstretched length of the cord is L_0, and its mass is m, much less than M. The "spring constant" for the cord is k. The block is released and stops at the lowest point. (a) Determine the tension in the string when the block is at this lowest point. (b) What is the length of the cord in this "stretched" position? (c) Find the speed of a transverse wave in the cord if the block is held in this lowest position.

51. ● An earthquake or a landslide can produce an ocean wave of short duration carrying great energy, called a tsunami. When its wavelength is large compared to the ocean depth d, the speed of a water wave is given approximately by $v = \sqrt{gd}$. (a) Explain why the amplitude of the wave increases as the wave approaches shore. What can you consider to be constant in the motion of any one wave crest? (b) Assume an earthquake occurs all along a tectonic plate boundary running north to south and produces a straight tsunami wave crest moving everywhere to the west. If the wave has amplitude 1.80 m when its speed is 200 m/s, what will be its amplitude where the water is 9.00 m deep? (c) Explain why the amplitude at the shore should be expected to be still greater, but cannot be meaningfully predicted by your model.

52. **Review problem.** A block of mass M, supported by a string, rests on a frictionless incline making an angle θ with the horizontal (Fig. P16.52). The length of the string is L, and its mass is $m \ll M$. Derive an expression for the

2 = intermediate;   3 = challenging;   □ = SSM/SG;   ▲ = ThomsonNOW;   = symbolic reasoning;   ● = qualitative reasoning

time interval required for a transverse wave to travel from one end of the string to the other.

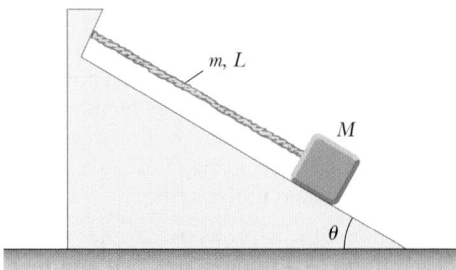

Figure P16.52

53. ● A string with linear density 0.500 g/m is held under tension 20.0 N. As a transverse sinusoidal wave propagates on the string, elements of the string move with maximum speed $v_{y, \text{max}}$. (a) Determine the power transmitted by the wave as a function of $v_{y, \text{max}}$. (b) State how the power depends on $v_{y, \text{max}}$. (c) Find the energy contained in a section of string 3.00 m long. Express it as a function of $v_{y, \text{max}}$ and the mass m_3 of this section. (d) Find the energy that the wave carries past a point in 6.00 s.

54. A sinusoidal wave in a rope is described by the wave function

$$y = (0.20 \text{ m}) \sin (0.75\pi x + 18\pi t)$$

where x and y are in meters and t is in seconds. The rope has a linear mass density of 0.250 kg/m. The tension in the rope is provided by an arrangement like the one illustrated in Figure 16.12. What is the mass of the suspended object?

55. A block of mass 0.450 kg is attached to one end of a cord of mass 0.003 20 kg; the other end of the cord is attached to a fixed point. The block rotates with constant angular speed in a circle on a horizontal, frictionless table. Through what angle does the block rotate in the time interval during which a transverse wave travels along the string from the center of the circle to the block?

56. A wire of density ρ is tapered so that its cross-sectional area varies with x according to

$$A = (1.0 \times 10^{-3}x + 0.010) \text{ cm}^2$$

(a) The tension in the wire is T. Derive a relationship for the speed of a wave as a function of position. (b) **What If?** Assume the wire is aluminum and is under a tension of 24.0 N. Determine the wave speed at the origin and at $x = 10.0$ m.

57. A rope of total mass m and length L is suspended vertically. Show that a transverse pulse travels the length of the rope in a time interval $\Delta t = 2\sqrt{L/g}$. *Suggestion*: First find an expression for the wave speed at any point a distance x from the lower end by considering the rope's tension as resulting from the weight of the segment below that point.

58. Assume an object of mass M is suspended from the bottom of the rope in Problem 57. (a) Show that the time interval for a transverse pulse to travel the length of the rope is

$$\Delta t = 2\sqrt{\frac{L}{mg}}\left(\sqrt{M + m} - \sqrt{M}\right)$$

What If? (b) Show that the expression in part (a) reduces to the result of Problem 57 when $M = 0$. (c) Show that for $m \ll M$, the expression in part (a) reduces to

$$\Delta t = \sqrt{\frac{mL}{Mg}}$$

59. It is stated in Problem 57 that a pulse travels from the bottom to the top of a hanging rope of length L in a time interval $\Delta t = 2\sqrt{L/g}$. Use this result to answer the following questions. (It is not necessary to set up any new integrations.) (a) Over what time interval does a pulse travel halfway up the rope? Give your answer as a fraction of the quantity $2\sqrt{L/g}$. (b) A pulse starts traveling up the rope. How far has it traveled after a time interval $\sqrt{L/g}$?

60. If a loop of chain is spun at high speed, it can roll along the ground like a circular hoop without collapsing. Consider a chain of uniform linear mass density μ whose center of mass travels to the right at a high speed v_0. (a) Determine the tension in the chain in terms of μ and v_0. (b) If the loop rolls over a bump, the resulting deformation of the chain causes two transverse pulses to propagate along the chain, one moving clockwise and one moving counterclockwise. What is the speed of the pulses traveling along the chain? (c) Through what angle does each pulse travel during the time interval over which the loop makes one revolution?

61. **Review problem.** An aluminum wire is clamped at each end under zero tension at room temperature. Reducing the temperature, which results in a decrease in the wire's equilibrium length, increases the tension in the wire. What strain $(\Delta L/L)$ results in a transverse wave speed of 100 m/s? Take the cross-sectional area of the wire to be equal to 5.00×10^{-6} m², the density to be 2.70×10^3 kg/m³, and Young's modulus to be 7.00×10^{10} N/m².

62. (a) Show that the speed of longitudinal waves along a spring of force constant k is $v = \sqrt{kL/\mu}$, where L is the unstretched length of the spring and μ is the mass per unit length. (b) A spring with a mass of 0.400 kg has an unstretched length of 2.00 m and a force constant of 100 N/m. Using the result you obtained in part (a), determine the speed of longitudinal waves along this spring.

63. A pulse traveling along a string of linear mass density μ is described by the wave function

$$y = \left[A_0 e^{-bx}\right] \sin (kx - \omega t)$$

where the factor in brackets is said to be the amplitude. (a) What is the power $\mathcal{P}(x)$ carried by this wave at a point x? (b) What is the power carried by this wave at the origin? (c) Compute the ratio $\mathcal{P}(x)/\mathcal{P}(0)$.

64. An earthquake on the ocean floor in the Gulf of Alaska produces a tsunami that reaches Hilo, Hawaii, 4 450 km away, in a time interval of 9 h 30 min. Tsunamis have enormous wavelengths (100 to 200 km), and the propagation speed for these waves is $v \approx \sqrt{g\overline{d}}$, where $\overline{d}$ is the average depth of the water. From the information given, find the average wave speed and the average ocean depth between Alaska and Hawaii. (This method was used in 1856 to estimate the average depth of the Pacific Ocean

long before soundings were made to give a direct determination.)

65. A string on a musical instrument is held under tension T and extends from the point $x = 0$ to the point $x = L$. The string is overwound with wire in such a way that its mass per unit length $\mu(x)$ increases uniformly from μ_0 at $x = 0$ to μ_L at $x = L$. (a) Find an expression for $\mu(x)$ as a function of x over the range $0 \leq x \leq L$. (b) Show that the time interval required for a transverse pulse to travel the length of the string is given by

$$\Delta t = \frac{2L\left(\mu_L + \mu_0 + \sqrt{\mu_L \mu_0}\right)}{3\sqrt{T}\left(\sqrt{\mu_L} + \sqrt{\mu_0}\right)}$$

Answers to Quick Quizzes

16.1 **(i),** (b). It is longitudinal because the disturbance (the shift of position of the people) is parallel to the direction in which the wave travels. **(ii),** (a). It is transverse because the people stand up and sit down (vertical motion), whereas the wave moves either to the left or to the right.

16.2 **(i),** (c). The wave speed is determined by the medium, so it is unaffected by changing the frequency. **(ii),** (b). Because the wave speed remains the same, the result of doubling the frequency is that the wavelength is half as large. **(iii),** (d). The amplitude of a wave is unrelated to the wave speed, so we cannot determine the new amplitude without further information.

16.3 (c). With a larger amplitude, an element of the string has more energy associated with its simple harmonic motion, so the element passes through the equilibrium position with a higher maximum transverse speed.

16.4 Only answers (f) and (h) are correct. Choices (a) and (b) affect the transverse speed of a particle of the string, but not the wave speed along the string. Choices (c) and (d) change the amplitude. Choices (e) and (g) increase the time interval by decreasing the wave speed.

16.5 (d). Doubling the amplitude of the wave causes the power to be larger by a factor of 4. In choice (a), halving the linear mass density of the string causes the power to change by a factor of 0.71, and the rate decreases. In choice (b), doubling the wavelength of the wave halves the frequency and causes the power to change by a factor of 0.25, and the rate decreases. In choice (c), doubling the tension in the string changes the wave speed and causes the power to change by a factor of 1.4, which is not as large as in choice (d).

Human ears have evolved to detect sound waves and interpret them as music or speech. Some animals, such as this young bat-eared fox, have ears adapted for the detection of very weak sounds. (Getty Images)

17 Sound Waves

Sound waves travel through any material medium with a speed that depends on the properties of the medium. As sound waves travel through air, the elements of air vibrate to produce changes in density and pressure along the direction of motion of the wave. If the source of the sound waves vibrates sinusoidally, the pressure variations are also sinusoidal. The mathematical description of sinusoidal sound waves is very similar to that of sinusoidal waves on strings, which were discussed in Chapter 16.

Sound waves are divided into three categories that cover different frequency ranges. (1) *Audible waves* lie within the range of sensitivity of the human ear. They can be generated in a variety of ways, such as by musical instruments, human voices, or loudspeakers. (2) *Infrasonic waves* have frequencies below the audible range. Elephants can use infrasonic waves to communicate with one another, even when separated by many kilometers. (3) *Ultrasonic waves* have frequencies above the audible range. You may have used a "silent" whistle to retrieve your dog. Dogs easily hear the ultrasonic sound this whistle emits, although humans cannot detect it at all. Ultrasonic waves are also used in medical imaging.

This chapter begins with a discussion of the speed of sound waves and then wave intensity, which is a function of wave amplitude. We then provide an alternative description of the intensity of sound waves that compresses the wide range of intensities to which the ear is sensitive into a smaller range for convenience. The effects of the motion of sources and listeners on the frequency of a sound are also investigated. Finally, we explore digital reproduction of sound, focusing in particular on sound systems used in modern motion pictures.

17.1 Speed of Sound Waves

Let us describe pictorially the motion of a one-dimensional longitudinal pulse moving through a long tube containing a compressible gas as shown in Figure 17.1. A piston at the left end can be moved to the right to compress the gas and create the pulse. Before the piston is moved, the gas is undisturbed and of uniform density as represented by the uniformly shaded region in Figure 17.1a. When the piston is suddenly pushed to the right (Fig. 17.1b), the gas just in front of it is compressed (as represented by the more heavily shaded region); the pressure and density in this region are now higher than they were before the piston moved. When the piston comes to rest (Fig. 17.1c), the compressed region of the gas continues to move to the right, corresponding to a longitudinal pulse traveling through the tube with speed v.

The speed of sound waves in a medium depends on the compressibility and density of the medium. If the medium is a liquid or a gas and has a bulk modulus B (see Section 12.4) and density ρ, the speed of sound waves in that medium is

$$v = \sqrt{\frac{B}{\rho}} \qquad (17.1)$$

It is interesting to compare this expression with Equation 16.18 for the speed of transverse waves on a string, $v = \sqrt{T/\mu}$. In both cases, the wave speed depends on an elastic property of the medium (bulk modulus B or string tension T) and on an inertial property of the medium (ρ or μ). In fact, the speed of all mechanical waves follows an expression of the general form

$$v = \sqrt{\frac{\text{elastic property}}{\text{inertial property}}}$$

For longitudinal sound waves in a solid rod of material, for example, the speed of sound depends on Young's modulus Y and the density ρ. Table 17.1 (page 476) provides the speed of sound in several different materials.

The speed of sound also depends on the temperature of the medium. For sound traveling through air, the relationship between wave speed and air temperature is

$$v = (331 \text{ m/s})\sqrt{1 + \frac{T_C}{273°C}}$$

where 331 m/s is the speed of sound in air at 0°C and T_C is the air temperature in degrees Celsius. Using this equation, one finds that at 20°C, the speed of sound in air is approximately 343 m/s.

This information provides a convenient way to estimate the distance to a thunderstorm. First count the number of seconds between seeing the flash of lightning and hearing the thunder. Dividing this time by 3 gives the approximate distance to the lightning in kilometers because 343 m/s is approximately $\frac{1}{3}$ km/s. Dividing the time in seconds by 5 gives the approximate distance to the lightning in miles because the speed of sound is approximately $\frac{1}{5}$ mi/s.

Undisturbed gas

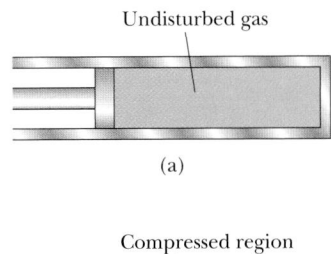

(a)

Compressed region

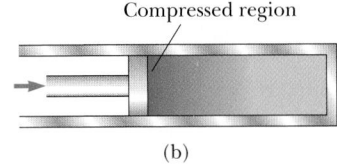

(b)

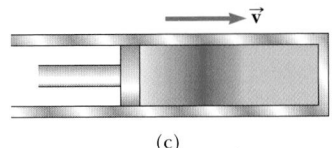

(c)

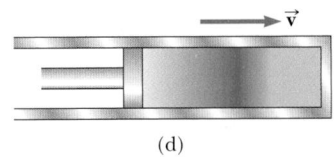

(d)

Figure 17.1 Motion of a longitudinal pulse through a compressible gas. The compression (darker region) is produced by the moving piston.

TABLE 17.1

Speed of Sound in Various Media

Medium	v (m/s)	Medium	v (m/s)	Medium	v (m/s)
Gases		**Liquids at 25°C**		**Solids**[a]	
Hydrogen (0°C)	1 286	Glycerol	1 904	Pyrex glass	5 640
Helium (0°C)	972	Seawater	1 533	Iron	5 950
Air (20°C)	343	Water	1 493	Aluminum	6 420
Air (0°C)	331	Mercury	1 450	Brass	4 700
Oxygen (0°C)	317	Kerosene	1 324	Copper	5 010
		Methyl alcohol	1 143	Gold	3 240
		Carbon tetrachloride	926	Lucite	2 680
				Lead	1 960
				Rubber	1 600

[a] Values given are for propagation of longitudinal waves in bulk media. Speeds for longitudinal waves in thin rods are smaller, and speeds of transverse waves in bulk are smaller yet.

17.2 Periodic Sound Waves

One can produce a one-dimensional periodic sound wave in a long, narrow tube containing a gas by means of an oscillating piston at one end as shown in Active Figure 17.2. The darker parts of the colored areas in this figure represent regions in which the gas is compressed and the density and pressure are above their equilibrium values. A compressed region is formed whenever the piston is pushed into the tube. This compressed region, called a **compression**, moves through the tube, continuously compressing the region just in front of itself. When the piston is pulled back, the gas in front of it expands and the pressure and density in this region fall below their equilibrium values (represented by the lighter parts of the colored areas in Active Fig. 17.2). These low-pressure regions, called **rarefactions**, also propagate along the tube, following the compressions. Both regions move at the speed of sound in the medium.

As the piston oscillates sinusoidally, regions of compression and rarefaction are continuously set up. The distance between two successive compressions (or two successive rarefactions) equals the wavelength λ of the sound wave. As these regions travel through the tube, any small element of the medium moves with simple harmonic motion parallel to the direction of the wave. If $s(x, t)$ is the position of a small element relative to its equilibrium position,[1] we can express this harmonic position function as

$$s(x, t) = s_{max} \cos (kx - \omega t) \tag{17.2}$$

where s_{max} is the maximum position of the element relative to equilibrium. This parameter is often called the **displacement amplitude** of the wave. The parameter k is the wave number, and ω is the angular frequency of the wave. Notice that the displacement of the element is along x, in the direction of propagation of the sound wave, which means we are describing a longitudinal wave.

The variation in the gas pressure ΔP measured from the equilibrium value is also periodic. For the position function in Equation 17.2, ΔP is given by

$$\Delta P = \Delta P_{max} \sin (kx - \omega t) \tag{17.3}$$

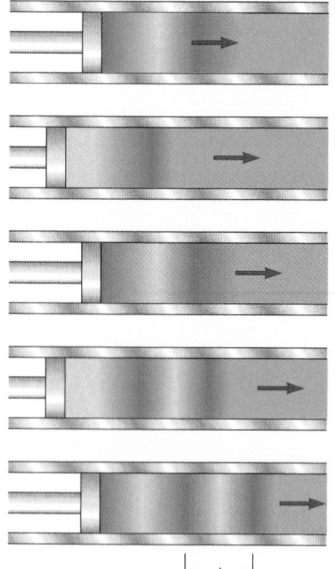

ACTIVE FIGURE 17.2

A longitudinal wave propagating through a gas-filled tube. The source of the wave is an oscillating piston at the left.

Sign in at www.thomsonedu.com and go to ThomsonNOW to adjust the frequency of the piston.

[1] We use $s(x, t)$ here instead of $y(x, t)$ because the displacement of elements of the medium is not perpendicular to the x direction.

where **the pressure amplitude ΔP_{max}**—which is the maximum change in pressure from the equilibrium value—is given by

$$\Delta P_{max} = \rho v \omega s_{max} \qquad (17.4)$$

Equation 17.3 is derived in Example 17.1.

A sound wave may be considered to be either a displacement wave or a pressure wave. A comparison of Equations 17.2 and 17.3 shows that **the pressure wave is 90° out of phase with the displacement wave**. Graphs of these functions are shown in Figure 17.3. The pressure variation is a maximum when the displacement from equilibrium is zero, and the displacement from equilibrium is a maximum when the pressure variation is zero.

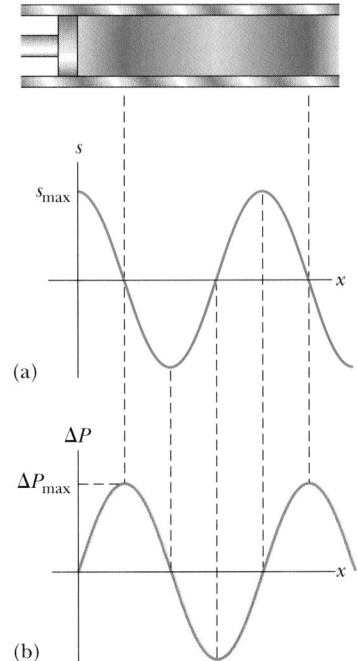

Figure 17.3 (a) Displacement amplitude and (b) pressure amplitude versus position for a sinusoidal longitudinal wave.

Quick Quiz 17.1 If you blow across the top of an empty soft-drink bottle, a pulse of sound travels down through the air in the bottle. At the moment the pulse reaches the bottom of the bottle, what is the correct description of the displacement of elements of air from their equilibrium positions and the pressure of the air at this point? (a) The displacement and pressure are both at a maximum. (b) The displacement and pressure are both at a minimum. (c) The displacement is zero, and the pressure is a maximum. (d) The displacement is zero, and the pressure is a minimum.

EXAMPLE 17.1	**Derivation of Equation 17.3**

Derive the expression for the pressure variation in a sound wave given by Equation 17.3.

SOLUTION

Conceptualize Consider a thin, disk-shaped element of gas whose flat faces are parallel to the piston in Active Figure 17.2. This element will undergo changes in position, pressure, and density as a sound wave propagates through the gas.

Categorize This derivation combines elastic properties of a gas (Chapter 12) with the wave phenomena discussed in this chapter.

Analyze The element of gas has a thickness Δx in the horizontal direction and a cross-sectional area A, so its volume is $V_i = A \Delta x$. When a sound wave displaces the element, the disk's two flat faces move through different distances s. The change in volume ΔV of the element when a sound wave displaces the element is equal to $A \Delta s$, where Δs is the difference between the values of s between the two flat faces of the disk.

From the definition of bulk modulus (see Eq. 12.8), express the pressure variation in the element of gas as a function of its change in volume:

$$\Delta P = -B \frac{\Delta V}{V_i}$$

Substitute for the initial volume and the change in volume of the element:

$$\Delta P = -B \frac{A \Delta s}{A \Delta x} = -B \frac{\Delta s}{\Delta x}$$

Let the thickness Δx of the disk approach zero so that the ratio $\Delta s/\Delta x$ becomes a partial derivative:

$$\Delta P = -B \frac{\partial s}{\partial x}$$

Substitute the position function given by Equation 17.2:

$$\Delta P = -B \frac{\partial}{\partial x}[s_{max} \cos(kx - \omega t)] = B s_{max} k \sin(kx - \omega t)$$

Use Equation 17.1 to express the bulk modulus as $B = \rho v^2$ and substitute:

$$\Delta P = \rho v^2 s_{max} k \sin (kx - \omega t)$$

Use Equation 16.11 in the form $k = \omega/v$ and substitute:

$$\Delta P = \rho v \omega s_{max} \sin (kx - \omega t)$$

Because the sine function has a maximum value of 1, identify the maximum value of the pressure variation as $\Delta P_{max} = \rho v \omega s_{max}$ (see Eq. 17.4) and substitute for this combination in the previous expression:

$$\Delta P = \Delta P_{max} \sin (kx - \omega t)$$

Finalize   This final expression for the pressure variation of the air in a sound wave matches Equation 17.3.

17.3   Intensity of Periodic Sound Waves

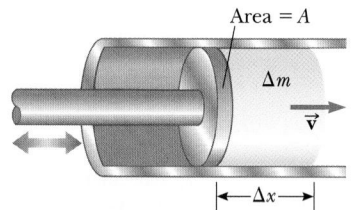

Area = A

Figure 17.4   An oscillating piston transfers energy to the air in the tube, causing the element of air of length Δx and mass Δm to oscillate with an amplitude s_{max}.

In Chapter 16, we showed that a wave traveling on a taut string transports energy. The same concept applies to sound waves. Consider an element of air of mass Δm and length Δx in front of a piston of area A oscillating with a frequency ω as shown in Figure 17.4. The piston transmits energy to this element of air in the tube, and the energy is propagated away from the piston by the sound wave. To evaluate the rate of energy transfer for the sound wave, let's evaluate the kinetic energy of this element of air, which is undergoing simple harmonic motion. A procedure similar to that in Section 16.5 in which we evaluated the rate of energy transfer for a wave on a string shows that the kinetic energy in one wavelength of the sound wave is

$$K_\lambda = \tfrac{1}{4}(\rho A)\omega^2 s_{max}^2 \lambda$$

As in the case of the string wave in Section 16.5, the total potential energy for one wavelength has the same value as the total kinetic energy; therefore, the total mechanical energy for one wavelength is

$$E_\lambda = K_\lambda + U_\lambda = \tfrac{1}{2}(\rho A)\omega^2 s_{max}^2 \lambda$$

As the sound wave moves through the air, this amount of energy passes by a given point during one period of oscillation. Hence, the rate of energy transfer is

$$\mathcal{P} = \frac{E_\lambda}{T} = \frac{\tfrac{1}{2}(\rho A)\omega^2 s_{max}^2 \lambda}{T} = \tfrac{1}{2}(\rho A)\omega^2 s_{max}^2 \left(\frac{\lambda}{T}\right) = \tfrac{1}{2}\rho A v \omega^2 s_{max}^2$$

where v is the speed of sound in air. Compare this expression with Equation 16.21 for a wave on a string.

We define the **intensity** I of a wave, or the power per unit area, as the rate at which the energy transported by the wave transfers through a unit area A perpendicular to the direction of travel of the wave:

$$I \equiv \frac{\mathcal{P}}{A} \qquad (17.5)$$

In this case, the intensity is therefore

◀ Intensity of a sound wave

$$I = \tfrac{1}{2}\rho v (\omega s_{max})^2$$

Hence, the intensity of a periodic sound wave is proportional to the square of the displacement amplitude and to the square of the angular frequency. This expression can also be written in terms of the pressure amplitude ΔP_{max}; in this case, we use Equation 17.4 to obtain

$$I = \frac{(\Delta P_{max})^2}{2\rho v} \qquad (17.6)$$

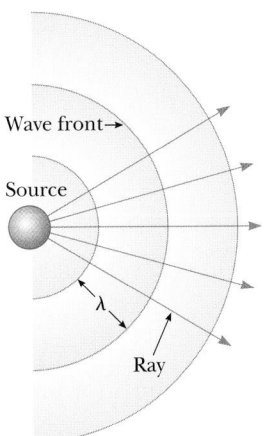

Figure 17.5   Spherical waves emitted by a point source. The circular arcs represent the spherical wave fronts that are concentric with the source. The rays are radial lines pointing outward from the source, perpendicular to the wave fronts.

Now consider a point source emitting sound waves equally in all directions. From everyday experience, we know that the intensity of sound decreases as we move farther from the source. When a source emits sound equally in all directions, the result is a **spherical wave**. Figure 17.5 shows these spherical waves as a series of circular arcs concentric with the source. Each arc represents a surface over which the phase of the wave is constant. We call such a surface of constant phase a **wave front**. The distance between adjacent wave fronts that have the same phase is the wavelength λ of the wave. The radial lines pointing outward from the source are called **rays**.

The average power $\mathcal{P}_{avg}$ emitted by the source must be distributed uniformly over each spherical wave front of area $4\pi r^2$. Hence, the wave intensity at a distance r from the source is

$$I = \frac{\mathcal{P}_{avg}}{A} = \frac{\mathcal{P}_{avg}}{4\pi r^2} \tag{17.7}$$

◄ Inverse-square behavior of intensity for a point source

This inverse-square law, which is reminiscent of the behavior of gravity in Chapter 13, states that the intensity decreases in proportion to the square of the distance from the source.

Quick Quiz 17.2   A vibrating guitar string makes very little sound if it is not mounted on the guitar body. Why does the sound have greater intensity if the string is attached to the guitar body? (a) The string vibrates with more energy. (b) The energy leaves the guitar at a greater rate. (c) The sound power is spread over a larger area at the listener's position. (d) The sound power is concentrated over a smaller area at the listener's position. (e) The speed of sound is higher in the material of the guitar body. (f) None of these answers is correct.

EXAMPLE 17.2   Hearing Limits

The faintest sounds the human ear can detect at a frequency of 1 000 Hz correspond to an intensity of about 1.00×10^{-12} W/m², which is called *threshold of hearing*. The loudest sounds the ear can tolerate at this frequency correspond to an intensity of about 1.00 W/m², the *threshold of pain*. Determine the pressure amplitude and displacement amplitude associated with these two limits.

SOLUTION

Conceptualize   Think about the quietest environment you have ever experienced. It is likely that the intensity of sound in even this quietest environment is higher than the threshold of hearing.

Categorize   Because we are given intensities and asked to calculate pressure and displacement amplitudes, this problem requires the concepts discussed in this section.

Analyze To find the pressure amplitude at the threshold of hearing, use Equation 17.6, taking the speed of sound waves in air to be $v = 343$ m/s and the density of air to be $\rho = 1.20$ kg/m³:

$$\Delta P_{max} = \sqrt{2\rho v I}$$
$$= \sqrt{2(1.20 \text{ kg/m}^3)(343 \text{ m/s})(1.00 \times 10^{-12} \text{ W/m}^2)}$$
$$= 2.87 \times 10^{-5} \text{ N/m}^2$$

Calculate the corresponding displacement amplitude using Equation 17.4, recalling that $\omega = 2\pi f$ (Eq. 16.9):

$$s_{max} = \frac{\Delta P_{max}}{\rho v \omega} = \frac{2.87 \times 10^{-5} \text{ N/m}^2}{(1.20 \text{ kg/m}^3)(343 \text{ m/s})(2\pi \times 1\,000 \text{ Hz})}$$
$$= 1.11 \times 10^{-11} \text{ m}$$

In a similar manner, one finds that the loudest sounds the human ear can tolerate correspond to a pressure amplitude of 28.7 N/m^2 and a displacement amplitude equal to 1.11×10^{-5} m.

Finalize Because atmospheric pressure is about 10^5 N/m², the result for the pressure amplitude tells us that the ear is sensitive to pressure fluctuations as small as 3 parts in 10^{10}! The displacement amplitude is also a remarkably small number! If we compare this result for s_{max} to the size of an atom (about 10^{-10} m), we see that the ear is an extremely sensitive detector of sound waves.

EXAMPLE 17.3   **Intensity Variations of a Point Source**

A point source emits sound waves with an average power output of 80.0 W.

(A) Find the intensity 3.00 m from the source.

SOLUTION

Conceptualize Imagine a small loudspeaker sending sound out at an average rate of 80.0 W uniformly in all directions. You are standing 3.00 m away from the speakers. As the sound propagates, the energy of the sound waves is spread out over an ever-expanding sphere.

Categorize We evaluate the intensity from a given equation, so we categorize this example as a substitution problem.

Because a point source emits energy in the form of spherical waves, use Equation 17.7 to find the intensity:

$$I = \frac{\mathcal{P}_{avg}}{4\pi r^2} = \frac{80.0 \text{ W}}{4\pi (3.00 \text{ m})^2} = 0.707 \text{ W/m}^2$$

This intensity is close to the threshold of pain.

(B) Find the distance at which the intensity of the sound is 1.00×10^{-8} W/m².

SOLUTION

Solve for r in Equation 17.7 and use the given value for I:

$$r = \sqrt{\frac{\mathcal{P}_{avg}}{4\pi I}} = \sqrt{\frac{80.0 \text{ W}}{4\pi (1.00 \times 10^{-8} \text{ W/m}^2)}}$$
$$= 2.52 \times 10^4 \text{ m}$$

Sound Level in Decibels

Example 17.2 illustrates the wide range of intensities the human ear can detect. Because this range is so wide, it is convenient to use a logarithmic scale, where the **sound level** β (Greek letter beta) is defined by the equation

Sound level in decibels ▶

$$\beta \equiv 10 \log \left(\frac{I}{I_0} \right) \tag{17.8}$$

The constant I_0 is the *reference intensity*, taken to be at the threshold of hearing ($I_0 = 1.00 \times 10^{-12}$ W/m^2), and I is the intensity in watts per square meter to which the sound level β corresponds, where β is measured[2] in **decibels** (dB). On this scale, the threshold of pain ($I = 1.00$ W/m^2) corresponds to a sound level of $\beta = 10 \log [(1$ W/m$^2)/(10^{-12}$ W/m$^2)] = 10 \log (10^{12}) = 120$ dB, and the threshold of hearing corresponds to $\beta = 10 \log [(10^{-12}$ W/m$^2)/(10^{-12}$ W/m$^2)] = 0$ dB.

Prolonged exposure to high sound levels may seriously damage the human ear. Ear plugs are recommended whenever sound levels exceed 90 dB. Recent evidence suggests that "noise pollution" may be a contributing factor to high blood pressure, anxiety, and nervousness. Table 17.2 gives some typical sound levels.

Quick Quiz 17.3   Increasing the intensity of a sound by a factor of 100 causes the sound level to increase by what amount? (a) 100 dB   (b) 20 dB   (c) 10 dB   (d) 2 dB

TABLE 17.2

Sound Levels

Source of Sound	β (dB)
Nearby jet airplane	150
Jackhammer; machine gun	130
Siren; rock concert	120
Subway; power lawn mower	100
Busy traffic	80
Vacuum cleaner	70
Normal conversation	50
Mosquito buzzing	40
Whisper	30
Rustling leaves	10
Threshold of hearing	0

EXAMPLE 17.4   **Sound Levels**

Two identical machines are positioned the same distance from a worker. The intensity of sound delivered by each operating machine at the worker's location is 2.0×10^{-7} W/m^2.

(A) Find the sound level heard by the worker when one machine is operating.

SOLUTION

Conceptualize   Imagine a situation in which one source of sound is active and is then joined by a second identical source, such as one person speaking and then a second person speaking at the same time or one musical instrument playing and then being joined by a second instrument.

Categorize   Because we are asked for a sound level, we will perform calculations with Equation 17.8.

Analyze   Use Equation 17.8 to calculate the sound level at the worker's location with one machine operating:

$$\beta_1 = 10 \log \left(\frac{2.0 \times 10^{-7} \text{ W/m}^2}{1.00 \times 10^{-12} \text{ W/m}^2} \right) = 10 \log (2.0 \times 10^5) = \boxed{53 \text{ dB}}$$

(B) Find the sound level heard by the worker when two machines are operating.

SOLUTION

Use Equation 17.8 to calculate the sound level at the worker's location with double the intensity:

$$\beta_2 = 10 \log \left(\frac{4.0 \times 10^{-7} \text{ W/m}^2}{1.00 \times 10^{-12} \text{ W/m}^2} \right) = 10 \log (4.0 \times 10^5) = \boxed{56 \text{ dB}}$$

Finalize   These results show that when the intensity is doubled, the sound level increases by only 3 dB.

What If?   *Loudness* is a psychological response to a sound. It depends on both the intensity and the frequency of the sound. As a rule of thumb, a doubling in loudness is approximately associated with an increase in sound level of 10 dB. (This rule of thumb is relatively inaccurate at very low or very high frequencies.) If the loudness of the machines in this example is to be doubled, how many machines at the same distance from the worker must be running?

---

[2] The unit *bel* is named after the inventor of the telephone, Alexander Graham Bell (1847–1922). The prefix *deci-* is the SI prefix that stands for 10^{-1}.

Answer Using the rule of thumb, a doubling of loudness corresponds to a sound level increase of 10 dB. Therefore,

$$\beta_2 - \beta_1 = 10 \text{ dB} = 10 \log\left(\frac{I_2}{I_0}\right) - 10 \log\left(\frac{I_1}{I_0}\right) = 10 \log\left(\frac{I_2}{I_1}\right)$$

$$\log\left(\frac{I_2}{I_1}\right) = 1 \quad \rightarrow \quad I_2 = 10 I_1$$

Therefore, ten machines must be operating to double the loudness.

Loudness and Frequency

The discussion of sound level in decibels relates to a *physical* measurement of the strength of a sound. Let us now extend our discussion from Example 17.4 concerning the *psychological* "measurement" of the strength of a sound.

Of course, we don't have instruments in our bodies that can display numerical values of our reactions to stimuli. We have to "calibrate" our reactions somehow by comparing different sounds to a reference sound, but that is not easy to accomplish. For example, earlier we mentioned that the threshold intensity is 10^{-12} W/m², corresponding to an intensity level of 0 dB. In reality, this value is the threshold only for a sound of frequency 1 000 Hz, which is a standard reference frequency in acoustics. If we perform an experiment to measure the threshold intensity at other frequencies, we find a distinct variation of this threshold as a function of frequency. For example, at 100 Hz, a barely audible sound must have an intensity level of about 30 dB! Unfortunately, there is no simple relationship between physical measurements and psychological "measurements." The 100-Hz, 30-dB sound is psychologically "equal" to the 1 000-Hz, 0-dB sound (both are just barely audible), but they are not physically equal (30 dB ≠ 0 dB).

By using test subjects, the human response to sound has been studied, and the results are shown in the white area of Figure 17.6 along with the approximate frequency and sound-level ranges of other sound sources. The lower curve of the white area corresponds to the threshold of hearing. Its variation with frequency is clear from this diagram. Notice that humans are sensitive to frequencies ranging from about 20 Hz to about 20 000 Hz. The upper bound of the white area is the

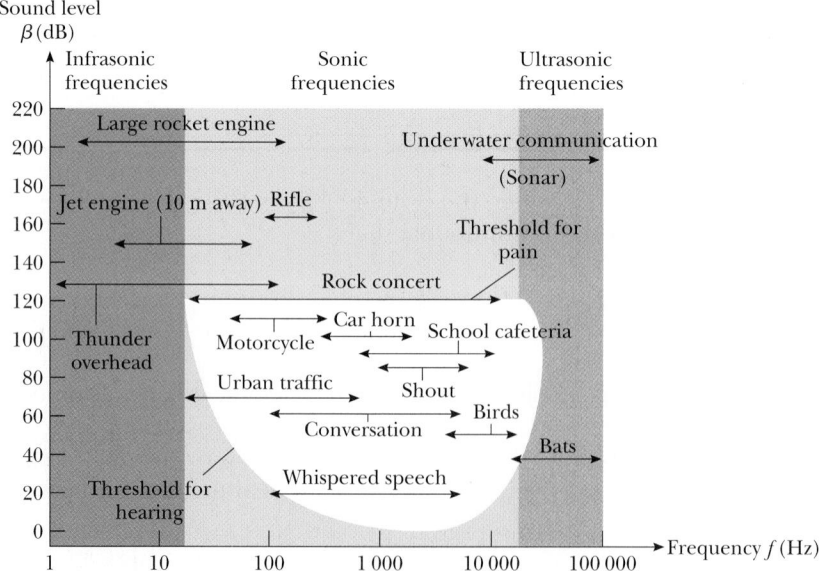

Figure 17.6 Approximate ranges of frequency and sound level of various sources and that of normal human hearing, shown by the white area. (From R. L. Reese, *University Physics*, Pacific Grove, Brooks/Cole, 2000.)

threshold of pain. Here the boundary of the white area is straight because the psychological response is relatively independent of frequency at this high sound level.

The most dramatic change with frequency is in the lower left region of the white area, for low frequencies and low intensity levels. Our ears are particularly insensitive in this region. If you are listening to your stereo and the bass (low frequencies) and treble (high frequencies) sound balanced at a high volume, try turning the volume down and listening again. You will probably notice that the bass seems weak, which is due to the insensitivity of the ear to low frequencies at low sound levels as shown in Figure 17.6.

17.4   The Doppler Effect

Perhaps you have noticed how the sound of a vehicle's horn changes as the vehicle moves past you. The frequency of the sound you hear as the vehicle approaches you is higher than the frequency you hear as it moves away from you. This experience is one example of the **Doppler effect**.[3]

To see what causes this apparent frequency change, imagine you are in a boat that is lying at anchor on a gentle sea where the waves have a period of $T = 3.0$ s. Hence, every 3.0 s a crest hits your boat. Figure 17.7a shows this situation, with the water waves moving toward the left. If you set your watch to $t = 0$ just as one crest hits, the watch reads 3.0 s when the next crest hits, 6.0 s when the third crest hits, and so on. From these observations, you conclude that the wave frequency is $f = 1/T = 1/(3.0 \text{ s}) = 0.33$ Hz. Now suppose you start your motor and head directly into the oncoming waves as in Figure 17.7b. Again you set your watch to $t = 0$ as a crest hits the front (the bow) of your boat. Now, however, because you are moving toward the next wave crest as it moves toward you, it hits you less than 3.0 s after the first hit. In other words, the period you observe is shorter than the 3.0-s period you observed when you were stationary. Because $f = 1/T$, you observe a higher wave frequency than when you were at rest.

If you turn around and move in the same direction as the waves (Fig. 17.7c), you observe the opposite effect. You set your watch to $t = 0$ as a crest hits the back (the stern) of the boat. Because you are now moving away from the next crest, more than 3.0 s has elapsed on your watch by the time that crest catches you. Therefore, you observe a lower frequency than when you were at rest.

These effects occur because the *relative* speed between your boat and the waves depends on the direction of travel and on the speed of your boat. When you are moving toward the right in Figure 17.7b, this relative speed is higher than that of the wave speed, which leads to the observation of an increased frequency. When you turn around and move to the left, the relative speed is lower, as is the observed frequency of the water waves.

Let's now examine an analogous situation with sound waves in which the water waves become sound waves, the water becomes the air, and the person on the boat becomes an observer listening to the sound. In this case, an observer O is moving and a sound source S is stationary. For simplicity, we assume the air is also stationary and the observer moves directly toward the source (Active Fig. 17.8). The observer moves with a speed v_O toward a stationary point source ($v_S = 0$), where *stationary* means at rest with respect to the medium, air.

If a point source emits sound waves and the medium is uniform, the waves move at the same speed in all directions radially away from the source; the result is a spherical wave as mentioned in Section 17.3. The distance between adjacent wave fronts equals the wavelength λ. In Active Figure 17.8, the circles are the intersections of these three-dimensional wave fronts with the two-dimensional paper.

We take the frequency of the source in Active Figure 17.8 to be f, the wavelength to be λ, and the speed of sound to be v. If the observer were also stationary,

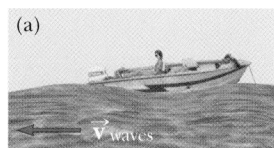

Figure 17.7 (a) Waves moving toward a stationary boat. The waves travel to the left, and their source is far to the right of the boat, out of the frame of the photograph. (b) The boat moving toward the wave source. (c) The boat moving away from the wave source.

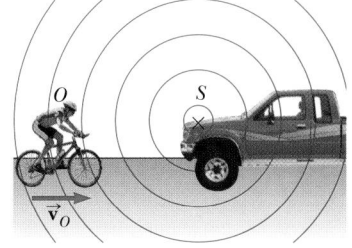

ACTIVE FIGURE 17.8

An observer O (the cyclist) moves with a speed v_O toward a stationary point source S, the horn of a parked truck. The observer hears a frequency f' that is greater than the source frequency.

Sign in at www.thomsonedu.com and go to ThomsonNOW to adjust the speed of the observer.

[3] Named after Austrian physicist Christian Johann Doppler (1803–1853), who in 1842 predicted the effect for both sound waves and light waves.

he would detect wave fronts at a frequency f. (That is, when $v_O = 0$ and $v_S = 0$, the observed frequency equals the source frequency.) When the observer moves toward the source, the speed of the waves relative to the observer is $v' = v + v_O$, as in the case of the boat in Figure 17.7, but the wavelength λ is unchanged. Hence, using Equation 16.12, $v = \lambda f$, we can say that the frequency f' heard by the observer is *increased* and is given by

$$f' = \frac{v'}{\lambda} = \frac{v + v_O}{\lambda}$$

Because $\lambda = v/f$, we can express f' as

$$f' = \left(\frac{v + v_O}{v}\right)f \quad \text{(observer moving toward source)} \tag{17.9}$$

If the observer is moving away from the source, the speed of the wave relative to the observer is $v' = v - v_O$. The frequency heard by the observer in this case is *decreased* and is given by

$$f' = \left(\frac{v - v_O}{v}\right)f \quad \text{(observer moving away from source)} \tag{17.10}$$

In general, whenever an observer moves with a speed v_O relative to a stationary source, the frequency heard by the observer is given by Equation 17.9, with a sign convention: a positive value is substituted for v_O when the observer moves toward the source, and a negative value is substituted when the observer moves away from the source.

Now suppose the source is in motion and the observer is at rest. If the source moves directly toward observer A in Active Figure 17.9a, the wave fronts heard by the observer are closer together than they would be if the source were not moving. As a result, the wavelength λ' measured by observer A is shorter than the wavelength λ of the source. During each vibration, which lasts for a time interval T (the period), the source moves a distance $v_S T = v_S/f$ and the wavelength is *shortened* by this amount. Therefore, the observed wavelength λ' is

$$\lambda' = \lambda - \Delta\lambda = \lambda - \frac{v_S}{f}$$

Because $\lambda = v/f$, the frequency f' heard by observer A is

$$f' = \frac{v}{\lambda'} = \frac{v}{\lambda - (v_S/f)} = \frac{v}{(v/f) - (v_S/f)}$$

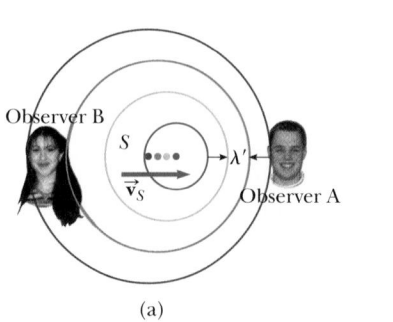

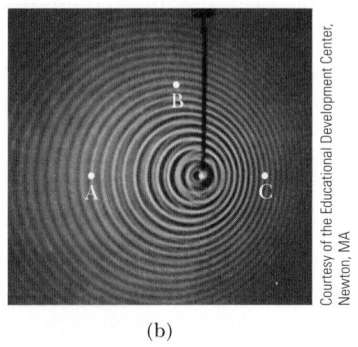

Courtesy of the Educational Development Center, Newton, MA

(a) (b)

ACTIVE FIGURE 17.9

(a) A source S moving with a speed v_S toward a stationary observer A and away from a stationary observer B. Observer A hears an increased frequency, and observer B hears a decreased frequency. (b) The Doppler effect in water, observed in a ripple tank. A point source is moving to the right with speed v_S. Letters shown in the photo refer to Quick Quiz 17.4.

Sign in at www.thomsonedu.com and go to ThomsonNOW to adjust the speed of the source.

$$f' = \left(\frac{v}{v - v_S}\right)f \quad \text{(source moving toward observer)} \qquad \textbf{(17.11)}$$

That is, the observed frequency is *increased* whenever the source is moving toward the observer.

When the source moves away from a stationary observer, as is the case for observer B in Active Figure 17.9a, the observer measures a wavelength λ' that is *greater* than λ and hears a *decreased* frequency:

$$f' = \left(\frac{v}{v + v_S}\right)f \quad \text{(source moving away from observer)} \qquad \textbf{(17.12)}$$

We can express the general relationship for the observed frequency when a source is moving and an observer is at rest as Equation 17.11, with the same sign convention applied to v_S as was applied to v_O: a positive value is substituted for v_S when the source moves toward the observer, and a negative value is substituted when the source moves away from the observer.

Finally, combining Equations 17.9 and 17.11 gives the following general relationship for the observed frequency:

$$f' = \left(\frac{v + v_O}{v - v_S}\right)f \qquad \textbf{(17.13)}$$

◄ General Doppler-shift expression

In this expression, the signs for the values substituted for v_O and v_S depend on the direction of the velocity. A positive value is used for motion of the observer or the source *toward* the other (associated with an *increase* in observed frequency), and a negative value is used for motion of one *away from* the other (associated with a *decrease* in observed frequency).

Although the Doppler effect is most typically experienced with sound waves, it is a phenomenon common to all waves. For example, the relative motion of source and observer produces a frequency shift in light waves. The Doppler effect is used in police radar systems to measure the speeds of motor vehicles. Likewise, astronomers use the effect to determine the speeds of stars, galaxies, and other celestial objects relative to the Earth.

PITFALL PREVENTION 17.1
Doppler Effect Does Not Depend on Distance

Some people think that the Doppler effect depends on the distance between the source and the observer. Although the intensity of a sound varies as the distance changes, the apparent frequency depends only on the relative speed of source and observer. As you listen to an approaching source, you will detect increasing intensity but constant frequency. As the source passes, you will hear the frequency suddenly drop to a new constant value and the intensity begin to decrease.

Quick Quiz 17.4   Consider detectors of water waves at three locations A, B, and C in Active Figure 17.9b. Which of the following statements is true? (a) The wave speed is highest at location A. (b) The wave speed is highest at location C. (c) The detected wavelength is largest at location B. (d) The detected wavelength is largest at location C. (e) The detected frequency is highest at location C. (f) The detected frequency is highest at location A.

Quick Quiz 17.5   You stand on a platform at a train station and listen to a train approaching the station at a constant velocity. While the train approaches, but before it arrives, what do you hear? (a) the intensity and the frequency of the sound both increasing   (b) the intensity and the frequency of the sound both decreasing   (c) the intensity increasing and the frequency decreasing   (d) the intensity decreasing and the frequency increasing   (e) the intensity increasing and the frequency remaining the same   (f) the intensity decreasing and the frequency remaining the same

---

EXAMPLE 17.5   **The Broken Clock Radio**

Your clock radio awakens you with a steady and irritating sound of frequency 600 Hz. One morning, it malfunctions and cannot be turned off. In frustration, you drop the clock radio out of your fourth-story dorm window, 15.0 m from the ground. Assume the speed of sound is 343 m/s. As you listen to the falling clock radio, what frequency do you hear just before you hear it striking the ground?

SOLUTION

Conceptualize   The speed of the clock radio increases as it falls. Therefore, it is a source of sound moving away from you with an increasing speed so the frequency you hear should be less than 600 Hz.

Categorize   We categorize this problem as one in which we must combine our understanding of falling objects with that of the frequency shift due to the Doppler effect.

Analyze   Because the clock radio is modeled as a particle under constant acceleration due to gravity, use Equation 2.13 to express the speed of the source of sound:

$$v_S = v_{yi} + a_y t = 0 - gt = -gt$$

Use Equation 17.13 to determine the Doppler-shifted frequency heard from the falling clock radio:

$$(1) \quad f' = \left[\frac{v + 0}{v - (-gt)} \right] f = \left(\frac{v}{v + gt} \right) f$$

From Equation 2.16, find the time at which the clock radio strikes the ground:

$$y_f = y_i + v_{yi}t - \tfrac{1}{2}gt^2$$

$$-15.0 \text{ m} = 0 + 0 - \tfrac{1}{2}(9.80 \text{ m/s}^2)t^2$$

$$t = 1.75 \text{ s}$$

From Equation (1), evaluate the Doppler-shifted frequency just as the clock radio strikes the ground:

$$f' = \left[\frac{343 \text{ m/s}}{343 \text{ m/s} + (9.80 \text{ m/s}^2)(1.75 \text{ s})} \right] (600 \text{ Hz})$$

$$= \boxed{571 \text{ Hz}}$$

Finalize   The frequency is lower than the actual frequency of 600 Hz because the clock radio is moving away from you. If it were to fall from a higher floor so that it passes below $y = -15.0$ m, the clock radio would continue to accelerate and the frequency would continue to drop.

EXAMPLE 17.6   Doppler Submarines

A submarine (sub A) travels through water at a speed of 8.00 m/s, emitting a sonar wave at a frequency of 1 400 Hz. The speed of sound in the water is 1 533 m/s. A second submarine (sub B) is located such that both submarines are traveling directly toward each other. The second submarine is moving at 9.00 m/s.

(A) What frequency is detected by an observer riding on sub B as the subs approach each other?

SOLUTION

Conceptualize   Even though the problem involves subs moving in water, there is a Doppler effect just like there is when you are in a moving car and listening to a sound moving through the air from another car.

Categorize   Because both subs are moving, we categorize this problem as one involving the Doppler effect for both a moving source and a moving observer.

Analyze   Use Equation 17.13 to find the Doppler-shifted frequency heard by the observer in sub B, being careful with the signs of the source and observer velocities:

$$f' = \left(\frac{v + v_O}{v - v_S} \right) f$$

$$f' = \left[\frac{1\ 533 \text{ m/s} + (+9.00 \text{ m/s})}{1\ 533 \text{ m/s} - (+8.00 \text{ m/s})} \right] (1\ 400 \text{ Hz}) = \boxed{1\ 416 \text{ Hz}}$$

(B) The subs barely miss each other and pass. What frequency is detected by an observer riding on sub B as the subs recede from each other?

SOLUTION

Use Equation 17.13 to find the Doppler-shifted frequency heard by the observer in sub B, again being careful with the signs of the source and observer velocities:

$$f' = \left(\frac{v + v_O}{v - v_S} \right) f$$

$$f' = \left[\frac{1\ 533\ \text{m/s} + (-9.00\ \text{m/s})}{1\ 533\ \text{m/s} - (-8.00\ \text{m/s})} \right] (1\ 400\ \text{Hz}) = \boxed{1\ 385\ \text{Hz}}$$

Finalize   Notice that the frequency drops from 1 416 Hz to 1 385 Hz as the subs pass. This effect is similar to the drop in frequency you hear when a car passes by you while blowing its horn.

What If?   While the subs are approaching each other, some of the sound from sub A reflects from sub B and returns to sub A. If this sound were to be detected by an observer on sub A, what is its frequency?

Answer   The sound of apparent frequency 1 416 Hz found in part (A) is reflected from a moving source (sub B) and then detected by a moving observer (sub A). Therefore, the frequency detected by sub A is

$$f'' = \left(\frac{v + v_O}{v - v_S} \right) f'$$

$$= \left[\frac{1\ 533\ \text{m/s} + (+8.00\ \text{m/s})}{1\ 533\ \text{m/s} - (+9.00\ \text{m/s})} \right] (1\ 416\ \text{Hz}) = 1\ 432\ \text{Hz}$$

This technique is used by police officers to measure the speed of a moving car. Microwaves are emitted from the police car and reflected by the moving car. By detecting the Doppler-shifted frequency of the reflected microwaves, the police officer can determine the speed of the moving car.

Shock Waves

Now consider what happens when the speed v_S of a source *exceeds* the wave speed v. This situation is depicted graphically in Figure 17.10a. The circles represent spherical wave fronts emitted by the source at various times during its motion. At $t = 0$, the source is at S_0, and at a later time t, the source is at S_n. At the time t, the wave front centered at S_0 reaches a radius of vt. In this same time interval, the

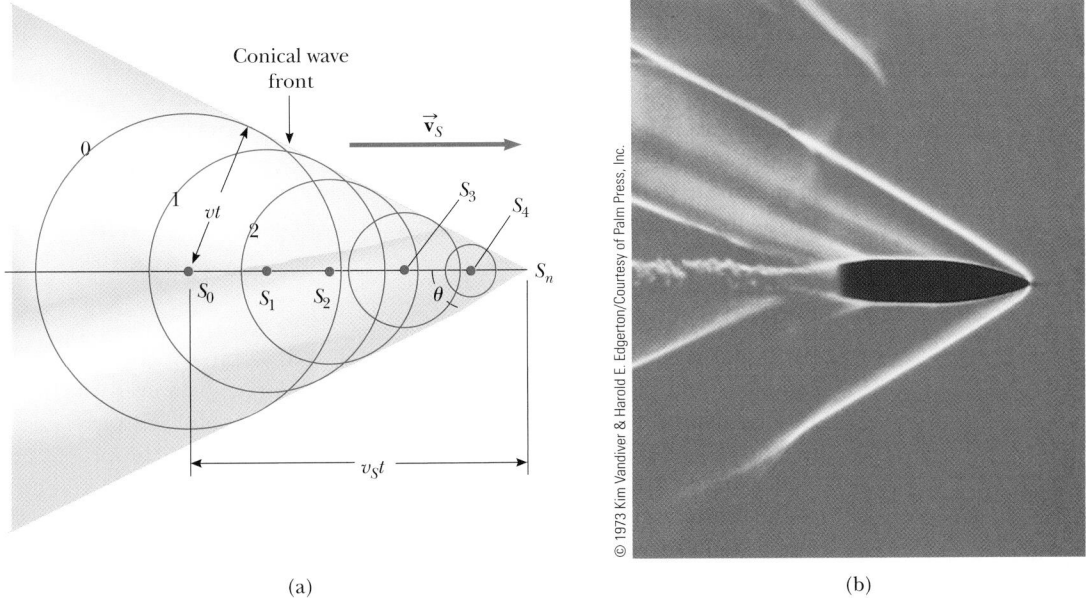

(a)   (b)

Figure 17.10   (a) A representation of a shock wave produced when a source moves from S_0 to S_n with a speed v_S, which is greater than the wave speed v in the medium. The envelope of the wave fronts forms a cone whose apex half-angle is given by $\sin \theta = v/v_S$. (b) A stroboscopic photograph of a bullet moving at supersonic speed through the hot air above a candle. Notice the shock wave in the vicinity of the bullet.

© 1973 Kim Vandiver & Harold E. Edgerton/Courtesy of Palm Press, Inc.

Figure 17.11 The V-shaped bow wave of a boat is formed because the boat speed is greater than the speed of the water waves it generates. A bow wave is analogous to a shock wave formed by an airplane traveling faster than sound.

source travels a distance $v_S t$ to S_n. At the instant the source is at S_n, waves are just beginning to be generated at this location; hence, the wave front has zero radius at this point. The tangent line drawn from S_n to the wave front centered on S_0 is tangent to all other wave fronts generated at intermediate times. Therefore, the envelope of these wave fronts is a cone whose apex half-angle θ (the "Mach angle") is given by

$$\sin \theta = \frac{vt}{v_S t} = \frac{v}{v_S}$$

The ratio v_S/v is referred to as the *Mach number*, and the conical wave front produced when $v_S > v$ (supersonic speeds) is known as a *shock wave*. An interesting analogy to shock waves is the V-shaped wave fronts produced by a boat (the bow wave) when the boat's speed exceeds the speed of the surface-water waves (Fig. 17.11).

Jet airplanes traveling at supersonic speeds produce shock waves, which are responsible for the loud "sonic boom" one hears. The shock wave carries a great deal of energy concentrated on the surface of the cone, with correspondingly great pressure variations. Such shock waves are unpleasant to hear and can cause damage to buildings when aircraft fly supersonically at low altitudes. In fact, an airplane flying at supersonic speeds produces a double boom because two shock waves are formed, one from the nose of the plane and one from the tail. People near the path of a space shuttle as it glides toward its landing point often report hearing what sounds like two very closely spaced cracks of thunder.

Quick Quiz 17.6 An airplane flying with a constant velocity moves from a cold air mass into a warm air mass. Does the Mach number (a) increase, (b) decrease, or (c) stay the same?

17.5 Digital Sound Recording

The first sound recording device, the phonograph, was invented by Thomas Edison in the 19th century. Sound waves were recorded in early phonographs by encoding the sound waveforms as variations in the depth of a continuous groove cut into tin foil wrapped around a cylinder. During playback, as a needle follows along the groove of the rotating cylinder, the needle is pushed back and forth according to the sound waves encoded on the record. The needle is attached to a diaphragm and a horn, making the sound intense enough to be heard.

As the development of the phonograph continued, sound was recorded on cardboard cylinders coated with wax. During the last decade of the 19th century and the first half of the 20th century, sound was recorded on disks made of shellac and clay. In 1948, the plastic phonograph disk was introduced and dominated the recording industry market until the advent of digital compact discs in the 1980s.

Digital Recording

In digital recording, information is converted to binary code (ones and zeros), similar to the dots and dashes of Morse code. First, the waveform of the sound is *sampled*, typically at the rate of 44 100 times per second. Figure 17.12a illustrates this process. Between each pair of blue lines in the figure, the pressure of the wave is measured and converted to a voltage. Therefore, there are 44 100 numbers associated with each second of the sound being sampled. The sampling frequency is much higher than the upper range of human hearing, about 20 000 Hz, so all frequencies of audible sound are adequately sampled at this rate.

These measurements are then converted to *binary numbers*, which are numbers expressed using base 2 rather than base 10. Table 17.3 shows some sample binary numbers. Generally, voltage measurements are recorded in 16-bit "words," where

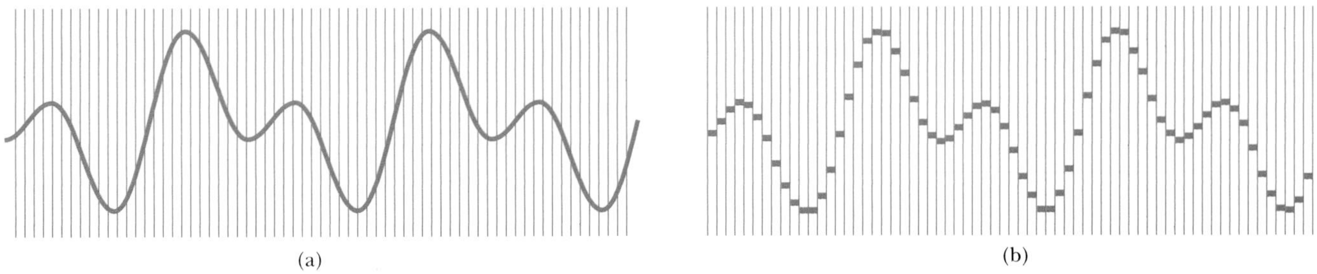

Figure 17.12 (a) Sound is digitized by electronically sampling the sound waveform at periodic intervals. During each time interval between the blue lines, a number is recorded for the average voltage during the interval. The sampling rate shown here is much slower than the actual sampling rate of 44 100 samples per second. (b) The reconstruction of the sound wave sampled in (a). Notice the stepwise reconstruction rather than the continuous waveform in (a).

TABLE 17.3

Sample Binary Numbers

Number in Base 10	Number in Binary	Sum
1	0000000000000001	1
2	0000000000000010	2+0
3	0000000000000011	2+1
10	0000000000001010	8+0+2+0
37	0000000000100101	32+0+0+4+0+1
275	0000000100010011	256+0+0+0+16+0+0+2+1

each bit is a one or a zero. Therefore, the number of different voltage levels that can be assigned codes is $2^{16} = 65\,536$. The number of bits in one second of sound is $16 \times 44\,100 = 705\,600$. It is these strings of ones and zeros, in 16-bit words, that are recorded on the surface of a compact disc.

Figure 17.13 shows a magnification of the surface of a compact disc. Two types of areas—*lands* and *pits*—are detected by the laser playback system. The lands are untouched regions of the disc surface that are highly reflective. The pits, which are areas burned into the surface, scatter light rather than reflecting it back to the detection system. The playback system samples the reflected light 705 600 times per second. When the laser moves from a pit to a flat or from a flat to a pit, the reflected light changes during the sampling and the bit is recorded as a one. If there is no change during the sampling, the bit is recorded as a zero.

The binary numbers read from the compact disc are converted back to voltages, and the waveform is reconstructed as shown in Figure 17.12b. Because the sampling rate is so high, it is not evident in the sound that the waveform is constructed from step-wise discrete voltages.

Courtesy of University of Miami, Music Engineering

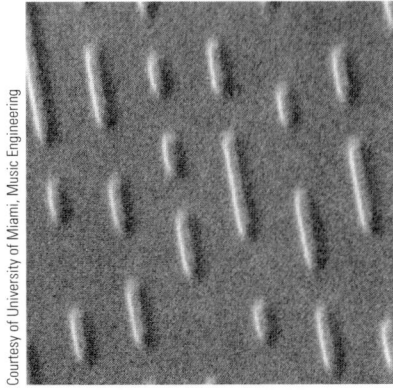

Figure 17.13 The surface of a compact disc, showing the pits. Transitions between pits and lands correspond to binary ones. Regions without transitions correspond to binary zeros.

The advantage of digital recording is in the high fidelity of the sound. With analog recording, any small imperfection in the record surface or the recording equipment can cause a distortion of the waveform. For example, clipping all peaks of a waveform by 10% has a major effect on the spectrum of the sound in an analog recording. With digital recording, however, it takes a major imperfection to turn a one into a zero. If an imperfection causes the magnitude of a one to be 90% of the original value, it still registers as a one and there is no distortion. Another advantage of digital recording is that the information is extracted optically, so there is no mechanical wear on the disc.

EXAMPLE 17.7 How Big Are the Pits?

In Example 10.2, we mentioned that the speed with which the surface of a compact disc passes the laser is 1.3 m/s. What is the average length of the audio track on a compact disc associated with each bit of the audio information?

SOLUTION

Conceptualize Imagine the surface of the disc passing by the laser at 1.3 m/s. In one second, a 1.3-m length of audio track passes by the laser. This length includes 705 600 bits of audio information.

Categorize This example is a simple substitution problem.

From knowing the number of bits in a length of 1.3 m, find the average length per bit:

$$\text{Length per bit} = \frac{1.3 \text{ m}}{705\ 600 \text{ bits}} = 1.8 \times 10^{-6} \text{ m/bit}$$

$$= \boxed{1.8 \,\mu\text{m/bit}}$$

The average length per bit of *total* information on the compact disc is smaller than this value because there is additional information on the disc besides the audio information. This information includes error correction codes, song numbers, and timing codes. As a result, the shortest length per bit is actually about 0.8 μm.

EXAMPLE 17.8 What's the Number?

Audio data on a compact disc undergoes complicated processing so as to reduce a variety of errors in reading the data. Therefore, an audio "word" is not laid out linearly on the disc. Suppose data has been read from the disc, the error encoding has been removed, and the resulting audio word is

$$1\,0\,1\,1\,1\,0\,1\,1\,1\,0\,1\,1\,1\,0\,1\,1$$

What is the decimal number represented by this 16-bit word?

SOLUTION

Conceptualize When looking at the binary number above, it is most likely that, based on your lack of experience with binary representations, you will not be able to immediately identify the number. Remember, however, that it is just a string of multipliers of powers of 2, just like the numbers with which you are familiar are strings of multipliers of powers of 10.

Categorize This example is a straightforward problem in which we change a representation from binary code to decimal code.

We convert each of these bits to a power of 2 and add the results:

$$1 \times 2^{15} = 32\ 768 \qquad 1 \times 2^9 = 512 \qquad 1 \times 2^3 = 8$$
$$0 \times 2^{14} = 0 \qquad 1 \times 2^8 = 256 \qquad 0 \times 2^2 = 0$$
$$1 \times 2^{13} = 8\ 192 \qquad 1 \times 2^7 = 128 \qquad 1 \times 2^1 = 2$$
$$1 \times 2^{12} = 4\ 096 \qquad 0 \times 2^6 = 0 \qquad 1 \times 2^0 = 1$$
$$1 \times 2^{11} = 2\ 048 \qquad 1 \times 2^5 = 32$$
$$0 \times 2^{10} = 0 \qquad 1 \times 2^4 = 16 \qquad \text{sum} = \boxed{48\ 059}$$

This number is converted by the compact disc player into a voltage, representing one of the 44 100 values that is used to build one second of the electronic waveform representing the recorded sound.

17.6   Motion Picture Sound

Another interesting application of digital sound is the soundtrack of a motion picture. Early 20th-century movies recorded sound on phonograph records, which were synchronized with the action on the screen. Beginning with early newsreel films, the *variable-area optical soundtrack* process was introduced in which sound was recorded on an optical track on the film. The width of the transparent portion of the track varied according to the sound wave that was recorded. A photocell detecting light passing through the track converted the varying light intensity to a sound wave. As with phonograph recording, there are a number of difficulties with this recording system. For example, dirt or fingerprints on the film cause fluctuations in intensity and loss of fidelity.

Digital recording on film first appeared with *Dick Tracy* (1990), using the Cinema Digital Sound, or CDS, system. This system suffered from lack of an analog backup system in case of equipment failure and is no longer used in the film industry. It did, however, introduce the use of 5.1 channels of sound: left, center, right, right surround, left surround, and low frequency effects (LFE). The LFE channel, which is the "0.1 channel" of 5.1, carries very low frequencies for dramatic sound from explosions, earthquakes, and the like.

Current motion pictures are produced with three systems of digital sound recording:

Dolby digital. In Dolby digital format, 5.1 channels of digital sound are optically stored between the sprocket holes of the film. There is an analog optical backup in case the digital system fails. The first film to use this technique was *Batman Returns* (1992).

Digital theater sound (DTS). In DTS, 5.1 channels of sound are stored on a separate CD-ROM, which is synchronized to the film print by time codes on the film. There is an analog optical backup in case the digital system fails. The first film to use this technique was *Jurassic Park* (1993).

Sony dynamic digital sound (SDDS). In SDDS, eight full channels of digital sound are optically stored outside the sprocket holes on both sides of film. There is an analog optical backup in case the digital system fails. The first film to use this technique was *Last Action Hero* (1993). The existence of information on both sides of the film is a system of redundancy; in case one side is damaged, the system still operates. SDDS employs a full-spectrum LFE channel and two additional channels (left center and right center behind the screen).

Summary

DEFINITIONS

The **intensity** of a periodic sound wave, which is the power per unit area, is

$$I \equiv \frac{\mathscr{P}}{A} = \frac{(\Delta P_{max})^2}{2\rho v} \quad \textbf{(17.5, 17.6)}$$

The **sound level** of a sound wave in decibels is

$$\beta \equiv 10 \log\left(\frac{I}{I_0}\right) \quad \textbf{(17.8)}$$

The constant I_0 is a reference intensity, usually taken to be at the threshold of hearing (1.00×10^{-12} W/m²), and I is the intensity of the sound wave in watts per square meter.

CONCEPTS AND PRINCIPLES

Sound waves are longitudinal and travel through a compressible medium with a speed that depends on the elastic and inertial properties of that medium. The speed of sound in a liquid or gas having a bulk modulus B and density ρ is

$$v = \sqrt{\frac{B}{\rho}} \quad \textbf{(17.1)}$$

For sinusoidal sound waves, the variation in the position of an element of the medium is

$$s(x, t) = s_{max} \cos(kx - \omega t) \quad \textbf{(17.2)}$$

and the variation in pressure from the equilibrium value is

$$\Delta P = \Delta P_{max} \sin(kx - \omega t) \quad \textbf{(17.3)}$$

where ΔP_{max} is the **pressure amplitude**. The pressure wave is 90° out of phase with the displacement wave. The relationship between s_{max} and ΔP_{max} is

$$\Delta P_{max} = \rho v \omega s_{max} \quad \textbf{(17.4)}$$

The change in frequency heard by an observer whenever there is relative motion between a source of sound waves and the observer is called the **Doppler effect**. The observed frequency is

$$f' = \left(\frac{v + v_O}{v - v_S}\right)f \quad \textbf{(17.13)}$$

In this expression, the signs for the values substituted for v_O and v_S depend on the direction of the velocity. A positive value for the velocity of the observer or source is substituted if the velocity of one is toward the other, whereas a negative value represents a velocity of one away from the other.

In digital recording of sound, the sound waveform is sampled 44 100 times per second. The pressure of the wave for each sampling is measured and converted to a binary number. In playback, these binary numbers are read and used to build the original waveform.

Questions

☐ denotes answer available in *Student Solutions Manual/Study Guide;* **O** denotes objective question

1. **O** Table 17.1 shows that the speed of sound is typically an order of magnitude larger in solids than in gases. To what can this higher value be most directly attributed? (a) the difference in density between solids and gases (b) the difference in compressibility between solids and gases (c) the limited size of a solid object compared to a free gas (d) the impossibility of holding a gas under significant tension

2. If an alarm clock is placed in a good vacuum and then activated, no sound is heard. Explain.

3. A sonic ranger is a device that determines the distance to an object by sending out an ultrasonic sound pulse and measuring the time interval required for the wave to return by reflection from the object. Typically these devices cannot reliably detect an object that is less than half a meter from the sensor. Why is that?

4. A friend sitting in her car far down the road waves to you and beeps her horn at the same moment. How far away must she be for you to calculate the speed of sound to two significant figures by measuring the time interval required for the sound to reach you?

5. **O** Assume a change at the source of sound reduces the wavelength of a sound wave in air by a factor of 2. (i) What happens to its frequency? (a) It increases by a

factor of 4. (b) It increases by a factor of 2. (c) It is unchanged. (d) It decreases by a factor of 2. (e) It changes by an unpredictable factor. **(ii)** What happens to its speed? Choose from the same possibilities.

6. **O** A sound wave travels in air with a frequency of 500 Hz. If the wave travels from the air into water, **(i)** what happens to its frequency? (a) It increases. (b) It decreases. (c) It is unchanged. **(ii)** What happens to its wavelength? Choose from the same possibilities.

7. By listening to a band or orchestra, how can you determine that the speed of sound is the same for all frequencies?

8. **O** A point source broadcasts sound into a uniform medium. If the distance from the source is tripled, how does the intensity change? (a) It becomes one-ninth as large.   (b) It becomes one-third as large. (c) It is unchanged. (d) It becomes three times larger. (e) It becomes nine times larger.

9. **O** A church bell in a steeple rings once. At 300 m in front of the church, the maximum sound intensity is 2 μW/m^2. At 950 m behind the church, the maximum intensity is 0.2 μW/m^2. What is the main reason for the difference in the intensity? (a) Most of the sound is absorbed by the air before it gets far away from the source. (b) Most of the sound is absorbed by the ground as it travels away from the source. (c) The bell broadcasts the sound mostly toward the front. (d) At a larger distance, the power is spread over a larger area. (e) At a larger distance, the power is spread throughout a larger spherical volume.

10. **O** Of the following sounds, which is most likely to have a sound level of 60 dB? (a) a rock concert   (b) the turning of a page in this textbook   (c) dinner-table conversation (d) a cheering crowd at a football game

11. **O** With a sensitive sound level meter you measure the sound of a running spider as −10 dB. What does the negative sign imply? (a) The spider is moving away from you. (b) The frequency of the sound is too low to be audible to humans. (c) The intensity of the sound is too faint to be audible to humans. (d) You have made a mistake; negative signs do not fit with logarithms.

12. *The Tunguska event.* On June 30, 1908, a meteor burned up and exploded in the atmosphere above the Tunguska River valley in Siberia. It knocked down trees over thousands of square kilometers and started a forest fire, but produced no crater and apparently caused no human casualties. A witness sitting on his doorstep outside the zone of falling trees recalled events in the following sequence. He saw a moving light in the sky, brighter than the sun and descending at a low angle to the horizon. He felt his face become warm. He felt the ground shake. An invisible agent picked him up and immediately dropped him about a meter farther away from where the light had been. He heard a very loud protracted rumbling. Suggest an explanation for these observations and for the order in which they happened.

13. Explain what happens to the frequency of the echo of your car horn as you drive toward the wall of a canyon. What happens to the frequency as you move away from the wall?

14. **O** A source of sound vibrates with constant frequency. Rank the frequency of sound observed in the following cases from the highest to the lowest. If two frequencies are equal, show their equality in your ranking. Only one thing is moving at a time, and all the motions mentioned have the same speed, 25 m/s. (a) Source and observer are stationary in stationary air. (b) The source is moving toward the observer in still air. (c) The source is moving away from the observer in still air. (d) The observer is moving toward the source in still air. (e) The observer is moving away from the source in still air. (f) Source and observer are stationary, with a steady wind blowing from the source toward the observer. (g) Source and observer are stationary, with a steady wind blowing from the observer toward the source.

15. **O** Suppose an observer and a source of sound are both at rest and a strong wind is blowing away from the source toward the observer. **(i)** What effect does the wind have on the observed frequency? (a) It causes an increase. (b) It causes a decrease. (c) It causes no change. **(ii)** What effect does the wind have on the observed wavelength? Choose from the same possibilities. **(iii)** What effect does the wind have on the observed speed of the wave? Choose from the same possibilities.

16. How can an object move with respect to an observer so that the sound from it is not shifted in frequency?

Problems

WebAssign The Problems from this chapter may be assigned online in WebAssign.

ThomsonNOW Sign in at **www.thomsonedu.com** and go to ThomsonNOW to assess your understanding of this chapter's topics with additional quizzing and conceptual questions.

1, 2, 3 denotes straightforward, intermediate, challenging;   □ denotes full solution available in *Student Solutions Manual/Study Guide;* ▲ denotes coached solution with hints available at **www.thomsonedu.com;** denotes developing symbolic reasoning; ● denotes asking for qualitative reasoning; 💻 denotes computer useful in solving problem

Section 17.1 Speed of Sound Waves

> Problem 60 in Chapter 2 can also be assigned with this section.

1. ● Suppose you hear a clap of thunder 16.2 s after seeing the associated lightning stroke. The speed of sound in air is 343 m/s, and the speed of light in air is 3.00 × 10^8 m/s. How far are you from the lightning stroke? Do you need to know the value of the speed of light to answer? Explain.

2. Find the speed of sound in mercury, which has a bulk modulus of approximately 2.80×10^{10} N/m^2 and a density of 13 600 kg/m^3.

3. A dolphin in seawater at a temperature of 25°C makes a chirp. How much time passes before it hears an echo from the bottom of the ocean, 150 m below?

4. The speed of sound in air (in meters per second) depends on temperature according to the approximate expression

$$v = 331.5 + 0.607 T_C$$

where T_C is the Celsius temperature. In dry air, the temperature decreases about 1°C for every 150 m rise in altitude. (a) Assume this change is constant up to an altitude of 9 000 m. What time interval is required for the sound from an airplane flying at 9 000 m to reach the ground on a day when the ground temperature is 30°C? (b) **What If?** Compare your answer with the time interval required if the air were uniformly at 30°C. Which time interval is longer?

5. A flowerpot is knocked off a balcony 20.0 m above the sidewalk and falls toward an unsuspecting 1.75-m-tall man who is standing below. How close to the sidewalk can the flowerpot fall before it is too late for a warning shouted from the balcony to reach the man in time? Assume the man below requires 0.300 s to respond to the warning. The ambient temperature is 20°C.

6. A rescue plane flies horizontally at a constant speed searching for a disabled boat. When the plane is directly above the boat, the boat's crew blows a loud horn. By the time the plane's sound detector receives the horn's sound, the plane has traveled a distance equal to half its altitude above the ocean. Assuming it takes the sound 2.00 s to reach the plane, determine (a) the speed of the plane and (b) its altitude. Take the speed of sound to be 343 m/s.

7. A cowboy stands on horizontal ground between two parallel vertical cliffs. He is not midway between the cliffs. He fires a shot and hears its echoes. The second echo arrives 1.92 s after the first and 1.47 s before the third. Consider only the sound traveling parallel to the ground and reflecting from the cliffs. Take the speed of sound as 340 m/s. (a) What is the distance between the cliffs? (b) **What If?** If he can hear a fourth echo, how long after the third echo does it arrive?

Section 17.2 Periodic Sound Waves

Note: Use the following values as needed unless otherwise specified. The equilibrium density of air at 20°C is $\rho = 1.20$ kg/m^3 and the speed of sound is $v = 343$ m/s. Pressure variations ΔP are measured relative to atmospheric pressure, 1.013×10^5 N/m^2.

8. ● A sound wave propagates in air at 27°C with frequency 4.00 kHz. It passes through a region where the temperature gradually changes, and then it moves through air at 0°C. (a) What happens to the speed of the wave? (b) What happens to its frequency? (c) What happens to its wavelength? Give numerical answers to these questions to the extent possible and state your reasoning about what happens to the wave physically.

9. Ultrasound is used in medicine both for diagnostic imaging and for therapy. For diagnosis, short pulses of ultrasound are passed through the patient's body. An echo reflected from a structure of interest is recorded, and the distance to the structure can be determined from the time delay for the echo's return. A single transducer emits and detects the ultrasound. An image of the structure is obtained by reducing the data with a computer. With sound of low intensity, this technique is noninvasive and harmless. It is used to examine fetuses, tumors, aneurysms, gallstones, and many other structures. To reveal detail, the wavelength of the reflected ultrasound must be small compared to the size of the object reflecting the wave. (a) What is the wavelength of ultrasound with a frequency of 2.40 MHz, used in echocardiography to map the beating human heart? (b) In the whole set of imaging techniques, frequencies in the range 1.00 to 20.0 MHz are used. What is the range of wavelengths corresponding to this range of frequencies? The speed of ultrasound in human tissue is about 1 500 m/s (nearly the same as the speed of sound in water).

10. A sound wave in air has a pressure amplitude equal to 4.00×10^{-3} N/m^2. Calculate the displacement amplitude of the wave at a frequency of 10.0 kHz.

11. A sinusoidal sound wave is described by the displacement wave function

$$s(x, t) = (2.00 \ \mu\text{m}) \cos \left[(15.7 \ \text{m}^{-1})x - (858 \ \text{s}^{-1})t \right]$$

(a) Find the amplitude, wavelength, and speed of this wave. (b) Determine the instantaneous displacement from equilibrium of the elements of air at the position $x = 0.050 \ 0$ m at $t = 3.00$ ms. (c) Determine the maximum speed of the element's oscillatory motion.

12. As a certain sound wave travels through the air, it produces pressure variations (above and below atmospheric pressure) given by $\Delta P = 1.27 \sin (\pi x - 340\pi t)$ in SI units. Find (a) the amplitude of the pressure variations, (b) the frequency, (c) the wavelength in air, and (d) the speed of the sound wave.

13. Write an expression that describes the pressure variation as a function of position and time for a sinusoidal sound wave in air. Assume $\lambda = 0.100$ m and $\Delta P_{\text{max}} = 0.200$ N/m^2.

14. The tensile stress in a thick copper bar is 99.5% of its elastic breaking point of 13.0×10^{10} N/m^2. If a 500-Hz sound wave is transmitted through the material, (a) what displacement amplitude will cause the bar to break? (b) What is the maximum speed of the elements of copper at this moment? (c) What is the sound intensity in the bar?

15. ▲ An experimenter wishes to generate in air a sound wave that has a displacement amplitude of 5.50×10^{-6} m. The pressure amplitude is to be limited to 0.840 N/m^2. What is the minimum wavelength the sound wave can have?

Section 17.3 Intensity of Periodic Sound Waves

16. The area of a typical eardrum is about 5.00×10^{-5} m^2. Calculate the sound power incident on an eardrum at (a) the threshold of hearing and (b) the threshold of pain.

17. Calculate the sound level (in decibels) of a sound wave that has an intensity of 4.00 μW/m^2.

2 = intermediate;   3 = challenging;   ☐ = SSM/SG;   ▲ = ThomsonNOW;   ▨ = symbolic reasoning;   ● = qualitative reasoning

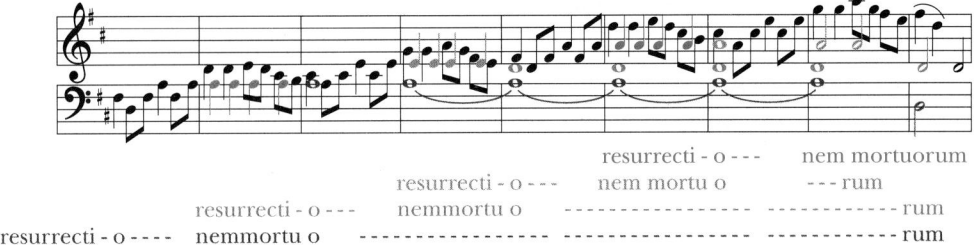

Figure P17.21   Bass (blue), tenor (green), alto (brown), and first soprano (red) parts for a portion of Bach's Mass in B Minor. The basses sing the foreground melody for two measures, then the tenors for two measures, then the altos, and then the first sopranos. For emphasis, this line is printed in black throughout. Parts for the second sopranos, violins, viola, flutes, oboes, and continuo are omitted. The tenor part is written as it is sung.

18. The tube depicted in Active Figure 17.2 is filled with air at 20°C and equilibrium pressure 1 atm. The diameter of the tube is 8.00 cm. The piston is driven at a frequency of 600 Hz with an amplitude of 0.120 cm. What power must be supplied to maintain the oscillation of the piston?

19. The intensity of a sound wave at a fixed distance from a speaker vibrating at 1.00 kHz is 0.600 W/m². (a) Determine the intensity that results if the frequency is increased to 2.50 kHz while a constant displacement amplitude is maintained. (b) Calculate the intensity if the frequency is reduced to 0.500 kHz and the displacement amplitude is doubled.

20. The intensity of a sound wave at a fixed distance from a speaker vibrating at a frequency f is I. (a) Determine the intensity that results if the frequency is increased to f' while a constant displacement amplitude is maintained. (b) Calculate the intensity if the frequency is reduced to $f/2$ and the displacement amplitude is doubled.

21. The most soaring vocal melody is in Johann Sebastian Bach's Mass in B Minor. A portion of the score for the Credo section, number 9, bars 25 to 33, appears in Figure P17.21. The repeating syllable O in the phrase "resurrectionem mortuorum" (the resurrection of the dead) is seamlessly passed from basses to tenors to altos to first sopranos, like a baton in a relay. Each voice carries the foreground melody up through a rising passage encompassing an octave or more. Together the voices carry it from D below middle C to A above a tenor's high C. In concert pitch, these notes are now assigned frequencies of 146.8 Hz and 880.0 Hz. (a) Find the wavelengths of the initial and final notes. (b) Assume the chorus sings the melody with a uniform sound level of 75.0 dB. Find the pressure amplitudes of the initial and final notes. (c) Find the displacement amplitudes of the initial and final notes. (d) **What If?** In Bach's time, before the invention of the tuning fork, frequencies were assigned to notes as a matter of immediate local convenience. Assume the rising melody was sung starting from 134.3 Hz and ending at 804.9 Hz. How would the answers to parts (a) through (c) change?

22. Show that the difference between decibel levels β_1 and β_2 of a sound is related to the ratio of the distances r_1 and r_2 from the sound source by

$$\beta_2 - \beta_1 = 20 \log \left(\frac{r_1}{r_2} \right)$$

23. ▲ A family ice show is held at an enclosed arena. The skaters perform to music with level 80.0 dB. This level is too loud for your baby, who yells at 75.0 dB. (a) What total sound intensity engulfs you? (b) What is the combined sound level?

24. A jackhammer, operated continuously at a construction site, behaves as a point source of spherical sound waves. A construction supervisor stands 50.0 m due north of this sound source and begins to walk due west. How far does she have to walk for the amplitude of the wave function to drop by a factor of 2.00?

25. The power output of a certain public address speaker is 6.00 W. Suppose it broadcasts equally in all directions. (a) Within what distance from the speaker would the sound be painful to the ear? (b) At what distance from the speaker would the sound be barely audible?

26. Two small speakers emit sound waves of different frequencies equally in all directions. Speaker A has an output of 1.00 mW, and speaker B has an output of 1.50 mW. Determine the sound level (in decibels) at point C in Figure P17.26 assuming (a) only speaker A emits sound, (b) only speaker B emits sound, and (c) both speakers emit sound.

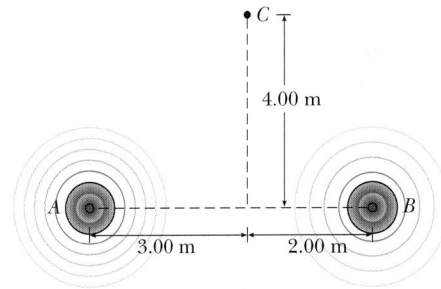

Figure P17.26

27. A firework charge is detonated many meters above the ground. At a distance of 400 m from the explosion, the acoustic pressure reaches a maximum of 10.0 N/m². Assume the speed of sound is constant at 343 m/s throughout the atmosphere over the region considered, the ground absorbs all the sound falling on it, and the air absorbs sound energy as described by the rate 7.00 dB/km. What is the sound level (in decibels) at 4.00 km from the explosion?

28. A fireworks rocket explodes at a height of 100 m above the ground. An observer on the ground directly under the explosion experiences an average sound intensity of 7.00×10^{-2} W/m² for 0.200 s. (a) What is the total sound energy of the explosion? (b) What is the sound level (in decibels) heard by the observer?

2 = intermediate;   3 = challenging;   ☐ = SSM/SG;   ▲ = ThomsonNOW;   ▨ = symbolic reasoning;   ● = qualitative reasoning

29. The sound level at a distance of 3.00 m from a source is 120 dB. At what distance is the sound level (a) 100 dB and (b) 10.0 dB?

30. The smallest change in sound level that a person can distinguish is approximately 1 dB. When you are standing next to your power lawn mower as it is running, can you hear the steady roar of your neighbor's lawn mower? Perform an order-of-magnitude calculation to substantiate your answer, stating the data you measure or estimate.

31. As the people sing in church, the sound level everywhere inside is 101 dB. No sound is transmitted through the massive walls, but all the windows and doors are open on a summer morning. Their total area is 22.0 m^2. (a) How much sound energy is radiated in 20.0 min? (b) Suppose the ground is a good reflector and sound radiates uniformly in all horizontal and upward directions. Find the sound level 1.00 km away.

Section 17.4 The Doppler Effect

32. Expectant parents are thrilled to hear their unborn baby's heartbeat, revealed by an ultrasonic motion detector. Suppose the fetus's ventricular wall moves in simple harmonic motion with an amplitude of 1.80 mm and a frequency of 115 per minute. (a) Find the maximum linear speed of the heart wall. Suppose the motion detector in contact with the mother's abdomen produces sound at 2 000 000.0 Hz, which travels through tissue at 1.50 km/s. (b) Find the maximum frequency at which sound arrives at the wall of the baby's heart. (c) Find the maximum frequency at which reflected sound is received by the motion detector. By electronically "listening" for echoes at a frequency different from the broadcast frequency, the motion detector can produce beeps of audible sound in synchronization with the fetal heartbeat.

33. A driver travels northbound on a highway at a speed of 25.0 m/s. A police car, traveling southbound at a speed of 40.0 m/s, approaches with its siren producing sound at a frequency of 2 500 Hz. (a) What frequency does the driver observe as the police car approaches? (b) What frequency does the driver detect after the police car passes him? (c) Repeat parts (a) and (b) for the case when the police car is traveling northbound.

34. A block with a speaker bolted to it is connected to a spring having spring constant $k = 20.0$ N/m as shown in Figure P17.34. The total mass of the block and speaker is 5.00 kg, and the amplitude of this unit's motion is 0.500 m. (a) The speaker emits sound waves of frequency 440 Hz. Determine the highest and lowest frequencies heard by the person to the right of the speaker. (b) If the maximum sound level heard by the person is 60.0 dB

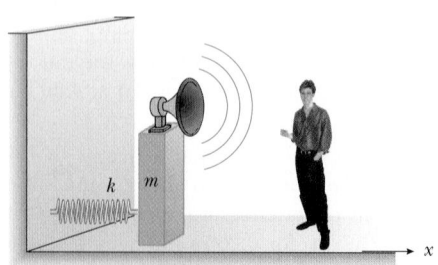

Figure P17.34

when he is closest to the speaker, 1.00 m away, what is the minimum sound level heard by the observer? Assume the speed of sound is 343 m/s.

35. ▲ Standing at a crosswalk, you hear a frequency of 560 Hz from the siren of an approaching ambulance. After the ambulance passes, the observed frequency of the siren is 480 Hz. Determine the ambulance's speed from these observations.

36. At the Winter Olympics, an athlete rides her luge down the track while a bell just above the wall of the chute rings continuously. When her sled passes the bell, she hears the frequency of the bell fall by the musical interval called a minor third. That is, the frequency she hears drops to five-sixths its original value. (a) Find the speed of sound in air at the ambient temperature −10.0°C. (b) Find the speed of the athlete.

37. A tuning fork vibrating at 512 Hz falls from rest and accelerates at 9.80 m/s^2. How far below the point of release is the tuning fork when waves of frequency 485 Hz reach the release point? Take the speed of sound in air to be 340 m/s.

38. A siren mounted on the roof of a firehouse emits sound at a frequency of 900 Hz. A steady wind is blowing with a speed of 15.0 m/s. Taking the speed of sound in calm air to be 343 m/s, find the wavelength of the sound (a) upwind of the siren and (b) downwind of the siren. Firefighters are approaching the siren from various directions at 15.0 m/s. What frequency does a firefighter hear (c) if she is approaching from an upwind position so that she is moving in the direction in which the wind is blowing and (d) if she is approaching from a downwind position and moving against the wind?

39. ▲ A supersonic jet traveling at Mach 3.00 at an altitude of 20 000 m is directly over a person at time $t = 0$ as shown in Figure P17.39. (a) At what time will the person encounter the shock wave? (b) Where will the plane be when the "boom" is finally heard? Assume the speed of sound in air is 335 m/s.

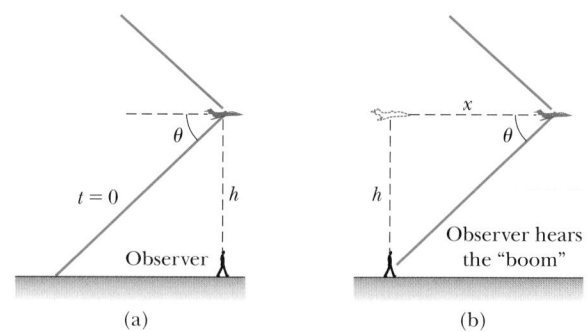

Figure P17.39

40. The loop of a circus ringmaster's whip travels at Mach 1.38 (that is, $v_S/v = 1.38$). What angle does the shock front make with the direction of the whip's motion?

41. When high-energy charged particles move through a transparent medium with a speed greater than the speed of light in that medium, a shock wave, or bow wave, of light is produced. This phenomenon is called the *Cerenkov effect*. When a nuclear reactor is shielded by a large pool of water, Cerenkov radiation can be seen as a blue glow in the vicinity of the reactor core due to high-speed electrons moving through the water. In a particular case, the Cerenkov radiation produces a wave front with an apex half-angle of 53.0°. Calculate the speed of the electrons in the water. The speed of light in water is 2.25×10^8 m/s.

Section 17.5 Digital Sound Recording

Section 17.6 Motion Picture Sound

42. ● This problem represents a possible (but not recommended) way to code instantaneous pressures in a sound wave into 16-bit digital words. Example 17.2 mentions that the pressure amplitude of a 120-dB sound is 28.7 N/m². Let this pressure variation be represented by the digital code 65 536. Let the digital word 0 on the recording represent zero pressure variation. Let other intermediate pressures be represented by digital words of intermediate size, in direct proportion to the pressure. (a) What digital word would represent the maximum pressure in a 40-dB sound? (b) Explain why this scheme works poorly for soft sounds. (c) Explain how this coding scheme would clip off half of the waveform of any sound, ignoring the actual shape of the wave and turning it into a string of zeros. By introducing sharp corners into every recorded waveform, this coding scheme would make everything sound like a buzzer or a kazoo.

Additional Problems

43. ● A 150-g glider moving at 2.30 m/s on an air track undergoes a completely inelastic collision with an originally stationary 200-g glider, and the two gliders latch together over a time interval of 7.00 ms. A student suggests that roughly half the missing mechanical energy goes into sound. Is this suggestion reasonable? To evaluate the idea, find the implied level of the sound 0.800 m from the gliders. If the student's idea is unreasonable, suggest a better idea.

44. ● Explain how the wave function

$$\Delta P(r, t) = \left(\frac{25.0 \text{ Pa} \cdot \text{m}}{r} \right) \sin (1.36r \text{ rad/m} - 2\,030t \text{ rad/s})$$

can apply to a wave radiating from a small source, with r being the radial distance from the center of the source to any point outside the source. Give the most detailed description of the wave that you can. Include answers to such questions as the following. Does the wave move more toward the right or the left? As it moves away from the source, what happens to its amplitude? Its speed? Its frequency? Its wavelength? Its power? Its intensity? What are representative values for each of these quantities? What can you say about the source of the wave? About the medium through which it travels?

45. ● A large set of unoccupied football bleachers has solid seats and risers. You stand on the field in front of the bleachers and sharply clap two wooden boards together once. The sound pulse you produce has no definite frequency and no wavelength. The sound you hear reflected from the bleachers has an identifiable frequency and may remind you of a short toot on a trumpet or of a buzzer or kazoo. Account for this sound. (a) Compute order-of-magnitude estimates for the frequency, wavelength, and duration of the sound, on the basis of data you specify. (b) Each face of a great Mayan pyramid is like a steep stairway with very narrow steps. Can it produce an echo of a handclap that sounds like the call of a bird? Explain your answer.

46. ● Spherical waves of wavelength 45.0 cm propagate outward from a point source. (a) Explain how the intensity at a distance of 240 cm compares with the intensity at a distance of 60.0 cm. (b) Explain how the amplitude at a distance of 240 cm compares with the amplitude at a distance of 60.0 cm. (c) Explain how the phase of the wave at a distance of 240 cm compares with the phase at 60.0 cm at the same moment.

47. A sound wave in a cylinder is described by Equations 17.2 through 17.4. Show that $\Delta P = \pm \rho v \omega \sqrt{s_{max}^2 - s^2}$.

48. Many artists sing very high notes in ad-lib ornaments and cadenzas. The highest note written for a singer in a published score was F-sharp above high C, 1.480 kHz, for Zerbinetta in the original version of Richard Strauss's opera *Ariadne auf Naxos*. (a) Find the wavelength of this sound in air. (b) Suppose people in the fourth row of seats hear this note with level 81.0 dB. Find the displacement amplitude of the sound. (c) **What If?** In response to complaints, Strauss later transposed the note down to F above high C, 1.397 kHz. By what increment did the wavelength change? (The Queen of the Night in Mozart's *Magic Flute* also sings F above high C.)

49. On a Saturday morning, pickup trucks and sport utility vehicles carrying garbage to the town dump form a nearly steady procession on a country road, all traveling at 19.7 m/s. From one direction, two trucks arrive at the dump every 3 min. A bicyclist is also traveling toward the dump, at 4.47 m/s. (a) With what frequency do the trucks pass the cyclist? (b) **What If?** A hill does not slow down the trucks, but makes the out-of-shape cyclist's speed drop to 1.56 m/s. How often do noisy, smelly, inefficient, garbage-dripping, road-hogging trucks whiz past the cyclist now?

50. **Review problem.** For a certain type of steel, stress is always proportional to strain with Young's modulus as shown in Table 12.1. The steel has the density listed for iron in Table 14.1. It will fail by bending permanently if subjected to compressive stress greater than its yield strength $\sigma_y = 400$ MPa. A rod 80.0 cm long, made of this steel, is fired at 12.0 m/s straight at a very hard wall or at another identical rod moving in the opposite direction. (a) The speed of a one-dimensional compressional wave moving along the rod is given by $v = \sqrt{Y/\rho}$, where Y is Young's modulus for the rod and ρ is the density. Calculate this speed. (b) After the front end of the rod hits the wall and stops, the back end of the rod keeps moving as described by Newton's first law until it is stopped by excess pressure in a sound wave moving back through the rod. What time interval elapses before the back end of the rod receives the message that it should stop? (c) How far has the back end of the rod moved in this time interval? Find (d) the strain and (e) the stress in the rod. (f) If it is not to fail, show that the maximum impact speed a rod can have is given by the expression $v = \sigma_y / \sqrt{\rho Y}$.

51. To permit measurement of her speed, a skydiver carries a buzzer emitting a steady tone at 1 800 Hz. A friend on the

ground at the landing site directly below listens to the amplified sound he receives. Assume the air is calm and the sound speed is 343 m/s, independent of altitude. While the skydiver is falling at terminal speed, her friend on the ground receives waves of frequency 2 150 Hz. (a) What is the skydiver's speed of descent? (b) **What If?** Suppose the skydiver can hear the sound of the buzzer reflected from the ground. What frequency does she receive?

52. Prove that sound waves propagate with a speed given by Equation 17.1. Proceed as follows. In Active Figure 17.2, consider a thin, cylindrical layer of air in the cylinder, with face area A and thickness Δx. Draw a free-body diagram of this thin layer. Show that $\Sigma F_x = ma_x$ implies that

$$-\frac{\partial(\Delta P)}{\partial x} A \, \Delta x = \rho A \, \Delta x \frac{\partial^2 s}{\partial t^2}$$

By substituting $\Delta P = -B(\partial s/\partial x)$, derive the following wave equation for sound:

$$\frac{B}{\rho} \frac{\partial^2 s}{\partial x^2} = \frac{\partial^2 s}{\partial t^2}$$

To a mathematical physicist, this equation demonstrates the existence of sound waves and determines their speed. As a physics student, you must take another step or two. Substitute into the wave equation the trial solution $s(x, t) = s_{max} \cos(kx - \omega t)$. Show that this function satisfies the wave equation provided that $\omega/k = \sqrt{B/\rho}$. This result reveals that sound waves exist provided they move with the speed $v = f\lambda = (2\pi f)(\lambda/2\pi) = \omega/k = \sqrt{B/\rho}$.

53. Two ships are moving along a line due east. The trailing vessel has a speed relative to a land-based observation point of 64.0 km/h, and the leading ship has a speed of 45.0 km/h relative to that point. The two ships are in a region of the ocean where the current is moving uniformly due west at 10.0 km/h. The trailing ship transmits a sonar signal at a frequency of 1 200.0 Hz. What frequency is monitored by the leading ship? Use 1 520 m/s as the speed of sound in ocean water.

54. A bat, moving at 5.00 m/s, is chasing a flying insect. If the bat emits a 40.0-kHz chirp and receives back an echo at 40.4 kHz, at what speed is the insect moving toward or away from the bat? (Take the speed of sound in air to be $v = 340$ m/s.)

55. Assume a loudspeaker broadcasts sound equally in all directions and produces sound with a level of 103 dB at a distance of 1.60 m from its center. (a) Find its sound power output. (b) If a salesperson claims to be giving you 150 W per channel, he is referring to the electrical power input to the speaker. Find the efficiency of the speaker, that is, the fraction of input power that is converted into useful output power.

56. A police car is traveling east at 40.0 m/s along a straight road, overtaking a car ahead of it moving east at 30.0 m/s. The police car has a malfunctioning siren that is stuck at 1 000 Hz. (a) Sketch the appearance of the wave fronts of the sound produced by the siren. Show the wave fronts both to the east and west of the police car. (b) What would be the wavelength in air of the siren sound if the police car were at rest? (c) What is the wavelength in front of the police car? (d) What is it behind

the police car? (e) What is the frequency heard by the driver being chased?

57. ● The speed of a one-dimensional compressional wave traveling along a thin copper rod is 3.56 km/s. A copper bar is given a sharp hammer blow at one end. A listener at the far end of the bar hears the sound twice, transmitted through the metal and through air at 0°C, with a time interval Δt between the two pulses. (a) Which sound arrives first? (b) Find the length of the bar as a function of Δt. (c) Evaluate the length of the bar if $\Delta t = 127$ ms. (d) Imagine that the copper were replaced by a much stiffer material through which sound would travel much faster. How would the answer to part (b) change? Would it go to a well-defined limit as the signal speed in the rod goes to infinity? Explain your answer.

58. An interstate highway has been built though a poor neighborhood in a city. In the afternoon, the sound level in a rented room is 80.0 dB as 100 cars pass outside the window every minute. Late at night, when the room's tenant is at work in a factory, the traffic flow is only five cars per minute. What is the average late-night sound level?

59. A meteoroid the size of a truck enters the earth's atmosphere at a speed of 20.0 km/s and is not significantly slowed before entering the ocean. (a) What is the Mach angle of the shock wave from the meteoroid in the atmosphere? (Use 331 m/s as the sound speed.) (b) Assuming the meteoroid survives the impact with the ocean surface, what is the (initial) Mach angle of the shock wave the meteoroid produces in the water? (Use the wave speed for seawater given in Table 17.1.)

60. Equation 17.7 states that at distance r away from a point source with power $\mathcal{P}_{avg}$, the wave intensity is

$$I = \frac{\mathcal{P}_{avg}}{4\pi r^2}$$

Study Active Figure 17.9 and prove that at distance r straight in front of a point source with power $\mathcal{P}_{avg}$ moving with constant speed v_S the wave intensity is

$$I = \frac{\mathcal{P}_{avg}}{4\pi r^2}\left(\frac{v - v_S}{v}\right)$$

61. ▲ With particular experimental methods, it is possible to produce and observe in a long, thin rod both a longitudinal wave and a transverse wave whose speed depends primarily on tension in the rod. The speed of the longitudinal wave is determined by Young's modulus and the density of the material according to the expression $v = \sqrt{Y/\rho}$. The transverse wave can be modeled as a wave in a stretched string. A particular metal rod is 150 cm long and has a radius of 0.200 cm and a mass of 50.9 g. Young's modulus for the material is 6.80×10^{10} N/m². What must the tension in the rod be if the ratio of the speed of longitudinal waves to the speed of transverse waves is 8.00?

62. The Doppler equation presented in the text is valid when the motion between the observer and the source occurs on a straight line so that the source and observer are moving either directly toward or directly away from each other. If this restriction is relaxed, one must use the more general Doppler equation

2 = intermediate; 3 = challenging; □ = SSM/SG; ▲ = ThomsonNOW; = symbolic reasoning; ● = qualitative reasoning

$$f' = \left(\frac{v + v_O \cos\theta_O}{v - v_S \cos\theta_S}\right)f$$

where θ_O and θ_S are defined in Figure P17.62a. (a) Show that if the observer and source are moving directly away from each other, the preceding equation reduces to Equation 17.13 with negative values for both v_O and v_S. (b) Use the preceding equation to solve the following problem. A train moves at a constant speed of 25.0 m/s toward the intersection shown in Figure P17.62b. A car is stopped near the crossing, 30.0 m from the tracks. If the train's horn emits a frequency of 500 Hz, what is the frequency heard by the passengers in the car when the train is 40.0 m from the intersection? Take the speed of sound to be 343 m/s.

63. Three metal rods are located relative to each other as shown in Figure P17.63, where $L_1 + L_2 = L_3$. The speed of sound in a rod is given by $v = \sqrt{Y/\rho}$, where Y is Young's modulus for the rod and ρ is the density. Values of density and Young's modulus for the three materials are $\rho_1 = 2.70 \times 10^3$ kg/m³, $Y_1 = 7.00 \times 10^{10}$ N/m², $\rho_2 = 11.3 \times 10^3$ kg/m³, $Y_2 = 1.60 \times 10^{10}$ N/m², $\rho_3 = 8.80 \times 10^3$ kg/m³, and $Y_3 = 11.0 \times 10^{10}$ N/m². (a) If $L_3 = 1.50$ m, what must the ratio L_1/L_2 be if a sound wave is to travel the length of rods 1 and 2 in the same time interval required for the wave to travel the length of rod 3? (b) The frequency of the source is 4.00 kHz. Determine the phase difference between the wave traveling along rods 1 and 2 and the one traveling along rod 3.

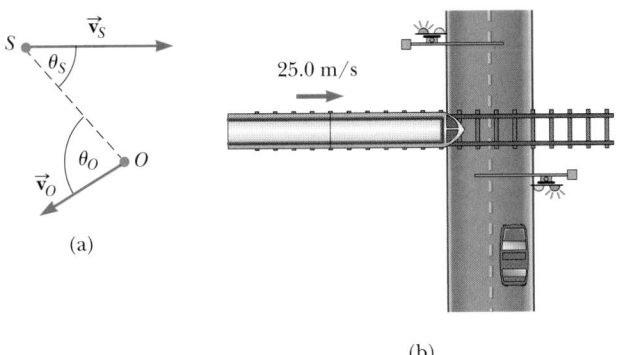

(a)

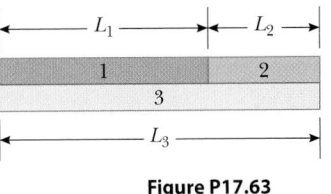

(b)

Figure P17.62

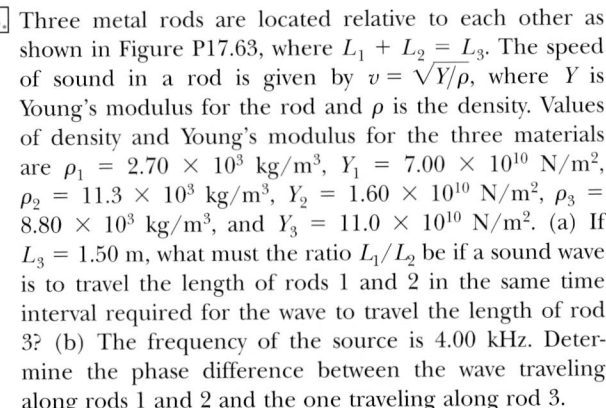

Figure P17.63

Answers to Quick Quizzes

17.1 (c). Because the bottom of the bottle is a rigid barrier, the displacement of elements of air at the bottom is zero. Because the pressure variation is a minimum or a maximum when the displacement is zero and because the pulse is moving downward, the pressure variation at the bottom is a maximum.

17.2 (b). The large area of the guitar body sets many elements of air into oscillation and allows the energy to leave the system by mechanical waves at a much larger rate than from the thin vibrating string.

17.3 (b). The factor of 100 is two powers of 10. The logarithm of 100 is 2, which multiplied by 10 gives 20 dB.

17.4 (e). The wave speed cannot be changed by moving the source, so choices (a) and (b) are incorrect. The

detected wavelength is largest at A, so choices (c) and (d) are incorrect. Choice (f) is incorrect because the detected frequency is lowest at A.

17.5 (e). The intensity of the sound increases because the train is moving closer to you. Because the train moves at a constant velocity, the Doppler-shifted frequency remains fixed.

17.6 (b). The Mach number is the ratio of the plane's speed (which does not change) to the speed of sound, which is greater in the warm air than in the cold. The denominator of this ratio increases, whereas the numerator stays constant. Therefore, the ratio as a whole—the Mach number—decreases.

2 = intermediate;   3 = challenging;   □ = SSM/SG;   ▲ = ThomsonNOW;   = symbolic reasoning;   ● = qualitative reasoning

Guitarist Carlos Santana takes advantage of standing waves on strings. He changes to higher notes on the guitar by pushing the strings against the frets on the fingerboard, shortening the lengths of the portions of the strings that vibrate. (Bettmann/Corbis)

18 Superposition and Standing Waves

The wave model was introduced in the previous two chapters. We have seen that waves are very different from particles. A particle is of zero size, whereas a wave has a characteristic size, its wavelength. Another important difference between waves and particles is that we can explore the possibility of two or more waves combining at one point in the same medium. Particles can be combined to form extended objects, but the particles must be at *different* locations. In contrast, two waves can both be present at the same location. The ramifications of this possibility are explored in this chapter.

When waves are combined in systems with boundary conditions, only certain allowed frequencies can exist and we say the frequencies are *quantized*. Quantization is a notion that is at the heart of quantum mechanics, a subject introduced formally in Chapter 40. There we show that waves under boundary conditions explain many of the quantum phenomena. In this chapter, we use quantization to understand the behavior of the wide array of musical instruments that are based on strings and air columns.

We also consider the combination of waves having different frequencies. When two sound waves having nearly the same frequency interfere, we hear variations in the loudness called *beats*. Finally, we discuss how any nonsinusoidal periodic wave can be described as a sum of sine and cosine functions.

18.1   Superposition and Interference

Many interesting wave phenomena in nature cannot be described by a single traveling wave. Instead, one must analyze these phenomena in terms of a combination of traveling waves. To analyze such wave combinations, we make use of the **superposition principle**:

> If two or more traveling waves are moving through a medium, the resultant value of the wave function at any point is the algebraic sum of the values of the wave functions of the individual waves.

◀ Superposition principle

Waves that obey this principle are called *linear waves*. In the case of mechanical waves, linear waves are generally characterized by having amplitudes much smaller than their wavelengths. Waves that violate the superposition principle are called *nonlinear waves* and are often characterized by large amplitudes. In this book, we deal only with linear waves.

One consequence of the superposition principle is that **two traveling waves can pass through each other without being destroyed or even altered**. For instance, when two pebbles are thrown into a pond and hit the surface at different locations, the expanding circular surface waves from the two locations do not destroy each other but rather pass through each other. The resulting complex pattern can be viewed as two independent sets of expanding circles.

Active Figure 18.1 (page 502) is a pictorial representation of the superposition of two pulses. The wave function for the pulse moving to the right is y_1, and the wave function for the pulse moving to the left is y_2. The pulses have the same speed but different shapes, and the displacement of the elements of the medium is in the positive y direction for both pulses. When the waves begin to overlap (Active Fig. 18.1b), the wave function for the resulting complex wave is given by $y_1 + y_2$. When the crests of the pulses coincide (Active Fig. 18.1c), the resulting wave given by $y_1 + y_2$ has a larger amplitude than that of the individual pulses. The two pulses finally separate and continue moving in their original directions (Active Fig. 18.1d). Notice that the pulse shapes remain unchanged after the interaction, as if the two pulses had never met!

The combination of separate waves in the same region of space to produce a resultant wave is called **interference**. For the two pulses shown in Active Figure 18.1, the displacement of the elements of the medium is in the positive y direction for both pulses, and the resultant pulse (created when the individual pulses overlap) exhibits an amplitude greater than that of either individual pulse. Because the displacements caused by the two pulses are in the same direction, we refer to their superposition as **constructive interference**.

◀ Constructive interference

Now consider two pulses traveling in opposite directions on a taut string where one pulse is inverted relative to the other as illustrated in Active Figure 18.2 (page 502). When these pulses begin to overlap, the resultant pulse is given by $y_1 + y_2$, but the values of the function y_2 are negative. Again, the two pulses pass through each other; because the displacements caused by the two pulses are in opposite directions, however, we refer to their superposition as **destructive interference**.

◀ Destructive interference

The superposition principle is the centerpiece of the **waves in interference model**. In many situations, both in acoustics and optics, waves combine according to this principle and exhibit interesting phenomena with practical applications.

Quick Quiz 18.1   Two pulses move in opposite directions on a string and are identical in shape except that one has positive displacements of the elements of the string and the other has negative displacements. At the moment the two pulses completely overlap on the string, what happens? (a) The energy associated with the pulses has disappeared. (b) The string is not moving. (c) The string forms a straight line. (d) The pulses have vanished and will not reappear.

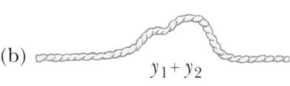

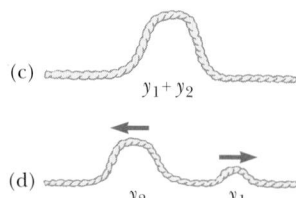

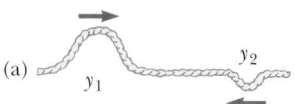

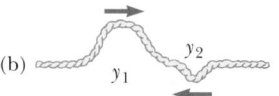

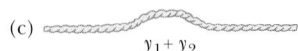

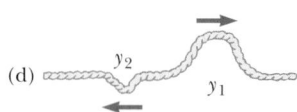

ACTIVE FIGURE 18.1

(a–d) Two pulses traveling on a stretched string in opposite directions pass through each other. When the pulses overlap, as shown in (b) and (c), the net displacement of the string equals the sum of the displacements produced by each pulse. Because each pulse produces positive displacements of the string, we refer to their superposition as *constructive interference*.

Sign in at www.thomsonedu.com and go to ThomsonNOW to choose the amplitude and orientation of each of the pulses and study the interference between them as they pass each other.

ACTIVE FIGURE 18.2

(a–d) Two pulses traveling in opposite directions and having displacements that are inverted relative to each other. When the two overlap in (c), their displacements partially cancel each other.

Sign in at www.thomsonedu.com and go to ThomsonNOW to choose the amplitude and orientation of each of the pulses and watch the interference as they pass each other.

Superposition of Sinusoidal Waves

Let us now apply the principle of superposition to two sinusoidal waves traveling in the same direction in a linear medium. If the two waves are traveling to the right and have the same frequency, wavelength, and amplitude but differ in phase, we can express their individual wave functions as

$$y_1 = A \sin (kx - \omega t) \qquad y_2 = A \sin (kx - \omega t + \phi)$$

where, as usual, $k = 2\pi/\lambda$, $\omega = 2\pi f$, and ϕ is the phase constant as discussed in Section 16.2. Hence, the resultant wave function y is

$$y = y_1 + y_2 = A[\sin (kx - \omega t) + \sin (kx - \omega t + \phi)]$$

To simplify this expression, we use the trigonometric identity

$$\sin a + \sin b = 2 \cos \left(\frac{a - b}{2}\right) \sin \left(\frac{a + b}{2}\right)$$

Letting $a = kx - \omega t$ and $b = kx - \omega t + \phi$, we find that the resultant wave function y reduces to

Resultant of two traveling ▶
sinusoidal waves

$$y = 2A \cos \left(\frac{\phi}{2}\right) \sin \left(kx - \omega t + \frac{\phi}{2}\right)$$

This result has several important features. The resultant wave function y also is sinusoidal and has the same frequency and wavelength as the individual waves because the sine function incorporates the same values of k and ω that appear in the original wave functions. The amplitude of the resultant wave is $2A \cos (\phi/2)$, and its phase is $\phi/2$. If the phase constant ϕ equals 0, then $\cos (\phi/2) = \cos 0 = 1$ and the amplitude of the resultant wave is $2A$, twice the amplitude of either individual wave. In this case, the waves are said to be everywhere *in phase* and therefore interfere constructively. That is, the crests and troughs of the individual waves y_1

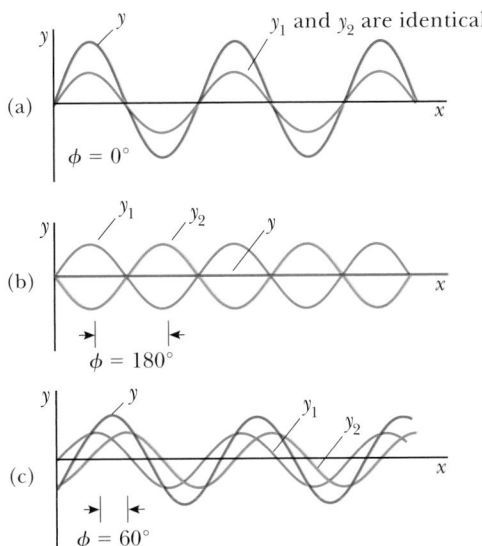

ACTIVE FIGURE 18.3

The superposition of two identical waves y_1 and y_2 (blue and green, respectively) to yield a resultant wave (red). (a) When y_1 and y_2 are in phase, the result is constructive interference. (b) When y_1 and y_2 are π rad out of phase, the result is destructive interference. (c) When the phase angle has a value other than 0 or π rad, the resultant wave y falls somewhere between the extremes shown in (a) and (b).

Sign in at www.thomsonedu.com and go to ThomsonNOW to change the phase relationship between the waves and observe the wave representing the superposition.

and y_2 occur at the same positions and combine to form the red curve y of amplitude $2A$ shown in Active Figure 18.3a. Because the individual waves are in phase, they are indistinguishable in Active Figure 18.3a, in which they appear as a single blue curve. In general, constructive interference occurs when $\cos(\phi/2) = \pm1$. That is true, for example, when $\phi = 0, 2\pi, 4\pi, \ldots$ rad, that is, when ϕ is an *even* multiple of π.

When ϕ is equal to π rad or to any *odd* multiple of π, then $\cos(\phi/2) = \cos(\pi/2) = 0$ and the crests of one wave occur at the same positions as the troughs of the second wave (Active Fig. 18.3b). Therefore, as a consequence of destructive interference, the resultant wave has *zero* amplitude everywhere. Finally, when the phase constant has an arbitrary value other than 0 or an integer multiple of π rad (Active Fig. 18.3c), the resultant wave has an amplitude whose value is somewhere between 0 and $2A$.

In the more general case in which the waves have the same wavelength but different amplitudes, the results are similar with the following exceptions. In the in-phase case, the amplitude of the resultant wave is not twice that of a single wave, but rather is the sum of the amplitudes of the two waves. When the waves are π rad out of phase, they do not completely cancel as in Active Figure 18.3b. The result is a wave whose amplitude is the difference in the amplitudes of the individual waves.

Interference of Sound Waves

One simple device for demonstrating interference of sound waves is illustrated in Figure 18.4. Sound from a loudspeaker S is sent into a tube at point P, where there is a T-shaped junction. Half the sound energy travels in one direction, and half travels in the opposite direction. Therefore, the sound waves that reach the receiver R can travel along either of the two paths. The distance along any path from speaker to receiver is called the **path length** r. The lower path length r_1 is fixed, but the upper path length r_2 can be varied by sliding the U-shaped tube, which is similar to that on a slide trombone. When the difference in the path lengths $\Delta r = |r_2 - r_1|$ is either zero or some integer multiple of the wavelength λ (that is, $\Delta r = n\lambda$, where $n = 0, 1, 2, 3, \ldots$), the two waves reaching the receiver at

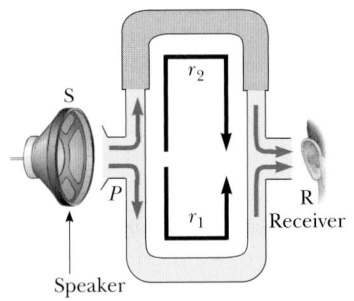

Figure 18.4 An acoustical system for demonstrating interference of sound waves. A sound wave from the speaker (S) propagates into the tube and splits into two parts at point P. The two waves, which combine at the opposite side, are detected at the receiver (R). The upper path length r_2 can be varied by sliding the upper section.

any instant are in phase and interfere constructively as shown in Active Figure 18.3a. For this case, a maximum in the sound intensity is detected at the receiver. If the path length r_2 is adjusted such that the path difference $\Delta r = \lambda/2, 3\lambda/2, \ldots,$ $n\lambda/2$ (for n odd), the two waves are exactly π rad, or 180°, out of phase at the receiver and hence cancel each other. In this case of destructive interference, no sound is detected at the receiver. This simple experiment demonstrates that a phase difference may arise between two waves generated by the same source when they travel along paths of unequal lengths. This important phenomenon will be indispensable in our investigation of the interference of light waves in Chapter 37.

EXAMPLE 18.1   **Two Speakers Driven by the Same Source**

Two identical loudspeakers placed 3.00 m apart are driven by the same oscillator (Fig. 18.5). A listener is originally at point O, located 8.00 m from the center of the line connecting the two speakers. The listener then moves to point P, which is a perpendicular distance 0.350 m from O, and she experiences the *first minimum* in sound intensity. What is the frequency of the oscillator?

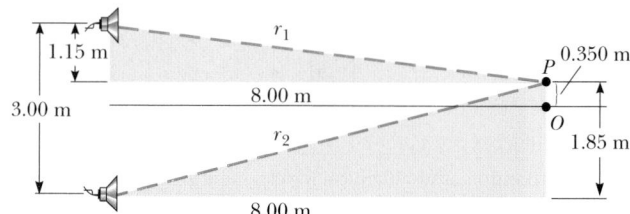

Figure 18.5 (Example 18.1) Two identical loudspeakers emit sound waves to a listener at P.

SOLUTION

Conceptualize In Figure 18.4, a sound wave enters a tube and is then *acoustically* split into two different paths before recombining at the other end. In this example, a signal representing the sound is *electrically* split and sent to two different loudspeakers. After leaving the speakers, the sound waves recombine at the position of the listener. Despite the difference in how the splitting occurs, the path difference discussion related to Figure 18.4 can be applied here.

Categorize Because the sound waves from two separate sources combine, we apply the waves in interference analysis model.

Analyze Figure 18.5 shows the physical arrangement of the speakers, along with two shaded right triangles that can be drawn on the basis of the lengths described in the problem. The first minimum occurs when the two waves reaching the listener at point P are 180° out of phase, in other words, when their path difference Δr equals $\lambda/2$.

From the shaded triangles, find the path lengths from the speakers to the listener:

$$r_1 = \sqrt{(8.00 \text{ m})^2 + (1.15 \text{ m})^2} = 8.08 \text{ m}$$

$$r_2 = \sqrt{(8.00 \text{ m})^2 + (1.85 \text{ m})^2} = 8.21 \text{ m}$$

Hence, the path difference is $r_2 - r_1 = 0.13$ m. Because this path difference must equal $\lambda/2$ for the first minimum, $\lambda = 0.26$ m.

To obtain the oscillator frequency, use Equation 16.12, $v = \lambda f$, where v is the speed of sound in air, 343 m/s:

$$f = \frac{v}{\lambda} = \frac{343 \text{ m/s}}{0.26 \text{ m}} = \boxed{1.3 \text{ kHz}}$$

Finalize This example enables us to understand why the speaker wires in a stereo system should be connected properly. When connected the wrong way—that is, when the positive (or red) wire is connected to the negative (or black) terminal on one of the speakers and the other is correctly wired—the speakers are said to be "out of phase," with one speaker moving outward while the other moves inward. As a consequence, the sound wave coming from one speaker destructively interferes with the wave coming from the other at point O in Figure 18.5. A rarefaction region due to one speaker is superposed on a compression region from the other speaker. Although the two sounds probably do not completely cancel each other (because the left and right stereo signals are usually not identical), a substantial loss of sound quality occurs at point O.

What If? What if the speakers were connected out of phase? What happens at point P in Figure 18.5?

Answer   In this situation, the path difference of $\lambda/2$ combines with a phase difference of $\lambda/2$ due to the incorrect wiring to give a full phase difference of λ. As a result, the waves are in phase and there is a *maximum* intensity at point P.

18.2   Standing Waves

The sound waves from the pair of loudspeakers in Example 18.1 leave the speakers in the forward direction, and we considered interference at a point in front of the speakers. Suppose we turn the speakers so that they face each other and then have them emit sound of the same frequency and amplitude. In this situation, two identical waves travel in opposite directions in the same medium as in Figure 18.6. These waves combine in accordance with the waves in interference model.

We can analyze such a situation by considering wave functions for two transverse sinusoidal waves having the same amplitude, frequency, and wavelength but traveling in opposite directions in the same medium:

$$y_1 = A \sin (kx - \omega t) \qquad y_2 = A \sin (kx + \omega t)$$

where y_1 represents a wave traveling in the $+x$ direction and y_2 represents one traveling in the $-x$ direction. Adding these two functions gives the resultant wave function y:

$$y = y_1 + y_2 = A \sin (kx - \omega t) + A \sin (kx + \omega t)$$

When we use the trigonometric identity $\sin (a \pm b) = \sin (a) \cos (b) \pm \cos (a) \sin (b)$, this expression reduces to

$$y = (2A \sin kx) \cos \omega t \qquad (18.1)$$

Equation 18.1 represents the wave function of a **standing wave**. A standing wave such as the one on a string shown in Figure 18.7 is an oscillation pattern *with a stationary outline* that results from the superposition of two identical waves traveling in opposite directions.

Notice that Equation 18.1 does not contain a function of $kx - \omega t$. Therefore, it is not an expression for a single traveling wave. When you observe a standing wave, there is no sense of motion in the direction of propagation of either original wave. Comparing Equation 18.1 with Equation 15.6, we see that it describes a special kind of simple harmonic motion. Every element of the medium oscillates in simple harmonic motion with the same angular frequency ω (according to the $\cos \omega t$ factor in the equation). The amplitude of the simple harmonic motion of a given

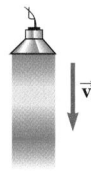

Figure 18.6   Two identical loudspeakers emit sound waves toward each other. When they overlap, identical waves traveling in opposite directions will combine to form standing waves.

PITFALL PREVENTION 18.2
Three Types of Amplitude

We need to distinguish carefully here between the **amplitude of the individual waves**, which is A, and the **amplitude of the simple harmonic motion of the elements of the medium**, which is $2A \sin kx$. A given element in a standing wave vibrates within the constraints of the *envelope* function $2A \sin kx$, where x is that element's position in the medium. Such vibration is in contrast to traveling sinusoidal waves, in which all elements oscillate with the same amplitude and the same frequency and the amplitude A of the wave is the same as the amplitude A of the simple harmonic motion of the elements. Furthermore, we can identify the **amplitude of the standing wave** as $2A$.

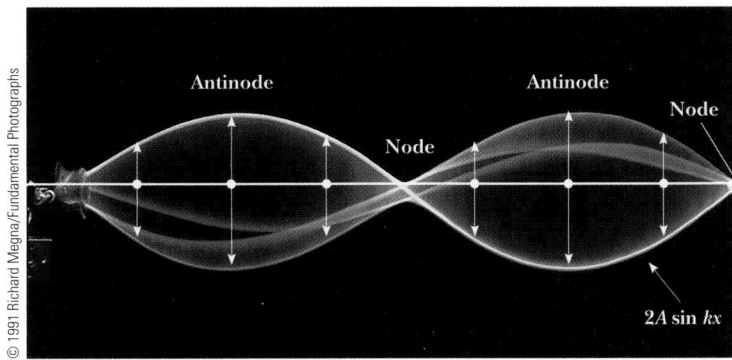

Figure 18.7   Multiflash photograph of a standing wave on a string. The time behavior of the vertical displacement from equilibrium of an individual element of the string is given by $\cos \omega t$. That is, each element vibrates at an angular frequency ω. The amplitude of the vertical oscillation of any element of the string depends on the horizontal position of the element. Each element vibrates within the confines of the envelope function $2A \sin kx$.

element (given by the factor $2A \sin kx$, the coefficient of the cosine function) depends on the location x of the element in the medium, however.

The amplitude of the simple harmonic motion of an element of the medium has a minimum value of zero when x satisfies the condition $\sin kx = 0$, that is, when

$$kx = 0, \pi, 2\pi, 3\pi, \ldots$$

Because $k = 2\pi/\lambda$, these values for kx give

Positions of nodes ▶

$$x = 0, \frac{\lambda}{2}, \lambda, \frac{3\lambda}{2}, \ldots = \frac{n\lambda}{2} \quad n = 0, 1, 2, 3, \ldots \tag{18.2}$$

These points of zero amplitude are called **nodes**.

The element of the medium with the *greatest* possible displacement from equilibrium has an amplitude of $2A$, which we define as the amplitude of the standing wave. The positions in the medium at which this maximum displacement occurs are called **antinodes**. The antinodes are located at positions for which the coordinate x satisfies the condition $\sin kx = \pm 1$, that is, when

$$kx = \frac{\pi}{2}, \frac{3\pi}{2}, \frac{5\pi}{2}, \ldots$$

Therefore, the positions of the antinodes are given by

Positions of antinodes ▶

$$x = \frac{\lambda}{4}, \frac{3\lambda}{4}, \frac{5\lambda}{4}, \ldots = \frac{n\lambda}{4} \quad n = 1, 3, 5, \ldots \tag{18.3}$$

Two nodes and two antinodes are labeled in the standing wave in Figure 18.7. The light blue curve labeled $2A \sin kx$ in Figure 18.7 represents one wavelength of the traveling waves that combine to form the standing wave. Figure 18.7 and Equations 18.2 and 18.3 provide the following important features of the locations of nodes and antinodes:

> The distance between adjacent antinodes is equal to $\lambda/2$.
> The distance between adjacent nodes is equal to $\lambda/2$.
> The distance between a node and an adjacent antinode is $\lambda/4$.

Wave patterns of the elements of the medium produced at various times by two transverse traveling waves moving in opposite directions are shown in Active Figure 18.8. The blue and green curves are the wave patterns for the individual travel-

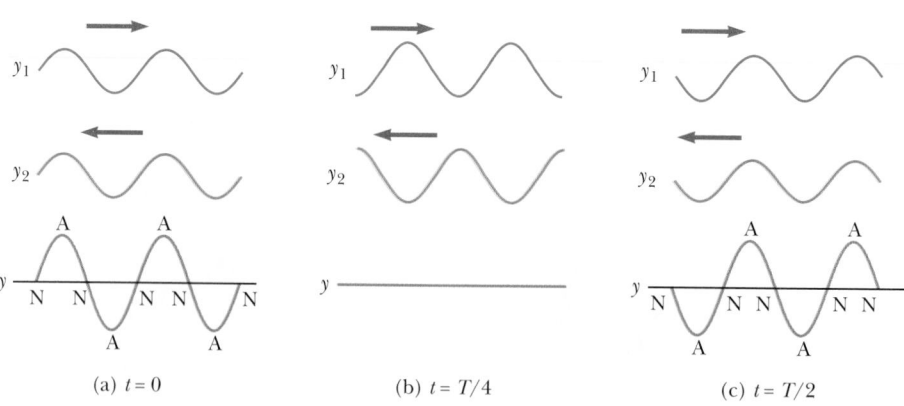

(a) $t = 0$ (b) $t = T/4$ (c) $t = T/2$

ACTIVE FIGURE 18.8

Standing-wave patterns produced at various times by two waves of equal amplitude traveling in opposite directions. For the resultant wave y, the nodes (N) are points of zero displacement and the antinodes (A) are points of maximum displacement.

Sign in at www.thomsonedu.com and go to ThomsonNOW to choose the wavelength of the waves and see the standing wave that results.

ing waves, and the brown curves are the wave patterns for the resultant standing wave. At $t = 0$ (Active Fig. 18.8a), the two traveling waves are in phase, giving a wave pattern in which each element of the medium is at rest and experiencing its maximum displacement from equilibrium. One quarter of a period later, at $t = T/4$ (Active Fig. 18.8b), the traveling waves have moved one quarter of a wavelength (one to the right and the other to the left). At this time, the traveling waves are out of phase, and each element of the medium is passing through the equilibrium position in its simple harmonic motion. The result is zero displacement for elements at all values of x; that is, the wave pattern is a straight line. At $t = T/2$ (Active Fig. 18.8c), the traveling waves are again in phase, producing a wave pattern that is inverted relative to the $t = 0$ pattern. In the standing wave, the elements of the medium alternate in time between the extremes shown in Active Figure 18.8a and c.

Quick Quiz 18.2   Consider a standing wave on a string as shown in Active Figure 18.8. Define the velocity of elements of the string as positive if they are moving upward in the figure. **(i)** At the moment the string has the shape shown by the brown curve in Active Figure 18.8a, what is the instantaneous velocity of elements along the string? (a) zero for all elements   (b) positive for all elements   (c) negative for all elements   (d) varies with the position of the element   **(ii)** From the same choices, at the moment the string has the shape shown by the brown curve in Active Figure 18.8b, what is the instantaneous velocity of elements along the string?

EXAMPLE 18.2   **Formation of a Standing Wave**

Two waves traveling in opposite directions produce a standing wave. The individual wave functions are

$$y_1 = (4.0 \text{ cm}) \sin (3.0x - 2.0t)$$

$$y_2 = (4.0 \text{ cm}) \sin (3.0x + 2.0t)$$

where x and y are measured in centimeters.

(A) Find the amplitude of the simple harmonic motion of the element of the medium located at $x = 2.3$ cm.

SOLUTION

Conceptualize   The waves described by the given equations are identical except for their directions of travel, so they indeed combine to form a standing wave as discussed in this section.

Categorize   We will substitute values into equations developed in this section, so we categorize this example as a substitution problem.

From the equations for the waves, we see that $A = 4.0$ cm, $k = 3.0$ rad/cm, and $\omega = 2.0$ rad/s. Use Equation 18.1 to write an expression for the standing wave:

$$y = (2A \sin kx) \cos \omega t = [(8.0 \text{ cm}) \sin 3.0x] \cos 2.0t$$

Find the amplitude of the simple harmonic motion of the element at the position $x = 2.3$ cm by evaluating the coefficient of the cosine function at this position:

$$y_{max} = (8.0 \text{ cm}) \sin 3.0x \big|_{x=2.3}$$

$$= (8.0 \text{ cm}) \sin (6.9 \text{ rad}) = \boxed{4.6 \text{ cm}}$$

(B) Find the positions of the nodes and antinodes if one end of the string is at $x = 0$.

SOLUTION

Find the wavelength of the traveling waves:

$$k = \frac{2\pi}{\lambda} = 3.0 \text{ rad/cm} \quad \rightarrow \quad \lambda = \frac{2\pi}{3.0} \text{ cm}$$

Use Equation 18.2 to find the locations of the nodes:

$$x = n\frac{\lambda}{2} = n\left(\frac{\pi}{3}\right) \text{ cm} \quad n = 0, 1, 2, 3, \ldots$$

Use Equation 18.3 to find the locations of the antinodes:

$$x = n\frac{\lambda}{4} = n\left(\frac{\pi}{6}\right) \text{ cm} \quad n = 1, 3, 5, 7, \ldots$$

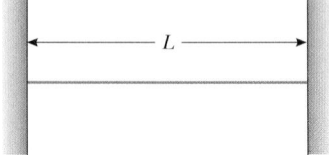

Figure 18.9 A string of length L fixed at both ends.

18.3 Standing Waves in a String Fixed at Both Ends

Consider a string of length L fixed at both ends as shown in Figure 18.9. We will use this system as a model for a guitar string or piano string. Standing waves can be set up in the string by a continuous superposition of waves incident on and reflected from the ends. Notice that there is a boundary condition for the waves on the string. Because the ends of the string are fixed, they must necessarily have zero displacement and are therefore nodes by definition. This boundary condition results in the string having a number of discrete natural patterns of oscillation, called **normal modes**, each of which has a characteristic frequency that is easily calculated. This situation in which only certain frequencies of oscillation are allowed is called **quantization**. Quantization is a common occurrence when waves are subject to boundary conditions and is a central feature in our discussions of quantum physics in the extended version of this text. Notice in Active Figure 18.8 that there are no boundary conditions, so standing waves of *any* frequency can be established; there is no quantization without boundary conditions. Because boundary conditions occur so often for waves, we identify an analysis model called the **waves under boundary conditions model** for the discussion that follows.

The normal modes of oscillation for the string in Figure 18.9 can be described by imposing the boundary conditions that the ends be nodes and that the nodes and antinodes be separated by one-fourth of a wavelength. The first normal mode that is consistent with these requirements, shown in Active Figure 18.10a, has nodes at its ends and one antinode in the middle. This normal mode is the longest-wavelength mode that is consistent with our boundary conditions. The first normal mode occurs when the wavelength λ_1 is equal to twice the length of the string, or $\lambda_1 = 2L$. The section of a standing wave from one node to the next node is called a *loop*. In the first normal mode, the string is vibrating in one loop. In the second normal mode (see Active Fig. 18.10b), the string vibrates in two loops. In this case, the wavelength λ_2 is equal to the length of the string, as expressed by $\lambda_2 = L$. The third normal mode (see Active Fig. 18.10c) corresponds to the case in which $\lambda_3 = 2L/3$, and our string vibrates in three loops. In general, the wavelengths of the various normal modes for a string of length L fixed at both ends are

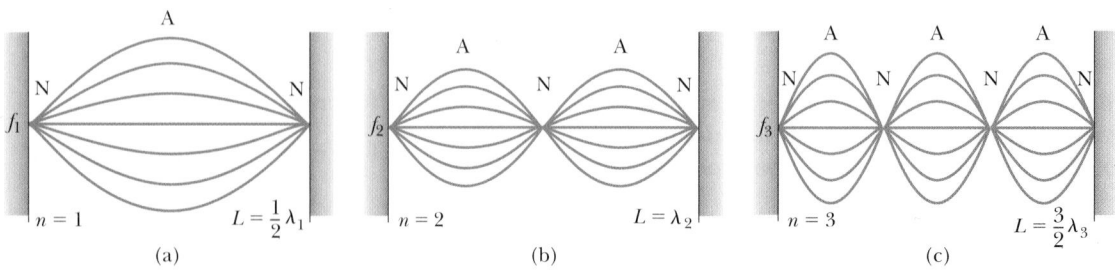

ACTIVE FIGURE 18.10

The normal modes of vibration of the string in Figure 18.9 form a harmonic series: (a) the fundamental, or first harmonic; (b) the second harmonic; (c) the third harmonic.

Sign in at www.thomsonedu.com and go to ThomsonNOW to choose the mode number and see the corresponding standing wave.

$$\lambda_n = \frac{2L}{n} \quad n = 1, 2, 3, \dots \qquad (18.4)$$

◀ Wavelengths of normal modes

where the index n refers to the nth normal mode of oscillation. These nodes are the *possible* modes of oscillation for the string. The *actual* modes that are excited on a string are discussed shortly.

The natural frequencies associated with the modes of oscillation are obtained from the relationship $f = v/\lambda$, where the wave speed v is the same for all frequencies. Using Equation 18.4, we find that the natural frequencies f_n of the normal modes are

$$f_n = \frac{v}{\lambda_n} = n\frac{v}{2L} \quad n = 1, 2, 3, \dots \qquad (18.5)$$

◀ Frequencies of normal modes as functions of wave speed and length of string

These natural frequencies are also called the *quantized frequencies* associated with the vibrating string fixed at both ends.

Because $v = \sqrt{T/\mu}$ (see Eq. 16.18) for waves on a string, where T is the tension in the string and μ is its linear mass density, we can also express the natural frequencies of a taut string as

$$f_n = \frac{n}{2L}\sqrt{\frac{T}{\mu}} \quad n = 1, 2, 3, \dots \qquad (18.6)$$

◀ Frequencies of normal modes as functions of string tension and linear mass density

The lowest frequency f_1, which corresponds to $n = 1$, is called either the **fundamental** or the **fundamental frequency** and is given by

$$f_1 = \frac{1}{2L}\sqrt{\frac{T}{\mu}} \qquad (18.7)$$

◀ Fundamental frequency of a taut string

The frequencies of the remaining normal modes are integer multiples of the fundamental frequency. Frequencies of normal modes that exhibit an integer-multiple relationship such as this form a **harmonic series**, and the normal modes are called **harmonics**. The fundamental frequency f_1 is the frequency of the first harmonic, the frequency $f_2 = 2f_1$ is the frequency of the second harmonic, and the frequency $f_n = nf_1$ is the frequency of the nth harmonic. Other oscillating systems, such as a drumhead, exhibit normal modes, but the frequencies are not related as integer multiples of a fundamental (see Section 18.6). Therefore, we do not use the term *harmonic* in association with these types of systems.

Let us examine further how the various harmonics are created in a string. To excite only a single harmonic, the string must be distorted into a shape that corresponds to that of the desired harmonic. After being released, the string vibrates at the frequency of that harmonic. This maneuver is difficult to perform, however, and is not how a string of a musical instrument is excited. If the string is distorted such that its shape is not that of just one harmonic, the resulting vibration includes a combination of various harmonics. Such a distortion occurs in musical instruments when the string is plucked (as in a guitar), bowed (as in a cello), or struck (as in a piano). When the string is distorted into a nonsinusoidal shape, only waves that satisfy the boundary conditions can persist on the string. These waves are the harmonics.

The frequency of a string that defines the musical note that it plays is that of the fundamental. The string's frequency can be varied by changing either the string's tension or its length. For example, the tension in guitar and violin strings is varied by a screw adjustment mechanism or by tuning pegs located on the neck of the instrument. As the tension is increased, the frequency of the normal modes increases in accordance with Equation 18.6. Once the instrument is "tuned," players vary the frequency by moving their fingers along the neck, thereby changing the length of the oscillating portion of the string. As the length is shortened, the frequency increases because, as Equation 18.6 specifies, the normal-mode frequencies are inversely proportional to string length.

Quick Quiz 18.3 When a standing wave is set up on a string fixed at both ends, which of the following statements is true? (a) The number of nodes is equal to the number of antinodes. (b) The wavelength is equal to the length of the string divided by an integer. (c) The frequency is equal to the number of nodes times the fundamental frequency. (d) The shape of the string at any instant shows a symmetry about the midpoint of the string.

EXAMPLE 18.3   Give Me a C Note!

Middle C on a piano has a fundamental frequency of 262 Hz, and the first A above middle C has a fundamental frequency of 440 Hz.

(A) Calculate the frequencies of the next two harmonics of the C string.

SOLUTION

Conceptualize Remember that the harmonics of a vibrating string have frequencies that are related by integer multiples of the fundamental.

Categorize This first part of the example is a simple substitution problem.

Knowing that the fundamental frequency is $f_1 = 262$ Hz, find the frequencies of the next harmonics by multiplying by integers:

$$f_2 = 2f_1 = \boxed{524 \text{ Hz}}$$

$$f_3 = 3f_1 = \boxed{786 \text{ Hz}}$$

(B) If the A and C strings have the same linear mass density μ and length L, determine the ratio of tensions in the two strings.

SOLUTION

Categorize This part of the example is more of an analysis problem than is part (A).

Analyze Use Equation 18.7 to write expressions for the fundamental frequencies of the two strings:

$$f_{1A} = \frac{1}{2L}\sqrt{\frac{T_A}{\mu}} \quad \text{and} \quad f_{1C} = \frac{1}{2L}\sqrt{\frac{T_C}{\mu}}$$

Divide the first equation by the second and solve for the ratio of tensions:

$$\frac{f_{1A}}{f_{1C}} = \sqrt{\frac{T_A}{T_C}} \rightarrow \frac{T_A}{T_C} = \left(\frac{f_{1A}}{f_{1C}}\right)^2 = \left(\frac{440}{262}\right)^2 = \boxed{2.82}$$

Finalize If the frequencies of piano strings were determined solely by tension, this result suggests that the ratio of tensions from the lowest string to the highest string on the piano would be enormous. Such large tensions would make it difficult to design a frame to support the strings. In reality, the frequencies of piano strings vary due to additional parameters, including the mass per unit length and the length of the string. The **What If?** below explores a variation in length.

What If? If you look inside a real piano, you'll see that the assumption made in part (B) is only partially true. The strings are not likely to have the same length. The string densities are equal, but suppose the length of the A string is only 64% of the length of the C string. What is the ratio of their tensions?

Answer Using Equation 18.7 again, we set up the ratio of frequencies:

$$\frac{f_{1A}}{f_{1C}} = \frac{L_C}{L_A}\sqrt{\frac{T_A}{T_C}} \rightarrow \frac{T_A}{T_C} = \left(\frac{L_A}{L_C}\right)^2\left(\frac{f_{1A}}{f_{1C}}\right)^2$$

$$\frac{T_A}{T_C} = (0.64)^2\left(\frac{440}{262}\right)^2 = 1.16$$

Notice that this result represents only a 16% increase in tension, compared with the 182% increase in part (B).

EXAMPLE 18.4	**Changing String Vibration with Water**

One end of a horizontal string is attached to a vibrating blade, and the other end passes over a pulley as in Figure 18.11a. A sphere of mass 2.00 kg hangs on the end of the string. The string is vibrating in its second harmonic. A container of water is raised under the sphere so that the sphere is completely submerged. In this configuration, the string vibrates in its fifth harmonic as shown in Figure 18.11b. What is the radius of the sphere?

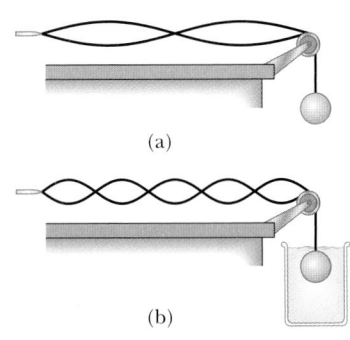

(a)

(b)

Figure 18.11 (Example 18.4) (a) When the sphere hangs in air, the string vibrates in its second harmonic. (b) When the sphere is immersed in water, the string vibrates in its fifth harmonic.

SOLUTION

Conceptualize Imagine what happens when the sphere is immersed in the water. The buoyant force acts upward on the sphere, reducing the tension in the string. The change in tension causes a change in the speed of waves on the string, which in turn causes a change in the wavelength. This altered wavelength results in the string vibrating in its fifth normal mode rather than the second.

Categorize The hanging sphere is modeled as a particle in equilibrium. One of the forces acting on it is the buoyant force from the water. We also apply the waves under boundary conditions model to the string.

Analyze Apply the particle in equilibrium model to the sphere in Figure 18.11a, identifying T_1 as the tension in the string as the sphere hangs in air:

$$\sum F = T_1 - mg = 0$$

$$T_1 = mg = (2.00 \text{ kg})(9.80 \text{ m/s}^2) = 19.6 \text{ N}$$

Apply the particle in equilibrium model to the sphere in Figure 18.11b, where T_2 is the tension in the string as the sphere is immersed in water:

$$T_2 + B - mg = 0$$

$$(1) \quad B = mg - T_2$$

The desired quantity, the radius of the sphere, will appear in the expression for the buoyant force B. Before proceeding in this direction, however, we must evaluate T_2 from the information about the standing wave.

Write the equation for the frequency of a standing wave on a string (Eq. 18.6) twice, once before the sphere is immersed and once after. Notice that the frequency f is the same in both cases because it is determined by the vibrating blade. In addition, the linear mass density μ and the length L of the vibrating portion of the string are the same in both cases. Divide the equations:

$$f = \frac{n_1}{2L}\sqrt{\frac{T_1}{\mu}} \quad \rightarrow \quad 1 = \frac{n_1}{n_2}\sqrt{\frac{T_1}{T_2}}$$
$$f = \frac{n_2}{2L}\sqrt{\frac{T_2}{\mu}}$$

Solve for T_2:

$$T_2 = \left(\frac{n_1}{n_2}\right)^2 T_1 = \left(\frac{2}{5}\right)^2 (19.6 \text{ N}) = 3.14 \text{ N}$$

Substitute this result into Equation (1):

$$B = mg - T_2 = 19.6 \text{ N} - 3.14 \text{ N} = 16.5 \text{ N}$$

Using Equation 14.5, express the buoyant force in terms of the radius of the sphere:

$$B = \rho_{\text{water}} g V_{\text{sphere}} = \rho_{\text{water}} g \left(\tfrac{4}{3}\pi r^3\right)$$

Solve for the radius of the sphere:

$$r = \left(\frac{3B}{4\pi\rho_{\text{water}}g}\right)^{1/3} = \left(\frac{3(16.5 \text{ N})}{4\pi(1\,000 \text{ kg/m}^3)(9.80 \text{ m/s}^2)}\right)^{1/3}$$

$$= 7.38 \times 10^{-2} \text{ m} = \boxed{7.38 \text{ cm}}$$

Finalize Notice that only certain radii of the sphere will result in the string vibrating in a normal mode; the speed of waves on the string must be changed to a value such that the length of the string is an integer multiple of half wavelengths. This limitation is a feature of the *quantization* that was introduced earlier in this chapter: the sphere radii that cause the string to vibrate in a normal mode are *quantized.*

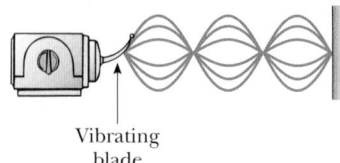

Vibrating
blade

Figure 18.12   Standing waves are set up in a string when one end is connected to a vibrating blade. When the blade vibrates at one of the natural frequencies of the string, large-amplitude standing waves are created.

18.4   Resonance

We have seen that a system such as a taut string is capable of oscillating in one or more normal modes of oscillation. **If a periodic force is applied to such a system, the amplitude of the resulting motion is greatest when the frequency of the applied force is equal to one of the natural frequencies of the system**. This phenomenon, known as *resonance*, was discussed in Section 15.7. Although a block–spring system or a simple pendulum has only one natural frequency, standing-wave systems have a whole set of natural frequencies, such as that given by Equation 18.6 for a string. Because an oscillating system exhibits a large amplitude when driven at any of its natural frequencies, these frequencies are often referred to as **resonance frequencies**.

Consider a taut string fixed at one end and connected at the opposite end to an oscillating blade as illustrated in Figure 18.12. The fixed end is a node, and the end connected to the blade is very nearly a node because the amplitude of the blade's motion is small compared with that of the elements of the string. As the blade oscillates, transverse waves sent down the string are reflected from the fixed end. As we learned in Section 18.3, the string has natural frequencies that are determined by its length, tension, and linear mass density (see Eq. 18.6). When the frequency of the blade equals one of the natural frequencies of the string, standing waves are produced and the string oscillates with a large amplitude. In this resonance case, the wave generated by the oscillating blade is in phase with the reflected wave and the string absorbs energy from the blade. If the string is driven at a frequency that is not one of its natural frequencies, the oscillations are of low amplitude and exhibit no stable pattern.

Resonance is very important in the excitation of musical instruments based on air columns. We shall discuss this application of resonance in Section 18.5.

18.5   Standing Waves in Air Columns

The waves under boundary conditions model can also be applied to sound waves in a column of air such as that inside an organ pipe. Standing waves are the result of interference between longitudinal sound waves traveling in opposite directions.

In a pipe closed at one end, **the closed end is a displacement node because the rigid barrier at this end does not allow longitudinal motion of the air**. Because the pressure wave is 90° out of phase with the displacement wave (see Section 17.2), **the closed end of an air column corresponds to a pressure antinode** (that is, a point of maximum pressure variation).

The open end of an air column is approximately a displacement antinode[1] and a pressure node. We can understand why no pressure variation occurs at an open end by noting that the end of the air column is open to the atmosphere; therefore, the pressure at this end must remain constant at atmospheric pressure.

You may wonder how a sound wave can reflect from an open end because there may not appear to be a change in the medium at this point: the medium through which the sound wave moves is air both inside and outside the pipe. Sound is a pressure wave, however, and a compression region of the sound wave is constrained by the sides of the pipe as long as the region is inside the pipe. As the compression region exits at the open end of the pipe, the constraint of the pipe is removed and the compressed air is free to expand into the atmosphere. Therefore, there is a change in the *character* of the medium between the inside of the pipe and the outside even though there is no change in the *material* of the medium. This change in character is sufficient to allow some reflection.

---

[1] Strictly speaking, the open end of an air column is not exactly a displacement antinode. A compression reaching an open end does not reflect until it passes beyond the end. For a tube of circular cross section, an end correction equal to approximately $0.6R$, where R is the tube's radius, must be added to the length of the air column. Hence, the effective length of the air column is longer than the true length L. We ignore this end correction in this discussion.

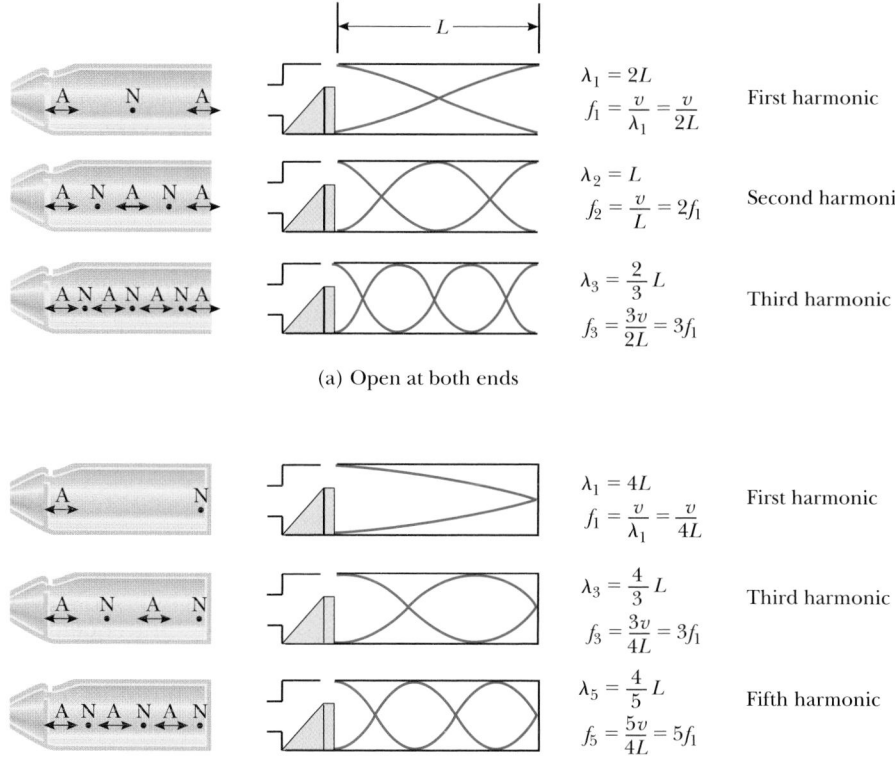

(a) Open at both ends

(b) Closed at one end, open at the other

Figure 18.13   Motion of elements of air in standing longitudinal waves in a pipe, along with schematic representations of the waves. In the schematic representations, the structure at the left end has the purpose of exciting the air column into a normal mode. The hole in the upper edge of the column ensures that the left end acts as an open end. The graphs represent the displacement amplitudes, not the pressure amplitudes. (a) In a pipe open at both ends, the harmonic series created consists of all integer multiples of the fundamental frequency: $f_1, 2f_1, 3f_1, \ldots$. (b) In a pipe closed at one end and open at the other, the harmonic series created consists of only odd-integer multiples of the fundamental frequency: $f_1, 3f_1, 5f_1, \ldots$.

With the boundary conditions of nodes or antinodes at the ends of the air column, we have a set of normal modes of oscillation as is the case for the string fixed at both ends. Therefore, the air column has quantized frequencies.

The first three normal modes of oscillation of a pipe open at both ends are shown in Figure 18.13a. Notice that both ends are displacement antinodes (approximately). In the first normal mode, the standing wave extends between two adjacent antinodes, which is a distance of half a wavelength. Therefore, the wavelength is twice the length of the pipe, and the fundamental frequency is $f_1 = v/2L$. As Figure 18.13a shows, the frequencies of the higher harmonics are $2f_1, 3f_1, \ldots$.

> In a pipe open at both ends, the natural frequencies of oscillation form a harmonic series that includes all integral multiples of the fundamental frequency.

Because all harmonics are present and because the fundamental frequency is given by the same expression as that for a string (see Eq. 18.5), we can express the natural frequencies of oscillation as

$$f_n = n\frac{v}{2L} \quad n = 1, 2, 3, \ldots \quad (18.8)$$

Despite the similarity between Equations 18.5 and 18.8, you must remember that v in Equation 18.5 is the speed of waves on the string, whereas v in Equation 18.8 is the speed of sound in air.

PITFALL PREVENTION 18.3
Sound Waves in Air Are Longitudinal, Not Transverse

The standing longitudinal waves are drawn as transverse waves in Figure 18.13. Because they are in the same direction as the propagation, it is difficult to draw longitudinal displacements. Therefore, it is best to interpret the red curves in Figure 18.13 as a graphical representation of the waves (our diagrams of string waves are pictorial representations), with the vertical axis representing horizontal displacement of the elements of the medium.

◄ Natural frequencies of a pipe open at both ends

If a pipe is closed at one end and open at the other, the closed end is a displacement node (see Fig. 18.13b). In this case, the standing wave for the fundamental mode extends from an antinode to the adjacent node, which is one-fourth of a wavelength. Hence, the wavelength for the first normal mode is $4L$, and the fundamental frequency is $f_1 = v/4L$. As Figure 18.13b shows, the higher-frequency waves that satisfy our conditions are those that have a node at the closed end and an antinode at the open end; hence, the higher harmonics have frequencies $3f_1, 5f_1, \ldots$.

> In a pipe closed at one end, the natural frequencies of oscillation form a harmonic series that includes only odd integral multiples of the fundamental frequency.

We express this result mathematically as

◀ Natural frequencies of a pipe closed at one end and open at the other

$$f_n = n\frac{v}{4L} \quad n = 1, 3, 5, \ldots \tag{18.9}$$

It is interesting to investigate what happens to the frequencies of instruments based on air columns and strings during a concert as the temperature rises. The sound emitted by a flute, for example, becomes sharp (increases in frequency) as the flute warms up because the speed of sound increases in the increasingly warmer air inside the flute (consider Eq. 18.8). The sound produced by a violin becomes flat (decreases in frequency) as the strings thermally expand because the expansion causes their tension to decrease (see Eq. 18.6).

Musical instruments based on air columns are generally excited by resonance. The air column is presented with a sound wave that is rich in many frequencies. The air column then responds with a large-amplitude oscillation to the frequencies that match the quantized frequencies in its set of harmonics. In many woodwind instruments, the initial rich sound is provided by a vibrating reed. In brass instruments, this excitation is provided by the sound coming from the vibration of the player's lips. In a flute, the initial excitation comes from blowing over an edge at the mouthpiece of the instrument in a manner similar to blowing across the opening of a bottle with a narrow neck. The sound of the air rushing across the edge has many frequencies, including one that sets the air cavity in the bottle into resonance.

Quick Quiz 18.4 A pipe open at both ends resonates at a fundamental frequency f_{open}. When one end is covered and the pipe is again made to resonate, the fundamental frequency is f_{closed}. Which of the following expressions describes how these two resonant frequencies compare? (a) $f_{\text{closed}} = f_{\text{open}}$ (b) $f_{\text{closed}} = \frac{1}{2}f_{\text{open}}$ (c) $f_{\text{closed}} = 2f_{\text{open}}$ (d) $f_{\text{closed}} = \frac{3}{2}f_{\text{open}}$

Quick Quiz 18.5 Balboa Park in San Diego has an outdoor organ. When the air temperature increases, the fundamental frequency of one of the organ pipes (a) stays the same, (b) goes down, (c) goes up, or (d) is impossible to determine.

EXAMPLE 18.5 | **Wind in a Culvert**

A section of drainage culvert 1.23 m in length makes a howling noise when the wind blows across its open ends.

(A) Determine the frequencies of the first three harmonics of the culvert if it is cylindrical in shape and open at both ends. Take $v = 343$ m/s as the speed of sound in air.

SOLUTION

Conceptualize The sound of the wind blowing across the end of the pipe contains many frequencies, and the culvert responds to the sound by vibrating at the natural frequencies of the air column.

Categorize   This example is a relatively simple substitution problem.

Find the frequency of the first harmonic of the culvert, modeling it as an air column open at both ends:

$$f_1 = \frac{v}{2L} = \frac{343 \text{ m/s}}{2(1.23 \text{ m})} = \boxed{139 \text{ Hz}}$$

Find the next harmonics by multiplying by integers:

$$f_2 = 2f_1 = \boxed{278 \text{ Hz}}$$

$$f_3 = 3f_1 = \boxed{417 \text{ Hz}}$$

(B) What are the three lowest natural frequencies of the culvert if it is blocked at one end?

SOLUTION

Find the frequency of the first harmonic of the culvert, modeling it as an air column closed at one end:

$$f_1 = \frac{v}{4L} = \frac{343 \text{ m/s}}{4(1.23 \text{ m})} = \boxed{69.7 \text{ Hz}}$$

Find the next two harmonics by multiplying by odd integers:

$$f_3 = 3f_1 = \boxed{209 \text{ Hz}}$$

$$f_5 = 5f_1 = \boxed{349 \text{ Hz}}$$

EXAMPLE 18.6   Measuring the Frequency of a Tuning Fork

A simple apparatus for demonstrating resonance in an air column is depicted in Figure 18.14. A vertical pipe open at both ends is partially submerged in water, and a tuning fork vibrating at an unknown frequency is placed near the top of the pipe. The length L of the air column can be adjusted by moving the pipe vertically. The sound waves generated by the fork are reinforced when L corresponds to one of the resonance frequencies of the pipe. For a certain pipe, the smallest value of L for which a peak occurs in the sound intensity is 9.00 cm.

(A) What is the frequency of the tuning fork?

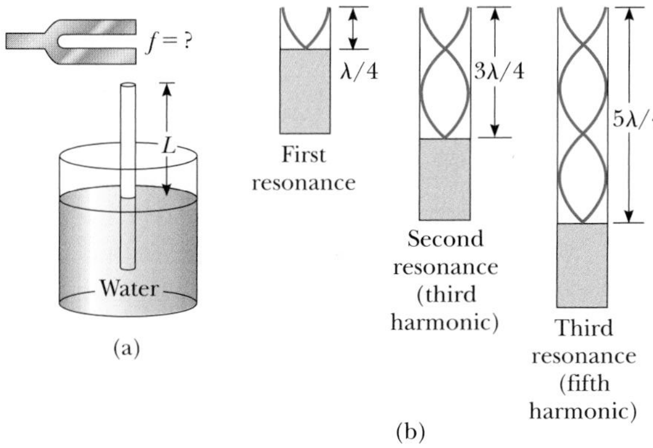

SOLUTION

Conceptualize   Consider how this problem differs from the preceding example. In the culvert, the length was fixed and the air column was presented with a mixture of very many frequencies. The pipe in this example is presented with one single frequency from the tuning fork, and the length of the pipe is varied until resonance is achieved.

Figure 18.14   (Example 18.6) (a) Apparatus for demonstrating the resonance of sound waves in a pipe closed at one end. The length L of the air column is varied by moving the pipe vertically while it is partially submerged in water. (b) The first three normal modes of the system shown in (a).

Categorize   This example is a simple substitution problem. Although the pipe is open at its lower end to allow the water to enter, the water's surface acts like a barrier. Therefore, this setup can be modeled as an air column closed at one end.

Use Equation 18.9 to find the fundamental frequency for $L = 0.090\ 0$ m:

$$f_1 = \frac{v}{4L} = \frac{343 \text{ m/s}}{4(0.090\ 0\ \text{m})} = \boxed{953 \text{ Hz}}$$

Because the tuning fork causes the air column to resonate at this frequency, this frequency must also be that of the tuning fork.

(B) What are the values of L for the next two resonance conditions?

SOLUTION

Use Equation 16.12 to find the wavelength of the sound wave from the tuning fork:

$$\lambda = \frac{v}{f} = \frac{343 \text{ m/s}}{953 \text{ Hz}} = 0.360 \text{ m}$$

Notice from Figure 18.14b that the length of the air column for the second resonance is $3\lambda/4$:

$$L = 3\lambda/4 = \boxed{0.270 \text{ m}}$$

Notice from Figure 18.14b that the length of the air column for the third resonance is $5\lambda/4$:

$$L = 5\lambda/4 = \boxed{0.450 \text{ m}}$$

18.6   Standing Waves in Rods and Membranes

Standing waves can also be set up in rods and membranes. A rod clamped in the middle and stroked parallel to the rod at one end oscillates as depicted in Figure 18.15a. The oscillations of the elements of the rod are longitudinal, and so the red curves in Figure 18.15 represent *longitudinal* displacements of various parts of the rod. For clarity, the displacements have been drawn in the transverse direction as they were for air columns. The midpoint is a displacement node because it is fixed by the clamp, whereas the ends are displacement antinodes because they are free to oscillate. The oscillations in this setup are analogous to those in a pipe open at both ends. The red lines in Figure 18.15a represent the first normal mode, for which the wavelength is $2L$ and the frequency is $f = v/2L$, where v is the speed of longitudinal waves in the rod. Other normal modes may be excited by clamping the rod at different points. For example, the second normal mode (Fig. 18.15b) is excited by clamping the rod a distance $L/4$ away from one end.

It is also possible to set up transverse standing waves in rods. Musical instruments that depend on transverse standing waves in rods include triangles, marimbas, xylophones, glockenspiels, chimes, and vibraphones. Other devices that make sounds from vibrating bars include music boxes and wind chimes.

Two-dimensional oscillations can be set up in a flexible membrane stretched over a circular hoop such as that in a drumhead. As the membrane is struck at some point, waves that arrive at the fixed boundary are reflected many times. The resulting sound is not harmonic because the standing waves have frequencies that are *not* related by integer multiples. Without this relationship, the sound may be more correctly described as *noise* rather than as music. The production of noise is in contrast to the situation in wind and stringed instruments, which produce sounds that we describe as musical.

Some possible normal modes of oscillation for a two-dimensional circular membrane are shown in Figure 18.16. Whereas nodes are *points* in one-dimensional standing waves on strings and in air columns, a two-dimensional oscillator has *curves* along which there is no displacement of the elements of the medium. The lowest normal mode, which has a frequency f_1, contains only one nodal curve; this curve runs around the outer edge of the membrane. The other possible normal modes show additional nodal curves that are circles and straight lines across the diameter of the membrane.

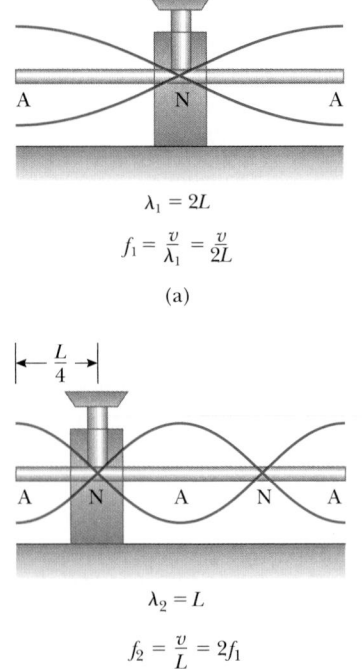

$$\lambda_1 = 2L$$

$$f_1 = \frac{v}{\lambda_1} = \frac{v}{2L}$$

(a)

$$\lambda_2 = L$$

$$f_2 = \frac{v}{L} = 2f_1$$

(b)

Figure 18.15 Normal-mode longitudinal vibrations of a rod of length L (a) clamped at the middle to produce the first normal mode and (b) clamped at a distance $L/4$ from one end to produce the second normal mode. Notice that the red curves represent oscillations parallel to the rod (longitudinal waves).

18.7   Beats: Interference in Time

The interference phenomena we have studied so far involve the superposition of two or more waves having the same frequency. Because the amplitude of the oscillation of elements of the medium varies with the position in space of the element

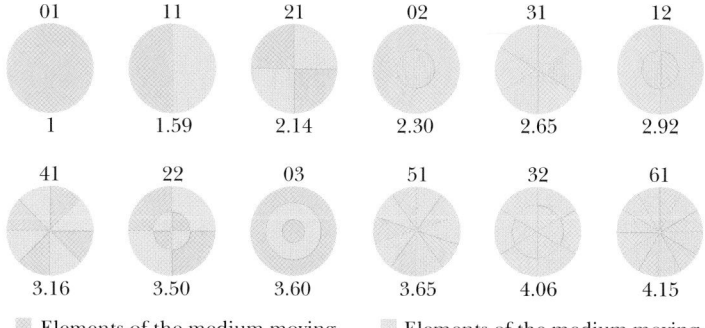

01	11	21	02	31	12
1	1.59	2.14	2.30	2.65	2.92
41	22	03	51	32	61
3.16	3.50	3.60	3.65	4.06	4.15

■ Elements of the medium moving out of the page at an instant of time.   ■ Elements of the medium moving into the page at an instant of time.

Figure 18.16   Representation of some of the normal modes possible in a circular membrane fixed at its perimeter. The pair of numbers above each pattern corresponds to the number of radial nodes and the number of circular nodes, respectively. Below each pattern is a factor by which the frequency of the mode is larger than that of the 01 mode. The frequencies of oscillation do not form a harmonic series because these factors are not integers. In each diagram, elements of the membrane on either side of a nodal line move in opposite directions, as indicated by the colors. (*Adapted from T. D. Rossing*, The Science of Sound, 2nd ed., *Reading, Massachusetts, Addison-Wesley Publishing Co., 1990*)

in such a wave, we refer to the phenomenon as *spatial interference*. Standing waves in strings and pipes are common examples of spatial interference.

Now let's consider another type of interference, one that results from the superposition of two waves having slightly *different* frequencies. In this case, when the two waves are observed at a point in space, they are periodically in and out of phase. That is, there is a *temporal* (time) alternation between constructive and destructive interference. As a consequence, we refer to this phenomenon as *interference in time* or *temporal interference*. For example, if two tuning forks of slightly different frequencies are struck, one hears a sound of periodically varying amplitude. This phenomenon is called **beating**.

> Beating is the periodic variation in amplitude at a given point due to the superposition of two waves having slightly different frequencies.

◀ Definition of beating

The number of amplitude maxima one hears per second, or the *beat frequency*, equals the difference in frequency between the two sources as we shall show below. The maximum beat frequency that the human ear can detect is about 20 beats/s. When the beat frequency exceeds this value, the beats blend indistinguishably with the sounds producing them.

Consider two sound waves of equal amplitude traveling through a medium with slightly different frequencies f_1 and f_2. We use equations similar to Equation 16.10 to represent the wave functions for these two waves at a point that we choose so that $kx = \pi/2$:

$$y_1 = A \sin\left(\frac{\pi}{2} - \omega_1 t\right) = A \cos\left(2\pi f_1 t\right)$$

$$y_2 = A \sin\left(\frac{\pi}{2} - \omega_2 t\right) = A \cos\left(2\pi f_2 t\right)$$

Using the superposition principle, we find that the resultant wave function at this point is

$$y = y_1 + y_2 = A\left(\cos 2\pi f_1 t + \cos 2\pi f_2 t\right)$$

The trigonometric identity

$$\cos a + \cos b = 2 \cos\left(\frac{a-b}{2}\right) \cos\left(\frac{a+b}{2}\right)$$

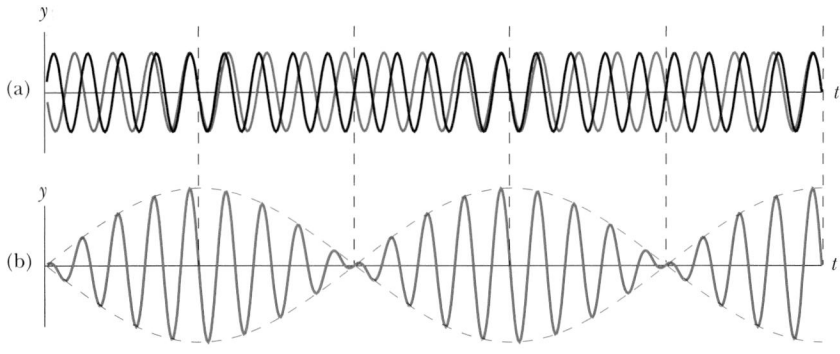

ACTIVE FIGURE 18.17

Beats are formed by the combination of two waves of slightly different frequencies. (a) The individual waves. (b) The combined wave. The envelope wave (dashed line) represents the beating of the combined sounds.

Sign in at www.thomsonedu.com and go to ThomsonNOW to choose the two frequencies and see the corresponding beats.

allows us to write the expression for y as

Resultant of two waves of different frequencies but equal amplitude ▶

$$y = \left[2A \cos 2\pi \left(\frac{f_1 - f_2}{2} \right) t \right] \cos 2\pi \left(\frac{f_1 + f_2}{2} \right) t \qquad \textbf{(18.10)}$$

Graphs of the individual waves and the resultant wave are shown in Active Figure 18.17. From the factors in Equation 18.10, we see that the resultant wave has an effective frequency equal to the average frequency $(f_1 + f_2)/2$. This wave is multiplied by an envelope wave given by the expression in the square brackets:

$$y_{\text{envelope}} = 2A \cos 2\pi \left(\frac{f_1 - f_2}{2} \right) t \qquad \textbf{(18.11)}$$

That is, the **amplitude and therefore the intensity of the resultant sound vary in time.** The dashed blue line in Active Figure 18.17b is a graphical representation of the envelope wave in Equation 18.11 and is a sine wave varying with frequency $(f_1 - f_2)/2$.

A maximum in the amplitude of the resultant sound wave is detected whenever

$$\cos 2\pi \left(\frac{f_1 - f_2}{2} \right) t = \pm 1$$

Hence, there are *two* maxima in each period of the envelope wave. Because the amplitude varies with frequency as $(f_1 - f_2)/2$, the number of beats per second, or the beat frequency f_{beat}, is twice this value. That is,

Beat frequency ▶

$$f_{\text{beat}} = |f_1 - f_2| \qquad \textbf{(18.12)}$$

For instance, if one tuning fork vibrates at 438 Hz and a second one vibrates at 442 Hz, the resultant sound wave of the combination has a frequency of 440 Hz (the musical note A) and a beat frequency of 4 Hz. A listener would hear a 440-Hz sound wave go through an intensity maximum four times every second.

EXAMPLE 18.7 **The Mistuned Piano Strings**

Two identical piano strings of length 0.750 m are each tuned exactly to 440 Hz. The tension in one of the strings is then increased by 1.0%. If they are now struck, what is the beat frequency between the fundamentals of the two strings?

SOLUTION

Conceptualize As the tension in one of the strings is changed, its fundamental frequency changes. Therefore, when both strings are played, they will have different frequencies and beats will be heard.

Categorize   We must combine our understanding of the waves under boundary conditions model for strings with our new knowledge of beats.

Analyze   Set up a ratio of the fundamental frequencies of the two strings using Equation 18.5:

$$\frac{f_2}{f_1} = \frac{(v_2/2L)}{(v_1/2L)} = \frac{v_2}{v_1}$$

Use Equation 16.18 to substitute for the wave speeds on the strings:

$$\frac{f_2}{f_1} = \frac{\sqrt{T_2/\mu}}{\sqrt{T_1/\mu}} = \sqrt{\frac{T_2}{T_1}}$$

Incorporate that the tension in one string is 1.0% larger than the other; that is, $T_2 = 1.010T_1$:

$$\frac{f_2}{f_1} = \sqrt{\frac{1.010T_1}{T_1}} = 1.005$$

Solve for the frequency of the tightened string:

$$f_2 = 1.005f_1 = 1.005(440 \text{ Hz}) = 442 \text{ Hz}$$

Find the beat frequency using Equation 18.12:

$$f_{\text{beat}} = 442 \text{ Hz} - 440 \text{ Hz} = \boxed{2 \text{ Hz}}$$

Finalize   Notice that a 1.0% mistuning in tension leads to an easily audible beat frequency of 2 Hz. A piano tuner can use beats to tune a stringed instrument by "beating" a note against a reference tone of known frequency. The tuner can then adjust the string tension until the frequency of the sound it emits equals the frequency of the reference tone. The tuner does so by tightening or loosening the string until the beats produced by it and the reference source become too infrequent to notice.

18.8   Nonsinusoidal Wave Patterns

It is relatively easy to distinguish the sounds coming from a violin and a saxophone even when they are both playing the same note. On the other hand, a person untrained in music may have difficulty distinguishing a note played on a clarinet from the same note played on an oboe. We can use the pattern of the sound waves from various sources to explain these effects.

When frequencies that are integer multiples of a fundamental frequency are combined to make a sound, the result is a *musical* sound. A listener can assign a pitch to the sound based on the fundamental frequency. Pitch is a psychological reaction to a sound that allows the listener to place the sound on a scale of low to high (bass to treble). Combinations of frequencies that are not integer multiples of a fundamental result in a *noise* rather than a musical sound. It is much harder for a listener to assign a pitch to a noise than to a musical sound.

The wave patterns produced by a musical instrument are the result of the superposition of frequencies that are integer multiples of a fundamental. This superposition results in the corresponding richness of musical tones. The human perceptive response associated with various mixtures of harmonics is the *quality* or *timbre* of the sound. For instance, the sound of the trumpet is perceived to have a "brassy" quality (that is, we have learned to associate the adjective *brassy* with that sound); this quality enables us to distinguish the sound of the trumpet from that of the saxophone, whose quality is perceived as "reedy." The clarinet and oboe, however, both contain air columns excited by reeds; because of this similarity, they have similar mixtures of frequencies and it is more difficult for the human ear to distinguish them on the basis of their sound quality.

The sound wave patterns produced by the majority of musical instruments are nonsinusoidal. Characteristic patterns produced by a tuning fork, a flute, and a clarinet, each playing the same note, are shown in Figure 18.18 (page 520). Each instrument has its own characteristic pattern. Notice, however, that despite the

PITFALL PREVENTION 18.4
Pitch Versus Frequency

Do not confuse the term *pitch* with *frequency*. Frequency is the physical measurement of the number of oscillations per second. Pitch is a psychological reaction to sound that enables a person to place the sound on a scale from high to low or from treble to bass. Therefore, frequency is the stimulus and pitch is the response. Although pitch is related mostly (but not completely) to frequency, they are not the same. A phrase such as "the pitch of the sound" is incorrect because pitch is not a physical property of the sound.

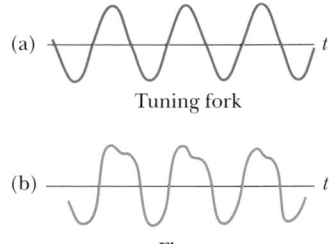

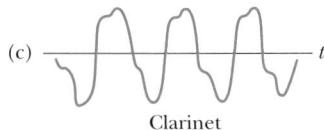

Figure 18.18 Sound wave patterns produced by (a) a tuning fork, (b) a flute, and (c) a clarinet, each at approximately the same frequency.

differences in the patterns, each pattern is periodic. This point is important for our analysis of these waves.

The problem of analyzing nonsinusoidal wave patterns appears at first sight to be a formidable task. If the wave pattern is periodic, however, **it can be represented as closely as desired by the combination of a sufficiently large number of sinusoidal waves that form a harmonic series**. In fact, we can represent any periodic function as a series of sine and cosine terms by using a mathematical technique based on **Fourier's theorem**.[2] The corresponding sum of terms that represents the periodic wave pattern is called a **Fourier series**. Let $y(t)$ be any function that is periodic in time with period T such that $y(t + T) = y(t)$. Fourier's theorem states that this function can be written as

Fourier's theorem ▶

$$y(t) = \sum (A_n \sin 2\pi f_n t + B_n \cos 2\pi f_n t) \tag{18.13}$$

where the lowest frequency is $f_1 = 1/T$. The higher frequencies are integer multiples of the fundamental, $f_n = nf_1$, and the coefficients A_n and B_n represent the amplitudes of the various waves. Figure 18.19 represents a harmonic analysis of the wave patterns shown in Figure 18.18. Each bar in the graph represents one of the terms in the series in Equation 18.13. Notice that a struck tuning fork pro-

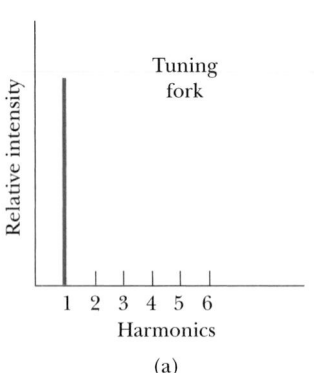

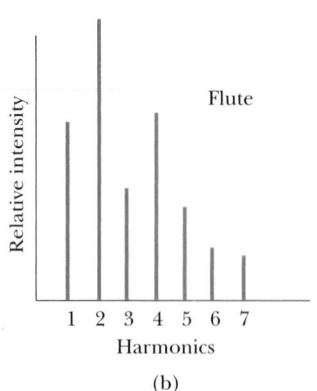

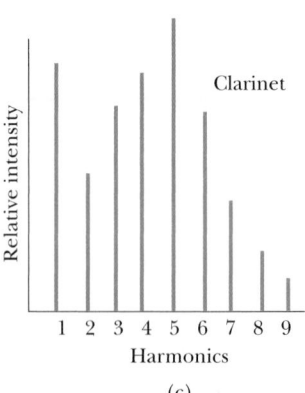

Figure 18.19 Harmonics of the wave patterns shown in Figure 18.18. Notice the variations in intensity of the various harmonics. Parts (a), (b), and (c) correspond to those in Figure 18.18.

[2] Developed by Jean Baptiste Joseph Fourier (1786–1830).

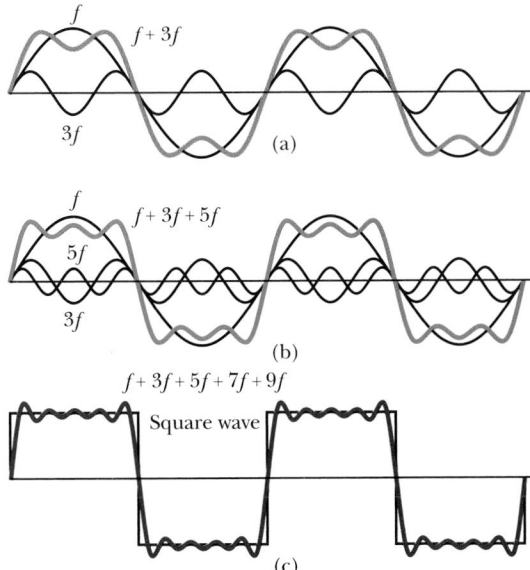

ACTIVE FIGURE 18.20

Fourier synthesis of a square wave, which is represented by the sum of odd multiples of the first harmonic, which has frequency f. (a) Waves of frequency f and $3f$ are added. (b) One more odd harmonic of frequency $5f$ is added. (c) The synthesis curve approaches closer to the square wave when odd frequencies up to $9f$ are added.

Sign in at www.thomsonedu.com and go to ThomsonNOW to add in harmonics with frequencies higher than $9f$ to try to synthesize a square wave.

duces only one harmonic (the first), whereas the flute and clarinet produce the first harmonic and many higher ones.

Notice the variation in relative intensity of the various harmonics for the flute and the clarinet. In general, any musical sound consists of a fundamental frequency f plus other frequencies that are integer multiples of f, all having different intensities.

We have discussed the *analysis* of a wave pattern using Fourier's theorem. The analysis involves determining the coefficients of the harmonics in Equation 18.13 from a knowledge of the wave pattern. The reverse process, called *Fourier synthesis,* can also be performed. In this process, the various harmonics are added together to form a resultant wave pattern. As an example of Fourier synthesis, consider the building of a square wave as shown in Active Figure 18.20. The symmetry of the square wave results in only odd multiples of the fundamental frequency combining in its synthesis. In Active Figure 18.20a, the orange curve shows the combination of f and $3f$. In Active Figure 18.20b, we have added $5f$ to the combination and obtained the green curve. Notice how the general shape of the square wave is approximated, even though the upper and lower portions are not flat as they should be.

Active Figure 18.20c shows the result of adding odd frequencies up to $9f$. This approximation (purple curve) to the square wave is better than the approximations in Active Figures 18.20a and 18.20b. To approximate the square wave as closely as possible, we must add all odd multiples of the fundamental frequency, up to infinite frequency.

Using modern technology, musical sounds can be generated electronically by mixing different amplitudes of any number of harmonics. These widely used electronic music synthesizers are capable of producing an infinite variety of musical tones.

Summary

ThomsonNOW™ Sign in at **www.thomsonedu.com** and go to ThomsonNOW to take a practice test for this chapter.

CONCEPTS AND PRINCIPLES

The **superposition principle** specifies that when two or more waves move through a medium, the value of the resultant wave function equals the algebraic sum of the values of the individual wave functions.

The phenomenon of **beating** is the periodic variation in intensity at a given point due to the superposition of two waves having slightly different frequencies.

Standing waves are formed from the combination of two sinusoidal waves having the same frequency, amplitude, and wavelength but traveling in opposite directions. The resultant standing wave is described by the wave function

$$y = (2A \sin kx) \cos \omega t \tag{18.1}$$

Hence, the amplitude of the standing wave is $2A$, and the amplitude of the simple harmonic motion of any particle of the medium varies according to its position as $2A \sin kx$. The points of zero amplitude (called **nodes**) occur at $x = n\lambda/2$ ($n = 0, 1, 2, 3, \ldots$). The maximum amplitude points (called **antinodes**) occur at $x = n\lambda/4$ ($n = 1, 3, 5, \ldots$). Adjacent antinodes are separated by a distance $\lambda/2$. Adjacent nodes also are separated by a distance $\lambda/2$.

ANALYSIS MODELS FOR PROBLEM SOLVING

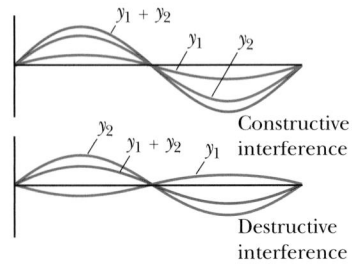

Waves in Interference. When two traveling waves having equal frequencies superimpose, the resultant wave has an amplitude that depends on the phase angle ϕ between the two waves. **Constructive interference** occurs when the two waves are in phase, corresponding to $\phi = 0, 2\pi, 4\pi, \ldots$ rad. **Destructive interference** occurs when the two waves are 180° out of phase, corresponding to $\phi = \pi, 3\pi, 5\pi, \ldots$ rad.

Waves Under Boundary Conditions. When a wave is subject to boundary conditions, only certain natural frequencies are allowed; we say that the frequencies are quantized.

For waves on a string fixed at both ends, the natural frequencies are

$$f_n = \frac{n}{2L}\sqrt{\frac{T}{\mu}} \quad n = 1, 2, 3, \ldots \tag{18.6}$$

where T is the tension in the string and μ is its linear mass density.

For sound waves in an air column open at both ends, the natural frequencies are

$$f_n = n\frac{v}{2L} \quad n = 1, 2, 3, \ldots \tag{18.8}$$

If an air column is open at one end and closed at the other, only odd harmonics are present and the natural frequencies are

$$f_n = n\frac{v}{4L} \quad n = 1, 3, 5, \ldots \tag{18.9}$$

Questions

☐ denotes answer available in *Student Solutions Manual/Study Guide;* **O** denotes objective question

1. Does the phenomenon of wave interference apply only to sinusoidal waves?

2. O A series of pulses, each of amplitude 0.1 m, is sent down a string that is attached to a post at one end. The pulses are reflected at the post and travel back along the string without loss of amplitude. What is the net displacement at a point on the string where two pulses are crossing? **(i)** First answer the question making the assumption the string is rigidly attached to the post. (a) 0.4 m (b) 0.2 m (c) 0.1 m (d) 0 **(ii)** Next assume the end at which reflection occurs is free to slide up and down. Choose your answer from the same possibilities.

3. O In Figure 18.4, a sound wave of wavelength 0.8 m divides into two equal parts that recombine to interfere constructively, with the original difference between their path lengths being $|r_2 - r_1| = 0.8$ m. Rank the following situations according to the intensity of sound at the receiver from the highest to the lowest. Assume the tube walls absorb no sound energy. Give equal ranks to situations in which the intensity is equal. (a) From its original position, the sliding section is moved out by 0.1 m. (b) Next it slides out an additional 0.1 m. (c) It slides out still another 0.1 m. (d) It slides out 0.1 m more.

4. When two waves interfere constructively or destructively, is there any gain or loss in energy? Explain.

5. O In Example 18.1, we investigated an oscillator at 1.3 kHz driving two identical side-by-side speakers. We found that a listener at the point O hears sound with maximum intensity, whereas a listener at point P hears a minimum. What is the intensity at P? (a) less than but close to the intensity at O (b) half the intensity at O (c) very low but not zero (d) zero

6. What limits the amplitude of motion of a real vibrating system that is driven at one of its resonant frequencies?

7. O Suppose all six strings of an acoustic guitar are played without fingering, that is, without being pressed down at any frets. What quantities are the same for all six strings? Choose each and every correct answer. (a) the fundamental frequency (b) the fundamental wavelength of the string wave (c) the fundamental wavelength of the sound emitted (d) the speed of the string wave (e) the speed of the sound emitted

8. O A string of length L, mass per unit length μ, and tension T is vibrating at its fundamental frequency. **(i)** If the length of the string is doubled, with all other factors held constant, what is the effect on the fundamental frequency? (a) It becomes four times larger. (b) It becomes two times larger. (c) It becomes $\sqrt{2}$ times larger. (d) It is unchanged. (e) It becomes $1/\sqrt{2}$ times as large. (f) It becomes one-half as large. (g) It becomes one-fourth as large. **(ii)** If the mass per unit length is doubled, with all other factors held constant, what is the effect on the fundamental frequency? Choose from the same possibilities. **(iii)** If the tension is doubled, with all other factors held constant, what is the effect on the fundamental frequency? Choose from the same possibilities.

9. O As oppositely moving pulses of the same shape (one upward, one downward) on a string pass through each other, at one particular instant the string shows no displacement from the equilibrium position at any point. What has happened to the energy carried by the pulses at this instant of time? (a) It was used up in producing the previous motion. (b) It is all potential energy. (c) It is all internal energy. (d) It is all kinetic energy. (e) It is momentum. (f) The positive energy of one pulse adds to zero with the negative energy of the other pulse. (g) Each pulse separately has zero total energy.

10. O Assume two identical sinusoidal waves are moving through the same medium in the same direction. Under what condition will the amplitude of the resultant wave be greater than either of the two original waves? (a) in all cases (b) only if the waves have no difference in phase (c) only if the phase difference is less than 90° (d) only if the phase difference is less than 120° (e) only if the phase difference is less than 180°

11. Explain how a musical instrument such as a piano may be tuned by using the phenomenon of beats.

12. O An archer shoots an arrow horizontally from the center of the string of a bow held vertically. After the arrow leaves it, the string of the bow will vibrate as a superposition of what standing-wave harmonics? (a) It vibrates only in harmonic number 1, the fundamental. (b) It vibrates only in the second harmonic. (c) It vibrates only in the odd-numbered harmonics 1, 3, 5, 7, ... (d) It vibrates only in the even-numbered harmonics 2, 4, 6, 8, ... (e) It vibrates in all harmonics. (f) None; it vibrates as a traveling wave rather than a standing wave. (g) None; it does not vibrate if the arrow leaves it with perfect symmetry as described.

13. A tuning fork by itself produces a faint sound. Try each one of the following four methods for obtaining a louder sound from it. Explain how each method works. Explain also any effect on the time interval for which the fork vibrates audibly. (a) Hold the edge of a sheet of paper against one vibrating tine. (b) Press the handle of the tuning fork against a chalkboard or a tabletop. (c) Hold the tuning fork above a column of air of properly chosen length as in Example 18.6. (d) Hold the tuning fork close to an open slot cut in a sheet of foam plastic or cardboard as shown in Figure Q18.13. The slot should be similar in

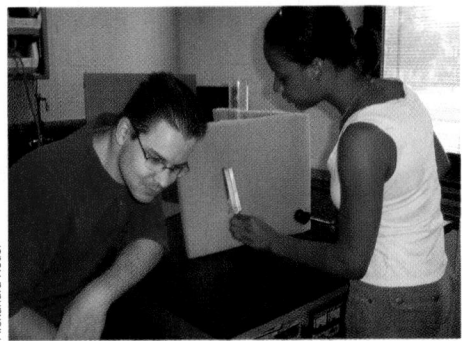

Figure Q18.13

size and shape to one tine of the fork. The motion of the tines should be perpendicular to the sheet.

14. Despite a reasonably steady hand, a person often spills his coffee when carrying it to his seat. Discuss resonance as a possible cause of this difficulty and devise a means for preventing the spills.

15. **O** A tuning fork is known to vibrate with frequency 262 Hz. When it is sounded along with a mandolin string, four beats are heard every second. Next, a bit of tape is put onto each tine of the tuning fork, and the tuning fork now produces five beats per second with the same mandolin string. What is the frequency of the string? (a) 257 Hz (b) 258 Hz (c) 262 Hz (d) 266 Hz (e) 267 Hz (f) This sequence of events could not happen.

16. An airplane mechanic notices that the sound from a twin-engine aircraft rapidly varies in loudness when both engines are running. What could be causing this variation from loud to soft?

Problems

WebAssign The Problems from this chapter may be assigned online in WebAssign.

ThomsonNOW™ Sign in at **www.thomsonedu.com** and go to ThomsonNOW to assess your understanding of this chapter's topics with additional quizzing and conceptual questions.

1, 2, 3 denotes straightforward, intermediate, challenging; ☐ denotes full solution available in *Student Solutions Manual/Study Guide;* ▲ denotes coached solution with hints available at **www.thomsonedu.com;** denotes developing symbolic reasoning; ● denotes asking for qualitative reasoning; ▪ denotes computer useful in solving problem

Section 18.1 Superposition and Interference

1. Two waves in one string are described by the wave functions

$$y_1 = (3.0 \text{ cm}) \cos (4.0x - 1.6t)$$

$$y_2 = (4.0 \text{ cm}) \sin (5.0x - 2.0t)$$

where y and x are in centimeters and t is in seconds. Find the superposition of the waves $y_1 + y_2$ at the points (a) $x = 1.00$, $t = 1.00$; (b) $x = 1.00$, $t = 0.500$; and (c) $x = 0.500$, $t = 0$. (Remember that the arguments of the trigonometric functions are in radians.)

2. Two pulses A and B are moving in opposite directions along a taut string with a speed of 2.00 cm/s. The amplitude of A is twice the amplitude of B. The pulses are shown in Figure P18.2 at $t = 0$. Sketch the shape of the string at $t = 1, 1.5, 2, 2.5,$ and 3 s.

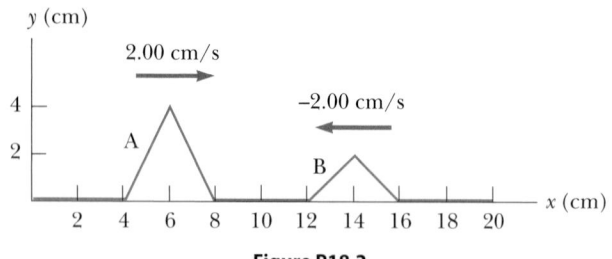

Figure P18.2

3. Two pulses traveling on the same string are described by

$$y_1 = \frac{5}{(3x - 4t)^2 + 2} \qquad y_2 = \frac{-5}{(3x + 4t - 6)^2 + 2}$$

(a) In which direction does each pulse travel? (b) At what instant do the two cancel everywhere? (c) At what point do the two pulses always cancel?

4. Two waves are traveling in the same direction along a stretched string. The waves are 90.0° out of phase. Each wave has an amplitude of 4.00 cm. Find the amplitude of the resultant wave.

5. ▲ Two traveling sinusoidal waves are described by the wave functions

$$y_1 = (5.00 \text{ m}) \sin [\pi(4.00x - 1\,200t)]$$

$$y_2 = (5.00 \text{ m}) \sin [\pi(4.00x - 1\,200t - 0.250)]$$

where x, y_1, and y_2 are in meters and t is in seconds. (a) What is the amplitude of the resultant wave? (b) What is the frequency of the resultant wave?

6. Two identical loudspeakers are placed on a wall 2.00 m apart. A listener stands 3.00 m from the wall directly in front of one of the speakers. A single oscillator is driving the speakers at a frequency of 300 Hz. (a) What is the phase difference between the two waves when they reach the observer? (b) **What If?** What is the frequency closest to 300 Hz to which the oscillator may be adjusted such that the observer hears minimal sound?

7. Two identical loudspeakers are driven by the same oscillator of frequency 200 Hz. The speakers are located on a vertical pole a distance of 4.00 m from each other. A man walks straight toward the lower speaker in a direction perpendicular to the pole as shown in Figure P18.7. (a) How many times will he hear a minimum in sound intensity? (b) How far is he from the pole at these moments? Take the speed of sound to be 330 m/s and ignore any sound reflection from the ground.

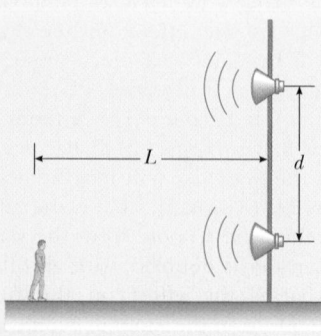

Figure P18.7 Problems 7 and 8.

8. Two identical loudspeakers are driven by the same oscillator of frequency f. The speakers are located a distance d from each other on a vertical pole. A man walks straight toward the lower speaker in a direction perpendicular to the pole as shown in Figure P18.7. (a) How many times will he hear a minimum in sound intensity? (b) How far is he from the pole at these moments? Let v represent the speed of sound and assume the ground does not reflect sound.

9. ▲ Two sinusoidal waves in a string are defined by the functions

$$y_1 = (2.00 \text{ cm}) \sin (20.0x - 32.0t)$$

$$y_2 = (2.00 \text{ cm}) \sin (25.0x - 40.0t)$$

where y_1, y_2, and x are in centimeters and t is in seconds. (a) What is the phase difference between these two waves at the point $x = 5.00$ cm at $t = 2.00$ s? (b) What is the positive x value closest to the origin for which the two phases differ by $\pm\pi$ at $t = 2.00$ s? (That is a location where the two waves add to zero.)

10. ● In air where the speed of sound is 344 m/s, two identical loudspeakers 10.0 m apart are driven by the same oscillator with a frequency of $f = 21.5$ Hz (Fig. P18.10). (a) Explain why a receiver at point A records a minimum in sound intensity from the two speakers. (b) If the receiver is moved in the plane of the speakers, what path should it take so that the intensity remains at a minimum? That is, determine the relationship between x and y (the coordinates of the receiver) that causes the receiver to record a minimum in sound intensity. (c) Can the receiver remain at a minimum and move far away from the two sources? If so, determine the limiting form of the path it must take. If not, explain how far it can go.

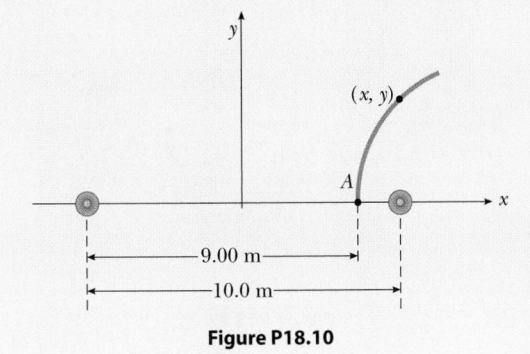

Figure P18.10

Section 18.2 Standing Waves

11. Two sinusoidal waves traveling in opposite directions interfere to produce a standing wave with the wave function

$$y = (1.50 \text{ m}) \sin (0.400x) \cos (200t)$$

where x is in meters and t is in seconds. Determine the wavelength, frequency, and speed of the interfering waves.

12. Verify by direct substitution that the wave function for a standing wave given in Equation 18.1,

$$y = (2A \sin kx) \cos \omega t$$

is a solution of the general linear wave equation, Equation 16.27:

$$\frac{\partial^2 y}{\partial x^2} = \frac{1}{v^2} \frac{\partial^2 y}{\partial t^2}$$

13. ▲ Two identical loudspeakers are driven in phase by a common oscillator at 800 Hz and face each other at a distance of 1.25 m. Locate the points along the line joining the two speakers where relative minima of sound pressure amplitude would be expected. (Use $v = 343$ m/s.)

14. ● ⬚ A standing wave is described by the function

$$y = 6 \sin \left(\frac{\pi}{2} x\right) \cos (100\pi t)$$

where x and y are in meters and t is in seconds. (a) Prepare a graph showing y as a function of x for $t = 0$, for $t = 5$ ms, for $t = 10$ ms, for $t = 15$ ms, and for $t = 20$ ms. (b) From the graph, identify the wavelength of the wave and explain how you do it. (c) From the graph, identify the frequency of the wave and explain how you do it. (d) From the equation, directly identify the wavelength of the wave and explain how you do it. (e) From the equation, directly identify the frequency and explain how you do it.

15. Two sinusoidal waves combining in a medium are described by the wave functions

$$y_1 = (3.0 \text{ cm}) \sin \pi(x + 0.60t)$$

$$y_2 = (3.0 \text{ cm}) \sin \pi(x - 0.60t)$$

where x is in centimeters and t is in seconds. Determine the maximum transverse position of an element of the medium at (a) $x = 0.250$ cm, (b) $x = 0.500$ cm, and (c) $x = 1.50$ cm. (d) Find the three smallest values of x corresponding to antinodes.

16. ● Two waves simultaneously present in a long string are given by the wave functions

$$y_1 = A \sin (kx - \omega t + \phi) \qquad y_2 = A \sin (kx + \omega t)$$

(a) Do the two traveling waves add to give a standing wave? Explain. (b) Is it still true that the nodes are one-half wavelength apart? Argue for your answer. (c) Are the nodes different in any way from the way they would be if ϕ were zero? Explain.

Section 18.3 Standing Waves in a String Fixed at Both Ends

17. Find the fundamental frequency and the next three frequencies that could cause standing wave patterns on a string that is 30.0 m long, has a mass per unit length of 9.00×10^{-3} kg/m, and is stretched to a tension of 20.0 N.

18. A string with a mass of 8.00 g and a length of 5.00 m has one end attached to a wall; the other end is draped over a small fixed pulley and attached to a hanging object with a mass of 4.00 kg. If the string is plucked, what is the fundamental frequency of its vibration?

19. In the arrangement shown in Figure P18.19, an object can be hung from a string (with linear mass density $\mu = 0.002\ 00$ kg/m) that passes over a light pulley. The string is connected to a vibrator (of constant frequency f), and the length of the string between point P and the pulley is $L = 2.00$ m. When the mass m of the object is either 16.0 kg or 25.0 kg, standing waves are observed; no standing waves are observed with any mass between these values, however. (a) What is the frequency of the vibrator? *Note:* The greater the tension in the string, the smaller the number of nodes in the standing wave. (b) What is the

largest object mass for which standing waves could be observed?

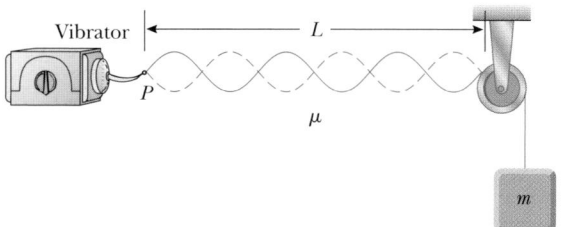

Figure P18.19

20. The top string of a guitar has a fundamental frequency of 330 Hz when it is allowed to vibrate as a whole, along all its 64.0-cm length from the neck to the bridge. A fret is provided for limiting vibration to just the lower two-thirds of the string. If the string is pressed down at this fret and plucked, what is the new fundamental frequency? (b) **What If?** The guitarist can play a "natural harmonic" by gently touching the string at the location of this fret and plucking the string at about one-sixth of the way along its length from the bridge. What frequency will be heard then?

21. The A string on a cello vibrates in its first normal mode with a frequency of 220 Hz. The vibrating segment is 70.0 cm long and has a mass of 1.20 g. (a) Find the tension in the string. (b) Determine the frequency of vibration when the string vibrates in three segments.

22. A violin string has a length of 0.350 m and is tuned to concert G, with $f_G = 392$ Hz. Where must the violinist place her finger to play concert A, with $f_A = 440$ Hz? If this position is to remain correct to one-half the width of a finger (that is, to within 0.600 cm), what is the maximum allowable percentage change in the string tension?

23. **Review problem**. A sphere of mass M is supported by a string that passes over a light horizontal rod of length L (Fig. P18.23). Given that the angle is θ and that f represents the fundamental frequency of standing waves in the portion of the string above the rod, determine the mass of this portion of the string.

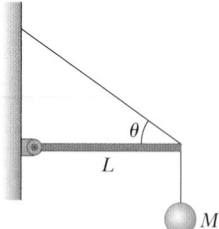

Figure P18.23

24. **Review problem**. A copper cylinder hangs at the bottom of a steel wire of negligible mass. The top end of the wire is fixed. When the wire is struck, it emits sound with a fundamental frequency of 300 Hz. The copper cylinder is then submerged in water so that half its volume is below the water line. Determine the new fundamental frequency.

25. A standing wave pattern is observed in a thin wire with a length of 3.00 m. The wave function is

$$y = (0.002 \text{ m}) \sin (\pi x) \cos (100\pi t)$$

where x is in meters and t is in seconds. (a) How many loops does this pattern exhibit? (b) What is the fundamental frequency of vibration of the wire? (c) **What If?** If the original frequency is held constant and the tension in the wire is increased by a factor of 9, how many loops are present in the new pattern?

Section 18.4 Resonance

26. ● The Bay of Fundy, Nova Scotia, has the highest tides in the world. Assume in midocean and at the mouth of the bay the Moon's gravity gradient and the Earth's rotation make the water surface oscillate with an amplitude of a few centimeters and a period of 12 h 24 min. At the head of the bay, the amplitude is several meters. Argue for or against the proposition that the tide is magnified by standing-wave resonance. Assume the bay has a length of 210 km and a uniform depth of 36.1 m. The speed of long-wavelength water waves is given by $\sqrt{gd}$, where d is the water's depth.

27. An earthquake can produce a *seiche* in a lake in which the water sloshes back and forth from end to end with remarkably large amplitude and long period. Consider a seiche produced in a rectangular farm pond as shown in the cross-sectional view of Figure P18.27. (The figure is not drawn to scale.) Suppose the pond is 9.15 m long and of uniform width and depth. You measure that a pulse produced at one end reaches the other end in 2.50 s. (a) What is the wave speed? (b) To produce the seiche, several people stand on the bank at one end and paddle together with snow shovels, moving them in simple harmonic motion. What should be the frequency of this motion?

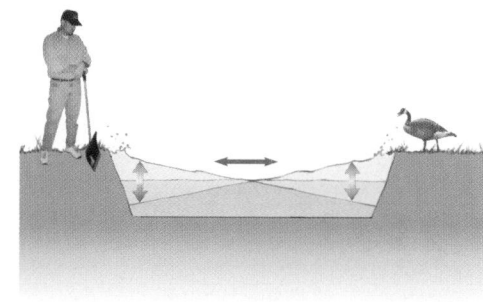

Figure P18.27

28. Figure P18.28a is a photograph of a vibrating wine glass. A special technique makes black and white stripes appear where the glass is moving, with closer spacing where the

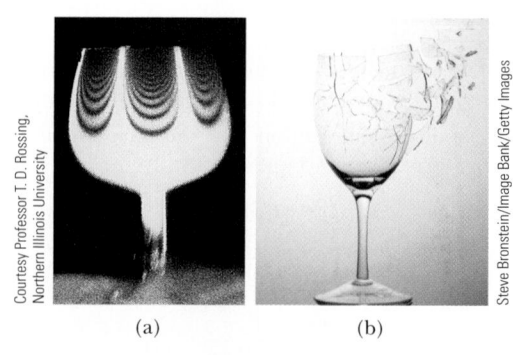

(a)   (b)

Figure P18.28

2 = intermediate;   3 = challenging;   □ = SSM/SG;   ▲ = ThomsonNOW;   ⬜ = symbolic reasoning;   ● = qualitative reasoning

amplitude is larger. Six nodes and six antinodes alternate around the rim of the glass in the vibration photographed, but consider instead the case of a standing-wave vibration with four nodes and four antinodes equally spaced around the 20.0-cm circumference of the rim of a goblet. If transverse waves move around the glass at 900 m/s, an opera singer would have to produce a high harmonic with what frequency to shatter the glass with a resonant vibration as shown in Figure P18.28b?

Section 18.5 Standing Waves in Air Columns

> Note: Unless otherwise specified, assume the speed of sound in air is 343 m/s at 20°C and is described by
>
> $$v = (331 \text{ m/s})\sqrt{1 + \frac{T_C}{273°}}$$
>
> at any Celsius temperature T_C.

29. Calculate the length of a pipe that has a fundamental frequency of 240 Hz assuming the pipe is (a) closed at one end and (b) open at both ends.

30. The overall length of a piccolo is 32.0 cm. The resonating air column vibrates as in a pipe open at both ends. (a) Find the frequency of the lowest note a piccolo can sound, assuming the speed of sound in air is 340 m/s. (b) Opening holes in the side effectively shortens the length of the resonant column. Assume the highest note a piccolo can sound is 4 000 Hz. Find the distance between adjacent antinodes for this mode of vibration.

31. The fundamental frequency of an open organ pipe corresponds to middle C (261.6 Hz on the chromatic musical scale). The third resonance of a closed organ pipe has the same frequency. What is the length of each pipe?

32. ● Do not stick anything into your ear! Estimate the length of your ear canal from its opening at the external ear to the eardrum. If you regard the canal as a narrow tube that is open at one end and closed at the other, at approximately what fundamental frequency would you expect your hearing to be most sensitive? Explain why you can hear especially soft sounds just around this frequency.

33. ▲ A shower stall has dimensions 86.0 cm × 86.0 cm × 210 cm. If you were singing in this shower, which frequencies would sound the richest (because of resonance)? Assume the stall acts as a pipe closed at both ends, with nodes at opposite sides. Assume the voices of various singers range from 130 Hz to 2 000 Hz. Let the speed of sound in the hot air be 355 m/s.

34. As shown in Figure P18.34, water is pumped into a tall vertical cylinder at a volume flow rate R. The radius of the cylinder is r, and at the open top of the cylinder a tuning

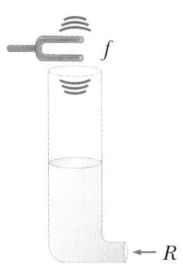

Figure P18.34

fork is vibrating with a frequency f. As the water rises, what time interval elapses between successive resonances?

35. ▲ Two adjacent natural frequencies of an organ pipe are determined to be 550 Hz and 650 Hz. Calculate the fundamental frequency and length of this pipe. (Use $v = 340$ m/s.)

36. ● A tunnel under a river is 2.00 km long. (a) At what frequencies can the air in the tunnel resonate? (b) Explain whether it would be good to make a rule against blowing your car horn when you are in the tunnel.

37. An air column in a glass tube is open at one end and closed at the other by a movable piston. The air in the tube is warmed above room temperature, and a 384-Hz tuning fork is held at the open end. Resonance is heard when the piston is 22.8 cm from the open end and again when it is 68.3 cm from the open end. (a) What speed of sound is implied by these data? (b) How far from the open end will the piston be when the next resonance is heard?

38. A tuning fork with a frequency of 512 Hz is placed near the top of the tube shown in Figure 18.14a. The water level is lowered so that the length L slowly increases from an initial value of 20.0 cm. Determine the next two values of L that correspond to resonant modes.

39. ● A student uses an audio oscillator of adjustable frequency to measure the depth of a water well. The student reports hearing two successive resonances at 51.5 Hz and 60.0 Hz. How deep is the well? Explain the precision you can ascribe to your answer.

40. With a particular fingering, a flute sounds a note with frequency 880 Hz at 20.0°C. The flute is open at both ends. (a) Find the air column length. (b) Find the frequency the flute produces at the beginning of the halftime performance at a late-season American football game, when the ambient temperature is −5.00°C and the musician has not had a chance to warm up the flute.

Section 18.6 Standing Waves in Rods and Membranes

41. An aluminum rod 1.60 m long is held at its center. It is stroked with a rosin-coated cloth to set up a longitudinal vibration. The speed of sound in a thin rod of aluminum is 5 100 m/s. (a) What is the fundamental frequency of the waves established in the rod? (b) What harmonics are set up in the rod held in this manner? (c) **What If?** What would be the fundamental frequency if the rod were copper, in which the speed of sound is 3 560 m/s?

42. An aluminum rod is clamped one-quarter of the way along its length and set into longitudinal vibration by a variable-frequency driving source. The lowest frequency that produces resonance is 4 400 Hz. The speed of sound in an aluminum rod is 5 100 m/s. Determine the length of the rod.

Section 18.7 Beats: Interference in Time

43. ▲ In certain ranges of a piano keyboard, more than one string is tuned to the same note to provide extra loudness. For example, the note at 110 Hz has two strings at this frequency. If one string slips from its normal tension of 600 N to 540 N, what beat frequency is heard when the hammer strikes the two strings simultaneously?

44. While attempting to tune the note C at 523 Hz, a piano tuner hears 2.00 beats/s between a reference oscillator and the string. (a) What are the possible frequencies of the string? (b) When she tightens the string slightly, she hears 3.00 beats/s. What is the frequency of the string now? (c) By what percentage should the piano tuner now change the tension in the string to bring it into tune?

45. A student holds a tuning fork oscillating at 256 Hz. He walks toward a wall at a constant speed of 1.33 m/s. (a) What beat frequency does he observe between the tuning fork and its echo? (b) How fast must he walk away from the wall to observe a beat frequency of 5.00 Hz?

46. When beats occur at a rate higher than about 20 per second, they are not heard individually but rather as a steady hum, called a *combination tone*. The player of a typical pipe organ can press a single key and make the organ produce sound with different fundamental frequencies. She can select and pull out different stops to make the same key for the note C produce sound at the following frequencies: 65.4 Hz from a so-called 8-foot pipe; 2 × 65.4 = 131 Hz from a 4-foot pipe; 3 × 65.4 = 196 Hz from a $2\frac{2}{3}$-foot pipe; 4 × 65.4 = 262 Hz from a 2-foot pipe; or any combination of these sounds. With notes at low frequencies, she obtains sound with the richest quality by pulling out all the stops. When an air leak develops in one of the pipes, that pipe cannot be used. If a leak occurs in an 8-foot pipe, playing a combination of other pipes can create the sensation of sound at the frequency that the 8-foot pipe would produce. Which sets of stops, among those listed, could be pulled out to do that?

Section 18.8 Nonsinusoidal Wave Patterns

47. An A-major chord consists of the notes called A, C#, and E. It can be played on a piano by simultaneously striking strings with fundamental frequencies of 440.00 Hz, 554.37 Hz, and 659.26 Hz. The rich consonance of the chord is associated with near equality of the frequencies of some of the higher harmonics of the three tones. Consider the first five harmonics of each string and determine which harmonics show near equality.

48. Suppose a flutist plays a 523-Hz C note with first harmonic displacement amplitude $A_1 = 100$ nm. From Figure 18.19b, read, by proportion, the displacement amplitudes of harmonics 2 through 7. Take them as the values A_2 through A_7 in the Fourier analysis of the sound and assume $B_1 = B_2 = \ldots = B_7 = 0$. Construct a graph of the waveform of the sound. Your waveform will not look exactly like the flute waveform in Figure 18.18b because you simplify by ignoring cosine terms; nevertheless, it produces the same sensation to human hearing.

Additional Problems

49. **Review problem.** The top end of a yo-yo string is held stationary. The yo-yo itself is much more massive than the string. It starts from rest and moves down with constant acceleration 0.800 m/s² as it unwinds from the string. The rubbing of the string against the edge of the yo-yo excites transverse standing-wave vibrations in the string.

Both ends of the string are nodes even as the length of the string increases. Consider the instant 1.20 s after the motion begins. (a) Show that the rate of change with time of the wavelength of the fundamental mode of oscillation is 1.92 m/s. (b) **What If?** Is the rate of change of the wavelength of the second harmonic also 1.92 m/s at this moment? Explain your answer. (c) **What If?** The experiment is repeated after more mass has been added to the yo-yo body. The mass distribution is kept the same so that the yo-yo still moves with downward acceleration 0.800 m/s². At the 1.20-s point in this case, is the rate of change of the fundamental wavelength of the string vibration still equal to 1.92 m/s? Explain. Is the rate of change of second harmonic wavelength the same as in part (b)? Explain.

50. A loudspeaker at the front of a room and an identical loudspeaker at the rear of the room are being driven by the same oscillator at 456 Hz. A student walks at a uniform rate of 1.50 m/s along the length of the room. She hears a single tone, repeatedly becoming louder and softer. (a) Model these variations as beats between the Doppler-shifted sounds the student receives. Calculate the number of beats the student hears each second. (b) **What If?** Model the two speakers as producing a standing wave in the room and the student as walking between antinodes. Calculate the number of intensity maxima the student hears each second. (c) Explain how the answers to parts (a) and (b) compare with each other.

51. On a marimba (Fig. P18.51), the wooden bar that sounds a tone when struck vibrates in a transverse standing wave having three antinodes and two nodes. The lowest frequency note is 87.0 Hz, produced by a bar 40.0 cm long. (a) Find the speed of transverse waves on the bar. (b) A resonant pipe suspended vertically below the center of the bar enhances the loudness of the emitted sound. If the pipe is open at the top end only and the speed of sound in air is 340 m/s, what is the length of the pipe required to resonate with the bar in part (a)?

Figure P18.51   Marimba players in Mexico City.

52. A nylon string has mass 5.50 g and length 86.0 cm. One end is tied to the floor and the other end to a small magnet, with a mass negligible compared to that of the string. A magnetic field (which we will study in Chapter 29) exerts an upward force of 1.30 N on the magnet wherever the magnet is located. At equilibrium, the string is vertical and motionless, with the magnet at the top. When it is carrying a small-amplitude wave, you may assume the string is always under uniform tension 1.30 N. (a) Find the speed of transverse waves on the string. (b) The string's vibration possibilities are a set of standing-wave states, each with a node at the fixed bottom end and an antinode at the free top end. Find the node–antinode distances for each one of the three simplest states. (c) Find the frequency of each of these states.

53. Two train whistles have identical frequencies of 180 Hz. When one train is at rest in the station and the other is moving nearby, a commuter standing on the station platform hears beats with a frequency of 2.00 beats/s when the whistles operate together. What are the two possible speeds and directions the moving train can have?

54. A string fixed at both ends and having a mass of 4.80 g, a length of 2.00 m, and a tension of 48.0 N vibrates in its second ($n = 2$) normal mode. What is the wavelength in air of the sound emitted by this vibrating string?

55. Two wires are welded together end to end. The wires are made of the same material, but the diameter of one is twice that of the other. They are subjected to a tension of 4.60 N. The thin wire has a length of 40.0 cm and a linear mass density of 2.00 g/m. The combination is fixed at both ends and vibrated in such a way that two antinodes are present, with the node between them being precisely at the weld. (a) What is the frequency of vibration? (b) What is the length of the thick wire?

56. A string of linear density 1.60 g/m is stretched between clamps 48.0 cm apart. The string does not stretch appreciably as the tension in it is steadily raised from 15.0 N at $t = 0$ to 25.0 N at $t = 3.50$ s. Therefore, the tension as a function of time is given by the expression $T = 15.0$ N + (10.0 N)$t/3.50$ s. The string is vibrating in its fundamental mode throughout this process. Find the number of oscillations it completes during the 3.50-s interval.

57. A standing wave is set up in a string of variable length and tension by a vibrator of variable frequency. Both ends of the string are fixed. When the vibrator has a frequency f, in a string of length L and under tension T, n antinodes are set up in the string. (a) If the length of the string is doubled, by what factor should the frequency be changed so that the same number of antinodes is produced? (b) If the frequency and length are held constant, what tension will produce $n + 1$ antinodes? (c) If the frequency is tripled and the length of the string is halved, by what factor should the tension be changed so that twice as many antinodes are produced?

58. **Review problem**. For the arrangement shown in Figure P18.58, $\theta = 30.0°$, the inclined plane and the small pulley

are frictionless, the string supports the object of mass M at the bottom of the plane, and the string has mass m that is small compared with M. The system is in equilibrium, and the vertical part of the string has a length h. Standing waves are set up in the vertical section of the string. (a) Find the tension in the string. (b) Model the shape of the string as one leg and the hypotenuse of a right triangle. Find the whole length of the string. (c) Find the mass per unit length of the string. (d) Find the speed of waves on the string. (e) Find the lowest frequency for a standing wave. (f) Find the period of the standing wave having three nodes. (g) Find the wavelength of the standing wave having three nodes. (h) Find the frequency of the beats resulting from the interference of the sound wave of lowest frequency generated by the string with another sound wave having a frequency that is 2.00% greater.

59. Two waves are described by the wave functions

$$y_1(x, t) = (5.0 \text{ m}) \sin (2.0x - 10t)$$

$$y_2(x, t) = (10 \text{ m}) \cos (2.0x - 10t)$$

where y_1, y_2, and x are in meters and t is in seconds. Show that the wave resulting from their superposition is also sinusoidal. Determine the amplitude and phase of this sinusoidal wave.

60. A quartz watch contains a crystal oscillator in the form of a block of quartz that vibrates by contracting and expanding. Two opposite faces of the block, 7.05 mm apart, are antinodes, moving alternately toward each other and away from each other. The plane halfway between these two faces is a node of the vibration. The speed of sound in quartz is 3.70 km/s. Find the frequency of the vibration. An oscillating electric voltage accompanies the mechanical oscillation; the quartz is described as *piezoelectric*. An electric circuit feeds in energy to maintain the oscillation and also counts the voltage pulses to keep time.

61. **Review problem**. A 12.0-kg object hangs in equilibrium from a string with a total length of $L = 5.00$ m and a linear mass density of $\mu = 0.001\,00$ kg/m. The string is wrapped around two light, frictionless pulleys that are separated by a distance of $d = 2.00$ m (Fig. P18.61a). (a) Determine the tension in the string. (b) At what frequency must the string between the pulleys vibrate to form the standing wave pattern shown in Figure P18.61b?

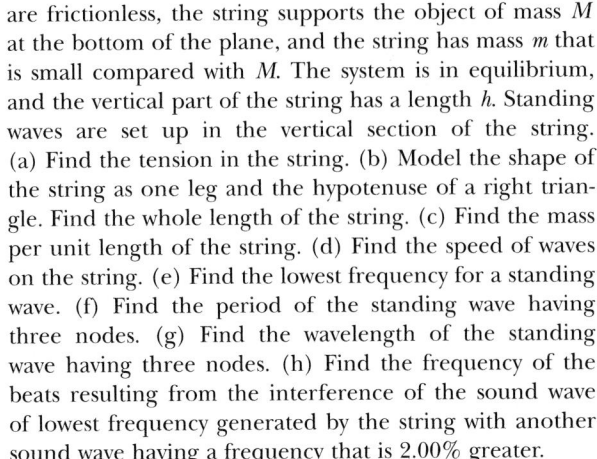

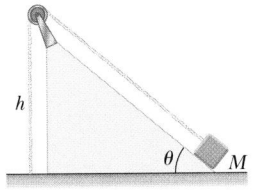

Figure P18.58

Figure P18.61

Answers to Quick Quizzes

18.1 (c). The pulses completely cancel each other in terms of displacement of elements of the string from equilibrium, but the string is still moving. A short time later, the string will be displaced again and the pulses will have passed each other.

18.2 (i), (a). The pattern shown at the bottom of Active Figure 18.8a corresponds to the extreme position of the string. All elements of the string have momentarily come to rest. (ii), (d). Near a nodal point, elements on one side of the point are moving upward at this instant and elements on the other side are moving downward.

18.3 (d). Choice (a) is incorrect because the number of nodes is one greater than the number of antinodes. Choice (b) is only true for half of the modes; it is not true for any odd-numbered mode. Choice (c) would be correct if we replace the word *nodes* with *antinodes*.

18.4 (b). With both ends open, the pipe has a fundamental frequency given by Equation 18.8: $f_{open} = v/2L$. With one end closed, the pipe has a fundamental frequency given by Equation 18.9:

$$f_{closed} = \frac{v}{4L} = \tfrac{1}{2}\frac{v}{2L} = \tfrac{1}{2}f_{open}$$

18.5 (c). The increase in temperature causes the speed of sound to go up. According to Equation 18.8, the result is an increase in the fundamental frequency of a given organ pipe.

PART 3

Thermodynamics

We now direct our attention to the study of thermodynamics, which involves situations in which the temperature or state (solid, liquid, gas) of a system changes due to energy transfers. As we shall see, thermodynamics is very successful in explaining the bulk properties of matter and the correlation between these properties and the mechanics of atoms and molecules.

Historically, the development of thermodynamics paralleled the development of the atomic theory of matter. By the 1820s, chemical experiments had provided solid evidence for the existence of atoms. At that time, scientists recognized that a connection between thermodynamics and the structure of matter must exist. In 1827, botanist Robert Brown reported that grains of pollen suspended in a liquid move erratically from one place to another as if under constant agitation. In 1905, Albert Einstein used kinetic theory to explain the cause of this erratic motion, known today as *Brownian motion*. Einstein explained this phenomenon by assuming the grains are under constant bombardment by "invisible" molecules in the liquid, which themselves move erratically. This explanation gave scientists insight into the concept of molecular motion and gave credence to the idea that matter is made up of atoms. A connection was thus forged between the everyday world and the tiny, invisible building blocks that make up this world.

Thermodynamics also addresses more practical questions. Have you ever wondered how a refrigerator is able to cool its contents, or what types of transformations occur in a power plant or in the engine of your automobile, or what happens to the kinetic energy of a moving object when the object comes to rest? The laws of thermodynamics can be used to provide explanations for these and other phenomena.

The Alyeska oil pipeline near the Tazlina River in Alaska. The oil in the pipeline is warm, and energy transferring from the pipeline could melt environmentally sensitive permafrost in the ground. The finned structures on top of the support posts are thermal radiators that allow the energy to be transferred into the air to protect the permafrost. (Topham Picturepoint/ The Image Works)

Why would someone designing a pipeline include these strange loops? Pipelines carrying liquids often contain such loops to allow for expansion and contraction as the temperature changes. We will study thermal expansion in this chapter. (Lowell Georgia/CORBIS)

19 Temperature

In our study of mechanics, we carefully defined such concepts as *mass, force,* **and** *kinetic energy* to facilitate our quantitative approach. Likewise, a quantitative description of thermal phenomena requires careful definitions of such important terms as *temperature, heat,* and *internal energy*. This chapter begins with a discussion of temperature.

Next, we consider the importance when studying thermal phenomena of the particular substance we are investigating. For example, gases expand appreciably when heated, whereas liquids and solids expand only slightly.

This chapter concludes with a study of ideal gases on the macroscopic scale. Here, we are concerned with the relationships among such quantities as pressure, volume, and temperature of a gas. In Chapter 21, we shall examine gases on a microscopic scale, using a model that represents the components of a gas as small particles.

19.1 Temperature and the Zeroth Law of Thermodynamics

We often associate the concept of temperature with how hot or cold an object feels when we touch it. In this way, our senses provide us with a qualitative indication of temperature. Our senses, however, are unreliable and often mislead us. For

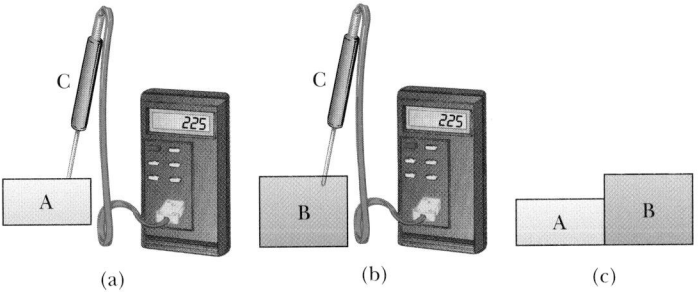

Figure 19.1   The zeroth law of thermodynamics. (a, b) If the temperatures of A and B are measured to be the same by placing them in thermal contact with a thermometer (object C), no energy will be exchanged between them when they are placed in thermal contact with each other (c).

example, if you remove a metal ice tray and a cardboard box of frozen vegetables from the freezer, the ice tray feels colder than the box *even though both are at the same temperature.* The two objects feel different because metal transfers energy by heat at a higher rate than cardboard does. What we need is a reliable and reproducible method for measuring the relative hotness or coldness of objects rather than the rate of energy transfer. Scientists have developed a variety of thermometers for making such quantitative measurements.

Two objects at different initial temperatures eventually reach some intermediate temperature when placed in contact with each other. For example, when hot water and cold water are mixed in a bathtub, the final temperature of the mixture is somewhere between the initial hot and cold temperatures. Likewise, when an ice cube is dropped into a cup of hot coffee, the ice cube melts and the coffee's temperature decreases.

Imagine that two objects are placed in an insulated container such that they interact with each other but not with the environment. If the objects are at different temperatures, energy is transferred between them, even if they are initially not in physical contact with each other. The energy transfer mechanisms from Chapter 8 that we will focus on are heat and electromagnetic radiation. For purposes of this discussion, let's assume two objects are in **thermal contact** with each other if energy can be exchanged between them by these processes due to a temperature difference. **Thermal equilibrium** is a situation in which two objects would not exchange energy by heat or electromagnetic radiation if they were placed in thermal contact.

Let's consider two objects A and B, which are not in thermal contact, and a third object C, which is our thermometer. We wish to determine whether A and B are in thermal equilibrium with each other. The thermometer (object C) is first placed in thermal contact with object A until thermal equilibrium is reached[1] as shown in Figure 19.1a. From that moment on, the thermometer's reading remains constant and we record this reading. The thermometer is then removed from object A and placed in thermal contact with object B as shown in Figure 19.1b. The reading is again recorded after thermal equilibrium is reached. If the two readings are the same, object A and object B are in thermal equilibrium with each other. If they are placed in contact with each other as in Figure 19.1c, there is no exchange of energy between them.

We can summarize these results in a statement known as the **zeroth law of thermodynamics** (the law of equilibrium):

> If objects A and B are separately in thermal equilibrium with a third object C, then A and B are in thermal equilibrium with each other.

◄   Zeroth law of
    thermodynamics

---

[1] We assume a negligible amount of energy transfers between the thermometer and object A during the equilibrium process. Without this assumption, which is also made for the thermometer and object B, the measurement of the temperature of an object disturbs the system so that the measured temperature is different from the initial temperature of the object. In practice, whenever you measure a temperature with a thermometer, you measure the disturbed system, not the original system.

This statement can easily be proved experimentally and is very important because it enables us to define temperature. We can think of **temperature** as the property that determines whether an object is in thermal equilibrium with other objects. **Two objects in thermal equilibrium with each other are at the same temperature.** Conversely, if two objects have different temperatures, they are not in thermal equilibrium with each other.

Quick Quiz 19.1 Two objects, with different sizes, masses, and temperatures, are placed in thermal contact. In which direction does the energy travel? (a) Energy travels from the larger object to the smaller object. (b) Energy travels from the object with more mass to the one with less mass. (c) Energy travels from the object at higher temperature to the object at lower temperature.

19.2 Thermometers and the Celsius Temperature Scale

Thermometers are devices used to measure the temperature of a system. All thermometers are based on the principle that some physical property of a system changes as the system's temperature changes. Some physical properties that change with temperature are (1) the volume of a liquid, (2) the dimensions of a solid, (3) the pressure of a gas at constant volume, (4) the volume of a gas at constant pressure, (5) the electric resistance of a conductor, and (6) the color of an object.

A common thermometer in everyday use consists of a mass of liquid—usually mercury or alcohol—that expands into a glass capillary tube when heated (Fig. 19.2). In this case, the physical property that changes is the volume of a liquid. Any temperature change in the range of the thermometer can be defined as being proportional to the change in length of the liquid column. The thermometer can be calibrated by placing it in thermal contact with a natural system that remains at constant temperature. One such system is a mixture of water and ice in thermal equilibrium at atmospheric pressure. On the **Celsius temperature scale,** this mixture is defined to have a temperature of zero degrees Celsius, which is written as 0°C; this temperature is called the *ice point* of water. Another commonly used system is a mixture of water and steam in thermal equilibrium at atmospheric pressure; its temperature is defined as 100°C, which is the *steam point* of water. Once the liquid levels in the thermometer have been established at these two points, the

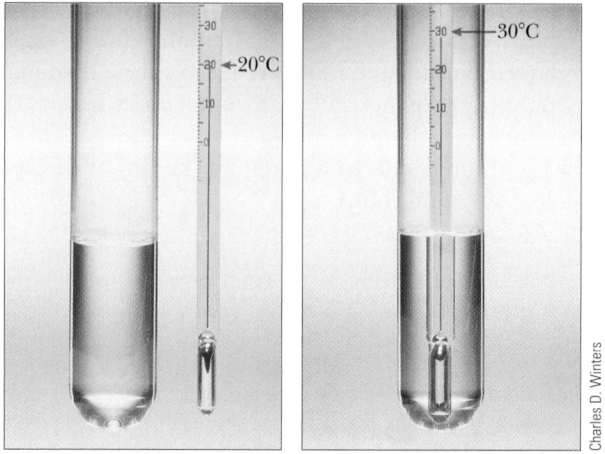

Figure 19.2 As a result of thermal expansion, the level of the mercury in the thermometer rises as the mercury is heated by water in the test tube.

length of the liquid column between the two points is divided into 100 equal segments to create the Celsius scale. Therefore, each segment denotes a change in temperature of one Celsius degree.

Thermometers calibrated in this way present problems when extremely accurate readings are needed. For instance, the readings given by an alcohol thermometer calibrated at the ice and steam points of water might agree with those given by a mercury thermometer only at the calibration points. Because mercury and alcohol have different thermal expansion properties, when one thermometer reads a temperature of, for example, 50°C, the other may indicate a slightly different value. The discrepancies between thermometers are especially large when the temperatures to be measured are far from the calibration points.[2]

An additional practical problem of any thermometer is the limited range of temperatures over which it can be used. A mercury thermometer, for example, cannot be used below the freezing point of mercury, which is −39°C, and an alcohol thermometer is not useful for measuring temperatures above 85°C, the boiling point of alcohol. To surmount this problem, we need a universal thermometer whose readings are independent of the substance used in it. The gas thermometer, discussed in the next section, approaches this requirement.

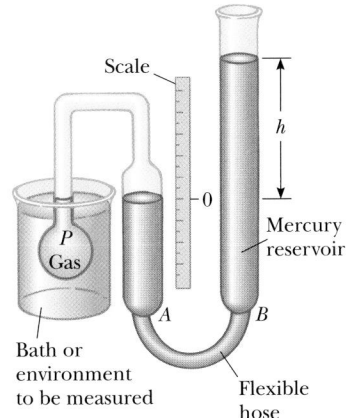

Figure 19.3 A constant-volume gas thermometer measures the pressure of the gas contained in the flask immersed in the bath. The volume of gas in the flask is kept constant by raising or lowering reservoir *B* to keep the mercury level in column *A* constant.

19.3 The Constant-Volume Gas Thermometer and the Absolute Temperature Scale

One version of a gas thermometer is the constant-volume apparatus shown in Figure 19.3. The physical change exploited in this device is the variation of pressure of a fixed volume of gas with temperature. The flask is immersed in an ice-water bath, and mercury reservoir *B* is raised or lowered until the top of the mercury in column *A* is at the zero point on the scale. The height *h*, the difference between the mercury levels in reservoir *B* and column *A*, indicates the pressure in the flask at 0°C.

The flask is then immersed in water at the steam point. Reservoir *B* is readjusted until the top of the mercury in column *A* is again at zero on the scale, which ensures that the gas's volume is the same as it was when the flask was in the ice bath (hence the designation "constant volume"). This adjustment of reservoir *B* gives a value for the gas pressure at 100°C. These two pressure and temperature values are then plotted as shown in Figure 19.4. The line connecting the two points serves as a calibration curve for unknown temperatures. (Other experiments show that a linear relationship between pressure and temperature is a very good assumption.) To measure the temperature of a substance, the gas flask of Figure 19.3 is placed in thermal contact with the substance and the height of reservoir *B* is adjusted until the top of the mercury column in *A* is at zero on the scale. The height of the mercury column in *B* indicates the pressure of the gas; knowing the pressure, the temperature of the substance is found using the graph in Figure 19.4.

Now suppose temperatures of different gases at different initial pressures are measured with gas thermometers. Experiments show that the thermometer readings are nearly independent of the type of gas used as long as the gas pressure is low and the temperature is well above the point at which the gas liquefies (Fig. 19.5). The agreement among thermometers using various gases improves as the pressure is reduced.

If we extend the straight lines in Figure 19.5 toward negative temperatures, we find a remarkable result: **in every case, the pressure is zero when the temperature is −273.15°C!** This finding suggests some special role that this particular temperature must play. It is used as the basis for the **absolute temperature scale,** which sets

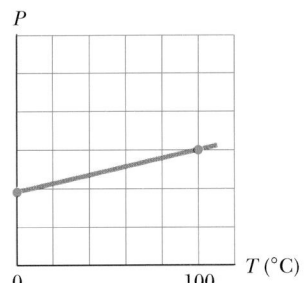

Figure 19.4 A typical graph of pressure versus temperature taken with a constant-volume gas thermometer. The two dots represent known reference temperatures (the ice and steam points of water).

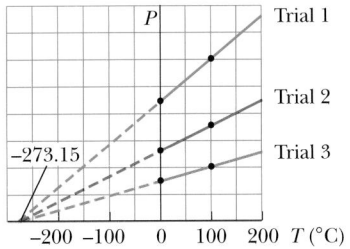

Figure 19.5 Pressure versus temperature for experimental trials in which gases have different pressures in a constant-volume gas thermometer. Notice that, for all three trials, the pressure extrapolates to zero at the temperature −273.15°C.

[2] Two thermometers that use the same liquid may also give different readings, due in part to difficulties in constructing uniform-bore glass capillary tubes.

−273.15°C as its zero point. This temperature is often referred to as **absolute zero**. It is indicated as a zero because at a lower temperature, the pressure of the gas would become negative, which is meaningless. The size of one degree on the absolute temperature scale is chosen to be identical to the size of one degree on the Celsius scale. Therefore, the conversion between these temperatures is

$$T_C = T - 273.15 \tag{19.1}$$

where T_C is the Celsius temperature and T is the absolute temperature.

Because the ice and steam points are experimentally difficult to duplicate and depend on atmospheric pressure, an absolute temperature scale based on two new fixed points was adopted in 1954 by the International Committee on Weights and Measures. The first point is absolute zero. The second reference temperature for this new scale was chosen as the **triple point of water,** which is the single combination of temperature and pressure at which liquid water, gaseous water, and ice (solid water) coexist in equilibrium. This triple point occurs at a temperature of 0.01°C and a pressure of 4.58 mm of mercury. On the new scale, which uses the unit *kelvin*, the temperature of water at the triple point was set at 273.16 kelvins, abbreviated 273.16 K. This choice was made so that the old absolute temperature scale based on the ice and steam points would agree closely with the new scale based on the triple point. This new absolute temperature scale (also called the **Kelvin scale**) employs the SI unit of absolute temperature, the **kelvin,** which is defined to be **1/273.16 of the difference between absolute zero and the temperature of the triple point of water**.

Figure 19.6 gives the absolute temperature for various physical processes and structures. The temperature of absolute zero (0 K) cannot be achieved, although laboratory experiments have come very close, reaching temperatures of less than one nanokelvin.

The Celsius, Fahrenheit, and Kelvin Temperature Scales[3]

Equation 19.1 shows that the Celsius temperature T_C is shifted from the absolute (Kelvin) temperature T by 273.15°. Because the size of one degree is the same on the two scales, a temperature difference of 5°C is equal to a temperature difference of 5 K. The two scales differ only in the choice of the zero point. Therefore, the ice-point temperature on the Kelvin scale, 273.15 K, corresponds to 0.00°C, and the Kelvin-scale steam point, 373.15 K, is equivalent to 100.00°C.

A common temperature scale in everyday use in the United States is the **Fahrenheit scale**. This scale sets the temperature of the ice point at 32°F and the temperature of the steam point at 212°F. The relationship between the Celsius and Fahrenheit temperature scales is

$$T_F = \tfrac{9}{5} T_C + 32°F \tag{19.2}$$

We can use Equations 19.1 and 19.2 to find a relationship between changes in temperature on the Celsius, Kelvin, and Fahrenheit scales:

$$\Delta T_C = \Delta T = \tfrac{5}{9} \Delta T_F \tag{19.3}$$

Of these three temperature scales, only the Kelvin scale is based on a true zero value of temperature. The Celsius and Fahrenheit scales are based on an arbitrary zero associated with one particular substance, water, on one particular planet, Earth. Therefore, if you encounter an equation that calls for a temperature T or that involves a ratio of temperatures, you *must* convert all temperatures to kelvins. If the equation contains a change in temperature ΔT, using Celsius temperatures will give you the correct answer, in light of Equation 19.3, but it is always *safest* to convert temperatures to the Kelvin scale.

[3] Named after Anders Celsius (1701–1744), Daniel Gabriel Fahrenheit (1686–1736), and William Thomson, Lord Kelvin (1824–1907), respectively.

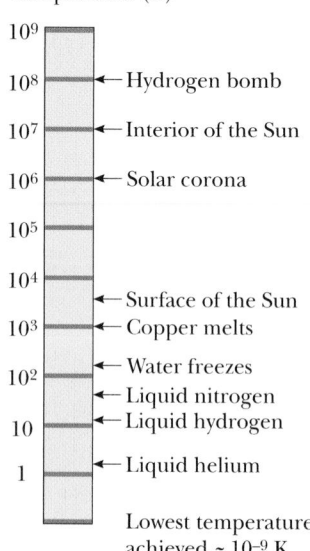

Temperature (K)

10^9

10^8 ← Hydrogen bomb

10^7 ← Interior of the Sun

10^6 ← Solar corona

10^5

10^4

     ← Surface of the Sun
10^3 ← Copper melts

10^2 ← Water freezes
     ← Liquid nitrogen
10 ← Liquid hydrogen

1 ← Liquid helium

Lowest temperature achieved ~ 10^{-9} K

Figure 19.6 Absolute temperatures at which various physical processes occur. Notice that the scale is logarithmic.

Quick Quiz 19.2   Consider the following pairs of materials. Which pair represents two materials, one of which is twice as hot as the other? (a) boiling water at 100°C, a glass of water at 50°C   (b) boiling water at 100°C, frozen methane at −50°C (c) an ice cube at −20°C, flames from a circus fire-eater at 233°C   (d) none of these pairs

---

EXAMPLE 19.1 | **Converting Temperatures**

On a day when the temperature reaches 50°F, what is the temperature in degrees Celsius and in kelvins?

SOLUTION

Conceptualize   In the United States, a temperature of 50°F is well understood. In many other parts of the world, however, this temperature might be meaningless because people are familiar with the Celsius temperature scale.

Categorize   This example is a simple substitution problem.

Substitute the given temperature into Equation 19.2: $T_C = \frac{5}{9}(T_F - 32) = \frac{5}{9}(50 - 32) = \boxed{10°C}$

Use Equation 19.1 to find the Kelvin temperature: $T = T_C + 273.15 = 10°C + 273.15 = \boxed{283\ K}$

A convenient set of weather-related temperature equivalents to keep in mind is that 0°C is (literally) freezing at 32°F, 10°C is cool at 50°F, 20°C is room temperature, 30°C is warm at 86°F, and 40°C is a hot day at 104°F.

19.4 Thermal Expansion of Solids and Liquids

Our discussion of the liquid thermometer makes use of one of the best-known changes in a substance: as its temperature increases, its volume increases. This phenomenon, known as **thermal expansion,** plays an important role in numerous engineering applications. For example, thermal-expansion joints such as those shown in Figure 19.7 must be included in buildings, concrete highways, railroad tracks, brick walls, and bridges to compensate for dimensional changes that occur as the temperature changes.

Thermal expansion is a consequence of the change in the *average* separation between the atoms in an object. To understand this concept, let's model the atoms as being connected by stiff springs as discussed in Section 15.3 and shown

(a)

(b)

Figure 19.7   (a) Thermal-expansion joints are used to separate sections of roadways on bridges. Without these joints, the surfaces would buckle due to thermal expansion on very hot days or crack due to contraction on very cold days. (b) The long, vertical joint is filled with a soft material that allows the wall to expand and contract as the temperature of the bricks changes.

in Figure 15.11b. At ordinary temperatures, the atoms in a solid oscillate about their equilibrium positions with an amplitude of approximately 10^{-11} m and a frequency of approximately 10^{13} Hz. The average spacing between the atoms is about 10^{-10} m. As the temperature of the solid increases, the atoms oscillate with greater amplitudes; as a result, the average separation between them increases.[4] Consequently, the object expands.

If thermal expansion is sufficiently small relative to an object's initial dimensions, the change in any dimension is, to a good approximation, proportional to the first power of the temperature change. Suppose an object has an initial length L_i along some direction at some temperature and the length increases by an amount ΔL for a change in temperature ΔT. Because it is convenient to consider the fractional change in length per degree of temperature change, we define the **average coefficient of linear expansion** as

$$\alpha \equiv \frac{\Delta L / L_i}{\Delta T}$$

PITFALL PREVENTION 19.2
Do Holes Become Larger or Smaller?

When an object's temperature is raised, every linear dimension increases in size. That includes any holes in the material, which expand in the same way as if the hole were filled with the material as shown in Active Figure 19.8. Keep in mind the notion of thermal expansion as being similar to a photographic enlargement.

Experiments show that α is constant for small changes in temperature. For purposes of calculation, this equation is usually rewritten as

$$\Delta L = \alpha L_i \, \Delta T \tag{19.4}$$

or as

$$L_f - L_i = \alpha L_i (T_f - T_i) \tag{19.5}$$

where L_f is the final length, T_i and T_f are the initial and final temperatures, respectively, and the proportionality constant α is the average coefficient of linear expansion for a given material and has units of $(°C)^{-1}$.

It may be helpful to think of thermal expansion as an effective magnification or as a photographic enlargement of an object. For example, as a metal washer is heated (Active Fig. 19.8), all dimensions, including the radius of the hole, increase according to Equation 19.4. **A cavity in a piece of material expands in the same way as if the cavity were filled with the material**.

Table 19.1 lists the average coefficients of linear expansion for various materials. For these materials, α is positive, indicating an increase in length with increasing temperature. That is not always the case, however. Some substances—calcite ($CaCO_3$) is one example—expand along one dimension (positive α) and contract along another (negative α) as their temperatures are increased.

Because the linear dimensions of an object change with temperature, it follows that surface area and volume change as well. The change in volume is proportional to the initial volume V_i and to the change in temperature according to the relationship

$$\Delta V = \beta V_i \, \Delta T \tag{19.6}$$

where β is the **average coefficient of volume expansion**. To find the relationship between β and α, assume the average coefficient of linear expansion of the solid is the same in all directions; that is, assume the material is *isotropic*. Consider a solid box of dimensions ℓ, w, and h. Its volume at some temperature T_i is $V_i = \ell w h$. If the temperature changes to $T_i + \Delta T$, its volume changes to $V_i + \Delta V$, where each dimension changes according to Equation 19.4. Therefore,

$$V_i + \Delta V = (\ell + \Delta \ell)(w + \Delta w)(h + \Delta h)$$

$$= (\ell + \alpha \ell \, \Delta T)(w + \alpha w \, \Delta T)(h + \alpha h \, \Delta T)$$

$$= \ell w h (1 + \alpha \, \Delta T)^3$$

$$= V_i [1 + 3\alpha \, \Delta T + 3(\alpha \, \Delta T)^2 + (\alpha \, \Delta T)^3]$$

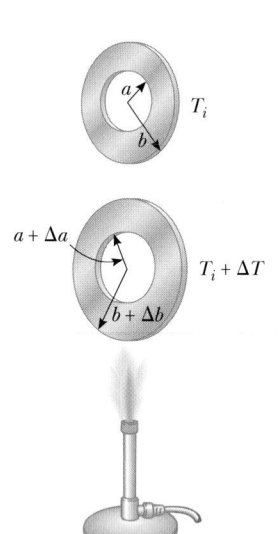

ACTIVE FIGURE 19.8

Thermal expansion of a homogeneous metal washer. As the washer is heated, all dimensions increase. (The expansion is exaggerated in this figure.)

Sign in at www.thomsonedu.com and go to ThomsonNOW to compare expansions for various temperatures of the burner and materials from which the washer is made.

[4] More precisely, thermal expansion arises from the *asymmetrical* nature of the potential energy curve for the atoms in a solid as shown in Figure 15.11a. If the oscillators were truly harmonic, the average atomic separations would not change regardless of the amplitude of vibration.

TABLE 19.1

Average Expansion Coefficients for Some Materials Near Room Temperature

Material	Average Linear Expansion Coefficient (α) $(°C)^{-1}$	Material	Average Volume Expansion Coefficient (β) $(°C)^{-1}$
Aluminum	24×10^{-6}	Alcohol, ethyl	1.12×10^{-4}
Brass and bronze	19×10^{-6}	Benzene	1.24×10^{-4}
Copper	17×10^{-6}	Acetone	1.5×10^{-4}
Glass (ordinary)	9×10^{-6}	Glycerin	4.85×10^{-4}
Glass (Pyrex)	3.2×10^{-6}	Mercury	1.82×10^{-4}
Lead	29×10^{-6}	Turpentine	9.0×10^{-4}
Steel	11×10^{-6}	Gasoline	9.6×10^{-4}
Invar (Ni–Fe alloy)	0.9×10^{-6}	Air[a] at 0°C	3.67×10^{-3}
Concrete	12×10^{-6}	Helium[a]	3.665×10^{-3}

[a] Gases do not have a specific value for the volume expansion coefficient because the amount of expansion depends on the type of process through which the gas is taken. The values given here assume the gas undergoes an expansion at constant pressure.

Dividing both sides by V_i and isolating the term $\Delta V/V_i$, we obtain the fractional change in volume:

$$\frac{\Delta V}{V_i} = 3\alpha \, \Delta T + 3(\alpha \, \Delta T)^2 + (\alpha \, \Delta T)^3$$

Because $\alpha \, \Delta T << 1$ for typical values of ΔT $(< \sim 100°C)$, we can neglect the terms $3(\alpha \, \Delta T)^2$ and $(\alpha \, \Delta T)^3$. Upon making this approximation, we see that

$$\frac{\Delta V}{V_i} = 3\alpha \, \Delta T \quad \rightarrow \quad \Delta V = (3\alpha)V_i \, \Delta T$$

Comparing this expression to Equation 19.6 shows that

$$\beta = 3\alpha$$

In a similar way, you can show that the change in area of a rectangular plate is given by $\Delta A = 2\alpha A_i \, \Delta T$ (see Problem 41).

As Table 19.1 indicates, each substance has its own characteristic average coefficient of expansion. A simple mechanism called a *bimetallic strip*, found in practical devices such as thermostats, uses the difference in coefficients of expansion for different materials. It consists of two thin strips of dissimilar metals bonded together. As the temperature of the strip increases, the two metals expand by different amounts and the strip bends as shown in Figure 19.9.

Quick Quiz 19.3   If you are asked to make a very sensitive glass thermometer, which of the following working liquids would you choose? (a) mercury   (b) alcohol   (c) gasoline   (d) glycerin

Quick Quiz 19.4   Two spheres are made of the same metal and have the same radius, but one is hollow and the other is solid. The spheres are taken through the same temperature increase. Which sphere expands more? (a) The solid sphere expands more. (b) The hollow sphere expands more. (c) They expand by the same amount. (d) There is not enough information to say.

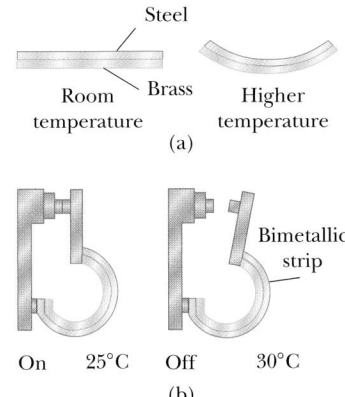

Figure 19.9   (a) A bimetallic strip bends as the temperature changes because the two metals have different expansion coefficients. (b) A bimetallic strip used in a thermostat to break or make electrical contact.

EXAMPLE 19.2   **Expansion of a Railroad Track**

A segment of steel railroad track has a length of 30.000 m when the temperature is 0.0°C.

(A) What is its length when the temperature is 40.0°C?

SOLUTION

Conceptualize   Because the rail is relatively long, we expect to obtain a measurable increase in length for a 40°C temperature increase.

Categorize   We will evaluate a length increase using the discussion of this section, so this example is a substitution problem.

Use Equation 19.4 and the value of the coeffi- $\Delta L = \alpha L_i \, \Delta T = [11 \times 10^{-6}(°C)^{-1}](30.000 \text{ m})(40.0°C) = 0.013 \text{ m}$
cient of linear expansion from Table 19.1:

Find the new length of the track: $L_f = 30.000 \text{ m} + 0.013 \text{ m} = \boxed{30.013 \text{ m}}$

(B) Suppose the ends of the rail are rigidly clamped at 0.0°C so that expansion is prevented. What is the thermal stress set up in the rail if its temperature is raised to 40.0°C?

SOLUTION

Categorize   This part of the example is an analysis problem because we need to use concepts from another chapter.

Analyze   The thermal stress is the same as the tensile stress in the situation in which the rail expands freely and is then compressed with a mechanical force F back to its original length.

Find the tensile stress from Equation 12.6 using $\text{Tensile stress} = \dfrac{F}{A} = Y\dfrac{\Delta L}{L_i}$
Young's modulus for steel from Table 12.1:

$$\frac{F}{A} = (20 \times 10^{10} \text{ N/m}^2)\left(\frac{0.013 \text{ m}}{30.000 \text{ m}}\right) = \boxed{8.7 \times 10^7 \text{ N/m}^2}$$

Finalize   The expansion in part (A) is 1.3 cm. This expansion is indeed measurable as predicted in the Conceptualize step. The thermal stress in part (B) can be avoided by leaving small expansion gaps between the rails.

What If?   What if the temperature drops to −40.0° C? What is the length of the unclamped segment?

Answer   The expression for the change in length in Equation 19.4 is the same whether the temperature increases or decreases. Therefore, if there is an increase in length of 0.013 m when the temperature increases by 40°C, there is a decrease in length of 0.013 m when the temperature decreases by 40°C. (We assume α is constant over the entire range of temperatures.) The new length at the colder temperature is 30.000 m − 0.013 m = 29.987 m.

EXAMPLE 19.3   **The Thermal Electrical Short**

A poorly designed electronic device has two bolts attached to different parts of the device that almost touch each other in its interior as in Figure 19.10. The steel and brass bolts are at different electric potentials, and if they touch, a short circuit will develop, damaging the device. (We will study electric potential in Chapter 25.) The initial gap between the ends of the bolts is 5.0 μm at 27°C. At what temperature will the bolts touch? Assume that the distance between the walls of the device is not affected by the temperature change.

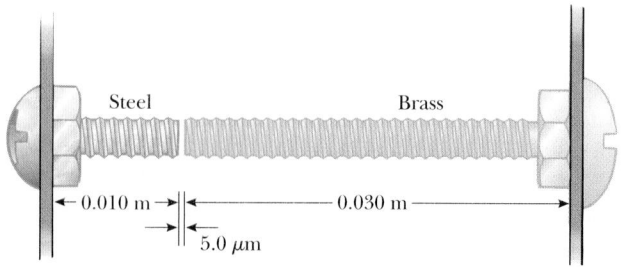

Figure 19.10   (Example 19.3) Two bolts attached to different parts of an electrical device are almost touching when the temperature is 27°C. As the temperature increases, the ends of the bolts move toward each other.

SOLUTION

Conceptualize   Imagine the ends of both bolts expanding into the gap between them as the temperature rises.

Categorize   We categorize this example as a thermal expansion problem in which the *sum* of the changes in length of the two bolts must equal the length of the initial gap between the ends.

Analyze   Set the sum of the length changes equal to the width of the gap:

$$\Delta L_{br} + \Delta L_{st} = \alpha_{br} L_{i,br}\, \Delta T + \alpha_{st} L_{i,st}\, \Delta T = 5.0 \times 10^{-6}\text{ m}$$

Solve for ΔT:

$$\Delta T = \frac{5.0 \times 10^{-6}\text{ m}}{\alpha_{br} L_{i,br} + \alpha_{st} L_{i,st}}$$

$$= \frac{5.0 \times 10^{-6}\text{ m}}{[19 \times 10^{-6}(^\circ\text{C})^{-1}](0.030\text{ m}) + [11 \times 10^{-6}(^\circ\text{C})^{-1}](0.010\text{ m})} = 7.4^\circ\text{C}$$

Find the temperature at which the bolts touch:

$$T = 27^\circ\text{C} + 7.4^\circ\text{C} = \boxed{34^\circ\text{C}}$$

Finalize   This temperature is possible if the air conditioning in the building housing the device fails for a long period on a very hot summer day.

The Unusual Behavior of Water

Liquids generally increase in volume with increasing temperature and have average coefficients of volume expansion about ten times greater than those of solids. Cold water is an exception to this rule as you can see from its density-versus-temperature curve shown in Figure 19.11. As the temperature increases from 0°C to 4°C, water contracts and its density therefore increases. Above 4°C, water expands with increasing temperature and so its density decreases. Therefore, the density of water reaches a maximum value of 1.000 g/cm³ at 4°C.

We can use this unusual thermal-expansion behavior of water to explain why a pond begins freezing at the surface rather than at the bottom. When the air temperature drops from, for example, 7°C to 6°C, the surface water also cools and consequently decreases in volume. The surface water is denser than the water below it, which has not cooled and decreased in volume. As a result, the surface water sinks, and warmer water from below is forced to the surface to be cooled. When the air temperature is between 4°C and 0°C, however, the surface water

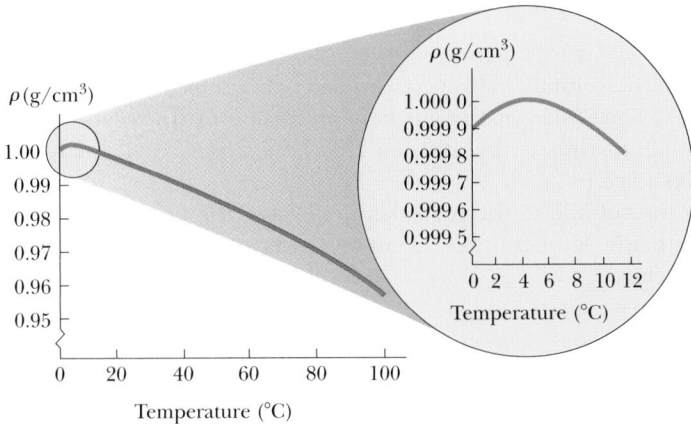

Figure 19.11   The variation in the density of water at atmospheric pressure with temperature. The inset at the right shows that the maximum density of water occurs at 4°C.

expands as it cools, becoming less dense than the water below it. The mixing process stops, and eventually the surface water freezes. As the water freezes, the ice remains on the surface because ice is less dense than water. The ice continues to build up at the surface, while water near the bottom remains at 4°C. If that were not the case, fish and other forms of marine life would not survive.

19.5 Macroscopic Description of an Ideal Gas

The volume expansion equation $\Delta V = \beta V_i \Delta T$ is based on the assumption that the material has an initial volume V_i before the temperature change occurs. Such is the case for solids and liquids because they have a fixed volume at a given temperature.

The case for gases is completely different. The interatomic forces within gases are very weak, and, in many cases, we can imagine these forces to be nonexistent and still make very good approximations. Therefore, *there is no equilibrium separation* for the atoms and no "standard" volume at a given temperature; the volume depends on the size of the container. As a result, we cannot express changes in volume ΔV in a process on a gas with Equation 19.6 because we have no defined volume V_i at the beginning of the process. Equations involving gases contain the volume V, rather than a *change* in the volume from an initial value, as a variable.

For a gas, it is useful to know how the quantities volume V, pressure P, and temperature T are related for a sample of gas of mass m. In general, the equation that interrelates these quantities, called the *equation of state*, is very complicated. If the gas is maintained at a very low pressure (or low density), however, the equation of state is quite simple and can be found experimentally. Such a low-density gas is commonly referred to as an **ideal gas**.[5] We can use the **ideal gas model** to make predictions that are adequate to describe the behavior of real gases at low pressures.

It is convenient to express the amount of gas in a given volume in terms of the number of moles n. One **mole** of any substance is that amount of the substance that contains **Avogadro's number** $N_A = 6.022 \times 10^{23}$ of constituent particles (atoms or molecules). The number of moles n of a substance is related to its mass m through the expression

$$n = \frac{m}{M} \tag{19.7}$$

where M is the molar mass of the substance. The molar mass of each chemical element is the atomic mass (from the periodic table; see Appendix C) expressed in grams per mole. For example, the mass of one He atom is 4.00 u (atomic mass units), so the molar mass of He is 4.00 g/mol.

Now suppose an ideal gas is confined to a cylindrical container whose volume can be varied by means of a movable piston as in Active Figure 19.12. If we assume the cylinder does not leak, the mass (or the number of moles) of the gas remains constant. For such a system, experiments provide the following information:

- When the gas is kept at a constant temperature, its pressure is inversely proportional to the volume. (This behavior is described historically as Boyle's law.)
- When the pressure of the gas is kept constant, the volume is directly proportional to the temperature. (This behavior is described historically as Charles's law.)
- When the volume of the gas is kept constant, the pressure is directly proportional to the temperature. (This behavior is described historically as Gay–Lussac's law.)

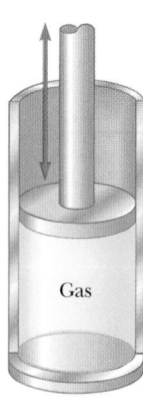

ACTIVE FIGURE 19.12

An ideal gas confined to a cylinder whose volume can be varied by means of a movable piston.

Sign in at www.thomsonedu.com and go to ThomsonNOW to choose to keep either the temperature or the pressure constant and verify Boyle's law and Charles's law.

---

[5] To be more specific, the assumptions here are that the temperature of the gas must not be too low (the gas must not condense into a liquid) or too high and that the pressure must be low. The concept of an ideal gas implies that the gas molecules do not interact except upon collision and that the molecular volume is negligible compared with the volume of the container. In reality, an ideal gas does not exist. Nonetheless, the concept of an ideal gas is very useful because real gases at low pressures behave as ideal gases do.

These observations are summarized by the **equation of state for an ideal gas:**

$$PV = nRT \qquad (19.8)$$

◀ Equation of state for an ideal gas

In this expression, also known as the **ideal gas law,** n is the number of moles of gas in the sample and R is a constant. Experiments on numerous gases show that as the pressure approaches zero, the quantity PV/nT approaches the same value R for all gases. For this reason, R is called the **universal gas constant.** In SI units, in which pressure is expressed in pascals ($1\ \text{Pa} = 1\ \text{N/m}^2$) and volume in cubic meters, the product PV has units of newton·meters, or joules, and R has the value

$$R = 8.314\ \text{J/mol} \cdot \text{K} \qquad (19.9)$$

If the pressure is expressed in atmospheres and the volume in liters ($1\ \text{L} = 10^3\ \text{cm}^3 = 10^{-3}\ \text{m}^3$), then R has the value

$$R = 0.082\ 06\ \text{L} \cdot \text{atm/mol} \cdot \text{K}$$

Using this value of R and Equation 19.8 shows that the volume occupied by 1 mol of any gas at atmospheric pressure and at 0°C (273 K) is 22.4 L.

The ideal gas law states that if the volume and temperature of a fixed amount of gas do not change, the pressure also remains constant. Consider a bottle of champagne that is shaken and then spews liquid when opened as shown in Figure 19.13. A common misconception is that the pressure inside the bottle is increased when the bottle is shaken. On the contrary, because the temperature of the bottle and its contents remains constant as long as the bottle is sealed, so does the pressure, as can be shown by replacing the cork with a pressure gauge. The correct explanation is as follows. Carbon dioxide gas resides in the volume between the liquid surface and the cork. The pressure of the gas in this volume is set higher than atmospheric pressure in the bottling process. Shaking the bottle displaces some of the carbon dioxide gas into the liquid, where it forms bubbles, and these bubbles become attached to the inside of the bottle. (No new gas is generated by shaking.) When the bottle is opened, the pressure is reduced to atmospheric pressure, which causes the volume of the bubbles to increase suddenly. If the bubbles are attached to the bottle (beneath the liquid surface), their rapid expansion expels liquid from the bottle. If the sides and bottom of the bottle are first tapped until no bubbles remain beneath the surface, however, the drop in pressure does not force liquid from the bottle when the champagne is opened.

The ideal gas law is often expressed in terms of the total number of molecules N. Because the number of moles n equals the ratio of the total number of molecules and Avogadro's number N_A, we can write Equation 19.8 as

$$PV = nRT = \frac{N}{N_\text{A}} RT$$

$$PV = Nk_\text{B}T \qquad (19.10)$$

where k_B is **Boltzmann's constant,** which has the value

$$k_\text{B} = \frac{R}{N_\text{A}} = 1.38 \times 10^{-23}\ \text{J/K} \qquad (19.11)$$

◀ Boltzmann's constant

It is common to call quantities such as P, V, and T the **thermodynamic variables** of an ideal gas. If the equation of state is known, one of the variables can always be expressed as some function of the other two.

Figure 19.13 A bottle of champagne is shaken and opened. Liquid spews out of the opening. A common misconception is that the pressure inside the bottle is increased by the shaking.

Steve Niedorf/Getty Images

PITFALL PREVENTION 19.3
So Many *k*s

There are a variety of physical quantities for which the letter k is used. Two we have seen previously are the force constant for a spring (Chapter 15) and the wave number for a mechanical wave (Chapter 16). Boltzmann's constant is another k, and we will see k used for thermal conductivity in Chapter 20 and for an electrical constant in Chapter 23. To make some sense of this confusing state of affairs, we use a subscript B for Boltzmann's constant to help us recognize it. In this book, you will see Boltzmann's constant as k_B, but you may see Boltzmann's constant in other resources as simply k.

Quick Quiz 19.5 A common material for cushioning objects in packages is made by trapping bubbles of air between sheets of plastic. This material is more effective at keeping the contents of the package from moving around inside the package on (a) a hot day   (b) a cold day   (c) either hot or cold days.

Quick Quiz 19.6 On a winter day, you turn on your furnace and the temperature of the air inside your home increases. Assume your home has the normal amount of leakage between inside air and outside air. Is the number of moles of air in your room at the higher temperature (a) larger than before, (b) smaller than before, or (c) the same as before?

EXAMPLE 19.4 | **Heating a Spray Can**

A spray can containing a propellant gas at twice atmospheric pressure (202 kPa) and having a volume of 125.00 cm³ is at 22°C. It is then tossed into an open fire. When the temperature of the gas in the can reaches 195°C, what is the pressure inside the can? Assume any change in the volume of the can is negligible.

SOLUTION

Conceptualize Intuitively, you should expect that the pressure of the gas in the container increases because of the increasing temperature.

Categorize We model the gas in the can as ideal and use the ideal gas law to calculate the new pressure.

Analyze Rearrange Equation 19.8:

$$(1) \quad \frac{PV}{T} = nR$$

No air escapes during the compression, so that n, and therefore nR, remains constant. Hence, set the initial value of the left side of Equation (1) equal to the final value:

$$(2) \quad \frac{P_i V_i}{T_i} = \frac{P_f V_f}{T_f}$$

Because the initial and final volumes of the gas are assumed to be equal, cancel the volumes:

$$(3) \quad \frac{P_i}{T_i} = \frac{P_f}{T_f}$$

Solve for P_f:

$$P_f = \left(\frac{T_f}{T_i}\right) P_i = \left(\frac{468 \text{ K}}{295 \text{ K}}\right)(202 \text{ kPa}) = \boxed{320 \text{ kPa}}$$

Finalize The higher the temperature, the higher the pressure exerted by the trapped gas as expected. If the pressure increases sufficiently, the can may explode. Because of this possibility, you should never dispose of spray cans in a fire.

What If? Suppose we include a volume change due to thermal expansion of the steel can as the temperature increases. Does that alter our answer for the final pressure significantly?

Answer Because the thermal expansion coefficient of steel is very small, we do not expect much of an effect on our final answer.

Find the change in the volume of the can using Equation 19.6 and the value for α for steel from Table 19.1:

$$\Delta V = \beta V_i \, \Delta T = 3\alpha V_i \, \Delta T$$
$$= 3[11 \times 10^{-6}(°C)^{-1}](125.00 \text{ cm}^3)(173°C) = 0.71 \text{ cm}^3$$

Start from Equation (2) again and find an equation for the final pressure:

$$P_f = \left(\frac{T_f}{T_i}\right)\left(\frac{V_i}{V_f}\right) P_i$$

This result differs from Equation (3) only in the factor V_i/V_f. Evaluate this factor:

$$\frac{V_i}{V_f} = \frac{125.00 \text{ cm}^3}{(125.00 \text{ cm}^3 + 0.71 \text{ cm}^3)} = 0.994 = 99.4\%$$

Therefore, the final pressure will differ by only 0.6% from the value calculated without considering the thermal expansion of the can. Taking 99.4% of the previous final pressure, the final pressure including thermal expansion is 318 kPa.

Summary

DEFINITIONS

Two objects are in **thermal equilibrium** with each other if they do not exchange energy when in thermal contact.	**Temperature** is the property that determines whether an object is in thermal equilibrium with other objects. **Two objects in thermal equilibrium with each other are at the same temperature**. The SI unit of absolute temperature is the **kelvin,** which is defined to be 1/273.16 of the difference between absolute zero and the temperature of the triple point of water.

CONCEPTS AND PRINCIPLES

The **zeroth law of thermodynamics** states that if objects A and B are separately in thermal equilibrium with a third object C, then objects A and B are in thermal equilibrium with each other.	When the temperature of an object is changed by an amount ΔT, its length changes by an amount ΔL that is proportional to ΔT and to its initial length L_i: $$\Delta L = \alpha L_i \, \Delta T \qquad \textbf{(19.4)}$$ where the constant α is the **average coefficient of linear expansion**. The **average coefficient of volume expansion** β for a solid is approximately equal to 3α.

An **ideal gas** is one for which PV/nT is constant. An ideal gas is described by the **equation of state,**

$$PV = nRT \qquad \textbf{(19.8)}$$

where n equals the number of moles of the gas, P is its pressure, V is its volume, R is the universal gas constant $(8.314 \, \text{J/mol} \cdot \text{K})$, and T is the absolute temperature of the gas. A real gas behaves approximately as an ideal gas if it has a low density.

Questions

□ denotes answer available in *Student Solutions Manual/Study Guide;* **O** denotes objective question

1. Is it possible for two objects to be in thermal equilibrium if they are not in contact with each other? Explain.

2. A piece of copper is dropped into a beaker of water. If the water's temperature rises, what happens to the temperature of the copper? Under what conditions are the water and copper in thermal equilibrium?

3. In describing his upcoming trip to the Moon and as portrayed in the movie *Apollo 13* (Universal, 1995), astronaut Jim Lovell said, "I'll be walking in a place where there's a 400-degree difference between sunlight and shadow." What is it that is hot in sunlight and cold in shadow? Suppose an astronaut standing on the Moon holds a thermometer in his gloved hand. Is the thermometer reading the temperature of the vacuum at the Moon's surface? Does it read any temperature? If so, what object or substance has that temperature?

4. **O** What would happen if the glass of a thermometer expanded more on warming than did the liquid in the tube? (a) The thermometer would break. (b) It could not be used for measuring temperature. (c) It could be used for temperatures only below room temperature. (d) You would have to hold it with the bulb on top. (e) Larger

numbers would be found closer to the bulb. (f) The numbers would not be evenly spaced.

5. **O** Suppose you empty a tray of ice cubes into a bowl partly full of water and cover the bowl. After one-half hour, the contents of the bowl come to thermal equilibrium, with more liquid water and less ice than you started with. Which of the following is true? (a) The temperature of the liquid water is higher than the temperature of the remaining ice. (b) The temperature of the liquid water is the same as that of the ice. (c) The temperature of the liquid water is less than that of the ice. (d) The comparative temperatures of the liquid water and ice depend on the amounts present.

6. **O** The coefficient of linear expansion of copper is $17 \times 10^{-6} \, (°\text{C})^{-1}$. The Statue of Liberty is 93 m tall on a summer morning when the temperature is 25°C. Assume the copper plates covering the statue are mounted edge to edge without expansion joints and do not buckle or bind on the framework supporting them as the day grows hot. What is the order of magnitude of the statue's increase in height? (a) 0.1 mm (b) 1 mm (c) 1 cm (d) 10 cm (e) 1 m (f) 10 m (g) none of these answers

7. Markings to indicate length are placed on a steel tape in a room that has a temperature of 22°C. Are measurements made with the tape on a day when the temperature is 27°C too long, too short, or accurate? Defend your answer.

8. Use a periodic table of the elements (see Appendix C) to determine the number of grams in one mole of (a) hydrogen, which has diatomic molecules; (b) helium; and (c) carbon monoxide.

9. What does the ideal gas law predict about the volume of a sample of gas at absolute zero? Why is this prediction incorrect?

10. O A rubber balloon is filled with 1 L of air at 1 atm and 300 K and is then put into a cryogenic refrigerator at 100 K. The rubber remains flexible as it cools. (i) What happens to the volume of the balloon? (a) It decreases to $\frac{1}{6}$ L. (b) It decreases to $\frac{1}{3}$ L. (c) It decreases to $1/\sqrt{3}$ L. (d) It is constant. (e) It increases. (ii) What happens to the pressure of the air in the balloon? (a) It decreases to $\frac{1}{6}$ atm. (b) It decreases to $\frac{1}{3}$ atm. (c) It decreases to $1/\sqrt{3}$ atm. (d) It is constant. (e) It increases.

11. O Two cylinders at the same temperature contain the same quantity of the same kind of gas. Is it possible that cylinder A has three times the volume of cylinder B? If so, what can you conclude about the pressures the gases exert? (a) The situation is not possible. (b) It is possible, but we can conclude nothing about the pressure. (c) It is possible only if the pressure in A is three times the pressure in B. (d) The pressures must be equal. (e) The pressure in A must be one-third the pressure in B.

12. O Choose every correct answer. The graph of pressure versus temperature in Figure 19.5 shows what for each sample of gas? (a) The pressure is proportional to the Celsius temperature. (b) The pressure is a linear function of the temperature. (c) The pressure increases at the same rate as the temperature. (d) The pressure increases with temperature at a constant rate.

13. O A cylinder with a piston contains a sample of a thin gas. The kind of gas and the sample size can be changed. The cylinder can be placed in different constant-temperature baths, and the piston can be held in different positions. Rank the following cases according to the pressure of the gas from the highest to the lowest, displaying any cases of equality. (a) A 2-mmol sample of oxygen is held at 300 K in a 100-cm³ container. (b) A 2-mmol sample of oxygen is held at 600 K in a 200-cm³ container. (c) A 2-mmol sample of oxygen is held at 600 K in a 300-cm³ container. (d) A 4-mmol sample of helium is held at 300 K in a 200-cm³ container. (e) A 4-mmol sample of helium is held at 250 K in a 200-cm³ container.

14. The pendulum of a certain pendulum clock is made of brass. When the temperature increases, does the period of the clock increase, decrease, or remain the same? Explain.

15. An automobile radiator is filled to the brim with water when the engine is cool. What happens to the water when the engine is running and the water has been raised to a high temperature? What do modern automobiles have in their cooling systems to prevent the loss of coolants?

16. Metal lids on glass jars can often be loosened by running hot water over them. Why does that work?

17. When the metal ring and metal sphere in Figure Q19.17 are both at room temperature, the sphere can barely be passed through the ring. After the sphere is warmed in a flame, it cannot be passed through the ring. Explain. **What If?** What if the ring is warmed and the sphere is left at room temperature? Does the sphere pass through the ring?

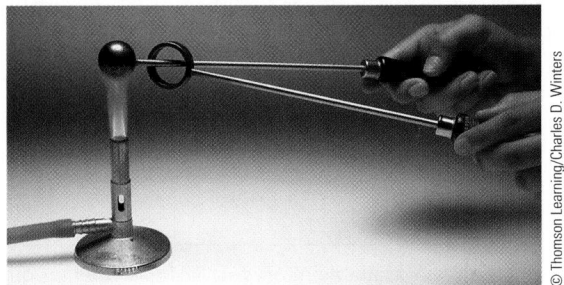

Figure Q19.17

Problems

WebAssign The Problems from this chapter may be assigned online in WebAssign.

ThomsonNOW™ Sign in at **www.thomsonedu.com** and go to ThomsonNOW to assess your understanding of this chapter's topics with additional quizzing and conceptual questions.

1, 2, 3 denotes straightforward, intermediate, challenging; ☐ denotes full solution available in *Student Solutions Manual/Study Guide;* ▲ denotes coached solution with hints available at **www.thomsonedu.com;** ▨ denotes developing symbolic reasoning; ● denotes asking for qualitative reasoning; ▥ denotes computer useful in solving problem

Section 19.2 Thermometers and the Celsius Temperature Scale

Section 19.3 The Constant-Volume Gas Thermometer and the Absolute Temperature Scale

1. ▲ A constant-volume gas thermometer is calibrated in dry ice (that is, evaporating carbon dioxide in the solid state, with a temperature of −80.0°C) and in boiling ethyl alcohol (78.0°C). The two pressures are 0.900 atm and 1.635 atm. (a) What Celsius value of absolute zero does the calibration yield? What is the pressure at (b) the freezing point of water and (c) the boiling point of water?

2. The temperature difference between the inside and the outside of an automobile engine is 450°C. Express this temperature difference on (a) the Fahrenheit scale and (b) the Kelvin scale.

3. Liquid nitrogen has a boiling point of −195.81°C at atmospheric pressure. Express this temperature (a) in degrees Fahrenheit and (b) in kelvins.

4. The melting point of gold is 1 064°C, and its boiling point is 2 660°C. (a) Express these temperatures in kelvins. (b) Compute the difference between these temperatures in Celsius degrees and kelvins.

Section 19.4 Thermal Expansion of Solids and Liquids

Note: Table 19.1 is available for use in solving problems in this section.

5. A copper telephone wire has essentially no sag between poles 35.0 m apart on a winter day when the temperature is −20.0°C. How much longer is the wire on a summer day when $T_C = 35.0°C$?

6. The concrete sections of a certain superhighway are designed to have a length of 25.0 m. The sections are poured and cured at 10.0°C. What minimum spacing should the engineer leave between the sections to eliminate buckling if the concrete is to reach a temperature of 50.0°C?

7. ▲ The active element of a certain laser is made of a glass rod 30.0 cm long and 1.50 cm in diameter. If the temperature of the rod increases by 65.0°C, what is the increase in (a) its length, (b) its diameter, and (c) its volume? Assume the average coefficient of linear expansion of the glass is 9.00×10^{-6} (°C)$^{-1}$.

8. **Review problem.** Inside the wall of a house, an L-shaped section of hot water pipe consists of a straight, horizontal piece 28.0 cm long, an elbow, and a straight vertical piece 134 cm long (Fig. P19.8). A stud and a second-story floorboard hold stationary the ends of this section of copper pipe. Find the magnitude and direction of the displacement of the pipe elbow when the water flow is turned on, raising the temperature of the pipe from 18.0°C to 46.5°C.

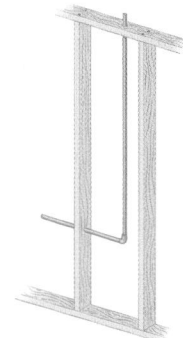

Figure P19.8

9. ● A thin brass ring of inner diameter 10.00 cm at 20.0°C is warmed and slipped over an aluminum rod of diameter 10.01 cm at 20.0°C. Assuming the average coefficients of linear expansion are constant, (a) to what temperature must this combination be cooled to separate the parts? Explain whether this separation is attainable. (b) **What If?** What if the aluminum rod were 10.02 cm in diameter?

10. ● At 20.0°C, an aluminum ring has an inner diameter of 5.000 0 cm and a brass rod has a diameter of 5.050 0 cm.

(a) If only the ring is warmed, what temperature must it reach so that it will just slip over the rod? (b) **What If?** If both the ring and the rod are warmed together, what temperature must they both reach so that the ring barely slips over the rod? Would this latter process work? Explain.

11. ● A volumetric flask made of Pyrex is calibrated at 20.0°C. It is filled to the 100-mL mark with 35.0°C acetone. (a) What is the volume of the acetone when it cools to 20.0°C? (b) How significant is the change in volume of the flask?

12. On a day that the temperature is 20.0°C, a concrete walk is poured in such a way that the ends of the walk are unable to move. (a) What is the stress in the cement on a hot day of 50.0°C? (b) Does the concrete fracture? Take Young's modulus for concrete to be 7.00×10^9 N/m^2 and the compressive strength to be 2.00×10^9 N/m^2.

13. A hollow aluminum cylinder 20.0 cm deep has an internal capacity of 2.000 L at 20.0°C. It is completely filled with turpentine and then slowly warmed to 80.0°C. (a) How much turpentine overflows? (b) If the cylinder is then cooled back to 20.0°C, how far below the cylinder's rim does the turpentine's surface recede?

14. ● The Golden Gate Bridge in San Francisco has a main span of length 1.28 km, one of the longest in the world. Imagine that a taut steel wire with this length and a cross-sectional area of 4.00×10^{-6} m^2 is laid on the bridge deck with its ends attached to the towers of the bridge and that on this summer day the temperature of the wire is 35.0°C. (a) When winter arrives, the towers stay the same distance apart and the bridge deck keeps the same shape as its expansion joints open. When the temperature drops to −10.0°C, what is the tension in the wire? Take Young's modulus for steel to be 20.0×10^{10} N/m^2. (b) Permanent deformation occurs if the stress in the steel exceeds its elastic limit of 3.00×10^8 N/m^2. At what temperature would the wire reach its elastic limit? (c) **What If?** Explain how your answers to parts (a) and (b) would change if the Golden Gate Bridge were twice as long.

15. A certain telescope forms an image of part of a cluster of stars on a square silicon charge-coupled detector chip 2.00 cm on each side. A star field is focused on the chip when it is first turned on, and its temperature is 20.0°C. The star field contains 5 342 stars scattered uniformly. To make the detector more sensitive, it is cooled to −100°C. How many star images then fit onto the chip? The average coefficient of linear expansion of silicon is 4.68×10^{-6} (°C)$^{-1}$.

Section 19.5 Macroscopic Description of an Ideal Gas

16. On your wedding day your lover gives you a gold ring of mass 3.80 g. Fifty years later its mass is 3.35 g. On the average, how many atoms were abraded from the ring during each second of your marriage? The molar mass of gold is 197 g/mol.

17. An automobile tire is inflated with air originally at 10.0°C and normal atmospheric pressure. During the process, the air is compressed to 28.0% of its original volume and the temperature is increased to 40.0°C. (a) What is the tire pressure? (b) After the car is driven at high speed, the tire's air temperature rises to 85.0°C and the tire's interior volume increases by 2.00%. What is the new tire pressure (absolute) in pascals?

18. Gas is contained in an 8.00-L vessel at a temperature of 20.0°C and a pressure of 9.00 atm. (a) Determine the number of moles of gas in the vessel. (b) How many molecules are in the vessel?

19. An auditorium has dimensions 10.0 m × 20.0 m × 30.0 m. How many molecules of air fill the auditorium at 20.0°C and a pressure of 101 kPa?

20. A cook puts 9.00 g of water in a 2.00-L pressure cooker and warms it to 500°C. What is the pressure inside the container?

21. ▲ The mass of a hot-air balloon and its cargo (not including the air inside) is 200 kg. The air outside is at 10.0°C and 101 kPa. The volume of the balloon is 400 m³. To what temperature must the air in the balloon be warmed before the balloon will lift off? (Air density at 10.0°C is 1.25 kg/m³.)

22. ● *Male-pattern dumbness.* Your father and your younger brother are confronted with the same puzzle. Your father's garden sprayer and your brother's water cannon both have tanks with a capacity of 5.00 L (Fig. P19.22). Your father puts a negligible amount of concentrated fertilizer into his tank. They both pour in 4.00 L of water and seal up their tanks, so the tanks also contain air at atmospheric pressure. Next, each uses a hand-operated piston pump to inject more air until the absolute pressure in the tank reaches 2.40 atm and it becomes too difficult to move the pump handle. Now each uses his device to spray out water—not air—until the stream becomes feeble as it does when the pressure in the tank reaches 1.20 atm. Then he must pump it up again, spray again, and so on. To accomplish spraying out all the water, each finds he must pump up the tank three times. Here is the puzzle: most of the water sprays out as a result of the second pumping. The first and the third pumping-up processes seem just as difficult as the second but result in a disappointingly small amount of water coming out. Account for this phenomenon.

Figure P19.22

23. ● (a) Find the number of moles in one cubic meter of an ideal gas at 20.0°C and atmospheric pressure. (b) For air, Avogadro's number of molecules has mass 28.9 g. Calculate the mass of one cubic meter of air. State how the result compares with the tabulated density of air.

24. At 25.0 m below the surface of the sea (density = 1 025 kg/m³), where the temperature is 5.00°C, a diver exhales an air bubble having a volume of 1.00 cm³. If the surface temperature of the sea is 20.0°C, what is the volume of the bubble just before it breaks the surface?

25. ● A cube 10.0 cm on each edge contains air (with equivalent molar mass 28.9 g/mol) at atmospheric pressure and temperature 300 K. Find (a) the mass of the gas, (b) the gravitational force exerted on it, and (c) the force it exerts on each face of the cube. (d) Comment on the physical reason such a small sample can exert such a great force.

26. Estimate the mass of the air in your bedroom. State the quantities you take as data and the value you measure or estimate for each.

27. The pressure gauge on a tank registers the gauge pressure, which is the difference between the interior and exterior pressure. When the tank is full of oxygen (O_2), it contains 12.0 kg of the gas at a gauge pressure of 40.0 atm. Determine the mass of oxygen that has been withdrawn from the tank when the pressure reading is 25.0 atm. Assume the temperature of the tank remains constant.

28. In state-of-the-art vacuum systems, pressures as low as 10^{-9} Pa are being attained. Calculate the number of molecules in a 1.00-m³ vessel at this pressure and a temperature of 27.0°C.

29. ● *How much water will a shearwater shear?* To measure how far below the ocean's surface a bird dives to catch a fish, Will Mackin used a method originated by Lord Kelvin for soundings by the British Navy. Mackin dusted the interiors of thin plastic tubes with powdered sugar and then sealed one end of each tube. Charging around on a rocky beach at night with a miner's headlamp, he would grab an Audubon's shearwater in its nest and attach a tube to its back. He would then catch the same bird the next night and remove the tube. After hundreds of captures, the birds thoroughly disliked him but were not permanently frightened away from the rookery. Assume in one trial, with a tube 6.50 cm long, he found that water had entered the tube to wash away the sugar over a distance of 2.70 cm from the open end. (a) Find the greatest depth to which the shearwater dove, assuming the air in the tube stayed at constant temperature. (b) Must the tube be attached to the bird in any particular orientation for this method to work? (Audubon's shearwater can dive to more than twice the depth you calculate, and larger species can dive nearly ten times deeper.)

30. A room of volume V contains air having equivalent molar mass M (in grams per mole). If the temperature of the room is raised from T_1 to T_2, what mass of air will leave the room? Assume the air pressure in the room is maintained at P_0.

Additional Problems

31. A student measures the length of a brass rod with a steel tape at 20.0°C. The reading is 95.00 cm. What will the tape indicate for the length of the rod when the rod and the tape are at (a) −15.0°C and (b) 55.0°C?

32. The density of gasoline is 730 kg/m³ at 0°C. Its average coefficient of volume expansion is $9.60 × 10^{-4}$ (°C)$^{-1}$. Assume 1.00 gal of gasoline occupies 0.003 80 m³. How many extra kilograms of gasoline would you get if you bought 10.0 gal of gasoline at 0°C rather than at 20.0°C from a pump that is not temperature compensated?

2 = intermediate;   3 = challenging;   □ = SSM/SG;   ▲ = ThomsonNOW;   ▨ = symbolic reasoning;   ● = qualitative reasoning

33. A mercury thermometer is constructed as shown in Figure P19.33. The capillary tube has a diameter of 0.004 00 cm, and the bulb has a diameter of 0.250 cm. Ignoring the expansion of the glass, find the change in height of the mercury column that occurs with a temperature change of 30.0°C.

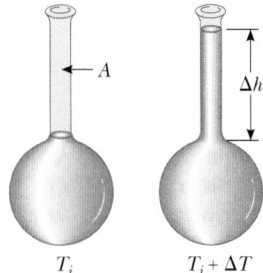

Figure P19.33   Problems 33 and 34.

34. ● A liquid with a coefficient of volume expansion β just fills a spherical shell of volume V_i at a temperature of T_i (Fig. P19.33). The shell is made of a material with an average coefficient of linear expansion α. The liquid is free to expand into an open capillary of area A projecting from the top of the sphere. (a) Assuming the temperature increases by ΔT, show that the liquid rises in the capillary by the amount Δh given by the equation $\Delta h = (V_i/A)(\beta - 3\alpha)\,\Delta T$. (b) For a typical system such as a mercury thermometer, why is it a good approximation to ignore the expansion of the shell?

35. Review problem. An aluminum pipe, 0.655 m long at 20.0°C and open at both ends, is used as a flute. The pipe is cooled to a low temperature, but then filled with air at 20.0°C as soon as you start to play it. After that, by how much does its fundamental frequency change as the metal rises in temperature from 5.00°C to 20.0°C?

36. Two metal bars are made of invar and one is made of aluminum. At 0°C, each of the three bars is drilled with two holes 40.0 cm apart. Pins are put through the holes to assemble the bars into an equilateral triangle. (a) First ignore the expansion of the invar. Find the angle between the invar bars as a function of Celsius temperature. (b) Is your answer accurate for negative as well as positive temperatures? Is it accurate for 0°C? (c) Solve the problem again, including the expansion of the invar. (d) Aluminum melts at 660°C and invar at 1 427°C. Assume the tabulated expansion coefficients are constant. What are the greatest and smallest attainable angles between the invar bars?

37. ● ▲ A liquid has a density ρ. (a) Show that the fractional change in density for a change in temperature ΔT is $\Delta\rho/\rho = -\beta\,\Delta T$. What does the negative sign signify? (b) Fresh water has a maximum density of 1.000 0 g/cm³ at 4.0°C. At 10.0°C, its density is 0.999 7 g/cm³. What is β for water over this temperature interval?

38. A cylinder is closed by a piston connected to a spring of constant 2.00×10^3 N/m (Fig. P19.38). With the spring relaxed, the cylinder is filled with 5.00 L of gas at a pressure of 1.00 atm and a temperature of 20.0°C. (a) If the piston has a cross-sectional area of 0.010 0 m² and negligible mass, how high will it rise when the temperature is raised to 250°C? (b) What is the pressure of the gas at 250°C?

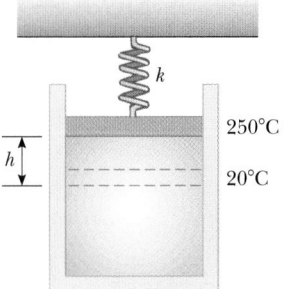

Figure P19.38

39. ▲ A vertical cylinder of cross-sectional area A is fitted with a tight-fitting, frictionless piston of mass m (Fig. P19.39). (a) If n moles of an ideal gas are in the cylinder at a temperature of T, what is the height h at which the piston is in equilibrium under its own weight? (b) What is the value for h if $n = 0.200$ mol, $T = 400$ K, $A = 0.008\ 00$ m², and $m = 20.0$ kg?

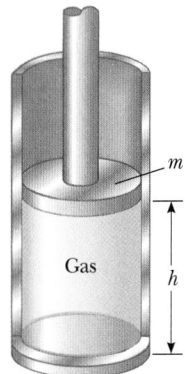

Figure P19.39

40. A bimetallic strip is made of two ribbons of different metals bonded together. (a) First assume the strip is originally straight. As the strip is warmed, the metal with the greater average coefficient of expansion expands more than the other, forcing the strip into an arc with the outer radius having a greater circumference (Fig. P19.40a, page 550). Derive an expression for the angle of bending θ as a function of the initial length of the strips, their average coefficients of linear expansion, the change in temperature, and the separation of the centers of the strips ($\Delta r = r_2 - r_1$). (b) Show that the angle of bending decreases to zero when ΔT decreases to zero and also when the two average coefficients of expansion become equal. (c) **What If?** What happens if the strip is cooled? (d) Figure P19.40b shows a compact spiral bimetallic strip in a home thermostat. If θ is interpreted as the angle of additional bending caused by a change in temperature, the equation from part (a) applies to it as well. The inner end of the spiral strip is fixed, and the outer end is free to move. Assume the metals are bronze and invar, the thickness of the strip is $2\,\Delta r = 0.500$ mm, and the overall length of the spiral strip is 20.0 cm. Find the angle through which the free end of the strip turns when the temperature changes by

2 = intermediate;   3 = challenging;   ☐ = SSM/SG;   ▲ = ThomsonNOW;   ▨ = symbolic reasoning;   ● = qualitative reasoning

1°C. The free end of the strip supports a capsule partly filled with mercury, visible above the strip in Figure P19.40b. When the capsule tilts, the mercury shifts from one end to the other to make or break an electrical contact switching the furnace on or off.

(a)   (b)

Figure P19.40

41. ● The rectangular plate shown in Figure P19.41 has an area A_i equal to ℓw. If the temperature increases by ΔT, each dimension increases according to the equation $\Delta L = \alpha L_i \Delta T$, where α is the average coefficient of linear expansion. Show that the increase in area is $\Delta A = 2\alpha A_i \Delta T$. What approximation does this expression assume?

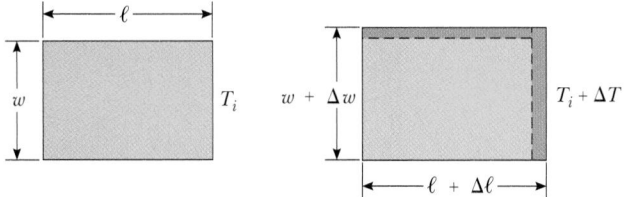

Figure P19.41

42. ● The measurement of the average coefficient of volume expansion for a liquid is complicated because the container also changes size with temperature. Figure P19.42 shows a simple means for overcoming this difficulty. With this apparatus, one arm of a U-tube is maintained at 0°C in an ice-water bath, and the other arm is maintained at a different temperature T_C in a constant-temperature bath. The connecting tube is horizontal. (a) Explain how use of this equipment permits determination of β for the liquid from measurements of the column heights h_0 and h_t of the liquid columns in the U-tube, without having to correct for expansion of the apparatus. (b) Derive the expression for β in terms of h_0, h_t, and T_C.

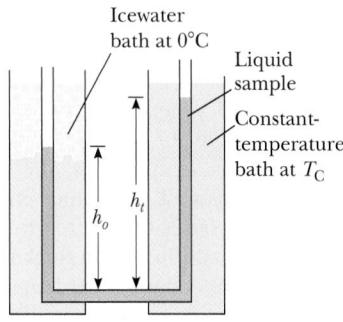

Figure P19.42

43. ● A copper rod and a steel rod are different in length by 5.00 cm at 0°C. The rods are warmed and cooled together. Is it possible that the length difference remains constant at all temperatures? Explain. Describe the lengths at 0°C as precisely as you can. Can you tell which rod is longer? Can you tell the lengths of the rods?

44. **Review problem**. A clock with a brass pendulum has a period of 1.000 s at 20.0°C. If the temperature increases to 30.0°C, (a) by how much does the period change and (b) how much time does the clock gain or lose in one week?

45. **Review problem**. Consider an object with any one of the shapes displayed in Table 10.2. What is the percentage increase in the moment of inertia of the object when it is warmed from 0°C to 100°C if it is composed of (a) copper or (b) aluminum? Assume the average linear expansion coefficients shown in Table 19.1 do not vary between 0°C and 100°C.

46. **Review problem**. (a) Derive an expression for the buoyant force on a spherical balloon, submerged in water, as a function of the depth below the surface, the volume of the balloon at the surface, the pressure at the surface, and the density of the water. (Assume the water temperature does not change with depth.) (b) Does the buoyant force increase or decrease as the balloon is submerged? (c) At what depth is the buoyant force one-half the surface value?

47. Two concrete spans of a 250-m-long bridge are placed end to end so that no room is allowed for expansion (Fig. P19.47a). If a temperature increase of 20.0°C occurs, what is the height y to which the spans rise when they buckle (Fig. P19.47b)?

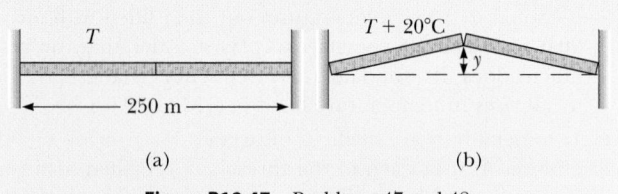

(a)   (b)

Figure P19.47 Problems 47 and 48.

48. Two concrete spans that form a bridge of length L are placed end to end so that no room is allowed for expansion (Fig. P19.47a). If a temperature increase of ΔT occurs, what is the height y to which the spans rise when they buckle (Fig. P19.47b)?

49. (a) Show that the density of an ideal gas occupying a volume V is given by $\rho = PM/RT$, where M is the molar mass. (b) Determine the density of oxygen gas at atmospheric pressure and 20.0°C.

50. ● (a) Take the definition of the coefficient of volume expansion to be

$$\beta = \frac{1}{V}\frac{dV}{dT}\bigg|_{P=\text{constant}} = \frac{1}{V}\frac{\partial V}{\partial T}$$

Use the equation of state for an ideal gas to show that the coefficient of volume expansion for an ideal gas at constant pressure is given by $\beta = 1/T$, where T is the absolute temperature. (b) What value does this expression predict for β at 0°C? State how this result compares with the experimental values for helium and air in Table

19.1. Notice that these values are much larger than the coefficients of volume expansion for most liquids and solids.

51. Starting with Equation 19.10, show that the total pressure *P* in a container filled with a mixture of several ideal gases is $P = P_1 + P_2 + P_3 + \ldots$, where $P_1, P_2, \ldots$, are the pressures that each gas would exert if it alone filled the container. (These individual pressures are called the *partial pressures* of the respective gases.) This result is known as *Dalton's law of partial pressures.*

52. ● **Review problem.** Following a collision in outer space, a copper disk at 850°C is rotating about its axis with an angular speed of 25.0 rad/s. As the disk radiates infrared light, its temperature falls to 20.0°C. No external torque acts on the disk. (a) Does the angular speed change as the disk cools? Explain how it changes or why it does not. (b) What is its angular speed at the lower temperature?

53. ● Helium gas is sold in steel tanks. If the helium is used to inflate a balloon, could the balloon lift the spherical tank the helium came in? Justify your answer. Steel will rupture if subjected to tensile stress greater than its yield strength of 5×10^8 N/m². *Suggestion:* You may consider a steel shell of radius *r* and thickness *t* having the density of iron and containing helium at high pressure and on the verge of breaking apart into two hemispheres.

54. A cylinder that has a 40.0-cm radius and is 50.0 cm deep is filled with air at 20.0°C and 1.00 atm (Fig. P19.54a). A 20.0-kg piston is now lowered into the cylinder, compressing the air trapped inside as it takes equilibrium height h_i (Fig. P19.54b). Finally, a 75.0-kg dog stands on the piston, further compressing the air, which remains at 20°C (Fig. P19.54c). (a) How far down (Δh) does the piston move when the dog steps onto it? (b) To what temperature should the gas be warmed to raise the piston and dog back to h_i?

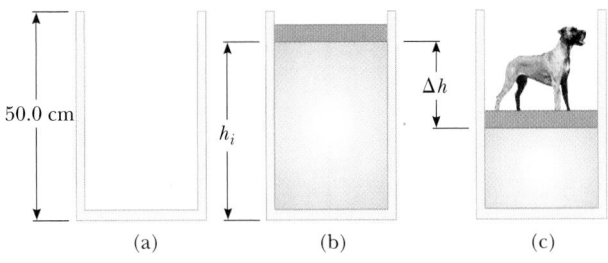

Figure P19.54

55. The relationship $L_f = L_i(1 + \alpha \, \Delta T)$ is a valid approximation when the average coefficient of expansion is small. If α is large, one must integrate the relationship $dL/dT = \alpha L$ to determine the final length. (a) Assuming that the coefficient of linear expansion is constant as *L* varies, determine a general expression for the final length. (b) Given a rod of length 1.00 m and a temperature change of 100.0°C, determine the error caused by the approximation when $\alpha = 2.00 \times 10^{-5}$ (°C)$^{-1}$ (a typical value for a metal) and when $\alpha = 0.020\,0$ (°C)$^{-1}$ (an unrealistically large value for comparison).

56. A steel wire and a copper wire, each of diameter 2.000 mm, are joined end to end. At 40.0°C, each has an unstretched length of 2.000 m. The wires are connected between two fixed supports 4.000 m apart on a tabletop. The steel wire extends from $x = -2.000$ m to $x = 0$, the copper wire extends from $x = 0$ to $x = 2.000$ m, and the tension is negligible. The temperature is then lowered to 20.0°C. At this lower temperature, find the tension in the wire and the *x* coordinate of the junction between the wires. (Refer to Tables 12.1 and 19.1.)

57. **Review problem.** A guitar string made of steel with a diameter of 1.00 mm is stretched between supports 80.0 cm apart. The temperature is 0.0°C. (a) Find the mass per unit length of this string. (Use the value 7.86×10^3 kg/m³ for the density.) (b) The fundamental frequency of transverse oscillations of the string is 200 Hz. What is the tension in the string? (c) The temperature is raised to 30.0°C. Find the resulting values of the tension and the fundamental frequency. Assume both the Young's modulus (Table 12.1) and the average coefficient of expansion (Table 19.1) have constant values between 0.0°C and 30.0°C.

58. In a chemical processing plant, a reaction chamber of fixed volume V_0 is connected to a reservoir chamber of fixed volume $4V_0$ by a passage containing a thermally insulating porous plug. The plug permits the chambers to be at different temperatures. It allows gas to pass from either chamber to the other, ensuring that the pressure is the same in both. At one point in the processing, both chambers contain gas at a pressure of 1.00 atm and a temperature of 27.0°C. Intake and exhaust valves to the pair of chambers are closed. The reservoir is maintained at 27.0°C while the reaction chamber is warmed to 400°C. What is the pressure in both chambers after these temperatures are achieved?

59. ⬛ A 1.00-km steel railroad rail is fastened securely at both ends when the temperature is 20.0°C. As the temperature increases, the rail buckles, taking the shape of an arc of a vertical circle. Find the height *h* of the center of the rail when the temperature is 25.0°C. You will need to solve a transcendental equation.

60. ● **Review problem.** A perfectly plane house roof makes an angle θ with the horizontal. When its temperature changes, between T_c before dawn each day and T_h in the middle of each afternoon, the roof expands and contracts uniformly with a coefficient of thermal expansion α_1. Resting on the roof is a flat, rectangular metal plate with expansion coefficient α_2, greater than α_1. The length of the plate is *L*, measured along the slope of the roof. The component of the plate's weight perpendicular to the roof is supported by a normal force uniformly distributed over the area of the plate. The coefficient of kinetic friction between the plate and the roof is μ_k. The plate is always at the same temperature as the roof, so we assume its temperature is continuously changing. Because of the difference in expansion coefficients, each bit of the plate is moving relative to the roof below it, except for points along a certain horizontal line running across the plate called the stationary line. If the temperature is rising, parts of the plate below the stationary line are moving down relative to the roof and feel a force of kinetic friction acting up the roof. Elements of area above the stationary line are sliding up the roof, and on them kinetic friction acts downward parallel to the roof. The stationary line occupies no area, so we assume no force of static fric-

tion acts on the plate while the temperature is changing. The plate as a whole is very nearly in equilibrium, so the net frictional force on it must be equal to the component of its weight acting down the incline. (a) Prove that the stationary line is at a distance of

$$\frac{L}{2}\left(1 - \frac{\tan\theta}{\mu_k}\right)$$

below the top edge of the plate. (b) Analyze the forces that act on the plate when the temperature is falling and prove that the stationary line is at that same distance above the bottom edge of the plate. (c) Show that the plate steps down the roof like an inchworm, moving each day by the distance

$$\frac{L}{\mu_k}(\alpha_2 - \alpha_1)(T_h - T_c)\tan\theta$$

(d) Evaluate the distance an aluminum plate moves each day if its length is 1.20 m, the temperature cycles between 4.00°C and 36.0°C, and the roof has slope 18.5°, coefficient of linear expansion 1.50×10^{-5} (°C)$^{-1}$, and coefficient of friction 0.420 with the plate. (e) **What If?** What if the expansion coefficient of the plate is less than that of the roof? Will the plate creep up the roof?

Answers to Quick Quizzes

19.1 (c). The direction of the transfer of energy depends only on temperature and not on the size of the object or on which object has more mass.

19.2 (c). The phrase "twice as hot" refers to a ratio of temperatures. When the given temperatures are converted to kelvins, only those in part (c) are in the correct ratio.

19.3 (c). Gasoline has the largest average coefficient of volume expansion.

19.4 (c). A cavity in a material expands in the same way as if it were filled with that material.

19.5 (a). On a cold day, the trapped air in the bubbles is reduced in pressure according to the ideal gas law. Therefore, the volume of the bubbles may be smaller than on a hot day and the package contents can shift more.

19.6 (b). Because of the increased temperature, the air expands. Consequently, some of the air leaks to the outside, leaving less air in the house.

In this photograph of Bow Lake in Banff National Park, Alberta, we see evidence of water in all three phases. In the lake is liquid water, and solid water in the form of snow appears on the ground. The clouds in the sky consist of liquid water droplets that have condensed from the gaseous water vapor in the air. Changes of a substance from one phase to another are a result of energy transfer. (Jacob Taposchaner/Getty Images)

20 The First Law of Thermodynamics

Until about 1850, the fields of thermodynamics and mechanics were considered to be two distinct branches of science. The law of conservation of energy seemed to describe only certain kinds of mechanical systems. Mid-19th-century experiments performed by Englishman James Joule and others, however, showed a strong connection between the transfer of energy by heat in thermal processes and the transfer of energy by work in mechanical processes. Today we know that mechanical energy can be transformed to internal energy, which is formally defined in this chapter. Once the concept of energy was generalized from mechanics to include internal energy, the law of conservation of energy emerged as a universal law of nature.

This chapter focuses on the concept of internal energy, the first law of thermodynamics, and some important applications of the first law. The first law of thermodynamics describes systems in which the only energy change is that of internal energy and the transfers of energy are by heat and work. A major difference in our discussion of work in this chapter from that in most of the chapters on mechanics is that we will consider work done on *deformable* systems.

20.1   Heat and Internal Energy

PITFALL PREVENTION 20.1
Internal Energy, Thermal Energy, and Bond Energy

When reading other physics books, you may see terms such as *thermal energy* and *bond energy*. Thermal energy can be interpreted as that part of the internal energy associated with random motion of molecules and, therefore, related to temperature. Bond energy is the intermolecular potential energy. Therefore,

Internal energy = thermal energy
+ bond energy

Although this breakdown is presented here for clarification with regard to other books, we will not use these terms because there is no need for them.

PITFALL PREVENTION 20.2
Heat, Temperature, and Internal Energy Are Different

As you read the newspaper or listen to the radio, be alert for incorrectly used phrases including the word *heat* and think about the proper word to be used in place of *heat*. Incorrect examples include "As the truck braked to a stop, a large amount of heat was generated by friction" and "The heat of a hot summer day . . ."

At the outset, it is important to make a major distinction between internal energy and heat, terms that are often incorrectly used interchangeably in popular language. **Internal energy is all the energy of a system that is associated with its microscopic components—atoms and molecules—when viewed from a reference frame at rest with respect to the center of mass of the system.** The last part of this sentence ensures that any bulk kinetic energy of the system due to its motion through space is not included in internal energy. Internal energy includes kinetic energy of random translational, rotational, and vibrational motion of molecules; vibrational potential energy associated with forces between atoms in molecules; and electric potential energy associated with forces between molecules. It is useful to relate internal energy to the temperature of an object, but this relationship is limited. We show in Section 20.3 that internal energy changes can also occur in the absence of temperature changes.

Heat is defined as the transfer of energy across the boundary of a system due to a temperature difference between the system and its surroundings. When you *heat* a substance, you are transferring energy into it by placing it in contact with surroundings that have a higher temperature. Such is the case, for example, when you place a pan of cold water on a stove burner. The burner is at a higher temperature than the water, and so the water gains energy. We shall also use the term *heat* to represent the amount of energy transferred by this method.

As an analogy to the distinction between heat and internal energy, consider the distinction between work and mechanical energy discussed in Chapter 7. The work done on a system is a measure of the amount of energy transferred to the system from its surroundings, whereas the mechanical energy (kinetic energy plus potential energy) of a system is a consequence of the motion and configuration of the system. Therefore, when a person does work on a system, energy is transferred from the person to the system. It makes no sense to talk about the work *of* a system; one can refer only to the work done *on* or *by* a system when some process has occurred in which energy has been transferred to or from the system. Likewise, it makes no sense to talk about the heat *of* a system; one can refer to heat only when energy has been transferred as a result of a temperature difference. Both heat and work are ways of changing the energy of a system.

Units of Heat

Early studies of heat focused on the resultant increase in temperature of a substance, which was often water. Initial notions of heat were based on a fluid called *caloric* that flowed from one substance to another and caused changes in temperature. From the name of this mythical fluid came an energy unit related to thermal processes, the **calorie (cal),** which is defined as **the amount of energy transfer necessary to raise the temperature of 1 g of water from 14.5°C to 15.5°C.**[1] (The "Calorie," written with a capital "C" and used in describing the energy content of foods, is actually a kilocalorie.) The unit of energy in the U.S. customary system is the **British thermal unit (Btu),** which is defined as **the amount of energy transfer required to raise the temperature of 1 lb of water from 63°F to 64°F.**

Once the relationship between energy in thermal and mechanical processes became clear, there was no need for a separate unit related to thermal processes. The *joule* has already been defined as an energy unit based on mechanical processes. Scientists are increasingly turning away from the calorie and the Btu and are using the joule when describing thermal processes. In this textbook, heat, work, and internal energy are usually measured in joules.

---

[1] Originally, the calorie was defined as the energy transfer necessary to raise the temperature of 1 g of water by 1°C. Careful measurements, however, showed that the amount of energy required to produce a 1°C change depends somewhat on the initial temperature; hence, a more precise definition evolved.

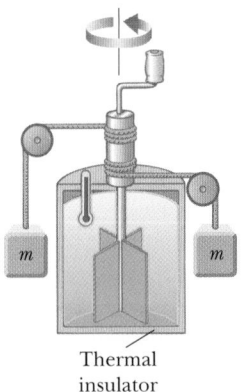

Figure 20.1 Joule's experiment for determining the mechanical equivalent of heat. The falling blocks rotate the paddles, causing the temperature of the water to increase.

Thermal insulator

The Mechanical Equivalent of Heat

In Chapters 7 and 8, we found that whenever friction is present in a mechanical system, the mechanical energy in the system decreases; in other words, mechanical energy is not conserved in the presence of nonconservative forces. Various experiments show that this mechanical energy does not simply disappear but is transformed into internal energy. You can perform such an experiment at home by hammering a nail into a scrap piece of wood. What happens to all the kinetic energy of the hammer once you have finished? Some of it is now in the nail as internal energy, as demonstrated by the nail being measurably warmer. Although this connection between mechanical and internal energy was first suggested by Benjamin Thompson, it was James Prescott Joule who established the equivalence of the decrease in mechanical energy and the increase in internal energy.

A schematic diagram of Joule's most famous experiment is shown in Figure 20.1. The system of interest is the water in a thermally insulated container. Work is done on the water by a rotating paddle wheel, which is driven by heavy blocks falling at a constant speed. If the energy lost in the bearings and through the walls is neglected, the loss in potential energy of the blocks–Earth system as the blocks fall equals the work done by the paddle wheel on the water. If the two blocks fall through a distance h, the loss in potential energy is $2mgh$, where m is the mass of one block; this energy causes the temperature of the water to increase due to friction between the paddles and the water. By varying the conditions of the experiment, Joule found that the loss in mechanical energy is proportional to the product of the mass of the water and the increase in water temperature. The proportionality constant was found to be approximately 4.18 J/g · °C. Hence, 4.18 J of mechanical energy raises the temperature of 1 g of water by 1°C. More precise measurements taken later demonstrated the proportionality to be 4.186 J/g · °C when the temperature of the water was raised from 14.5°C to 15.5°C. We adopt this "15-degree calorie" value:

$$1 \text{ cal} = 4.186 \text{ J} \qquad \textbf{(20.1)}$$

This equality is known, for purely historical reasons, as the **mechanical equivalent of heat**.

By kind permission of the President and Council of the Royal Society

JAMES PRESCOTT JOULE
British physicist (1818–1889)
Joule received some formal education in mathematics, philosophy, and chemistry from John Dalton but was in large part self-educated. Joule's research led to the establishment of the principle of conservation of energy. His study of the quantitative relationship among electrical, mechanical, and chemical effects of heat culminated in his announcement in 1843 of the amount of work required to produce a unit of energy, called the mechanical equivalent of heat.

EXAMPLE 20.1   **Losing Weight the Hard Way**

A student eats a dinner rated at 2 000 Calories. He wishes to do an equivalent amount of work in the gymnasium by lifting a 50.0-kg barbell. How many times must he raise the barbell to expend this much energy? Assume he raises the barbell 2.00 m each time he lifts it and he regains no energy when he lowers the barbell.

SOLUTION

Conceptualize Imagine the student raising the barbell. He is doing work on the system of the barbell and the Earth, so energy is leaving his body. The total amount of work that the student must do is 2 000 Calories.

Categorize We model the system of the barbell and the Earth as a nonisolated system.

Analyze Reduce the conservation of energy equation, Equation 8.2, to the appropriate expression for the system of the barbell and the Earth:

$$(1) \quad \Delta U_{total} = W_{total}$$

Express the change in gravitational potential energy of the system after the barbell is raised once:

$$\Delta U = mgh$$

Express the total amount of energy that must be transferred into the system by work for lifting the barbell n times, assuming energy is not regained when the barbell is lowered:

$$(2) \quad \Delta U_{total} = nmgh$$

Substitute Equation (2) into Equation (1):

$$nmgh = W_{total}$$

Solve for n:

$$n = \frac{W_{total}}{mgh}$$

$$= \frac{(2\ 000\ \text{Cal})}{(50.0\ \text{kg})(9.80\ \text{m/s}^2)(2.00\ \text{m})}\left(\frac{1.00 \times 10^3\ \text{cal}}{\text{Calorie}}\right)\left(\frac{4.186\ \text{J}}{1\ \text{cal}}\right)$$

$$= \boxed{8.54 \times 10^3 \text{ times}}$$

Finalize If the student is in good shape and lifts the barbell once every 5 s, it will take him about 12 h to perform this feat. Clearly, it is much easier for this student to lose weight by dieting.

In reality, the human body is not 100% efficient. Therefore, not all the energy transformed within the body from the dinner transfers out of the body by work done on the barbell. Some of this energy is used to pump blood and perform other functions within the body. Therefore, the 2 000 Calories can be worked off in less time than 12 h when these other energy requirements are included.

20.2 Specific Heat and Calorimetry

When energy is added to a system and there is no change in the kinetic or potential energy of the system, the temperature of the system usually rises. (An exception to this statement is the case in which a system undergoes a change of state—also called a *phase transition*—as discussed in the next section.) If the system consists of a sample of a substance, we find that the quantity of energy required to raise the temperature of a given mass of the substance by some amount varies from one substance to another. For example, the quantity of energy required to raise the temperature of 1 kg of water by 1°C is 4 186 J, but the quantity of energy required to raise the temperature of 1 kg of copper by 1°C is only 387 J. In the discussion that follows, we shall use heat as our example of energy transfer, but keep in mind that the temperature of the system could be changed by means of any method of energy transfer.

The **heat capacity** C of a particular sample is defined as the amount of energy needed to raise the temperature of that sample by 1°C. From this definition, we see that if energy Q produces a change ΔT in the temperature of a sample, then

$$Q = C\,\Delta T \tag{20.2}$$

The **specific heat** c of a substance is the heat capacity per unit mass. Therefore, if energy Q transfers to a sample of a substance with mass m and the temperature of the sample changes by ΔT, the specific heat of the substance is

TABLE 20.1

Specific Heats of Some Substances at 25°C and Atmospheric Pressure

Substance	Specific Heat c		Substance	Specific Heat c	
	J/kg · °C	**cal/g · °C**		**J/kg · °C**	**cal/g · °C**
Elemental solids			*Other solids*		
Aluminum	900	0.215	Brass	380	0.092
Beryllium	1 830	0.436	Glass	837	0.200
Cadmium	230	0.055	Ice (−5°C)	2 090	0.50
Copper	387	0.092 4	Marble	860	0.21
Germanium	322	0.077	Wood	1 700	0.41
Gold	129	0.030 8	*Liquids*		
Iron	448	0.107	Alcohol (ethyl)	2 400	0.58
Lead	128	0.030 5	Mercury	140	0.033
Silicon	703	0.168	Water (15°C)	4 186	1.00
Silver	234	0.056	*Gas*		
			Steam (100°C)	2 010	0.48

$$c \equiv \frac{Q}{m\,\Delta T}$$

(20.3) ◀ Specific heat

Specific heat is essentially a measure of how thermally insensitive a substance is to the addition of energy. The greater a material's specific heat, the more energy must be added to a given mass of the material to cause a particular temperature change. Table 20.1 lists representative specific heats.

From this definition, we can relate the energy Q transferred between a sample of mass m of a material and its surroundings to a temperature change ΔT as

$$Q = mc\,\Delta T$$

(20.4)

For example, the energy required to raise the temperature of 0.500 kg of water by 3.00°C is $Q = (0.500 \text{ kg})(4\ 186 \text{ J/kg} \cdot {}^\circ\text{C})(3.00{}^\circ\text{C}) = 6.28 \times 10^3$ J. Notice that when the temperature increases, Q and ΔT are taken to be positive and energy transfers into the system. When the temperature decreases, Q and ΔT are negative and energy transfers out of the system.

Specific heat varies with temperature. If, however, temperature intervals are not too great, the temperature variation can be ignored and c can be treated as a constant.[2] For example, the specific heat of water varies by only about 1% from 0°C to 100°C at atmospheric pressure. Unless stated otherwise, we shall neglect such variations.

Quick Quiz 20.1   Imagine you have 1 kg each of iron, glass, and water, and all three samples are at 10°C. (a) Rank the samples from lowest to highest temperature after 100 J of energy is added to each sample. (b) Rank the samples from least to greatest amount of energy transferred by heat if each sample increases in temperature by 20°C.

Notice from Table 20.1 that water has the highest specific heat of common materials. This high specific heat is in part responsible for the moderate temperatures found near large bodies of water. As the temperature of a body of water decreases during the winter, energy is transferred from the cooling water to the air by heat, increasing the internal energy of the air. Because of the high specific heat

PITFALL PREVENTION 20.3
An Unfortunate Choice of Terminology

The name *specific heat* is an unfortunate holdover from the days when thermodynamics and mechanics developed separately. A better name would be *specific energy transfer*, but the existing term is too entrenched to be replaced.

PITFALL PREVENTION 20.4
Energy Can Be Transferred by Any Method

The symbol Q represents the amount of energy transferred, but keep in mind that the energy transfer in Equation 20.4 could be by *any* of the methods introduced in Chapter 8; it does not have to be heat. For example, repeatedly bending a wire coat hanger raises the temperature at the bending point by *work*.

---

[2] The definition given by Equation 20.4 assumes the specific heat does not vary with temperature over the interval $\Delta T = T_f - T_i$. In general, if c varies with temperature over the interval, the correct expression for Q is $Q = m\int_{T_i}^{T_f} c\, dT$.

of water, a relatively large amount of energy is transferred to the air for even modest temperature changes of the water. The prevailing winds on the West Coast of the United States are toward the land (eastward). Hence, the energy liberated by the Pacific Ocean as it cools keeps coastal areas much warmer than they would otherwise be. As a result, West Coast states generally have more favorable winter weather than East Coast states, where the prevailing winds do not tend to carry the energy toward land.

Calorimetry

One technique for measuring specific heat involves heating a sample to some known temperature T_x, placing it in a vessel containing water of known mass and temperature $T_w < T_x$, and measuring the temperature of the water after equilibrium has been reached. This technique is called **calorimetry,** and devices in which this energy transfer occurs are called **calorimeters**. If the system of the sample and the water is isolated, the principle of conservation of energy requires that the amount of energy that leaves the sample (of unknown specific heat) equal the amount of energy that enters the water.[3] Conservation of energy allows us to write the mathematical representation of this energy statement as

$$Q_{cold} = -Q_{hot} \tag{20.5}$$

Suppose m_x is the mass of a sample of some substance whose specific heat we wish to determine. Let's call its specific heat c_x and its initial temperature T_x. Likewise, let m_w, c_w, and T_w represent corresponding values for the water. If T_f is the final equilibrium temperature after everything is mixed, Equation 20.4 shows that the energy transfer for the water is $m_w c_w (T_f - T_w)$, which is positive because $T_f > T_w$, and that the energy transfer for the sample of unknown specific heat is $m_x c_x (T_f - T_x)$, which is negative. Substituting these expressions into Equation 20.5 gives

$$m_w c_w (T_f - T_w) = -m_x c_x (T_f - T_x)$$

Solving for c_x gives

$$c_x = \frac{m_w c_w (T_f - T_w)}{m_x (T_x - T_f)}$$

PITFALL PREVENTION 20.5
Remember the Negative Sign

It is *critical* to include the negative sign in Equation 20.5. The negative sign in the equation is necessary for consistency with our sign convention for energy transfer. The energy transfer Q_{hot} has a negative value because energy is leaving the hot substance. The negative sign in the equation ensures that the right side is a positive number, consistent with the left side, which is positive because energy is entering the cold water.

EXAMPLE 20.2 | **Cooling a Hot Ingot**

A 0.050 0-kg ingot of metal is heated to 200.0°C and then dropped into a calorimeter containing 0.400 kg of water initially at 20.0°C. The final equilibrium temperature of the mixed system is 22.4°C. Find the specific heat of the metal.

SOLUTION

Conceptualize Imagine the process occurring in the system. Energy is leaving the hot ingot and going into the cold water, so the ingot cools off and the water warms up. Once both are at the same temperature, the energy transfer stops.

Categorize We use an equation developed in this section, so we categorize this example as a substitution problem.

Use Equation 20.4 to evaluate each side of Equation 20.5:

$$m_w c_w (T_f - T_w) = -m_x c_x (T_f - T_x)$$

$$(0.400 \text{ kg})(4 \text{ 186 J/kg} \cdot °\text{C})(22.4°\text{C} - 20.0°\text{C})$$

$$= -(0.050 \text{ 0 kg})(c_x)(22.4°\text{C} - 200.0°\text{C})$$

[3] For precise measurements, the water container should be included in our calculations because it also exchanges energy with the sample. Doing so would require that we know the container's mass and composition, however. If the mass of the water is much greater than that of the container, we can neglect the effects of the container.

Solve for the specific heat of the metal:

$$c_x = \boxed{453 \text{ J/kg} \cdot {}^\circ\text{C}}$$

The ingot is most likely iron as you can see by comparing this result with the data given in Table 20.1. The temperature of the ingot is initially above the steam point. Therefore, some of the water may vaporize when the ingot is dropped into the water. We assume the system is sealed and this steam cannot escape. Because the final equilibrium temperature is lower than the steam point, any steam that does result recondenses back into water.

What If? Suppose you are performing an experiment in the laboratory that uses this technique to determine the specific heat of a sample and you wish to decrease the overall uncertainty in your final result for c_x. Of the data given in this example, changing which value would be most effective in decreasing the uncertainty?

Answer The largest experimental uncertainty is associated with the small difference in temperature of 2.4°C for the water. For example, using the rules for propagation of uncertainty in Appendix Section B.8, an uncertainty of 0.1°C in each of T_f and T_w leads to an 8% uncertainty in their difference. For this temperature difference to be larger experimentally, the most effective change is to *decrease the amount of water*.

EXAMPLE 20.3   Fun Time for a Cowboy

A cowboy fires a silver bullet with a muzzle speed of 200 m/s into the pine wall of a saloon. Assume all the internal energy generated by the impact remains with the bullet. What is the temperature change of the bullet?

SOLUTION

Conceptualize Imagine similar experiences you may have had in which mechanical energy is transformed to internal energy when a moving object is stopped. For example, as mentioned in Section 20.1, a nail becomes warm after it is hit a few times with a hammer.

Categorize The bullet is modeled as an isolated system. No work is done on the system because the force from the wall moves through no displacement. This example is similar to the skateboarder pushing off a wall in Section 9.7. There, no work is done on the skateboarder by the wall, and potential energy stored in the body from previous meals is transformed to kinetic energy. Here, no work is done by the wall on the bullet, and kinetic energy is transformed to internal energy.

Analyze Reduce the conservation of energy equation, Equation 8.2, to the appropriate expression for the system of the bullet:

$$(1) \quad \Delta K + \Delta E_{\text{int}} = 0$$

The change in the bullet's internal energy is the same as that which would take place if energy were transferred by heat from a stove to the bullet. Using this concept, evaluate the change in internal energy of the bullet:

$$(2) \quad \Delta E_{\text{int}} = Q = mc\,\Delta T$$

Substitute Equation (2) into Equation (1):

$$(0 - \tfrac{1}{2}mv^2) + mc\,\Delta T = 0$$

Solve for ΔT, using 234 J/kg $\cdot$ °C as the specific heat of silver (see Table 20.1):

$$(3) \quad \Delta T = \frac{\tfrac{1}{2}mv^2}{mc} = \frac{v^2}{2c} = \frac{(200 \text{ m/s})^2}{2(234 \text{ J/kg} \cdot {}^\circ\text{C})} = \boxed{85.5{}^\circ\text{C}}$$

Finalize Notice that the result does not depend on the mass of the bullet.

What If? Suppose the cowboy runs out of silver bullets and fires a lead bullet at the same speed into the wall. Will the temperature change of the bullet be larger or smaller?

Answer   Table 20.1 shows that the specific heat of lead is 128 J/kg · °C, which is smaller than that for silver. Therefore, a given amount of energy input or transformation raises lead to a higher temperature than silver and the final temperature of the lead bullet will be larger. In Equation (3), let's substitute the new value for the specific heat:

$$\Delta T = \frac{v^2}{2c} = \frac{(200 \text{ m/s})^2}{2(128 \text{ J/kg} \cdot °\text{C})} = 156°\text{C}$$

There is no requirement that the silver and lead bullets have the same mass to determine this change in temperature. The only requirement is that they have the same speed.

20.3   Latent Heat

As we have seen in the preceding section, a substance can undergo a change in temperature when energy is transferred between it and its surroundings. In some situations, however, the transfer of energy does not result in a change in temperature. That is the case whenever the physical characteristics of the substance change from one form to another; such a change is commonly referred to as a **phase change**. Two common phase changes are from solid to liquid (melting) and from liquid to gas (boiling); another is a change in the crystalline structure of a solid. All such phase changes involve a change in the system's internal energy but no change in its temperature. The increase in internal energy in boiling, for example, is represented by the breaking of bonds between molecules in the liquid state; this bond breaking allows the molecules to move farther apart in the gaseous state, with a corresponding increase in intermolecular potential energy.

As you might expect, different substances respond differently to the addition or removal of energy as they change phase because their internal molecular arrangements vary. Also, the amount of energy transferred during a phase change depends on the amount of substance involved. (It takes less energy to melt an ice cube than it does to thaw a frozen lake.) If a quantity Q of energy transfer is required to change the phase of a mass m of a substance, the **latent heat** of the substance is defined as

$$L \equiv \frac{Q}{m} \tag{20.6}$$

This parameter is called latent heat (literally, the "hidden" heat) because this added or removed energy does not result in a temperature change. The value of L for a substance depends on the nature of the phase change as well as on the properties of the substance.

From the definition of latent heat, and again choosing heat as our energy transfer mechanism, the energy required to change the phase of a given mass m of a pure substance is

◀ Latent heat

$$Q = \pm mL \tag{20.7}$$

Latent heat of fusion L_f is the term used when the phase change is from solid to liquid (*to fuse* means "to combine by melting"), and **latent heat of vaporization** L_v is the term used when the phase change is from liquid to gas (the liquid "vaporizes").[4] The latent heats of various substances vary considerably as data in Table 20.2 show. The positive sign in Equation 20.7 is used when energy enters a system, causing melting or vaporization. The negative sign corresponds to energy leaving a system such that the system freezes or condenses.

PITFALL PREVENTION 20.6
Signs Are Critical

Sign errors occur very often when students apply calorimetry equations. For phase changes, use the correct explicit sign in Equation 20.7, depending on whether you are adding or removing energy from the substance. In Equation 20.4, there is no explicit sign to consider, but be sure your ΔT is *always* the final temperature minus the initial temperature. In addition, you must *always* include the negative sign on the right side of Equation 20.5.

---

[4] When a gas cools, it eventually *condenses*; that is, it returns to the liquid phase. The energy given up per unit mass is called the *latent heat of condensation* and is numerically equal to the latent heat of vaporization. Likewise, when a liquid cools, it eventually solidifies, and the *latent heat of solidification* is numerically equal to the latent heat of fusion.

TABLE 20.2

Latent Heats of Fusion and Vaporization

Substance	Melting Point (°C)	Latent Heat of Fusion (J/kg)	Boiling Point (°C)	Latent Heat of Vaporization (J/kg)
Helium	−269.65	5.23×10^3	−268.93	2.09×10^4
Nitrogen	−209.97	2.55×10^4	−195.81	2.01×10^5
Oxygen	−218.79	1.38×10^4	−182.97	2.13×10^5
Ethyl alcohol	−114	1.04×10^5	78	8.54×10^5
Water	0.00	3.33×10^5	100.00	2.26×10^6
Sulfur	119	3.81×10^4	444.60	3.26×10^5
Lead	327.3	2.45×10^4	1 750	8.70×10^5
Aluminum	660	3.97×10^5	2 450	1.14×10^7
Silver	960.80	8.82×10^4	2 193	2.33×10^6
Gold	1 063.00	6.44×10^4	2 660	1.58×10^6
Copper	1 083	1.34×10^5	1 187	5.06×10^6

To understand the role of latent heat in phase changes, consider the energy required to convert a 1.00-g cube of ice at −30.0°C to steam at 120.0°C. Figure 20.2 indicates the experimental results obtained when energy is gradually added to the ice. The results are presented as a graph of temperature of the system of the ice cube versus energy added to the system. Let's examine each portion of the red curve.

Part A.   On this portion of the curve, the temperature of the ice changes from −30.0°C to 0.0°C. Equation 20.4 indicates that the temperature varies linearly with the energy added, so the experimental result is a straight line on the graph. Because the specific heat of ice is 2 090 J/kg·°C, we can calculate the amount of energy added by using Equation 20.4:

$$Q = m_i c_i \, \Delta T = (1.00 \times 10^{-3} \text{ kg})(2\,090 \text{ J/kg} \cdot °\text{C})(30.0°\text{C}) = 62.7 \text{ J}$$

Part B.   When the temperature of the ice reaches 0.0°C, the ice–water mixture remains at this temperature—even though energy is being added—until all the ice melts. The energy required to melt 1.00 g of ice at 0.0°C is, from Equation 20.7,

$$Q = m_i L_f = (1.00 \times 10^{-3} \text{ kg})(3.33 \times 10^5 \text{ J/kg}) = 333 \text{ J}$$

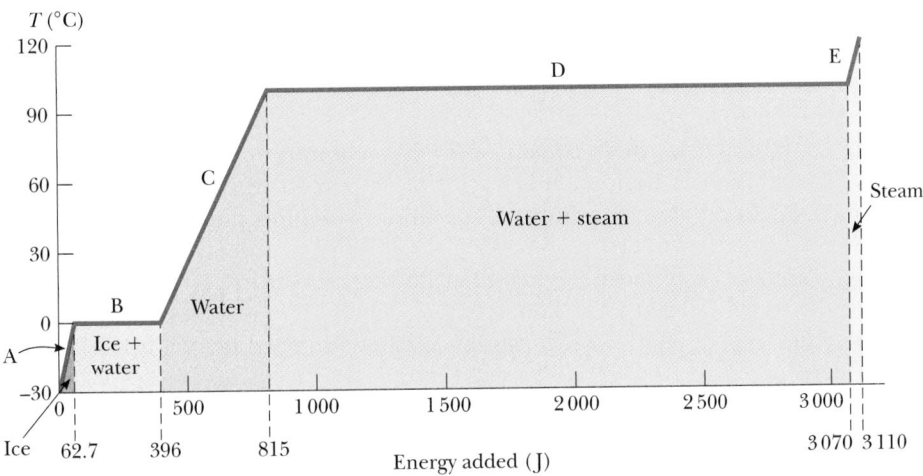

Figure 20.2   A plot of temperature versus energy added when 1.00 g of ice initially at −30.0°C is converted to steam at 120.0°C.

At this point, we have moved to the 396 J (= 62.7 J + 333 J) mark on the energy axis in Figure 20.2.

Part C. Between 0.0°C and 100.0°C, nothing surprising happens. No phase change occurs, and so all energy added to the water is used to increase its temperature. The amount of energy necessary to increase the temperature from 0.0°C to 100.0°C is

$$Q = m_w c_w \, \Delta T = (1.00 \times 10^{-3} \text{ kg})(4.19 \times 10^3 \text{ J/kg} \cdot °\text{C})(100.0°\text{C}) = 419 \text{ J}$$

Part D. At 100.0°C, another phase change occurs as the water changes from water at 100.0°C to steam at 100.0°C. Similar to the ice-water mixture in part B, the water-steam mixture remains at 100.0°C—even though energy is being added—until all the liquid has been converted to steam. The energy required to convert 1.00 g of water to steam at 100.0°C is

$$Q = m_w L_v = (1.00 \times 10^{-3} \text{ kg})(2.26 \times 10^6 \text{ J/kg}) = 2.26 \times 10^3 \text{ J}$$

Part E. On this portion of the curve, as in parts A and C, no phase change occurs; therefore, all energy added is used to increase the temperature of the steam. The energy that must be added to raise the temperature of the steam from 100.0°C to 120.0°C is

$$Q = m_s c_s \, \Delta T = (1.00 \times 10^{-3} \text{ kg})(2.01 \times 10^3 \text{ J/kg} \cdot °\text{C})(20.0°\text{C}) = 40.2 \text{ J}$$

The total amount of energy that must be added to change 1 g of ice at −30.0°C to steam at 120.0°C is the sum of the results from all five parts of the curve, which is 3.11 × 10³ J. Conversely, to cool 1 g of steam at 120.0°C to ice at −30.0°C, we must remove 3.11 × 10³ J of energy.

Notice in Figure 20.2 the relatively large amount of energy that is transferred into the water to vaporize it to steam. Imagine reversing this process, with a large amount of energy transferred out of steam to condense it into water. That is why a burn to your skin from steam at 100°C is much more damaging than exposure of your skin to water at 100°C. A very large amount of energy enters your skin from the steam, and the steam remains at 100°C for a long time while it condenses. Conversely, when your skin makes contact with water at 100°C, the water immediately begins to drop in temperature as energy transfers from the water to your skin.

If liquid water is held perfectly still in a very clean container, it is possible for the water to drop below 0°C without freezing into ice. This phenomenon, called **supercooling,** arises because the water requires a disturbance of some sort for the molecules to move apart and start forming the large open ice structure that makes the density of ice lower than that of water as discussed in Section 19.4. If supercooled water is disturbed, it suddenly freezes. The system drops into the lower-energy configuration of bound molecules of the ice structure, and the energy released raises the temperature back to 0°C.

Commercial hand warmers consist of liquid sodium acetate in a sealed plastic pouch. The solution in the pouch is in a stable supercooled state. When a disk in the pouch is clicked by your fingers, the liquid solidifies and the temperature increases, just like the supercooled water just mentioned. In this case, however, the freezing point of the liquid is higher than body temperature, so the pouch feels warm to the touch. To reuse the hand warmer, the pouch must be boiled until the solid liquefies. Then, as it cools, it passes below its freezing point into the super-cooled state.

It is also possible to create **superheating**. For example, clean water in a very clean cup placed in a microwave oven can sometimes rise in temperature beyond 100°C without boiling because the formation of a bubble of steam in the water requires scratches in the cup or some type of impurity in the water to serve as a nucleation site. When the cup is removed from the microwave oven, the super-

heated water can become explosive as bubbles form immediately and the hot
water is forced upward out of the cup.

Quick Quiz 20.2   Suppose the same process of adding energy to the ice cube is
performed as discussed above, but instead we graph the internal energy of the system as a function of energy input. What would this graph look like?

EXAMPLE 20.4	**Cooling the Steam**

What mass of steam initially at 130°C is needed to warm 200 g of water in a 100-g glass container from 20.0°C to
50.0°C?

SOLUTION

Conceptualize   Imagine placing water and steam together in a closed insulated container. The system eventually
reaches a uniform state of water with a final temperature of 50.0°C.

Categorize   Based on our conceptualization of this situation, we categorize this example as one involving calorimetry in which a phase change occurs.

Analyze   Write Equation 20.5 to describe the
calorimetry process:

$$(1) \quad Q_{cold} = -Q_{hot}$$

The steam undergoes three processes: a
decrease in temperature to 100°C, condensation into liquid water, and finally a decrease in
temperature of the water to 50.0°C. Find the
energy transfer in the first process using the
unknown mass m_s of the steam:

$$Q_1 = m_s c_s \, \Delta T = m_s (2.01 \times 10^3 \, \text{J/kg} \cdot \text{°C})(-30.0\text{°C})$$
$$= -m_s(6.03 \times 10^4 \, \text{J/kg})$$

Find the energy transfer in the second process,
being sure to use a negative sign in Equation
20.7 because energy is leaving the steam:

$$Q_2 = -m_s(2.26 \times 10^6 \, \text{J/kg})$$

Find the energy transfer in the third process:

$$Q_3 = m_s c_w \, \Delta T = m_s(4.19 \times 10^3 \, \text{J/kg} \cdot \text{°C}) \, (-50.0\text{°C})$$
$$= -m_s(2.09 \times 10^5 \, \text{J/kg})$$

Add the energy transfers in these three stages:

$$Q_{hot} = Q_1 + Q_2 + Q_3$$
$$Q_{hot} = -m_s[6.03 \times 10^4 \, \text{J/kg} + 2.26 \times 10^6 \, \text{J/kg} + 2.09 \times 10^5 \, \text{J/kg}]$$
$$(2) \quad Q_{hot} = -m_s(2.53 \times 10^6 \, \text{J/kg})$$

The 20.0°C water and the glass undergo only
one process, an increase in temperature to
50.0°C. Find the energy transfer in this process:

$$Q_{cold} = (0.200 \, \text{kg})(4.19 \times 10^3 \, \text{J/kg} \cdot \text{°C})(30.0\text{°C})$$
$$+ (0.100 \, \text{kg})(837 \, \text{J/kg} \cdot \text{°C})(30.0\text{°C})$$
$$(3) \quad Q_{cold} = 2.77 \times 10^4 \, \text{J}$$

Substitute Equations (2) and (3) into Equation (1) and solve for m_s:

$$2.77 \times 10^4 \, \text{J} = -[-m_s(2.53 \times 10^6 \, \text{J/kg})]$$
$$m_s = 1.09 \times 10^{-2} \, \text{kg} = \boxed{10.9 \, \text{g}}$$

What If?   What if the final state of the system is water at 100°C? Would we need more steam or less steam? How
would the analysis above change?

Answer   More steam would be needed to raise the temperature of the water and glass to 100°C instead of 50.0°C. There would be two major changes in the analysis. First, we would not have a term Q_3 for the steam because the water that condenses from the steam does not cool below 100°C. Second, in Q_{cold}, the temperature change would be 80.0°C instead of 30.0°C. For practice, show that the result is a required mass of steam of 31.8 g.

20.4   Work and Heat in Thermodynamic Processes

In thermodynamics, we describe the *state* of a system using such variables as pressure, volume, temperature, and internal energy. As a result, these quantities belong to a category called **state variables**. For any given configuration of the system, we can identify values of the state variables. (For mechanical systems, the state variables include kinetic energy K and potential energy U.) A state of a system can be specified only if the system is in thermal equilibrium internally. In the case of a gas in a container, internal thermal equilibrium requires that every part of the gas be at the same pressure and temperature.

A second category of variables in situations involving energy is **transfer variables**. These variables are those that appear on the right side of the conservation of energy equation, Equation 8.2. Such a variable has a nonzero value if a process occurs in which energy is transferred across the system's boundary. The transfer variable is positive or negative, depending on whether energy is entering or leaving the system. Because a transfer of energy across the boundary represents a change in the system, transfer variables are not associated with a given state of the system but, rather, with a *change* in the state of the system.

In the previous sections, we discussed heat as a transfer variable. In this section, we study another important transfer variable for thermodynamic systems, work. Work performed on particles was studied extensively in Chapter 7, and here we investigate the work done on a deformable system, a gas. Consider a gas contained in a cylinder fitted with a movable piston (Fig. 20.3). At equilibrium, the gas occupies a volume V and exerts a uniform pressure P on the cylinder's walls and on the piston. If the piston has a cross-sectional area A, the force exerted by the gas on the piston is $F = PA$. Now let's assume that we push the piston inward and compress the gas **quasi-statically,** that is, slowly enough to allow the system to remain essentially in internal thermal equilibrium at all times. As the piston is pushed downward by an external force $\vec{\mathbf{F}} = -F\hat{\mathbf{j}}$ through a displacement of $d\vec{\mathbf{r}} = dy\hat{\mathbf{j}}$ (Fig. 20.3b), the work done on the gas is, according to our definition of work in Chapter 7,

Figure 20.3   Work is done on a gas contained in a cylinder at a pressure P as the piston is pushed downward so that the gas is compressed.

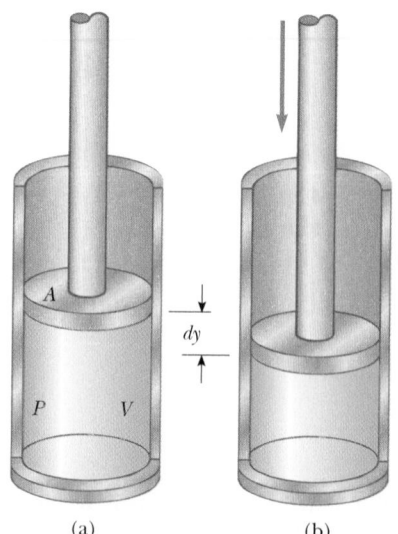

(a)   (b)

$$dW = \vec{\mathbf{F}} \cdot d\vec{\mathbf{r}} = -F\hat{\mathbf{j}} \cdot dy\hat{\mathbf{j}} = -F\,dy = -PA\,dy$$

where the magnitude F of the external force is equal to PA because the piston is always in equilibrium between the external force and the force from the gas. The mass of the piston is assumed to be negligible in this discussion. Because $A\,dy$ is the change in volume of the gas dV, we can express the work done on the gas as

$$dW = -P\,dV \qquad (20.8)$$

If the gas is compressed, dV is negative and the work done on the gas is positive. If the gas expands, dV is positive and the work done on the gas is negative. If the volume remains constant, the work done on the gas is zero. The total work done on the gas as its volume changes from V_i to V_f is given by the integral of Equation 20.8:

$$W = -\int_{V_i}^{V_f} P\,dV \qquad (20.9)$$

◀ Work done on a gas

To evaluate this integral, you must know how the pressure varies with volume during the process.

In general, the pressure is not constant during a process followed by a gas, but depends on the volume and temperature. If the pressure and volume are known at each step of the process, the state of the gas at each step can be plotted on a graphical representation called a **PV diagram** as in Active Figure 20.4. This type of diagram allows us to visualize a process through which a gas is progressing. The curve on a PV diagram is called the *path* taken between the initial and final states.

Notice that the integral in Equation 20.9 is equal to the area under a curve on a PV diagram. Therefore, we can identify an important use for PV diagrams:

> The work done on a gas in a quasi-static process that takes the gas from an initial state to a final state is the negative of the area under the curve on a PV diagram, evaluated between the initial and final states.

For the process of compressing a gas in a cylinder, the work done depends on the particular path taken between the initial and final states as Active Figure 20.4 suggests. To illustrate this important point, consider several different paths connecting i and f (Active Fig. 20.5). In the process depicted in Active Figure 20.5a, the volume of the gas is first reduced from V_i to V_f at constant pressure P_i and the pressure of the gas then increases from P_i to P_f by heating at constant volume V_f. The work done on the gas along this path is $-P_i(V_f - V_i)$. In Active Figure 20.5b, the pressure of the gas is increased from P_i to P_f at constant volume V_i and then the volume of the gas is reduced from V_i to V_f at constant pressure P_f. The work done on the gas is $-P_f(V_f - V_i)$. This value is greater than that for the process

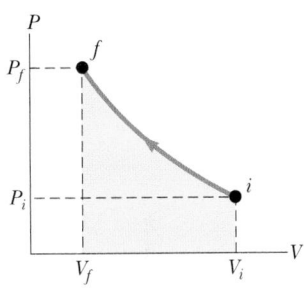

ACTIVE FIGURE 20.4

A gas is compressed quasi-statically (slowly) from state i to state f. The work done on the gas equals the negative of the area under the PV curve. The volume is decreasing, so this area is negative. Then the work done on the gas is positive. An outside agent must do positive work on the gas to compress it.

Sign in at www.thomsonedu.com and go to ThomsonNOW to compress the piston in Figure 20.3 and see the result on the PV diagram in this figure.

ACTIVE FIGURE 20.5

The work done on a gas as it is taken from an initial state to a final state depends on the path between these states.

Sign in at www.thomsonedu.com and go to ThomsonNOW to choose one of the three paths and see the movement of the piston in Figure 20.3 and of a point on the PV diagram in this figure.

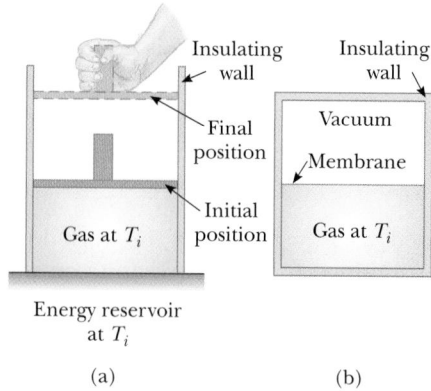

Figure 20.6   (a) A gas at temperature T_i expands slowly while absorbing energy from a reservoir to maintain a constant temperature. (b) A gas expands rapidly into an evacuated region after a membrane is broken.

described in Active Figure 20.5a because the piston is moved through the same displacement by a larger force. Finally, for the process described in Active Figure 20.5c, where both P and V change continuously, the work done on the gas has some value between the values obtained in the first two processes. To evaluate the work in this case, the function $P(V)$ must be known so that we can evaluate the integral in Equation 20.9.

The energy transfer Q into or out of a system by heat also depends on the process. Consider the situations depicted in Figure 20.6. In each case, the gas has the same initial volume, temperature, and pressure, and is assumed to be ideal. In Figure 20.6a, the gas is thermally insulated from its surroundings except at the bottom of the gas-filled region, where it is in thermal contact with an energy reservoir. An *energy reservoir* is a source of energy that is considered to be so great that a finite transfer of energy to or from the reservoir does not change its temperature. The piston is held at its initial position by an external agent such as a hand. When the force holding the piston is reduced slightly, the piston rises very slowly to its final position. Because the piston is moving upward, the gas is doing work on the piston. During this expansion to the final volume V_f, just enough energy is transferred by heat from the reservoir to the gas to maintain a constant temperature T_i.

Now consider the completely thermally insulated system shown in Figure 20.6b. When the membrane is broken, the gas expands rapidly into the vacuum until it occupies a volume V_f and is at a pressure P_f. In this case, the gas does no work because it does not apply a force; no force is required to expand into a vacuum. Furthermore, no energy is transferred by heat through the insulating wall.

The initial and final states of the ideal gas in Figure 20.6a are identical to the initial and final states in Figure 20.6b, but the paths are different. In the first case, the gas does work on the piston and energy is transferred slowly to the gas by heat. In the second case, no energy is transferred by heat and the value of the work done is zero. Therefore, **energy transfer by heat, like work done, depends on the initial, final, and intermediate states of the system**. In other words, because heat and work depend on the path, neither quantity is determined solely by the endpoints of a thermodynamic process.

20.5   The First Law of Thermodynamics

When we introduced the law of conservation of energy in Chapter 8, we stated that the change in the energy of a system is equal to the sum of all transfers of energy across the system's boundary. The **first law of thermodynamics** is a special case of the law of conservation of energy that describes processes in which only the internal energy[5] changes and the only energy transfers are by heat and work:

$$\Delta E_{int} = Q + W \qquad (20.10)$$

◀ First law of thermodynamics

An important consequence of the first law of thermodynamics is that there exists a quantity known as internal energy whose value is determined by the state of the system. The internal energy is therefore a state variable like pressure, volume, and temperature.

When a system undergoes an infinitesimal change in state in which a small amount of energy dQ is transferred by heat and a small amount of work dW is done, the internal energy changes by a small amount dE_{int}. Therefore, for infinitesimal processes we can express the first law as[6]

$$dE_{int} = dQ + dW$$

Let us investigate some special cases in which the first law can be applied. First, consider an *isolated system*, that is, one that does not interact with its surroundings. In this case, no energy transfer by heat takes place and the work done on the system is zero; hence, the internal energy remains constant. That is, because $Q = W = 0$, it follows that $\Delta E_{int} = 0$; therefore, $E_{int,i} = E_{int,f}$. We conclude that **the internal energy E_{int} of an isolated system remains constant**.

Next, consider the case of a system that can exchange energy with its surroundings and is taken through a **cyclic process**, that is, a process that starts and ends at the same state. In this case, the change in the internal energy must again be zero because E_{int} is a state variable; therefore, the energy Q added to the system must equal the negative of the work W done on the system during the cycle. That is, in a cyclic process,

$$\Delta E_{int} = 0 \quad \text{and} \quad Q = -W \quad \text{(cyclic process)}$$

On a PV diagram, a cyclic process appears as a closed curve. (The processes described in Active Figure 20.5 are represented by open curves because the initial and final states differ.) It can be shown that **in a cyclic process, the net work done on the system per cycle equals the area enclosed by the path representing the process on a PV diagram**.

20.6 Some Applications of the First Law of Thermodynamics

In this section, we consider applications of the first law to processes through which a gas is taken. As a model, let's consider the sample of gas contained in the piston-cylinder apparatus in Active Figure 20.7 (page 568). This figure shows work being done on the gas and energy transferring in by heat, so the internal energy of the gas is rising. In the following discussion of various processes, refer back to this figure and mentally alter the directions of the transfer of energy to reflect what is happening in the process.

Before we apply the first law of thermodynamics to specific systems, it is useful to first define some idealized thermodynamic processes. An **adiabatic process** is one during which no energy enters or leaves the system by heat; that is, $Q = 0$. An

---

[5] It is an unfortunate accident of history that the traditional symbol for internal energy is U, which is also the traditional symbol for potential energy as introduced in Chapter 7. To avoid confusion between potential energy and internal energy, we use the symbol E_{int} for internal energy in this book. If you take an advanced course in thermodynamics, however, be prepared to see U used as the symbol for internal energy in the first law.

[6] Notice that dQ and dW are not true differential quantities because Q and W are not state variables, but dE_{int} is. Because dQ and dW are *inexact differentials*, they are often represented by the symbols $đQ$ and $đW$. For further details on this point, see an advanced text on thermodynamics.

PITFALL PREVENTION 20.7
Dual Sign Conventions

Some physics and engineering books present the first law as $\Delta E_{int} = Q - W$, with a minus sign between the heat and work. The reason is that work is defined in these treatments as the work done *by* the gas rather than *on* the gas, as in our treatment. The equivalent equation to Equation 20.9 in these treatments defines work as $W = \int_{V_i}^{V_f} P\, dV$. Therefore, if positive work is done by the gas, energy is leaving the system, leading to the negative sign in the first law.

In your studies in other chemistry or engineering courses, or in your reading of other physics books, be sure to note which sign convention is being used for the first law.

PITFALL PREVENTION 20.8
The First Law

With our approach to energy in this book, the first law of thermodynamics is a special case of Equation 8.2. Some physicists argue that the first law is the general equation for energy conservation, equivalent to Equation 8.2. In this approach, the first law is applied to a closed system (so that there is no matter transfer), heat is interpreted so as to include electromagnetic radiation, and work is interpreted so as to include electrical transmission ("electrical work") and mechanical waves ("molecular work"). Keep that in mind if you run across the first law in your reading of other physics books.

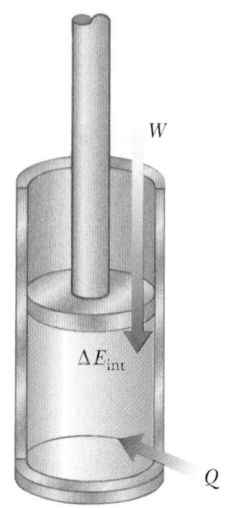

ACTIVE FIGURE 20.7

The first law of thermodynamics equates the change in internal energy E_{int} in a system to the net energy transfer to the system by heat Q and work W. In the situation shown here, the internal energy of the gas increases.

Sign in at www.thomsonedu.com and go to ThomsonNOW to choose one of the four processes for the gas discussed in this section and see the movement of the piston and of a point on a PV diagram.

adiabatic process can be achieved either by thermally insulating the walls of the system or by performing the process rapidly so that there is negligible time for energy to transfer by heat. Applying the first law of thermodynamics to an adiabatic process gives

$$\Delta E_{int} = W \quad \text{(adiabatic process)} \tag{20.11}$$

This result shows that if a gas is compressed adiabatically such that W is positive, then ΔE_{int} is positive and the temperature of the gas increases. Conversely, the temperature of a gas decreases when the gas expands adiabatically.

Adiabatic processes are very important in engineering practice. Some common examples are the expansion of hot gases in an internal combustion engine, the liquefaction of gases in a cooling system, and the compression stroke in a diesel engine.

The process described in Figure 20.6b, called an **adiabatic free expansion,** is unique. The process is adiabatic because it takes place in an insulated container. Because the gas expands into a vacuum, it does not apply a force on a piston as was depicted in Figure 20.6a, so no work is done on or by the gas. Therefore, in this adiabatic process, both $Q = 0$ and $W = 0$. As a result, $\Delta E_{int} = 0$ for this process as can be seen from the first law. That is, **the initial and final internal energies of a gas are equal in an adiabatic free expansion.** As we shall see in Chapter 21, the internal energy of an ideal gas depends only on its temperature. Therefore, we expect no change in temperature during an adiabatic free expansion. This prediction is in accord with the results of experiments performed at low pressures. (Experiments performed at high pressures for real gases show a slight change in temperature after the expansion due to intermolecular interactions, which represent a deviation from the model of an ideal gas.)

A process that occurs at constant pressure is called an **isobaric process.** In Active Figure 20.7, an isobaric process could be established by allowing the piston to move freely so that it is always in equilibrium between the net force from the gas pushing upward and the weight of the piston plus the force due to atmospheric pressure pushing downward. The first process in Active Figure 20.5a and the second process in Active Figure 20.5b are both isobaric.

In such a process, the values of the heat and the work are both usually nonzero. The work done on the gas in an isobaric process is simply

Isobaric process ▶

$$W = -P(V_f - V_i) \quad \text{(isobaric process)} \tag{20.12}$$

where P is the constant pressure of the gas during the process.

A process that takes place at constant volume is called an **isovolumetric process.** In Active Figure 20.7, clamping the piston at a fixed position would ensure an isovolumetric process. The second process in Active Figure 20.5a and the first process in Active Figure 20.5b are both isovolumetric.

Because the volume of the gas does not change in such a process, the work given by Equation 20.9 is zero. Hence, from the first law we see that in an isovolumetric process, because $W = 0$,

Isovolumetric process ▶

$$\Delta E_{int} = Q \quad \text{(isovolumetric process)} \tag{20.13}$$

This expression specifies that **if energy is added by heat to a system kept at constant volume, all the transferred energy remains in the system as an increase in its internal energy.** For example, when a can of spray paint is thrown into a fire, energy enters the system (the gas in the can) by heat through the metal walls of the can. Consequently, the temperature, and therefore the pressure, in the can increases until the can possibly explodes.

Isothermal process ▶

A process that occurs at constant temperature is called an **isothermal process.** This process can be established by immersing the cylinder in Active Figure 20.7 in an ice-water bath or by putting the cylinder in contact with some other constant-temperature reservoir. A plot of P versus V at constant temperature for an ideal gas yields a hyperbolic curve called an *isotherm.* The internal energy of an ideal gas is a function of temperature only. Hence, in an isothermal process involving an ideal gas, $\Delta E_{int} = 0$. For an isothermal process, we conclude from the first law that the energy transfer Q must be equal to the negative of the work done on the gas; that is, $Q = -W$. Any energy that enters the system by heat is transferred out of the system by work; as a result, no change in the internal energy of the system occurs in an isothermal process.

Quick Quiz 20.3 In the last three columns of the following table, fill in the boxes with the correct signs (−, +, or 0) for Q, W, and ΔE_{int}. For each situation, the system to be considered is identified.

Situation	System	Q	W	ΔE_{int}
(a) Rapidly pumping up a bicycle tire	Air in the pump			
(b) Pan of room-temperature water sitting on a hot stove	Water in the pan			
(c) Air quickly leaking out of a balloon	Air originally in the balloon			

Isothermal Expansion of an Ideal Gas

Suppose an ideal gas is allowed to expand quasi-statically at constant temperature. This process is described by the PV diagram shown in Figure 20.8. The curve is a hyperbola (see Appendix B, Eq. B.23), and the ideal gas law with T constant indicates that the equation of this curve is $PV = $ constant.

Let's calculate the work done on the gas in the expansion from state i to state f. The work done on the gas is given by Equation 20.9. Because the gas is ideal and the process is quasi-static, the ideal gas law is valid for each point on the path. Therefore,

$$W = -\int_{V_i}^{V_f} P \, dV = -\int_{V_i}^{V_f} \frac{nRT}{V} \, dV$$

Because T is constant in this case, it can be removed from the integral along with n and R:

$$W = -nRT \int_{V_i}^{V_f} \frac{dV}{V} = -nRT \ln V \Big|_{V_i}^{V_f}$$

To evaluate the integral, we used $\int (dx/x) = \ln x$. (See Appendix B.) Evaluating the result at the initial and final volumes gives

$$W = nRT \ln \left(\frac{V_i}{V_f} \right) \tag{20.14}$$

Numerically, this work W equals the negative of the shaded area under the PV curve shown in Figure 20.8. Because the gas expands, $V_f > V_i$ and the value for the work done on the gas is negative as we expect. If the gas is compressed, then $V_f < V_i$ and the work done on the gas is positive.

Quick Quiz 20.4 Characterize the paths in Figure 20.9 as isobaric, isovolumetric, isothermal, or adiabatic. For path B, $Q = 0$.

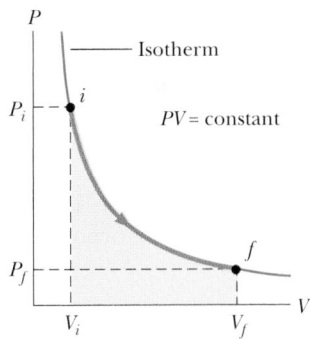

Figure 20.8 The PV diagram for an isothermal expansion of an ideal gas from an initial state to a final state. The curve is a hyperbola.

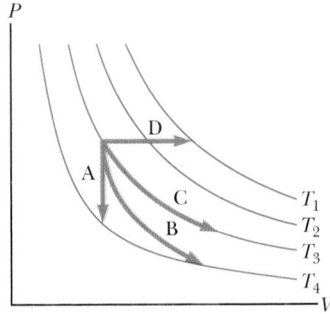

Figure 20.9 (Quick Quiz 20.4) Identify the nature of paths A, B, C, and D.

EXAMPLE 20.5 | **An Isothermal Expansion**

A 1.0-mol sample of an ideal gas is kept at 0.0°C during an expansion from 3.0 L to 10.0 L.

(A) How much work is done on the gas during the expansion?

SOLUTION

Conceptualize Run the process in your mind: the cylinder in Active Figure 20.7 is immersed in an ice-water bath, and the piston moves outward so that the volume of the gas increases.

Categorize We will evaluate parameters using equations developed in the preceding sections, so we categorize this example as a substitution problem. Because the temperature of the gas is fixed, the process is isothermal.

Substitute the given values into Equation 20.14:

$$W = nRT \ln \left(\frac{V_i}{V_f} \right)$$

$$= (1.0 \text{ mol})(8.31 \text{ J/mol} \cdot \text{K})(273 \text{ K}) \ln \left(\frac{3.0 \text{ L}}{10.0 \text{ L}} \right)$$

$$= \boxed{-2.7 \times 10^3 \text{ J}}$$

(B) How much energy transfer by heat occurs between the gas and its surroundings in this process?

SOLUTION

Find the heat from the first law:

$$\Delta E_{\text{int}} = Q + W$$

$$0 = Q + W$$

$$Q = -W = \boxed{2.7 \times 10^3 \text{ J}}$$

(C) If the gas is returned to the original volume by means of an isobaric process, how much work is done on the gas?

SOLUTION

Use Equation 20.12. The pressure is not given, so incorporate the ideal gas law:

$$W = -P(V_f - V_i) = -\frac{nRT_i}{V_i}(V_f - V_i)$$

$$= -\frac{(1.0 \text{ mol})(8.31 \text{ J/mol} \cdot \text{K})(273 \text{ K})}{10.0 \times 10^{-3} \text{ m}^3}(3.0 \times 10^{-3} \text{ m}^3 - 10.0 \times 10^{-3} \text{ m}^3)$$

$$= \boxed{1.6 \times 10^3 \text{ J}}$$

We used the initial temperature and volume to calculate the work done because the final temperature was unknown. The work done on the gas is positive because the gas is being compressed.

EXAMPLE 20.6   Boiling Water

Suppose 1.00 g of water vaporizes isobarically at atmospheric pressure (1.013×10^5 Pa). Its volume in the liquid state is $V_i = V_{\text{liquid}} = 1.00 \text{ cm}^3$, and its volume in the vapor state is $V_f = V_{\text{vapor}} = 1\,671 \text{ cm}^3$. Find the work done in the expansion and the change in internal energy of the system. Ignore any mixing of the steam and the surrounding air; imagine that the steam simply pushes the surrounding air out of the way.

SOLUTION

Conceptualize Notice that the temperature of the system does not change. There is a phase change occurring as the water evaporates to steam.

Categorize Because the expansion takes place at constant pressure, we categorize the process as isobaric. We will use equations developed in the preceding sections, so we categorize this example as a substitution problem.

Use Equation 20.12 to find the work done on the system as the air is pushed out of the way:

$$W = -P(V_f - V_i)$$

$$= -(1.013 \times 10^5 \text{ Pa})(1\,671 \times 10^{-6} \text{ m}^3 - 1.00 \times 10^{-6} \text{ m}^3)$$

$$= \boxed{-169 \text{ J}}$$

Use Equation 20.7 and the latent heat of vaporization for water to find the energy transferred into the system by heat:

$$Q = mL_v = (1.00 \times 10^{-3}\,\text{kg})(2.26 \times 10^6\,\text{J/kg}) = 2\,260\,\text{J}$$

Use the first law to find the change in internal energy of the system:

$$\Delta E_{int} = Q + W = 2\,260\,\text{J} + (-169\,\text{J}) = \boxed{2.09\,\text{kJ}}$$

The positive value for ΔE_{int} indicates that the internal energy of the system increases. The largest fraction of the energy (2 090 J/ 2 260 J = 93%) transferred to the liquid goes into increasing the internal energy of the system. The remaining 7% of the energy transferred leaves the system by work done by the steam on the surrounding atmosphere.

EXAMPLE 20.7   **Heating a Solid**

A 1.0-kg bar of copper is heated at atmospheric pressure so that its temperature increases from 20°C to 50°C.

(A) What is the work done on the copper bar by the surrounding atmosphere?

SOLUTION

Conceptualize   This example involves a solid, whereas the preceding two examples involved liquids and gases. For a solid, the change in volume due to thermal expansion is very small.

Categorize   Because the expansion takes place at constant atmospheric pressure, we categorize the process as isobaric.

Analyze   Calculate the change in volume of the copper bar using Equation 19.6, the average linear expansion coefficient for copper given in Table 19.1, and that $\beta = 3\alpha$:

$$\Delta V = \beta V_i\,\Delta T = 3\alpha V_i\,\Delta T$$
$$= 3[1.7 \times 10^{-5}(°\text{C})^{-1}]V_i(50°\text{C} - 20°\text{C}) = 1.5 \times 10^{-3}\,V_i$$

Use Equation 1.1 to express the initial volume of the bar in terms of the mass of the bar and the density of copper from Table 14.1:

$$\Delta V = (1.5 \times 10^{-3})\left(\frac{m}{\rho}\right) = (1.5 \times 10^{-3})\left(\frac{1.0\,\text{kg}}{8.92 \times 10^3\,\text{kg/m}^3}\right)$$
$$= 1.7 \times 10^{-7}\,\text{m}^3$$

Find the work done on the copper bar using Equation 20.12:

$$W = -P\,\Delta V = -(1.013 \times 10^5\,\text{N/m}^2)(1.7 \times 10^{-7}\,\text{m}^3)$$
$$= \boxed{-1.7 \times 10^{-2}\,\text{J}}$$

Because this work is negative, work is done *by* the copper bar on the atmosphere.

(B) How much energy is transferred to the copper bar by heat?

SOLUTION

Use Equation 20.4 and the specific heat of copper from Table 20.1:

$$Q = mc\,\Delta T = (1.0\,\text{kg})(387\,\text{J/kg}\cdot°\text{C})(50°\text{C} - 20°\text{C})$$
$$= \boxed{1.2 \times 10^4\,\text{J}}$$

(C) What is the increase in internal energy of the copper bar?

SOLUTION

Use the first law of thermodynamics:

$$\Delta E_{int} = Q + W = 1.2 \times 10^4\,\text{J} + (-1.7 \times 10^{-2}\,\text{J})$$
$$= \boxed{1.2 \times 10^4\,\text{J}}$$

Finalize   Most of the energy transferred into the system by heat goes into increasing the internal energy of the copper bar. The fraction of energy used to do work on the surrounding atmosphere is only about 10^{-6}. Hence, when the thermal expansion of a solid or a liquid is analyzed, the small amount of work done on or by the system is usually ignored.

TABLE 20.3

Thermal Conductivities

Substance	Thermal Conductivity (W/m · °C)
Metals (at 25°C)	
Aluminum	238
Copper	397
Gold	314
Iron	79.5
Lead	34.7
Silver	427
Nonmetals (approximate values)	
Asbestos	0.08
Concrete	0.8
Diamond	2 300
Glass	0.8
Ice	2
Rubber	0.2
Water	0.6
Wood	0.08
Gases (at 20°C)	
Air	0.023 4
Helium	0.138
Hydrogen	0.172
Nitrogen	0.023 4
Oxygen	0.023 8

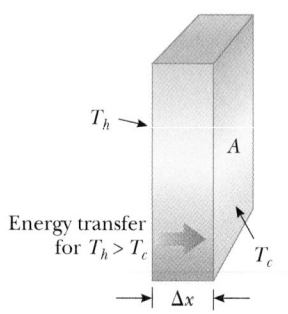

Figure 20.10 Energy transfer through a conducting slab with a cross-sectional area A and a thickness Δx. The opposite faces are at different temperatures T_c and T_h.

Law of thermal conduction ▶

20.7 Energy Transfer Mechanisms

In Chapter 8, we introduced a global approach to the energy analysis of physical processes through Equation 8.1, $\Delta E_{\text{system}} = \Sigma T$, where T represents energy transfer, which can occur by several mechanisms. Earlier in this chapter, we discussed two of the terms on the right side of this equation, work W and heat Q. In this section, we explore more details about heat as a means of energy transfer and two other energy transfer methods often related to temperature changes: convection (a form of matter transfer T_{MT}) and electromagnetic radiation T_{ER}.

Thermal Conduction

The process of energy transfer by heat can also be called **conduction** or **thermal conduction**. In this process, the transfer can be represented on an atomic scale as an exchange of kinetic energy between microscopic particles—molecules, atoms, and free electrons—in which less-energetic particles gain energy in collisions with more-energetic particles. For example, if you hold one end of a long metal bar and insert the other end into a flame, you will find that the temperature of the metal in your hand soon increases. The energy reaches your hand by means of conduction. Initially, before the rod is inserted into the flame, the microscopic particles in the metal are vibrating about their equilibrium positions. As the flame raises the temperature of the rod, the particles near the flame begin to vibrate with greater and greater amplitudes. These particles, in turn, collide with their neighbors and transfer some of their energy in the collisions. Slowly, the amplitudes of vibration of metal atoms and electrons farther and farther from the flame increase until eventually those in the metal near your hand are affected. This increased vibration is detected by an increase in the temperature of the metal and of your potentially burned hand.

The rate of thermal conduction depends on the properties of the substance being heated. For example, it is possible to hold a piece of asbestos in a flame indefinitely, which implies that very little energy is conducted through the asbestos. In general, metals are good thermal conductors and materials such as asbestos, cork, paper, and fiberglass are poor conductors. Gases also are poor conductors because the separation distance between the particles is so great. Metals are good thermal conductors because they contain large numbers of electrons that are relatively free to move through the metal and so can transport energy over large distances. Therefore, in a good conductor such as copper, conduction takes place by means of both the vibration of atoms and the motion of free electrons.

Conduction occurs only if there is a difference in temperature between two parts of the conducting medium. Consider a slab of material of thickness Δx and cross-sectional area A. One face of the slab is at a temperature T_c, and the other face is at a temperature $T_h > T_c$ (Fig. 20.10). Experimentally, it is found that energy Q transfers in a time interval Δt from the hotter face to the colder one. The rate $\mathcal{P} = Q/\Delta t$ at which this energy transfer occurs is found to be proportional to the cross-sectional area and the temperature difference $\Delta T = T_h - T_c$ and inversely proportional to the thickness:

$$\mathcal{P} = \frac{Q}{\Delta t} \propto A \frac{\Delta T}{\Delta x}$$

Notice that $\mathcal{P}$ has units of watts when Q is in joules and Δt is in seconds. That is not surprising because $\mathcal{P}$ is *power*, the rate of energy transfer by heat. For a slab of infinitesimal thickness dx and temperature difference dT, we can write the **law of thermal conduction** as

$$\mathcal{P} = kA \left| \frac{dT}{dx} \right| \tag{20.15}$$

where the proportionality constant k is the **thermal conductivity** of the material and $\left| dT/dx \right|$ is the **temperature gradient** (the rate at which temperature varies with position).

Suppose a long, uniform rod of length L is thermally insulated so that energy cannot escape by heat from its surface except at the ends as shown in Figure 20.11. One end is in thermal contact with an energy reservoir at temperature T_c, and the other end is in thermal contact with a reservoir at temperature $T_h > T_c$. When a steady state has been reached, the temperature at each point along the rod is constant in time. In this case, if we assume k is not a function of temperature, the temperature gradient is the same everywhere along the rod and is

$$\left|\frac{dT}{dx}\right| = \frac{T_h - T_c}{L}$$

Therefore, the rate of energy transfer by conduction through the rod is

$$\mathcal{P} = kA\left(\frac{T_h - T_c}{L}\right) \qquad \textbf{(20.16)}$$

Substances that are good thermal conductors have large thermal conductivity values, whereas good thermal insulators have low thermal conductivity values. Table 20.3 lists thermal conductivities for various substances. Notice that metals are generally better thermal conductors than nonmetals.

For a compound slab containing several materials of thicknesses L_1, L_2, ... and thermal conductivities k_1, k_2, ..., the rate of energy transfer through the slab at steady state is

$$\mathcal{P} = \frac{A(T_h - T_c)}{\sum\limits_i (L_i/k_i)} \qquad \textbf{(20.17)}$$

where T_c and T_h are the temperatures of the outer surfaces (which are held constant) and the summation is over all slabs. Example 20.8 shows how Equation 20.17 results from a consideration of two thicknesses of materials.

Quick Quiz 20.5   You have two rods of the same length and diameter, but they are formed from different materials. The rods are used to connect two regions at different temperatures so that energy transfers through the rods by heat. They can be connected in series as in Figure 20.12a or in parallel as in Figure 20.12b. In which case is the rate of energy transfer by heat larger? (a) The rate is larger when the rods are in series. (b) The rate is larger when the rods are in parallel. (c) The rate is the same in both cases.

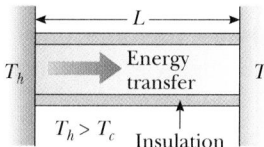

Figure 20.11   Conduction of energy through a uniform, insulated rod of length L. The opposite ends are in thermal contact with energy reservoirs at different temperatures.

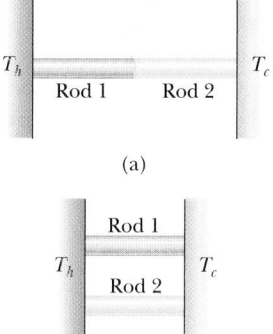

Figure 20.12 (Quick Quiz 20.5) In which case is the rate of energy transfer larger?

EXAMPLE 20.8   **Energy Transfer Through Two Slabs**

Two slabs of thickness L_1 and L_2 and thermal conductivities k_1 and k_2 are in thermal contact with each other as shown in Figure 20.13. The temperatures of their outer surfaces are T_c and T_h, respectively, and $T_h > T_c$. Determine the temperature at the interface and the rate of energy transfer by conduction through the slabs in the steady-state condition.

SOLUTION

Conceptualize   Notice the phrase "in the steady-state condition." We interpret this phrase to mean that energy transfers through the compound slab at the same rate at all points. Otherwise, energy would be building up or disappearing at some point. Furthermore, the temperature varies with position in the two slabs, most likely at different rates in each part of the compound slab. When the system is in steady state, the interface is at some fixed temperature T.

Categorize   We categorize this example as an equilibrium thermal conduction problem and impose the condition that the power is the same in both slabs of material.

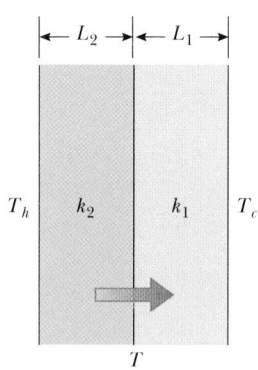

Figure 20.13 (Example 20.8) Energy transfer by conduction through two slabs in thermal contact with each other. At steady state, the rate of energy transfer through slab 1 equals the rate of energy transfer through slab 2.

Analyze Use Equation 20.16 to express the rate at which energy is transferred through slab 1:

$$(1) \quad \mathcal{P}_1 = k_1 A\left(\frac{T - T_c}{L_1}\right)$$

Express the rate at which energy is transferred through slab 2:

$$(2) \quad \mathcal{P}_2 = k_2 A\left(\frac{T_h - T}{L_2}\right)$$

Set these two rates equal to represent the equilibrium situation:

$$k_1 A\left(\frac{T - T_c}{L_1}\right) = k_2 A\left(\frac{T_h - T}{L_2}\right)$$

Solve for T:

$$(3) \quad T = \frac{k_1 L_2 T_c + k_2 L_1 T_h}{k_1 L_2 + k_2 L_1}$$

Substitute Equation (3) into either Equation (1) or Equation (2):

$$(4) \quad \mathcal{P} = \frac{A(T_h - T_c)}{(L_1/k_1) + (L_2/k_2)}$$

Finalize Extension of this procedure to several slabs of materials leads to Equation 20.17.

What If? Suppose you are building an insulated container with two layers of insulation and the rate of energy transfer determined by Equation (4) turns out to be too high. You have enough room to increase the thickness of one of the two layers by 20%. How would you decide which layer to choose?

Answer To decrease the power as much as possible, you must increase the denominator in Equation (4) as much as possible. Whichever thickness you choose to increase, L_1 or L_2, you increase the corresponding term L/k in the denominator by 20%. For this percentage change to represent the largest absolute change, you want to take 20% of the larger term. Therefore, you should increase the thickness of the layer that has the larger value of L/k.

Home Insulation

In engineering practice, the term L/k for a particular substance is referred to as the **R-value** of the material. Therefore, Equation 20.17 reduces to

$$\mathcal{P} = \frac{A(T_h - T_c)}{\displaystyle\sum_i R_i} \tag{20.18}$$

where $R_i = L_i/k_i$. The R-values for a few common building materials are given in Table 20.4. In the United States, the insulating properties of materials used in

TABLE 20.4

R-Values for Some Common Building Materials

Material	R-value (ft² · °F · h/Btu)
Hardwood siding (1 in. thick)	0.91
Wood shingles (lapped)	0.87
Brick (4 in. thick)	4.00
Concrete block (filled cores)	1.93
Fiberglass insulation (3.5 in. thick)	10.90
Fiberglass insulation (6 in. thick)	18.80
Fiberglass board (1 in. thick)	4.35
Cellulose fiber (1 in. thick)	3.70
Flat glass (0.125 in. thick)	0.89
Insulating glass (0.25-in. space)	1.54
Air space (3.5 in. thick)	1.01
Stagnant air layer	0.17
Drywall (0.5 in. thick)	0.45
Sheathing (0.5 in. thick)	1.32

buildings are usually expressed in U.S. customary units, not SI units. Therefore, in Table 20.4, *R*-values are given as a combination of British thermal units, feet, hours, and degrees Fahrenheit.

At any vertical surface open to the air, a very thin stagnant layer of air adheres to the surface. One must consider this layer when determining the *R*-value for a wall. The thickness of this stagnant layer on an outside wall depends on the speed of the wind. Energy transfer through the walls of a house on a windy day is greater than that on a day when the air is calm. A representative *R*-value for this stagnant layer of air is given in Table 20.4.

EXAMPLE 20.9   **The *R*-Value of a Typical Wall**

Calculate the total *R*-value for a wall constructed as shown in Figure 20.14a. Starting outside the house (toward the front in the figure) and moving inward, the wall consists of 4 in. of brick, 0.5 in. of sheathing, an air space 3.5 in. thick, and 0.5 in. of drywall.

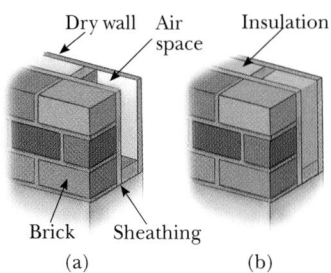

Figure 20.14   (Example 20.9) An exterior house wall containing (a) an air space and (b) insulation.

SOLUTION

Conceptualize   Use Figure 20.14 to help conceptualize the structure of the wall. Do not forget the stagnant air layers inside and outside the house.

Categorize   We will use specific equations developed in this section on home insulation, so we categorize this example as a substitution problem.

Use Table 20.4 to find the *R*-value of each layer:

$$R_1 \text{ (outside stagnant air layer)} = 0.17 \text{ ft}^2 \cdot {}^\circ\text{F} \cdot \text{h/Btu}$$

$$R_2 \text{ (brick)} = 4.00 \text{ ft}^2 \cdot {}^\circ\text{F} \cdot \text{h/Btu}$$

$$R_3 \text{ (sheathing)} = 1.32 \text{ ft}^2 \cdot {}^\circ\text{F} \cdot \text{h/Btu}$$

$$R_4 \text{ (air space)} = 1.01 \text{ ft}^2 \cdot {}^\circ\text{F} \cdot \text{h/Btu}$$

$$R_5 \text{ (drywall)} = 0.45 \text{ ft}^2 \cdot {}^\circ\text{F} \cdot \text{h/Btu}$$

$$R_6 \text{ (inside stagnant air layer)} = 0.17 \text{ ft}^2 \cdot {}^\circ\text{F} \cdot \text{h/Btu}$$

Add the *R*-values to obtain the total *R*-value for the wall:

$$R_{\text{total}} = R_1 + R_2 + R_3 + R_4 + R_5 + R_6 = \boxed{7.12 \text{ ft}^2 \cdot {}^\circ\text{F} \cdot \text{h/Btu}}$$

What If?   Suppose you are not happy with this total *R*-value for the wall. You cannot change the overall structure, but you can fill the air space as in Figure 20.14b. To *maximize* the total *R*-value, what material should you choose to fill the air space?

Answer   Looking at Table 20.4, we see that 3.5 in. of fiberglass insulation is more than ten times as effective as 3.5 in. of air. Therefore, we should fill the air space with fiberglass insulation. The result is that we add $10.90 \text{ ft}^2 \cdot {}^\circ\text{F} \cdot \text{h/Btu}$ of *R*-value, and we lose $1.01 \text{ ft}^2 \cdot {}^\circ\text{F} \cdot \text{h/Btu}$ due to the air space we have replaced. The new total *R*-value is equal to $7.12 \text{ ft}^2 \cdot {}^\circ\text{F} \cdot \text{h/Btu} + 9.89 \text{ ft}^2 \cdot {}^\circ\text{F} \cdot \text{h/Btu} = 17.01 \text{ ft}^2 \cdot {}^\circ\text{F} \cdot \text{h/Btu}$.

Convection

At one time or another, you probably have warmed your hands by holding them over an open flame. In this situation, the air directly above the flame is heated and expands. As a result, the density of this air decreases and the air rises. This hot air warms your hands as it flows by. **Energy transferred by the movement of a warm substance is said to have been transferred by convection.** When resulting from differences in density, as with air around a fire, the process is referred to as *natural convection*. Airflow at a beach is an example of natural convection, as is the mixing

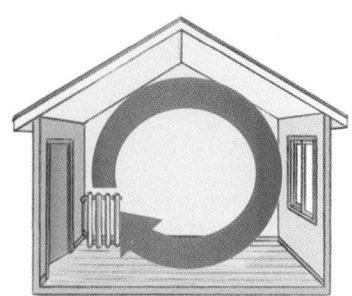

Figure 20.15 Convection currents are set up in a room warmed by a radiator.

that occurs as surface water in a lake cools and sinks (see Section 19.4). When the heated substance is forced to move by a fan or pump, as in some hot-air and hot-water heating systems, the process is called *forced convection*.

If it were not for convection currents, it would be very difficult to boil water. As water is heated in a teakettle, the lower layers are warmed first. This water expands and rises to the top because its density is lowered. At the same time, the denser, cool water at the surface sinks to the bottom of the kettle and is heated.

The same process occurs when a room is heated by a radiator. The hot radiator warms the air in the lower regions of the room. The warm air expands and rises to the ceiling because of its lower density. The denser, cooler air from above sinks, and the continuous air current pattern shown in Figure 20.15 is established.

Radiation

The third means of energy transfer we shall discuss is **thermal radiation**. All objects radiate energy continuously in the form of electromagnetic waves (see Chapter 34) produced by thermal vibrations of the molecules. You are likely familiar with electromagnetic radiation in the form of the orange glow from an electric stove burner, an electric space heater, or the coils of a toaster.

The rate at which an object radiates energy is proportional to the fourth power of its absolute temperature. Known as **Stefan's law**, this behavior is expressed in equation form as

Stefan's law ▶

$$\mathcal{P} = \sigma A e T^4 \qquad\qquad (20.19)$$

where $\mathcal{P}$ is the power in watts of electromagnetic waves radiated from the surface of the object, σ is a constant equal to $5.669\,6 \times 10^{-8}$ W/m$^2 \cdot$K^4, A is the surface area of the object in square meters, e is the **emissivity**, and T is the surface temperature in kelvins. The value of e can vary between zero and unity depending on the properties of the surface of the object. The emissivity is equal to the **absorptivity**, which is the fraction of the incoming radiation that the surface absorbs. A mirror has very low absorptivity because it reflects almost all incident light. Therefore, a mirror surface also has a very low emissivity. At the other extreme, a black surface has high absorptivity and high emissivity. An **ideal absorber** is defined as an object that absorbs all the energy incident on it, and for such an object, $e = 1$. An object for which $e = 1$ is often referred to as a **black body**. We shall investigate experimental and theoretical approaches to radiation from a black body in Chapter 40.

Every second, approximately 1 370 J of electromagnetic radiation from the Sun passes perpendicularly through each 1 m^2 at the top of the Earth's atmosphere. This radiation is primarily visible and infrared light accompanied by a significant amount of ultraviolet radiation. We shall study these types of radiation in detail in Chapter 34. Enough energy arrives at the surface of the Earth each day to supply all our energy needs on this planet hundreds of times over, if only it could be captured and used efficiently. The growth in the number of solar energy–powered houses built in the United States reflects the increasing efforts being made to use this abundant energy.

What happens to the atmospheric temperature at night is another example of the effects of energy transfer by radiation. If there is a cloud cover above the Earth, the water vapor in the clouds absorbs part of the infrared radiation emitted by the Earth and re-emits it back to the surface. Consequently, temperature levels at the surface remain moderate. In the absence of this cloud cover, there is less in the way to prevent this radiation from escaping into space; therefore, the temperature decreases more on a clear night than on a cloudy one.

As an object radiates energy at a rate given by Equation 20.19, it also absorbs electromagnetic radiation from the surroundings, which consist of other objects that radiate energy. If the latter process did not occur, an object would eventually radiate all its energy and its temperature would reach absolute zero. If an object is at a temperature T and its surroundings are at an average temperature T_0, the net rate of energy gained or lost by the object as a result of radiation is

$$\mathcal{P}_{\text{net}} = \sigma A e (T^4 - T_0^4) \qquad \textbf{(20.20)}$$

When an object is in equilibrium with its surroundings, it radiates and absorbs energy at the same rate and its temperature remains constant. When an object is hotter than its surroundings, it radiates more energy than it absorbs and its temperature decreases.

The Dewar Flask

The *Dewar flask*[7] is a container designed to minimize energy transfers by conduction, convection, and radiation. Such a container is used to store cold or hot liquids for long periods of time. (An insulated bottle, such as a Thermos, is a common household equivalent of a Dewar flask.) The standard construction (Fig. 20.16) consists of a double-walled Pyrex glass vessel with silvered walls. The space between the walls is evacuated to minimize energy transfer by conduction and convection. The silvered surfaces minimize energy transfer by radiation because silver is a very good reflector and has very low emissivity. A further reduction in energy loss is obtained by reducing the size of the neck. Dewar flasks are commonly used to store liquid nitrogen (boiling point 77 K) and liquid oxygen (boiling point 90 K).

To confine liquid helium (boiling point 4.2 K), which has a very low heat of vaporization, it is often necessary to use a double Dewar system in which the Dewar flask containing the liquid is surrounded by a second Dewar flask. The space between the two flasks is filled with liquid nitrogen.

Newer designs of storage containers use "super insulation" that consists of many layers of reflecting material separated by fiberglass. All this material is in a vacuum, and no liquid nitrogen is needed with this design.

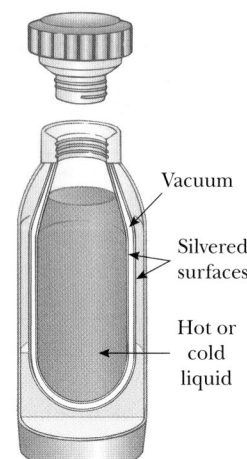

Figure 20.16 A cross-sectional view of a Dewar flask, which is used to store hot or cold substances.

---

[7] Invented by Sir James Dewar (1842–1923).

Summary

ThomsonNOW™ Sign in at **www.thomsonedu.com** and go to ThomsonNOW to take a practice test for this chapter.

DEFINITIONS

Internal energy is all a system's energy that is associated with the system's microscopic components. Internal energy includes kinetic energy of random translation, rotation, and vibration of molecules, vibrational potential energy within molecules, and potential energy between molecules.

    Heat is the transfer of energy across the boundary of a system resulting from a temperature difference between the system and its surroundings. The symbol Q represents the amount of energy transferred by this process.

A **calorie** is the amount of energy necessary to raise the temperature of 1 g of water from 14.5°C to 15.5°C.

    The **heat capacity** C of any sample is the amount of energy needed to raise the temperature of the sample by 1°C.

    The **specific heat** c of a substance is the heat capacity per unit mass:

$$c \equiv \frac{Q}{m\,\Delta T} \qquad \textbf{(20.3)}$$

    The **latent heat** of a substance is defined as the ratio of the energy necessary to cause a phase change to the mass of the substance:

$$L \equiv \frac{Q}{m} \qquad \textbf{(20.6)}$$

(continued)

CONCEPTS AND PRINCIPLES

The energy Q required to change the temperature of a mass m of a substance by an amount ΔT is

$$Q = mc\,\Delta T \qquad \textbf{(20.4)}$$

where c is the specific heat of the substance.

The energy required to change the phase of a pure substance of mass m is

$$Q = \pm mL \qquad \textbf{(20.7)}$$

where L is the latent heat of the substance and depends on the nature of the phase change and the substance. The positive sign is used if energy is entering the system, and the negative sign is used if energy is leaving the system.

The **work** done on a gas as its volume changes from some initial value V_i to some final value V_f is

$$W = -\int_{V_i}^{V_f} P\,dV \qquad \textbf{(20.9)}$$

where P is the pressure of the gas, which may vary during the process. To evaluate W, the process must be fully specified; that is, P and V must be known during each step. The work done depends on the path taken between the initial and final states.

The **first law of thermodynamics** states that when a system undergoes a change from one state to another, the change in its internal energy is

$$\Delta E_{\text{int}} = Q + W \qquad \textbf{(20.10)}$$

where Q is the energy transferred into the system by heat and W is the work done on the system. Although Q and W both depend on the path taken from the initial state to the final state, the quantity ΔE_{int} does not depend on the path.

In a **cyclic process** (one that originates and terminates at the same state), $\Delta E_{\text{int}} = 0$ and therefore $Q = -W$. That is, the energy transferred into the system by heat equals the negative of the work done on the system during the process.

In an **adiabatic process**, no energy is transferred by heat between the system and its surroundings ($Q = 0$). In this case, the first law gives $\Delta E_{\text{int}} = W$. In the **adiabatic free expansion** of a gas, $Q = 0$ and $W = 0$, so $\Delta E_{\text{int}} = 0$. That is, the internal energy of the gas does not change in such a process.

An **isobaric process** is one that occurs at constant pressure. The work done on a gas in such a process is $W = -P(V_f - V_i)$.

An **isovolumetric process** is one that occurs at constant volume. No work is done in such a process, so $\Delta E_{\text{int}} = Q$.

An **isothermal process** is one that occurs at constant temperature. The work done on an ideal gas during an isothermal process is

$$W = nRT \ln\left(\frac{V_i}{V_f}\right) \qquad \textbf{(20.14)}$$

Conduction can be viewed as an exchange of kinetic energy between colliding molecules or electrons. The rate of energy transfer by conduction through a slab of area A is

$$\mathcal{P} = kA\left|\frac{dT}{dx}\right| \qquad \textbf{(20.15)}$$

where k is the **thermal conductivity** of the material from which the slab is made and $|dT/dx|$ is the **temperature gradient**.

In **convection**, a warm substance transfers energy from one location to another.

All objects emit **thermal radiation** in the form of electromagnetic waves at the rate

$$\mathcal{P} = \sigma A e T^4 \qquad \textbf{(20.19)}$$

Questions

☐ denotes answer available in *Student Solutions Manual/Study Guide;* **O** denotes objective question

1. Clearly distinguish among temperature, heat, and internal energy.

2. **O** Ethyl alcohol has about half the specific heat of water. Assume equal amounts of energy are transferred by heat into equal-mass liquid samples of alcohol and water in separate insulated containers. The water rises in temperature by 25°C. How much will the alcohol rise in temperature? (a) 12°C (b) 25°C (c) 50°C (d) It depends on the rate of energy transfer. (e) It will not rise in temperature.

3. What is wrong with the following statement: "Given any two bodies, the one with the higher temperature contains more heat."

4. **O** Beryllium has roughly one-half the specific heat of liquid water (H_2O). Rank the quantities of energy input required to produce the following changes from the largest to the smallest. In your ranking, note any cases of equality. (a) raising the temperature of 1 kg of H_2O from 20°C to 26°C (b) raising the temperature of 2 kg of H_2O from 20°C to 23°C (c) raising the temperature of 2 kg of H_2O from 1°C to 4°C (d) raising the temperature of 2 kg of beryllium from −1°C to 2°C (e) raising the temperature of 2 kg of H_2O from −1°C to 2°C

5. Why is a person able to remove a piece of dry aluminum foil from a hot oven with bare fingers, whereas a burn results if there is moisture on the foil?

6. The air temperature above coastal areas is profoundly influenced by the large specific heat of water. One reason is that the energy released when 1 m³ of water cools by 1°C will raise the temperature of a much larger volume of air by 1°C. Find this volume of air. The specific heat of air is approximately 1 kJ/kg · °C. Take the density of air to be 1.3 kg/m³.

7. **O** Assume you are measuring the specific heat of a sample of originally hot metal by the method of mixtures as described in Example 20.2. Because your calorimeter is not perfectly insulating, energy can transfer by heat between the contents of the calorimeter and the room. To obtain the most accurate result for the specific heat of the metal, you should use water with which initial temperature? (a) slightly lower than room temperature (b) the same as room temperature (c) slightly above room temperature (d) whatever you like because the initial temperature makes no difference.

8. Using the first law of thermodynamics, explain why the *total* energy of an isolated system is always constant.

9. **O** A person shakes a sealed insulated bottle containing hot coffee for a few minutes. **(i)** What is the change in the temperature of the coffee? (a) a large decrease (b) a slight decrease (c) no change (d) a slight increase (e) a large increase **(ii)** What is the change in the internal energy of the coffee? Choose from the same possibilities.

10. Is it possible to convert internal energy to mechanical energy? Explain with examples.

11. A tile floor in a bathroom may feel uncomfortably cold to your bare feet, but a carpeted floor in an adjoining room at the same temperature will feel warm. Why?

12. It is the morning of a day that will become hot. You just purchased drinks for a picnic and are loading them, with ice, into a chest in the back of your car. You have a wool blanket. Should you wrap it around the chest? Would doing so help to keep the beverages cool, or should you expect the wool blanket to warm them up? Your little sister tells you emphatically that she would not like to be wrapped up in a wool blanket on a hot day. Explain your answers and your response to her.

13. When camping in a canyon on a still night, a camper notices that as soon as the sun strikes the surrounding peaks, a breeze begins to stir. What causes the breeze?

14. **O** A poker is a stiff, nonflammable rod used to push burning logs around in a fireplace. For ease of use and safety, the poker should be made from a material (a) with high specific heat and high thermal conductivity, (b) with low specific heat and low thermal conductivity, (c) with low specific heat and high thermal conductivity, or (d) with high specific heat and low thermal conductivity.

15. **O** Star *A* has twice the radius and twice the absolute temperature of star *B*. What is the ratio of the power output of star *A* to that of star *B*? The emissivity of both stars is essentially 1. (a) 4 (b) 8 (c) 16 (d) 32 (e) 64

16. If water is a poor thermal conductor, why can the temperature throughout a pot of water be raised quickly when it is placed over a flame?

17. You need to pick up a very hot cooking pot in your kitchen. You have a pair of hot pads. To be able to pick up the pot most comfortably, should you soak the pads in cold water or keep them dry?

18. Suppose you pour hot coffee for your guests, and one of them wants to drink it with cream, several minutes later, and then as warm as possible. To have the warmest coffee, should the person add the cream just after the coffee is poured or just before drinking? Explain.

19. **O** Warning signs seen on highways just before a bridge are "Caution—Bridge freezes before road surface," or "Bridge may be icy." Which of the three energy transfer processes discussed in Section 20.7 is most important in causing ice to form on a bridge surface before it does on the rest of the road surface on very cold days? (a) conduction (b) convection (c) radiation (d) none of these choices because the ice freezes without a change in temperature

20. A physics teacher drops one marshmallow into a flask of liquid nitrogen, waits for the most energetic boiling to stop, fishes it out with tongs, shakes it off, pops it into his mouth, chews it up, and swallows it. Clouds of ice crystals issue from his mouth as he crunches noisily and comments on the sweet taste. How can he do that without injury? *Caution:* Liquid nitrogen can be a dangerous substance. You should *not* try this demonstration yourself. The teacher might be badly injured if he did not shake the marshmallow off, if he touched the tongs to a tooth, or if he did not start with a mouthful of saliva.

21. In 1801, Humphry Davy rubbed together pieces of ice inside an icehouse. He made sure that nothing in the environment was at a higher temperature than the rubbed pieces. He observed the production of drops of liquid water. Make a table listing this and other experiments or processes to illustrate each of the following situations. (a) A system can absorb energy by heat, increase in internal energy, and increase in temperature. (b) A system can absorb energy by heat and increase in internal energy without an increase in temperature. (c) A system can absorb energy by heat without increasing in temperature or in internal energy. (d) A system can increase in internal energy and in temperature without absorbing energy by heat. (e) A system can increase in internal energy without absorbing energy by heat or increasing in temperature. (f) **What If?** If a system's temperature increases, is it necessarily true that its internal energy increases?

22. Consider the opening photograph for Part 3 (page 531). Discuss the roles of conduction, convection, and radiation in the operation of the cooling fins on the support posts of the Alaskan oil pipeline.

Problems

WebAssign The Problems from this chapter may be assigned online in WebAssign.

ThomsonNOW™ Sign in at **www.thomsonedu.com** and go to ThomsonNOW to assess your understanding of this chapter's topics with additional quizzing and conceptual questions.

1, 2, 3 denotes straightforward, intermediate, challenging; ☐ denotes full solution available in *Student Solutions Manual/Study Guide;* ▲ denotes coached solution with hints available at **www.thomsonedu.com;** denotes developing symbolic reasoning; ● denotes asking for qualitative reasoning; ▪ denotes computer useful in solving problem

Section 20.1 Heat and Internal Energy

1. On his honeymoon, James Joule tested the conversion of mechanical energy into internal energy by measuring temperatures of falling water. If water at the top of a Swiss waterfall has a temperature of 10.0°C and then falls 50.0 m, what maximum temperature at the bottom could Joule expect? He did not succeed in measuring the temperature change, partly because evaporation cooled the falling water and also because his thermometer was not sufficiently sensitive.

2. Consider Joule's apparatus described in Figure 20.1. The mass of each of the two blocks is 1.50 kg, and the insulated tank is filled with 200 g of water. What is the increase in the temperature of the water after the blocks fall through a distance of 3.00 m?

Section 20.2 Specific Heat and Calorimetry

3. The temperature of a silver bar rises by 10.0°C when it absorbs 1.23 kJ of energy by heat. The mass of the bar is 525 g. Determine the specific heat of silver.

4. ● The *Nova* laser at Lawrence Livermore National Laboratory in California was used in early studies of initiating controlled nuclear fusion (Section 45.4). It delivered a power of 1.60×10^{13} W over a time interval of 2.50 ns. Explain how its energy output in one such time interval compares with the energy required to make a pot of tea by warming 0.800 kg of water from 20.0°C to 100°C.

5. Systematic use of solar energy can yield a large saving in the cost of winter space heating for a typical house in the northern United States. If the house has good insulation, you may model it as losing energy by heat steadily at the rate 6 000 W on a day in April when the average exterior temperature is 4°C and when the conventional heating system is not used at all. The passive solar energy collector can consist simply of very large windows in a room facing south. Sunlight shining in during the daytime is absorbed by the floor, interior walls, and objects in the room, raising their temperature to 38.0°C. As the sun goes down, insulating draperies or shutters are closed over the windows. During the period between 5:00 p.m. and 7:00 a.m., the temperature of the house will drop and a sufficiently large "thermal mass" is required to keep it from dropping too far. The thermal mass can be a large quantity of stone (with specific heat 850 J/kg·°C) in the floor and the interior walls exposed to sunlight. What mass of stone is required if the temperature is not to drop below 18.0°C overnight?

6. An aluminum cup of mass 200 g contains 800 g of water in thermal equilibrium at 80.0°C. The combination of cup and water is cooled uniformly so that the temperature decreases by 1.50°C per minute. At what rate is energy being removed by heat? Express your answer in watts.

7. ▲ A 1.50-kg iron horseshoe initially at 600°C is dropped into a bucket containing 20.0 kg of water at 25.0°C. What is the final temperature? (Ignore the heat capacity of the container and assume a negligible amount of water boils away.)

8. ● An electric drill with a steel drill bit of mass 27.0 g and diameter 0.635 cm is used to drill into a cubical steel block of mass 240 g. Assume steel has the same properties as iron. The cutting process can be modeled as happening at one point on the circumference of the bit. This point moves in a spiral at constant speed 40.0 m/s and exerts a force of constant magnitude 3.20 N on the block. As shown in Figure P20.8, a groove in the bit carries the chips up to the top of the block, where they form a pile around the hole. The block is held in a clamp made of material of low thermal conductivity, and the drill bit is held in a chuck also made of this material. We consider turning the drill on for a time interval of 15.0 s. This time interval is sufficiently short that the steel objects lose only a negligible amount of energy by conduction, convection, and radiation into their environment. Nevertheless, 15 s is long enough for conduction within the steel to bring it all to a uniform temperature. The temperature is promptly measured with a thermometer probe, shown in the side of

the block in the figure. (a) Suppose the drill bit is sharp and cuts three-quarters of the way through the block during 15 s. Find the temperature change of the whole quantity of steel. (b) **What If?** Now suppose the drill bit is dull and cuts only one-eighth of the way through the block. Identify the temperature change of the whole quantity of steel in this case. (c) What pieces of data, if any, are unnecessary for the solution? Explain.

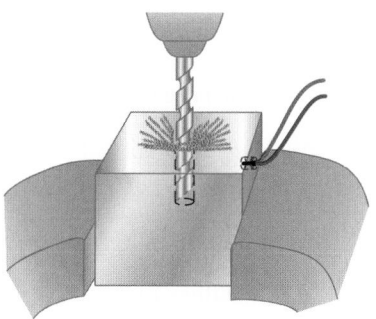

Figure P20.8

9. ● An aluminum calorimeter with a mass of 100 g contains 250 g of water. The calorimeter and water are in thermal equilibrium at 10.0°C. Two metallic blocks are placed into the water. One is a 50.0-g piece of copper at 80.0°C. The other has a mass of 70.0 g and is originally at a temperature of 100°C. The entire system stabilizes at a final temperature of 20.0°C. (a) Determine the specific heat of the unknown sample. (b) Using the data in Table 20.1, can you make a positive identification of the unknown material? Can you identify a possible material? Explain your answers.

10. ● A 3.00-g copper penny at 25.0°C drops 50.0 m to the ground. (a) Assuming 60.0% of the change in potential energy of the penny–Earth system goes into increasing the internal energy of the penny, determine the penny's final temperature. (b) **What If?** Does the result depend on the mass of the penny? Explain.

11. A combination of 0.250 kg of water at 20.0°C, 0.400 kg of aluminum at 26.0°C, and 0.100 kg of copper at 100°C is mixed in an insulated container and allowed to come to thermal equilibrium. Ignore any energy transfer to or from the container and determine the final temperature of the mixture.

12. Two thermally insulated vessels are connected by a narrow tube fitted with a valve that is initially closed. One vessel of volume 16.8 L contains oxygen at a temperature of 300 K and a pressure of 1.75 atm. The other vessel of volume 22.4 L contains oxygen at a temperature of 450 K and a pressure of 2.25 atm. When the valve is opened, the gases in the two vessels mix and the temperature and pressure become uniform throughout. (a) What is the final temperature? (b) What is the final pressure?

Section 20.3 Latent Heat

13. How much energy is required to change a 40.0-g ice cube from ice at −10.0°C to steam at 110°C?

14. A 50.0-g copper calorimeter contains 250 g of water at 20.0°C. How much steam must be condensed into the water if the final temperature of the system is to reach 50.0°C?

15. A 3.00-g lead bullet at 30.0°C is fired at a speed of 240 m/s into a large block of ice at 0°C, in which it becomes embedded. What quantity of ice melts?

16. Steam at 100°C is added to ice at 0°C. (a) Find the amount of ice melted and the final temperature when the mass of steam is 10.0 g and the mass of ice is 50.0 g. (b) **What If?** Repeat when the mass of steam is 1.00 g and the mass of ice is 50.0 g.

17. A 1.00-kg block of copper at 20.0°C is dropped into a large vessel of liquid nitrogen at 77.3 K. How many kilograms of nitrogen boil away by the time the copper reaches 77.3 K? (The specific heat of copper is 0.092 0 cal/g · °C. The latent heat of vaporization of nitrogen is 48.0 cal/g.)

18. ● An automobile has a mass of 1 500 kg, and its aluminum brakes have an overall mass of 6.00 kg. (a) Assume all the mechanical energy that disappears when the car stops is deposited in the brakes and no energy is transferred out of the brakes by heat. The brakes are originally at 20.0°C. How many times can the car be stopped from 25.0 m/s before the brakes start to melt? (b) Identify some effects ignored in part (a) that are important in a more realistic assessment of the warming of the brakes.

19. ▲ In an insulated vessel, 250 g of ice at 0°C is added to 600 g of water at 18.0°C. (a) What is the final temperature of the system? (b) How much ice remains when the system reaches equilibrium?

20. **Review problem**. The following equation describes a process that occurs so rapidly that negligible energy is transferred between the system and the environment by conduction, convection, or radiation:

$$\tfrac{1}{2}(0.012\ 0\ \text{kg})(300\ \text{m/s})^2 + \tfrac{1}{2}(0.008\ 00\ \text{kg})(400\ \text{m/s})^2$$

$$= \tfrac{1}{2}(0.020\ 0\ \text{kg})(20\ \text{m/s})^2$$

$$+ (0.020\ 0\ \text{kg})(128\ \text{J/kg} \cdot °\text{C})(327.3°\text{C} - 30.0°\text{C})$$

$$+ m_\ell(2.45 \times 10^4\ \text{J/kg})$$

(a) Write a problem for which the equation will appear in the solution. Give the data, describe the system, and describe the process going on. Let the problem end with the statement, "Describe the state of the system immediately thereafter." (b) Solve the problem, including calculating the unknown in the equation and identifying its physical meaning.

Section 20.4 Work and Heat in Thermodynamic Processes

Problems 4 and 27 in Chapter 7 can also be assigned with this section.

21. ▲ A sample of ideal gas is expanded to twice its original volume of 1.00 m³ in a quasi-static process for which $P = \alpha V^2$, with $\alpha = 5.00$ atm/m⁶, as shown in Figure P20.21. How much work is done on the expanding gas?

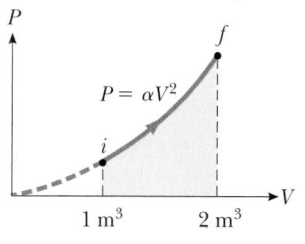

Figure P20.21

22. (a) Determine the work done on a fluid that expands from i to f as indicated in Figure P20.22. (b) **What If?** How much work is performed on the fluid if it is compressed from f to i along the same path?

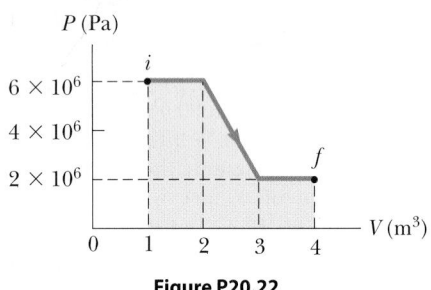

Figure P20.22

23. ▲ An ideal gas is enclosed in a cylinder with a movable piston on top of it. The piston has a mass of 8 000 g and an area of 5.00 cm² and is free to slide up and down, keeping the pressure of the gas constant. How much work is done on the gas as the temperature of 0.200 mol of the gas is raised from 20.0°C to 300°C?

24. An ideal gas is enclosed in a cylinder that has a movable piston on top. The piston has a mass m and an area A and is free to slide up and down, keeping the pressure of the gas constant. How much work is done on the gas as the temperature of n mol of the gas is raised from T_1 to T_2?

25. ● One mole of an ideal gas is warmed slowly so that it goes from the PV state (P_i, V_i), to $(3P_i, 3V_i)$, in such a way that the pressure of the gas is directly proportional to the volume. (a) How much work is done on the gas in the process? (b) How is the temperature of the gas related to its volume during this process?

Section 20.5 The First Law of Thermodynamics

26. A gas is taken through the cyclic process described in Figure P20.26. (a) Find the net energy transferred to the system by heat during one complete cycle. (b) **What If?** If the cycle is reversed—that is, the process follows the path $ACBA$—what is the net energy input per cycle by heat?

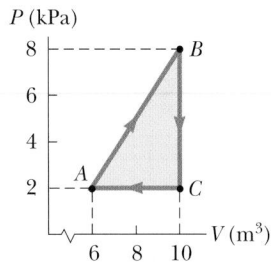

Figure P20.26   Problems 26 and 29.

27. A thermodynamic system undergoes a process in which its internal energy decreases by 500 J. Over the same time interval, 220 J of work is done on the system. Find the energy transferred to or from it by heat.

28. A sample of an ideal gas goes through the process shown in Figure P20.28. From A to B, the process is adiabatic; from B to C, it is isobaric with 100 kJ of energy entering the system by heat. From C to D, the process is isothermal; from D to A, it is isobaric with 150 kJ of energy leaving the

system by heat. Determine the difference in internal energy $E_{int,B} - E_{int,A}$.

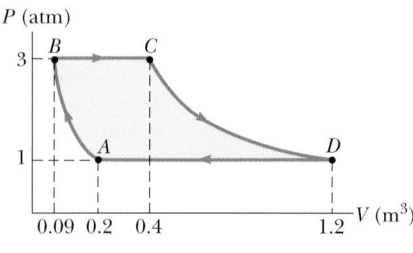

Figure P20.28

29. Consider the cyclic process depicted in Figure P20.26. If Q is negative for the process BC and ΔE_{int} is negative for the process CA, what are the signs of Q, W, and ΔE_{int} that are associated with each process?

Section 20.6 Some Applications of the First Law of Thermodynamics

30. One mole of an ideal gas does 3 000 J of work on its surroundings as it expands isothermally to a final pressure of 1.00 atm and volume of 25.0 L. Determine (a) the initial volume and (b) the temperature of the gas.

31. An ideal gas initially at 300 K undergoes an isobaric expansion at 2.50 kPa. If the volume increases from 1.00 m³ to 3.00 m³ and 12.5 kJ is transferred to the gas by heat, what are (a) the change in its internal energy and (b) its final temperature?

32. A 1.00-kg block of aluminum is warmed at atmospheric pressure so that its temperature increases from 22.0°C to 40.0°C. Find (a) the work done on the aluminum, (b) the energy added to it by heat, and (c) the change in its internal energy.

33. How much work is done on the steam when 1.00 mol of water at 100°C boils and becomes 1.00 mol of steam at 100°C at 1.00 atm pressure? Assume the steam to behave as an ideal gas. Determine the change in internal energy of the material as it vaporizes.

34. An ideal gas initially at P_i, V_i, and T_i is taken through a cycle as shown in Figure P20.34. (a) Find the net work done on the gas per cycle. (b) What is the net energy added by heat to the system per cycle? (c) Obtain a numerical value for the net work done per cycle for 1.00 mol of gas initially at 0°C.

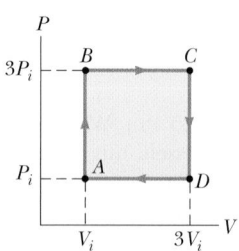

Figure P20.34

35. A 2.00-mol sample of helium gas initially at 300 K and 0.400 atm is compressed isothermally to 1.20 atm. Noting that the helium behaves as an ideal gas, find (a) the final volume of the gas, (b) the work done on the gas, and (c) the energy transferred by heat.

36. In Figure P20.36, the change in internal energy of a gas that is taken from A to C is +800 J. The work done on the gas along path ABC is −500 J. (a) How much energy must be added to the system by heat as it goes from A through B to C? (b) If the pressure at point A is five times that of point C, what is the work done on the system in going from C to D? (c) What is the energy exchanged with the surroundings by heat as the cycle goes from C to A along the green path? (d) If the change in internal energy in going from point D to point A is +500 J, how much energy must be added to the system by heat as it goes from point C to point D?

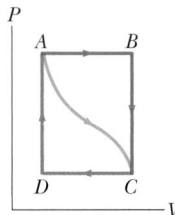

Figure P20.36

Section 20.7 Energy Transfer Mechanisms

37. A glass windowpane has an area of 3.00 m² and a thickness of 0.600 cm. If the temperature difference between its faces is 25.0°C, what is the rate of energy transfer by conduction through the window?

38. A thermal window with an area of 6.00 m² is constructed of two layers of glass, each 4.00 mm thick, separated from each other by an air space of 5.00 mm. If the inside surface is at 20.0°C and the outside is at −30.0°C, what is the rate of energy transfer by conduction through the window?

39. A bar of gold (Au) is in thermal contact with a bar of silver (Ag) of the same length and area (Fig. P20.39). One end of the compound bar is maintained at 80.0°C, and the opposite end is at 30.0°C. When the energy transfer reaches steady state, what is the temperature at the junction?

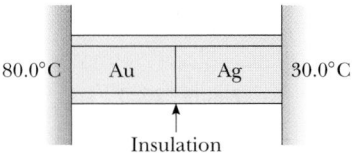

Figure P20.39

40. Calculate the R-value of (a) a window made of a single pane of flat glass $\frac{1}{8}$ in. thick and (b) a thermal window made of two single panes each $\frac{1}{8}$ in. thick and separated by a $\frac{1}{4}$-in. air space. (c) By what factor is the transfer of energy by heat through the window reduced by using the thermal window instead of the single-pane window?

41. A student is trying to decide what to wear. His bedroom is at 20.0°C. His skin temperature is 35.0°C. The area of his exposed skin is 1.50 m². People all over the world have skin that is dark in the infrared, with emissivity about 0.900. Find the net energy loss from his body by radiation in 10.0 min.

42. The surface of the Sun has a temperature of about 5 800 K. The radius of the Sun is 6.96×10^8 m. Calculate the total energy radiated by the Sun each second. Assume the emissivity is 0.986.

43. ● For bacteriological testing of water supplies and in medical clinics, samples must routinely be incubated for 24 h at 37°C. A standard constant-temperature bath with electric heating and thermostatic control is not practical in war-torn places and developing countries without continuously operating electric power lines. Peace Corps volunteer and MIT engineer Amy Smith invented a low-cost, low-maintenance incubator to fill the need. It consists of a foam-insulated box containing several packets of a waxy material that melts at 37.0°C, interspersed among tubes, dishes, or bottles containing the test samples and growth medium (bacteria food). Outside the box, the waxy material is first melted by a stove or solar energy collector. Then the waxy material is put into the box to keep the test samples warm as it solidifies. The heat of fusion of the phase-change material is 205 kJ/kg. Model the insulation as a panel with surface area 0.490 m², thickness 4.50 cm, and conductivity 0.012 0 W/m · °C. Assume the exterior temperature is 23.0°C for 12.0 h and 16.0°C for 12.0 h. (a) What mass of the waxy material is required to conduct the bacteriological test? (b) Explain why your calculation can be done without knowing the mass of the test samples or of the insulation.

44. A large, hot pizza floats in outer space after being jettisoned as refuse from a Vogon spacecraft. What is the order of magnitude (a) of its rate of energy loss and (b) of its rate of temperature change? List the quantities you estimate and the value you estimate for each.

45. The tungsten filament of a certain 100-W lightbulb radiates 2.00 W of light. (The other 98 W is carried away by convection and conduction.) The filament has a surface area of 0.250 mm² and an emissivity of 0.950. Find the filament's temperature. (The melting point of tungsten is 3 683 K.)

46. At high noon, the Sun delivers 1 000 W to each square meter of a blacktop road. If the hot asphalt loses energy only by radiation, what is its steady-state temperature?

47. ● At our distance from the Sun, the intensity of solar radiation is 1 370 W/m². The temperature of the Earth is affected by the so-called greenhouse effect of the atmosphere, which makes our planet's emissivity for visible light higher than its emissivity for infrared light. For comparison, consider a spherical object of radius r with no atmosphere at the same distance from the Sun as the Earth. Assume its emissivity is the same for all kinds of electromagnetic waves and its temperature is uniform over its surface. Explain why the projected area over which it absorbs sunlight is πr^2 and the surface area over which it radiates is $4\pi r^2$. Compute its steady-state temperature. Is it chilly? Your calculation applies to (1) the average temperature of the Moon, (2) astronauts in mortal danger aboard the crippled *Apollo 13* spacecraft, and (3) global catastrophe on the Earth if widespread fires caused a layer of soot to accumulate throughout the upper atmosphere so that most of the radiation from the Sun were absorbed there rather than at the surface below the atmosphere.

48. Two lightbulbs have cylindrical filaments much greater in length than in diameter. The evacuated lightbulbs are identical except that one operates at a filament temperature of

2 = intermediate;   3 = challenging;   □ = SSM/SG;   ▲ = ThomsonNOW;   ▨ = symbolic reasoning;   ● = qualitative reasoning

2 100°C and the other operates at 2 000°C. (a) Find the ratio of the power emitted by the hotter lightbulb to that emitted by the cooler lightbulb. (b) With the lightbulbs operating at the same respective temperatures, the cooler one is to be altered so that it emits the same power as the hotter one, by making the filament of the cooler lightbulb thicker. By what factor should the radius of this filament be increased?

Additional Problems

49. A 75.0-kg cross-country skier moves horizontally across snow at 0°C. The coefficient of friction between the skis and the snow is 0.200. Assume all the internal energy generated by friction is added to the snow, which sticks to her skis until it melts. How far does she have to ski to melt 1.00 kg of snow?

50. On a cold winter day you buy roasted chestnuts from a street vendor. You put the change he gives you—coins constituting 9.00 g of copper at −12.0°C—into the pocket of your down parka. Your pocket already contains 14.0 g of silver coins at 30.0°C. After a short time interval, the temperature of the copper coins is 4.00°C and is increasing at a rate of 0.500°C/s. At this moment, (a) what is the temperature of the silver coins and (b) at what rate is it changing?

51. An aluminum rod 0.500 m in length and with a cross-sectional area of 2.50 cm² is inserted into a thermally insulated vessel containing liquid helium at 4.20 K. The rod is initially at 300 K. (a) If one half of the rod is inserted into the helium, how many liters of helium boil off by the time the inserted half cools to 4.20 K? (Assume the upper half does not yet cool.) (b) If the upper end of the rod is maintained at 300 K, what is the approximate boil-off rate of liquid helium after the lower half has reached 4.20 K? (Aluminum has thermal conductivity of 31.0 J/s · cm · K at 4.2 K; ignore its temperature variation. Aluminum has a specific heat of 0.210 cal/g · °C and density of 2.70 g/cm³. The density of liquid helium is 0.125 g/cm³.)

52. ● One mole of an ideal gas is contained in a cylinder with a movable piston. The initial pressure, volume, and temperature are P_i, V_i, and T_i, respectively. Find the work done on the gas in the following processes. In operational terms, describe how to carry out each process. Show each process on a PV diagram: (a) an isobaric compression in which the final volume is one-half the initial volume (b) an isothermal compression in which the final pressure is four times the initial pressure (c) an isovolumetric process in which the final pressure is three times the initial pressure

53. A *flow calorimeter* is an apparatus used to measure the specific heat of a liquid. The technique of flow calorimetry involves measuring the temperature difference between the input and output points of a flowing stream of the liquid while energy is added by heat at a known rate. A liquid of density ρ flows through the calorimeter with volume flow rate R. At steady state, a temperature difference ΔT is established between the input and output points when energy is supplied at the rate $\mathcal{P}$. What is the specific heat of the liquid?

54. **Review problem.** Continue the analysis of Problem 52 in Chapter 19. Following a collision between a large spacecraft and an asteroid, a copper disk of radius 28.0 m and thickness 1.20 m, at a temperature of 850°C, is floating in space, rotating about its axis with an angular speed of 25.0 rad/s. As the disk radiates infrared light, its temperature falls to 20.0°C. No external torque acts on the disk. (a) Find the change in kinetic energy of the disk. (b) Find the change in internal energy of the disk. (c) Find the amount of energy it radiates.

55. **Review problem.** A 670-kg meteorite happens to be composed of aluminum. When it is far from the Earth, its temperature is −15°C and it moves with a speed of 14.0 km/s relative to the planet. As it crashes into the Earth, assume the resulting additional internal energy is shared equally between the meteor and the planet and all the material of the meteor rises momentarily to the same final temperature. Find this temperature. Assume the specific heat of liquid and of gaseous aluminum is 1 170 J/kg · °C.

56. Water in an electric teakettle is boiling. The power absorbed by the water is 1.00 kW. Assuming the pressure of vapor in the kettle equals atmospheric pressure, determine the speed of effusion of vapor from the kettle's spout if the spout has a cross-sectional area of 2.00 cm².

57. ▲ A solar cooker consists of a curved reflecting surface that concentrates sunlight onto the object to be warmed (Fig. P20.57). The solar power per unit area reaching the Earth's surface at the location is 600 W/m². The cooker faces the Sun and has a face diameter of 0.600 m. Assume 40.0% of the incident energy is transferred to 0.500 L of water in an open container, initially at 20.0°C. Over what time interval does the water completely boil away? (Ignore the heat capacity of the container.)

Figure P20.57

58. (a) In air at 0°C, a 1.60-kg copper block at 0°C is set sliding at 2.50 m/s over a sheet of ice at 0°C. Friction brings the block to rest. Find the mass of the ice that melts. To describe the process of slowing down, identify the energy input Q, the work input W, the change in internal energy ΔE_{int}, and the change in mechanical energy ΔK for the block and also for the ice. (b) A 1.60-kg block of ice at 0°C is set sliding at 2.50 m/s over a sheet of copper at 0°C. Friction brings the block to rest. Find the mass of the ice that melts. Identify Q, W, ΔE_{int}, and ΔK for the block and for the metal sheet during the process. (c) A thin 1.60-kg slab of copper at 20°C is set sliding at 2.50 m/s over an identical stationary slab at the same temperature. Friction quickly stops the motion. Assuming no energy is lost to the environment by heat, find the change in temperature of both objects. Identify Q, W, ΔE_{int}, and ΔK for each object during the process.

59. A cooking vessel on a slow burner contains 10.0 kg of water and an unknown mass of ice in equilibrium at 0°C at time $t = 0$. The temperature of the mixture is measured at various times, and the result is plotted in Figure P20.59. During the first 50.0 minutes, the mixture remains at 0°C. From 50.0 min to 60.0 min, the temperature increases to 2.00°C. Ignoring the heat capacity of the vessel, determine the initial mass of the ice.

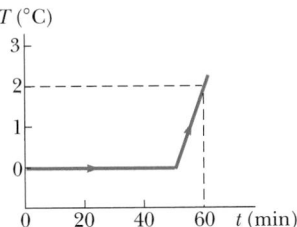

Figure P20.59

60. A pond of water at 0°C is covered with a layer of ice 4.00 cm thick. If the air temperature stays constant at −10.0°C, what time interval is required for the ice thickness to increase to 8.00 cm? *Suggestion:* Use Equation 20.16 in the form

$$\frac{dQ}{dt} = kA\frac{\Delta T}{x}$$

and note that the incremental energy dQ extracted from the water through the thickness x of ice is the amount required to freeze a thickness dx of ice. That is, $dQ = L\rho A\,dx$, where ρ is the density of the ice, A is the area, and L is the latent heat of fusion.

61. The average thermal conductivity of the walls (including the windows) and roof of the house depicted in Figure P20.61 is 0.480 W/m · °C, and their average thickness is 21.0 cm. The house is kept warm with natural gas having a heat of combustion (that is, the energy provided per cubic meter of gas burned) of 9 300 kcal/m³. How many cubic meters of gas must be burned each day to maintain an inside temperature of 25.0°C if the outside temperature is 0.0°C? Disregard radiation and the energy lost by heat through the ground.

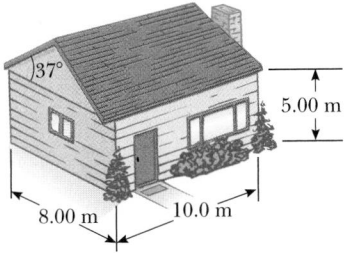

Figure P20.61

62. The inside of a hollow cylinder is maintained at a temperature T_a while the outside is at a lower temperature, T_b (Fig. P20.62). The wall of the cylinder has a thermal conductivity k. Ignoring end effects, show that the rate of energy conduction from the inner to the outer surface in the radial direction is

$$\frac{dQ}{dt} = 2\pi Lk\left[\frac{T_a - T_b}{\ln(b/a)}\right]$$

Suggestions: The temperature gradient is dT/dr. Notice that a radial energy current passes through a concentric cylinder of area $2\pi rL$.

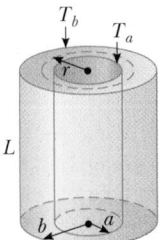

Figure P20.62

63. The passenger section of a jet airliner is in the shape of a cylindrical tube with a length of 35.0 m and an inner radius of 2.50 m. Its walls are lined with an insulating material 6.00 cm in thickness and having a thermal conductivity of 4.00×10^{-5} cal/s · cm · °C. A heater must maintain the interior temperature at 25.0°C while the outside temperature is −35.0°C. What power must be supplied to the heater? (You may use the result of Problem 62.)

64. ● A student measures the following data in a calorimetry experiment designed to determine the specific heat of aluminum:

Initial temperature of water and calorimeter:	70°C
Mass of water:	0.400 kg
Mass of calorimeter:	0.040 kg
Specific heat of calorimeter:	0.63 kJ/kg · °C
Initial temperature of aluminum:	27°C
Mass of aluminum:	0.200 kg
Final temperature of mixture:	66.3°C

Use these data to determine the specific heat of aluminum. Explain whether your result is within 15% of the value listed in Table 20.1.

65. ● A spherical shell has inner radius 3.00 cm and outer radius 7.00 cm. It is made of material with thermal conductivity $k = 0.800$ W/m · °C. The interior is maintained at temperature 5°C and the exterior at 40°C. After an interval of time, the shell reaches a steady state with the temperature at each point within it remaining constant in time. (a) Explain why the rate of energy transfer $\mathcal{P}$ must be the same through each spherical surface, of radius r, within the shell and must satisfy

$$\frac{dT}{dr} = \frac{\mathcal{P}}{4\pi kr^2}$$

(b) Next, prove that

$$\int_{5°C}^{40°C} dT = \frac{\mathcal{P}}{4\pi k}\int_{3\text{ cm}}^{7\text{ cm}} r^{-2}\,dr$$

(c) Find the rate of energy transfer through the shell.
(d) Prove that

$$\int_{5°C}^{T} dT = (1.84\text{ m} \cdot °C)\int_{3\text{ cm}}^{r} r^{-2}\,dr$$

(e) Find the temperature within the shell as a function of radius. (f) Find the temperature at $r = 5.00$ cm, halfway through the shell.

66. ● During periods of high activity, the Sun has more sunspots than usual. Sunspots are cooler than the rest of the luminous layer of the Sun's atmosphere (the photosphere). Paradoxically, the total power output of the active Sun is not lower than average but is the same or slightly higher than average. Work out the details of the following crude model of this phenomenon. Consider a patch of the photosphere with an area of 5.10×10^{14} m². Its emissivity is 0.965. (a) Find the power it radiates if its temperature is uniformly 5 800 K, corresponding to the quiet Sun. (b) To represent a sunspot, assume 10.0% of the patch area is at 4 800 K and the other 90.0% is at 5 890 K. That is, a section with the surface area of the Earth is 1 000 K cooler than before and a section nine times larger is 90 K warmer. Find the average temperature of the patch. State how it compares with 5 800 K. (c) Find the power output of the patch. State how it compares with the answer to part (a). (The next sunspot maximum is expected around the year 2012.)

Answers to Quick Quizzes

20.1 **(i)** Water, glass, iron. Because water has the highest specific heat (4 186 J/kg · °C), it has the smallest change in temperature. Glass is next (837 J/kg · °C), and iron is last (448 J/kg · °C). **(i)** Iron, glass, water. For a given temperature increase, the energy transfer by heat is proportional to the specific heat.

20.2 The figure shows a graphical representation of the internal energy of the ice as a function of energy added. Notice that this graph looks quite different from Figure 20.2 in that it doesn't have the flat portions during the phase changes. Regardless of how the temperature is varying in Figure 20.2, the internal energy of the system simply increases linearly with energy input.

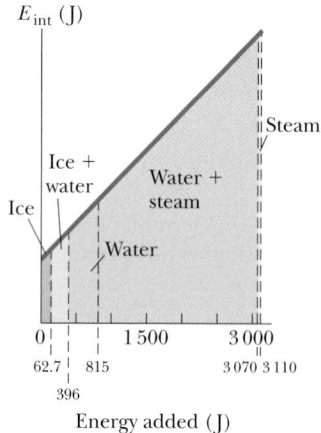

20.3

Situation	System	Q	W	ΔE_{int}
(a) Rapidly pumping up a bicycle tire	Air in the pump	0	+	+
(b) Pan of room-temperature water sitting on a hot stove	Water in the pan	+	0	+
(c) Air quickly leaking out of a balloon	Air originally in the balloon	0	−	−

(a) Because the pumping is rapid, no energy enters or leaves the system by heat. Because $W > 0$ when work is done *on* the system, it is positive here. Therefore, $\Delta E_{int} = Q + W$ must be positive. The air in the pump is warmer. (b) There is no work done either on or by the system, but energy transfers into the water by heat from the hot burner, making both Q and ΔE_{int} positive. (c) Again no energy transfers into or out of the system by heat, but the air molecules escaping from the balloon do work on the surrounding air molecules as they push them out of the way. Therefore, W is negative and ΔE_{int} is negative. The decrease in internal energy is evident because the escaping air becomes cooler.

20.4 Path A is isovolumetric, path B is adiabatic, path C is isothermal, and path D is isobaric.

20.5 (b). In parallel, the rods present a larger area through which energy can transfer and a smaller length.

Dogs do not have sweat glands like humans do. In hot weather, a dog pants to promote evaporation from the tongue. In this chapter, we show that evaporation is a cooling process based on the removal of molecules with high kinetic energy from a liquid. (Frank Oberle/Getty Images)

21.1 Molecular Model of an Ideal Gas

21.2 Molar Specific Heat of an Ideal Gas

21.3 Adiabatic Processes for an Ideal Gas

21.4 The Equipartition of Energy

21.5 Distribution of Molecular Speeds

21 The Kinetic Theory of Gases

In Chapter 19, we discussed the properties of an ideal gas by using such macro-scopic variables as pressure, volume, and temperature. Such large-scale properties can be related to a description on a microscopic scale, where matter is treated as a collection of molecules. Applying Newton's laws of motion in a statistical manner to a collection of particles provides a reasonable description of thermodynamic processes. To keep the mathematics relatively simple, we shall consider primarily the behavior of gases because in gases the interactions between molecules are much weaker than they are in liquids or solids.

21.1 Molecular Model of an Ideal Gas

We begin this chapter by developing a microscopic model of an ideal gas, called **kinetic theory**. In developing this model, we make the following assumptions:

1. **The number of molecules in the gas is large, and the average separation between them is large compared with their dimensions**. In other words, the molecules occupy a negligible volume in the container. That is consistent with the ideal gas model, in which we model the molecules as particles.
2. **The molecules obey Newton's laws of motion, but as a whole they move randomly**. By "randomly" we mean that any molecule can move in any direction with any speed.

◄ Assumptions of the molecular model of an ideal gas

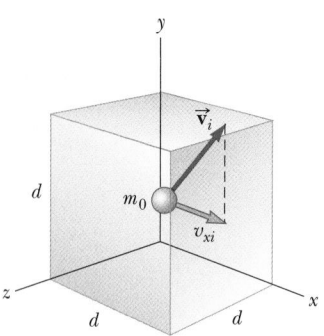

Figure 21.1 A cubical box with sides of length d containing an ideal gas. The molecule shown moves with velocity $\vec{\mathbf{v}}_i$.

3. **The molecules interact only by short-range forces during elastic collisions.** That is consistent with the ideal gas model, in which the molecules exert no long-range forces on each other.
4. **The molecules make elastic collisions with the walls.** These collisions lead to the macroscopic pressure on the walls of the container.
5. **The gas under consideration is a pure substance; that is, all molecules are identical.**

Although we often picture an ideal gas as consisting of single atoms, the behavior of molecular gases approximates that of ideal gases rather well at low pressures. Usually, molecular rotations or vibrations have no effect on the motions considered here.

For our first application of kinetic theory, let us derive an expression for the pressure of N molecules of an ideal gas in a container of volume V in terms of microscopic quantities. The container is a cube with edges of length d (Fig. 21.1). We shall first focus our attention on one of these molecules of mass m_0 and assume it is moving so that its component of velocity in the x direction is v_{xi} as in Active Figure 21.2. (The subscript i here refers to the ith molecule, not to an initial value. We will combine the effects of all the molecules shortly.) As the molecule collides elastically with any wall (assumption 4), its velocity component perpendicular to the wall is reversed because the mass of the wall is far greater than the mass of the molecule. Because the momentum component p_{xi} of the molecule is $m_0 v_{xi}$ before the collision and $-m_0 v_{xi}$ after the collision, the change in the x component of the momentum of the molecule is

$$\Delta p_{xi} = -m_0 v_{xi} - (m_0 v_{xi}) = -2 m_0 v_{xi}$$

Because the molecules obey Newton's laws (assumption 2), we can apply the impulse-momentum theorem (Eq. 9.8) to the molecule to give

$$\bar{F}_{i,\text{ on molecule}}\, \Delta t_{\text{collision}} = \Delta p_{xi} = -2 m_0 v_{xi}$$

where $\bar{F}_{i,\text{ on molecule}}$ is the x component of the average force[1] the wall exerts on the molecule during the collision and $\Delta t_{\text{collision}}$ is the duration of the collision. For the molecule to make another collision with the same wall after this first collision, it must travel a distance of $2d$ in the x direction (across the container and back). Therefore, the time interval between two collisions with the same wall is

$$\Delta t = \frac{2d}{v_{xi}}$$

The force that causes the change in momentum of the molecule in the collision with the wall occurs only during the collision. We can, however, average the force over the time interval for the molecule to move across the cube and back. Sometime during this time interval the collision occurs, so the change in momentum for this time interval is the same as that for the short duration of the collision. Therefore, we can rewrite the impulse-momentum theorem as

$$\bar{F}_i\, \Delta t = -2 m_0 v_{xi}$$

where $\bar{F}_i$ is the average force component over the time interval for the molecule to move across the cube and back. Because exactly one collision occurs for each such time interval, this result is also the long-term average force on the molecule over long time intervals containing any number of multiples of Δt.

This equation and the preceding one enable us to express the x component of the long-term average force exerted by the wall on the molecule as

$$\bar{F}_i = -\frac{2 m_0 v_{xi}}{\Delta t} = -\frac{2 m_0 v_{xi}^2}{2d} = -\frac{m_0 v_{xi}^2}{d}$$

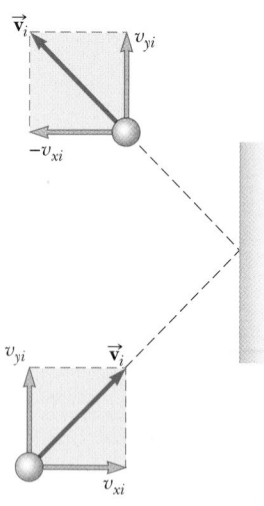

ACTIVE FIGURE 21.2

A molecule makes an elastic collision with the wall of the container. Its x component of momentum is reversed, while its y component remains unchanged. In this construction, we assume the molecule moves in the xy plane.

Sign in at www.thomsonedu.com and go to ThomsonNOW to observe molecules within a container making collisions with the walls of the container and with each other.

---

[1] For this discussion, we use a bar over a variable to represent the average value of the variable, such as $\bar{F}$ for the average force, rather than the subscript "avg" that we have used before. This notation is to save confusion because we already have a number of subscripts on variables.

Now, by Newton's third law, the x component of the long-term average force exerted by the *molecule* on the *wall* is equal in magnitude and opposite in direction:

$$\bar{F}_{i,\text{ on wall}} = -\bar{F}_i = -\left(-\frac{m_0 v_{xi}^2}{d}\right) = \frac{m_0 v_{xi}^2}{d}$$

The total average force $\bar{F}$ exerted by the gas on the wall is found by adding the average forces exerted by the individual molecules. Adding terms such as that above for all molecules gives

$$\bar{F} = \sum_{i=1}^{N} \frac{m_0 v_{xi}^2}{d} = \frac{m_0}{d}\sum_{i=1}^{N} v_{xi}^2$$

where we have factored out the length of the box and the mass m_0 because assumption 5 tells us that all the molecules are the same. We now impose assumption 1, that the number of molecules is large. For a small number of molecules, the actual force on the wall would vary with time. It would be nonzero during the short interval of a collision of a molecule with the wall and zero when no molecule happens to be hitting the wall. For a very large number of molecules such as Avogadro's number, however, these variations in force are smoothed out so that the average force given above is the same over *any* time interval. Therefore, the *constant* force F on the wall due to the molecular collisions is

$$F = \frac{m_0}{d}\sum_{i=1}^{N} v_{xi}^2$$

To proceed further, let's consider how to express the average value of the square of the x component of the velocity for N molecules. The traditional average of a set of values is the sum of the values over the number of values:

$$\overline{v_x^2} = \frac{\sum_{i=1}^{N} v_{xi}^2}{N}$$

The numerator of this expression is contained in the right side of the preceding equation. Therefore, by combining the two expressions the total force on the wall can be written

$$F = \frac{m_0}{d}N\overline{v_x^2} \tag{21.1}$$

Now let's focus again on one molecule with velocity components v_{xi}, v_{yi}, and v_{zi}. The Pythagorean theorem relates the square of the speed of the molecule to the squares of the velocity components:

$$v_i^2 = v_{xi}^2 + v_{yi}^2 + v_{zi}^2$$

Hence, the average value of v^2 for all the molecules in the container is related to the average values of v_x^2, v_y^2, and v_z^2 according to the expression

$$\overline{v^2} = \overline{v_x^2} + \overline{v_y^2} + \overline{v_z^2}$$

Because the motion is completely random (assumption 2), the average values $\overline{v_x^2}$, $\overline{v_y^2}$, and $\overline{v_z^2}$ are equal to each other. Using this fact and the preceding equation, we find that

$$\overline{v^2} = 3\overline{v_x^2}$$

Therefore, from Equation 21.1, the total force exerted on the wall is

$$F = \tfrac{1}{3}N\frac{m_0\overline{v^2}}{d}$$

Using this expression, we can find the total pressure exerted on the wall:

$$P = \frac{F}{A} = \frac{F}{d^2} = \tfrac{1}{3} N \frac{m_0 \overline{v^2}}{d^3} = \tfrac{1}{3} \left(\frac{N}{V} \right) m_0 \overline{v^2}$$

Relationship between ▶
pressure and molecular
kinetic energy

$$P = \tfrac{2}{3} \left(\frac{N}{V} \right) \left(\tfrac{1}{2} m_0 \overline{v^2} \right) \qquad (21.2)$$

This result indicates that **the pressure of a gas is proportional to the number of molecules per unit volume and to the average translational kinetic energy of the molecules**, $\tfrac{1}{2} m_0 \overline{v^2}$. In analyzing this simplified model of an ideal gas, we obtain an important result that relates the macroscopic quantity of pressure to a microscopic quantity, the average value of the square of the molecular speed. Therefore, a key link between the molecular world and the large-scale world has been established.

Notice that Equation 21.2 verifies some features of pressure with which you are probably familiar. One way to increase the pressure inside a container is to increase the number of molecules per unit volume N/V in the container. That is what you do when you add air to a tire. The pressure in the tire can also be increased by increasing the average translational kinetic energy of the air molecules in the tire. That can be accomplished by increasing the temperature of that air, which is why the pressure inside a tire increases as the tire warms up during long road trips. The continuous flexing of the tire as it moves along the road surface results in work done on the rubber as parts of the tire distort, causing an increase in internal energy of the rubber. The increased temperature of the rubber results in the transfer of energy by heat into the air inside the tire. This transfer increases the air's temperature, and this increase in temperature in turn produces an increase in pressure.

Molecular Interpretation of Temperature

We can gain some insight into the meaning of temperature by first writing Equation 21.2 in the form

$$PV = \tfrac{2}{3} N \left(\tfrac{1}{2} m_0 \overline{v^2} \right)$$

Let's now compare this expression with the equation of state for an ideal gas (Eq. 19.10):

$$PV = N k_B T$$

Recall that the equation of state is based on experimental facts concerning the macroscopic behavior of gases. Equating the right sides of these expressions gives

Temperature is ▶
proportional to average
kinetic energy

$$T = \frac{2}{3 k_B} \left(\tfrac{1}{2} m_0 \overline{v^2} \right) \qquad (21.3)$$

This result tells us that temperature is a direct measure of average molecular kinetic energy. By rearranging Equation 21.3, we can relate the translational molecular kinetic energy to the temperature:

Average kinetic energy per ▶
molecule

$$\tfrac{1}{2} m_0 \overline{v^2} = \tfrac{3}{2} k_B T \qquad (21.4)$$

That is, the average translational kinetic energy per molecule is $\tfrac{3}{2} k_B T$. Because $\overline{v_x^2} = \tfrac{1}{3} \overline{v^2}$, it follows that

$$\tfrac{1}{2} m_0 \overline{v_x^2} = \tfrac{1}{2} k_B T \qquad (21.5)$$

In a similar manner, for the y and z directions,

$$\tfrac{1}{2} m_0 \overline{v_y^2} = \tfrac{1}{2} k_B T \quad \text{and} \quad \tfrac{1}{2} m_0 \overline{v_z^2} = \tfrac{1}{2} k_B T$$

Therefore, each translational degree of freedom contributes an equal amount of energy, $\tfrac{1}{2} k_B T$, to the gas. (In general, a "degree of freedom" refers to an indepen-

TABLE 21.1

Some Root-Mean-Square (rms) Speeds

Gas	Molar Mass (g/mol)	v_{rms} at 20°C (m/s)	Gas	Molar Mass (g/mol)	v_{rms} at 20°C (m/s)
H_2	2.02	1902	NO	30.0	494
He	4.00	1352	O_2	32.0	478
H_2O	18.0	637	CO_2	44.0	408
Ne	20.2	602	SO_2	64.1	338
N_2 or CO	28.0	511			

dent means by which a molecule can possess energy.) A generalization of this result, known as the **theorem of equipartition of energy**, is as follows:

> Each degree of freedom contributes $\frac{1}{2}k_B T$ to the energy of a system, where possible degrees of freedom are those associated with translation, rotation, and vibration of molecules.

◀ Theorem of equipartition of energy

The total translational kinetic energy of N molecules of gas is simply N times the average energy per molecule, which is given by Equation 21.4:

$$K_{tot\ trans} = N(\tfrac{1}{2}m_0\overline{v^2}) = \tfrac{3}{2}Nk_B T = \tfrac{3}{2}nRT \qquad (21.6)$$

◀ Total translational kinetic energy of N molecules

where we have used $k_B = R/N_A$ for Boltzmann's constant and $n = N/N_A$ for the number of moles of gas. If the gas molecules possess only translational kinetic energy, Equation 21.6 represents the internal energy of the gas. This result implies that **the internal energy of an ideal gas depends only on the temperature**. We will follow up on this point in Section 21.2.

The square root of $\overline{v^2}$ is called the *root-mean-square* (rms) *speed* of the molecules. From Equation 21.4, we find that the rms speed is

$$v_{rms} = \sqrt{\overline{v^2}} = \sqrt{\frac{3k_B T}{m_0}} = \sqrt{\frac{3RT}{M}} \qquad (21.7)$$

◀ Root-mean-square speed

where M is the molar mass in kilograms per mole and is equal to $m_0 N_A$. This expression shows that, at a given temperature, lighter molecules move faster, on the average, than do heavier molecules. For example, at a given temperature, hydrogen molecules, whose molar mass is 2.02×10^{-3} kg/mol, have an average speed approximately four times that of oxygen molecules, whose molar mass is 32.0×10^{-3} kg/mol. Table 21.1 lists the rms speeds for various molecules at 20°C.

PITFALL PREVENTION 21.1
The Square Root of the Square?

Taking the square root of $\overline{v^2}$ does not "undo" the square because we have taken an average *between* squaring and taking the square root. Although the square root of $(\overline{v})^2$ is $\overline{v} = v_{avg}$ because the squaring is done after the averaging, the square root of $\overline{v^2}$ is *not* v_{avg}, but rather v_{rms}.

Quick Quiz 21.1 Two containers hold an ideal gas at the same temperature and pressure. Both containers hold the same type of gas, but container B has twice the volume of container A. **(i)** What is the average translational kinetic energy per molecule in container B? (a) twice that of container A   (b) the same as that of container A   (c) half that of container A   (d) impossible to determine   **(ii)** From the same choices, describe the internal energy of the gas in container B.

EXAMPLE 21.1   **A Tank of Helium**

A tank used for filling helium balloons has a volume of 0.300 m³ and contains 2.00 mol of helium gas at 20.0°C. Assume the helium behaves like an ideal gas.

(A) What is the total translational kinetic energy of the gas molecules?

SOLUTION

Conceptualize Imagine a microscopic model of a gas in which you can watch the molecules move about the container more rapidly as the temperature increases.

Categorize We evaluate parameters with equations developed in the preceding discussion, so this example is a substitution problem.

Use Equation 21.6 with $n = 2.00$ mol and $T = 293$ K:

$$K_{\text{tot trans}} = \tfrac{3}{2}nRT = \tfrac{3}{2}(2.00 \text{ mol})(8.31 \text{ J/mol} \cdot \text{K})(293 \text{ K})$$

$$= \boxed{7.30 \times 10^3 \text{ J}}$$

(B) What is the average kinetic energy per molecule?

SOLUTION

Use Equation 21.4:

$$\tfrac{1}{2}m_0\overline{v^2} = \tfrac{3}{2}k_B T = \tfrac{3}{2}(1.38 \times 10^{-23} \text{ J/K})(293 \text{ K})$$

$$= \boxed{6.07 \times 10^{-21} \text{ J}}$$

What If? What if the temperature is raised from 20.0°C to 40.0°C? Because 40.0 is twice as large as 20.0, is the total translational energy of the molecules of the gas twice as large at the higher temperature?

Answer The expression for the total translational energy depends on the temperature, and the value for the temperature must be expressed in kelvins, not in degrees Celsius. Therefore, the ratio of 40.0 to 20.0 is *not* the appropriate ratio. Converting the Celsius temperatures to kelvins, 20.0°C is 293 K and 40.0°C is 313 K. Therefore, the total translational energy increases by a factor of only 313 K/293 K = 1.07.

21.2   Molar Specific Heat of an Ideal Gas

Consider an ideal gas undergoing several processes such that the change in temperature is $\Delta T = T_f - T_i$ for all processes. The temperature change can be achieved by taking a variety of paths from one isotherm to another as shown in Figure 21.3. Because ΔT is the same for each path, the change in internal energy ΔE_{int} is the same for all paths. The work W done on the gas (the negative of the area under the curves) is different for each path. Therefore, from the first law of thermodynamics, the heat associated with a given change in temperature does *not* have a unique value as discussed in Section 20.4.

We can address this difficulty by defining specific heats for two special processes: isovolumetric and isobaric. Because the number of moles is a convenient measure of the amount of gas, we define the **molar specific heats** associated with these processes as follows:

$$Q = nC_V \, \Delta T \quad \text{(constant volume)} \tag{21.8}$$

$$Q = nC_P \, \Delta T \quad \text{(constant pressure)} \tag{21.9}$$

where C_V is the **molar specific heat at constant volume** and C_P is the **molar specific heat at constant pressure**. When energy is added to a gas by heat at constant pressure, not only does the internal energy of the gas increase, but (negative) work is done on the gas because of the change in volume. Therefore, the heat Q in Equation 21.9 must account for both the increase in internal energy and the transfer of energy out of the system by work. For this reason, Q is greater in Equation 21.9 than in Equation 21.8 for given values of n and ΔT. Therefore, C_P is greater than C_V.

In the previous section, we found that the temperature of a gas is a measure of the average translational kinetic energy of the gas molecules. This kinetic energy is associated with the motion of the center of mass of each molecule. It does not include the energy associated with the internal motion of the molecule, namely,

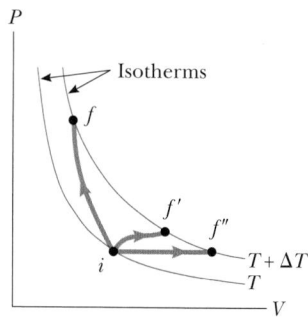

Figure 21.3 An ideal gas is taken from one isotherm at temperature T to another at temperature $T + \Delta T$ along three different paths.

vibrations and rotations about the center of mass. That should not be surprising because the simple kinetic theory model assumes a structureless molecule.

So, let's first consider the simplest case of an ideal monatomic gas, that is, a gas containing one atom per molecule such as helium, neon, or argon. When energy is added to a monatomic gas in a container of fixed volume, all the added energy goes into increasing the translational kinetic energy of the atoms. There is no other way to store the energy in a monatomic gas. Therefore, from Equation 21.6, we see that the internal energy E_{int} of N molecules (or n mol) of an ideal monatomic gas is

$$E_{int} = K_{tot\ trans} = \tfrac{3}{2}Nk_B T = \tfrac{3}{2}nRT \qquad \textbf{(21.10)}$$

◀ **Internal energy of an ideal monatomic gas**

For a monatomic ideal gas, E_{int} is a function of T only and the functional relationship is given by Equation 21.10. In general, the internal energy of any ideal gas is a function of T only and the exact relationship depends on the type of gas.

If energy is transferred by heat to a system at constant volume, no work is done on the system. That is, $W = -\int P\,dV = 0$ for a constant-volume process. Hence, from the first law of thermodynamics,

$$Q = \Delta E_{int} \qquad \textbf{(21.11)}$$

In other words, all the energy transferred by heat goes into increasing the internal energy of the system. A constant-volume process from i to f for an ideal gas is described in Active Figure 21.4, where ΔT is the temperature difference between the two isotherms. Substituting the expression for Q given by Equation 21.8 into Equation 21.11, we obtain

$$\Delta E_{int} = nC_V\,\Delta T \qquad \textbf{(21.12)}$$

If the molar specific heat is constant, we can express the internal energy of a gas as

$$E_{int} = nC_V T$$

This equation applies to all ideal gases, those gases having more than one atom per molecule as well as monatomic ideal gases. In the limit of infinitesimal changes, we can use Equation 21.12 to express the molar specific heat at constant volume as

$$C_V = \frac{1}{n}\frac{dE_{int}}{dT} \qquad \textbf{(21.13)}$$

Let's now apply the results of this discussion to a monatomic gas. Substituting the internal energy from Equation 21.10 into Equation 21.13 gives

$$C_V = \tfrac{3}{2}R \qquad \textbf{(21.14)}$$

This expression predicts a value of $C_V = \tfrac{3}{2}R = 12.5\ \text{J/mol}\cdot\text{K}$ for *all* monatomic gases. This prediction is in excellent agreement with measured values of molar specific heats for such gases as helium, neon, argon, and xenon over a wide range of temperatures (Table 21.2, page 594). Small variations in Table 21.2 from the predicted values are because real gases are not ideal gases. In real gases, weak intermolecular interactions occur, which are not addressed in our ideal gas model.

Now suppose the gas is taken along the constant-pressure path $i \rightarrow f'$ shown in Active Figure 21.4. Along this path, the temperature again increases by ΔT. The energy that must be transferred by heat to the gas in this process is $Q = nC_P\,\Delta T$. Because the volume changes in this process, the work done on the gas is $W = -P\,\Delta V$, where P is the constant pressure at which the process occurs. Applying the first law of thermodynamics to this process, we have

$$\Delta E_{int} = Q + W = nC_P\,\Delta T + (-P\,\Delta V) \qquad \textbf{(21.15)}$$

In this case, the energy added to the gas by heat is channeled as follows. Part of it leaves the system by work (that is, the gas moves a piston through a displacement), and the remainder appears as an increase in the internal energy of the gas. The

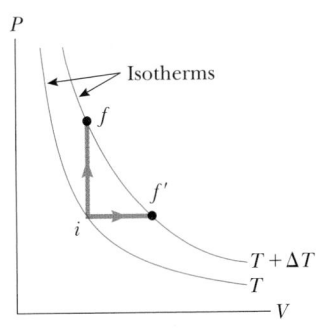

ACTIVE FIGURE 21.4

Energy is transferred by heat to an ideal gas in two ways. For the constant-volume path $i \rightarrow f$, all the energy goes into increasing the internal energy of the gas because no work is done. Along the constant-pressure path $i \rightarrow f'$, part of the energy transferred in by heat is transferred out by work.

Sign in at www.thomsonedu.com and go to ThomsonNOW to choose initial and final temperatures for one mole of an ideal gas undergoing constant-volume and constant-pressure processes and measure Q, W, ΔE_{int}, C_V, and C_P.

TABLE 21.2

Molar Specific Heats of Various Gases

Gas	Molar Specific Heat (J/mol · K)[a]			
	C_P	C_V	$C_P - C_V$	$\gamma = C_P/C_V$
Monatomic gases				
He	20.8	12.5	8.33	1.67
Ar	20.8	12.5	8.33	1.67
Ne	20.8	12.7	8.12	1.64
Kr	20.8	12.3	8.49	1.69
Diatomic gases				
H_2	28.8	20.4	8.33	1.41
N_2	29.1	20.8	8.33	1.40
O_2	29.4	21.1	8.33	1.40
CO	29.3	21.0	8.33	1.40
Cl_2	34.7	25.7	8.96	1.35
Polyatomic gases				
CO_2	37.0	28.5	8.50	1.30
SO_2	40.4	31.4	9.00	1.29
H_2O	35.4	27.0	8.37	1.30
CH_4	35.5	27.1	8.41	1.31

[a] All values except that for water were obtained at 300 K.

change in internal energy for the process $i \rightarrow f'$, however, is equal to that for the process $i \rightarrow f$ because E_{int} depends only on temperature for an ideal gas and ΔT is the same for both processes. In addition, because $PV = nRT$, note that for a constant-pressure process, $P\Delta V = nR\,\Delta T$. Substituting this value for $P\Delta V$ into Equation 21.15 with $\Delta E_{int} = nC_V\,\Delta T$ (Eq. 21.12) gives

$$nC_V\,\Delta T = nC_P\,\Delta T - nR\,\Delta T$$

$$C_P - C_V = R \tag{21.16}$$

This expression applies to *any* ideal gas. It predicts that the molar specific heat of an ideal gas at constant pressure is greater than the molar specific heat at constant volume by an amount R, the universal gas constant (which has the value 8.31 J/mol · K). This expression is applicable to real gases as the data in Table 21.2 show.

Because $C_V = \frac{3}{2}R$ for a monatomic ideal gas, Equation 21.16 predicts a value $C_P = \frac{5}{2}R = 20.8$ J/mol·K for the molar specific heat of a monatomic gas at constant pressure. The ratio of these molar specific heats is a dimensionless quantity γ (Greek letter gamma):

◀ Ratio of molar specific heats for a monatomic ideal gas

$$\gamma = \frac{C_P}{C_V} = \frac{5R/2}{3R/2} = \frac{5}{3} = 1.67 \tag{21.17}$$

Theoretical values of C_V, C_P, and γ are in excellent agreement with experimental values obtained for monatomic gases, but they are in serious disagreement with the values for the more complex gases (see Table 21.2). That is not surprising; the value $C_V = \frac{3}{2}R$ was derived for a monatomic ideal gas, and we expect some additional contribution to the molar specific heat from the internal structure of the more complex molecules. In Section 21.4, we describe the effect of molecular structure on the molar specific heat of a gas. The internal energy—and hence the molar specific heat—of a complex gas must include contributions from the rotational and the vibrational motions of the molecule.

In the case of solids and liquids heated at constant pressure, very little work is done because the thermal expansion is small. Consequently, C_P and C_V are approximately equal for solids and liquids.

Quick Quiz 21.2   **(i)** How does the internal energy of an ideal gas change as it follows path $i \rightarrow f$ in Active Figure 21.4? (a) E_{int} increases. (b) E_{int} decreases. (c) E_{int} stays the same. (d) There is not enough information to determine how E_{int} changes. **(ii)** From the same choices, how does the internal energy of an ideal gas change as it follows path $f \rightarrow f'$ along the isotherm labeled $T + \Delta T$ in Active Figure 21.4?

EXAMPLE 21.2   **Heating a Cylinder of Helium**

A cylinder contains 3.00 mol of helium gas at a temperature of 300 K.

(A) If the gas is heated at constant volume, how much energy must be transferred by heat to the gas for its temperature to increase to 500 K?

SOLUTION

Conceptualize   Run the process in your mind with the help of the piston–cylinder arrangement in Figure 19.12.

Categorize   Because the gas maintains a constant volume, the piston in Figure 19.12 is locked in place. We evaluate parameters with equations developed in the preceding discussion, so this example is a substitution problem.

Use Equation 21.8 to find the energy transfer:

$$Q_1 = nC_V \, \Delta T$$

Substitute the given values:

$$Q_1 = (3.00 \text{ mol})(12.5 \text{ J/mol} \cdot \text{K})(500 \text{ K} - 300 \text{ K})$$

$$= \boxed{7.50 \times 10^3 \text{ J}}$$

(B) How much energy must be transferred by heat to the gas at constant pressure to raise the temperature to 500 K?

SOLUTION

Categorize   Because the gas maintains a constant pressure, the piston in Figure 19.12 is free to move, so the piston is modeled as a particle in equilibrium.

Use Equation 21.9 to find the energy transfer:

$$Q_2 = nC_P \, \Delta T$$

Substitute the given values:

$$Q_2 = (3.00 \text{ mol})(20.8 \text{ J/mol} \cdot \text{K})(500 \text{ K} - 300 \text{ K})$$

$$= \boxed{12.5 \times 10^3 \text{ J}}$$

This value is larger than Q_1 because of the transfer of energy out of the gas by work in the constant pressure process.

21.3   Adiabatic Processes for an Ideal Gas

As noted in Section 20.6, an **adiabatic process** is one in which no energy is transferred by heat between a system and its surroundings. For example, if a gas is compressed (or expanded) rapidly, very little energy is transferred out of (or into) the system by heat, so the process is nearly adiabatic. Such processes occur in the cycle of a gasoline engine, which is discussed in detail in Chapter 22. Another example of an adiabatic process is the slow expansion of a gas that is thermally insulated from its surroundings. All three variables in the ideal gas law—P, V, and T—change during an adiabatic process.

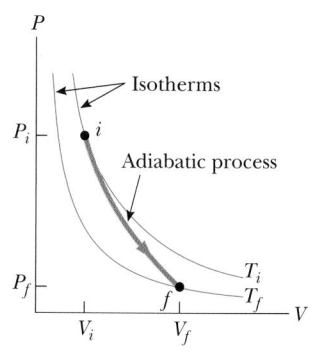

Figure 21.5 The PV diagram for an adiabatic expansion of an ideal gas. Notice that $T_f < T_i$ in this process, so the temperature of the gas decreases.

Let's imagine an adiabatic gas process involving an infinitesimal change in volume dV and an accompanying infinitesimal change in temperature dT. The work done on the gas is $-P\,dV$. Because the internal energy of an ideal gas depends only on temperature, the change in the internal energy in an adiabatic process is the same as that for an isovolumetric process between the same temperatures, $dE_{int} = nC_V\,dT$ (Eq. 21.12). Hence, the first law of thermodynamics, $\Delta E_{int} = Q + W$, with $Q = 0$ becomes

$$dE_{int} = nC_V\,dT = -P\,dV$$

Taking the total differential of the equation of state of an ideal gas, $PV = nRT$, gives

$$P\,dV + V\,dP = nR\,dT$$

Eliminating dT from these two equations, we find that

$$P\,dV + V\,dP = -\frac{R}{C_V}P\,dV$$

Substituting $R = C_P - C_V$ and dividing by PV gives

$$\frac{dV}{V} + \frac{dP}{P} = -\left(\frac{C_P - C_V}{C_V}\right)\frac{dV}{V} = (1 - \gamma)\frac{dV}{V}$$

$$\frac{dP}{P} + \gamma\frac{dV}{V} = 0$$

Integrating this expression, we have

$$\ln P + \gamma \ln V = \text{constant}$$

which is equivalent to

▶ Relationship between P and V for an adiabatic process involving an ideal gas

$$PV^\gamma = \text{constant} \qquad (21.18)$$

The PV diagram for an adiabatic expansion is shown in Figure 21.5. Because $\gamma > 1$, the PV curve is steeper than it would be for an isothermal expansion. By the definition of an adiabatic process, no energy is transferred by heat into or out of the system. Hence, from the first law, we see that ΔE_{int} is negative (work is done *by* the gas, so its internal energy decreases) and so ΔT also is negative. Therefore, the temperature of the gas decreases ($T_f < T_i$) during an adiabatic expansion.[2] Conversely, the temperature increases if the gas is compressed adiabatically. Applying Equation 21.18 to the initial and final states, we see that

$$P_iV_i^\gamma = P_fV_f^\gamma \qquad (21.19)$$

▶ Relationship between T and V for an adiabatic process involving an ideal gas

Using the ideal gas law, we can express Equation 21.19 as

$$T_iV_i^{\gamma-1} = T_fV_f^{\gamma-1} \qquad (21.20)$$

EXAMPLE 21.3 **A Diesel Engine Cylinder**

Air at 20.0°C in the cylinder of a diesel engine is compressed from an initial pressure of 1.00 atm and volume of 800.0 cm³ to a volume of 60.0 cm³. Assume air behaves as an ideal gas with $\gamma = 1.40$ and the compression is adiabatic. Find the final pressure and temperature of the air.

SOLUTION

Conceptualize Imagine what happens if a gas is compressed into a smaller volume. Our discussion above and Figure 21.5 tell us that the pressure and temperature both increase.

Categorize We categorize this example as a problem involving an adiabatic process.

---

[2] In the adiabatic free expansion discussed in Section 20.6, the temperature remains constant. In this unique process, no work is done because the gas expands into a vacuum. In general, the temperature decreases in an adiabatic expansion in which work is done.

Analyze   Use Equation 21.19 to find the final pressure:

$$P_f = P_i \left(\frac{V_i}{V_f} \right)^{\gamma} = (1.00 \text{ atm}) \left(\frac{800.0 \text{ cm}^3}{60.0 \text{ cm}^3} \right)^{1.40}$$

$$= \boxed{37.6 \text{ atm}}$$

Use the ideal gas law to find the final temperature:

$$\frac{P_i V_i}{T_i} = \frac{P_f V_f}{T_f}$$

$$T_f = \frac{P_f V_f}{P_i V_i} T_i = \frac{(37.6 \text{ atm})(60.0 \text{ cm}^3)}{(1.00 \text{ atm})(800.0 \text{ cm}^3)} (293 \text{ K})$$

$$= 826 \text{ K} = \boxed{553°\text{C}}$$

Finalize   The temperature of the gas increases by a factor of 826 K/293 K = 2.82. The high compression in a diesel engine raises the temperature of the fuel enough to cause its combustion without the use of spark plugs.

21.4   The Equipartition of Energy

Predictions based on our model for molar specific heat agree quite well with the behavior of monatomic gases, but not with the behavior of complex gases (see Table 21.2). The value predicted by the model for the quantity $C_P - C_V = R$, however, is the same for all gases. This similarity is not surprising because this difference is the result of the work done on the gas, which is independent of its molecular structure.

To clarify the variations in C_V and C_P in gases more complex than monatomic gases, let's explore further the origin of molar specific heat. So far, we have assumed the sole contribution to the internal energy of a gas is the translational kinetic energy of the molecules. The internal energy of a gas, however, includes contributions from the translational, vibrational, and rotational motion of the molecules. The rotational and vibrational motions of molecules can be activated by collisions and therefore are "coupled" to the translational motion of the molecules. The branch of physics known as *statistical mechanics* has shown that, for a large number of particles obeying the laws of Newtonian mechanics, the available energy is, on average, shared equally by each independent degree of freedom. Recall from Section 21.1 that the equipartition theorem states that, at equilibrium, each degree of freedom contributes $\frac{1}{2}k_B T$ of energy per molecule.

Let's consider a diatomic gas whose molecules have the shape of a dumbbell (Fig. 21.6). In this model, the center of mass of the molecule can translate in the x, y, and z directions (Fig. 21.6a). In addition, the molecule can rotate about three mutually perpendicular axes (Fig. 21.6b). The rotation about the y axis can be neglected because the molecule's moment of inertia I_y and its rotational energy $\frac{1}{2}I_y \omega^2$ about this axis are negligible compared with those associated with the x and z axes. (If the two atoms are modeled as particles, then I_y is identically zero.) Therefore, there are five degrees of freedom for translation and rotation: three associated with the translational motion and two associated with the rotational motion. Because each degree of freedom contributes, on average, $\frac{1}{2}k_B T$ of energy per molecule, the internal energy for a system of N molecules, ignoring vibration for now, is

$$E_{\text{int}} = 3N(\tfrac{1}{2}k_B T) + 2N(\tfrac{1}{2}k_B T) = \tfrac{5}{2}Nk_B T = \tfrac{5}{2}nRT$$

We can use this result and Equation 21.13 to find the molar specific heat at constant volume:

$$C_V = \frac{1}{n}\frac{dE_{\text{int}}}{dT} = \frac{1}{n}\frac{d}{dT}\left(\tfrac{5}{2}nRT\right) = \tfrac{5}{2}R \qquad \textbf{(21.21)}$$

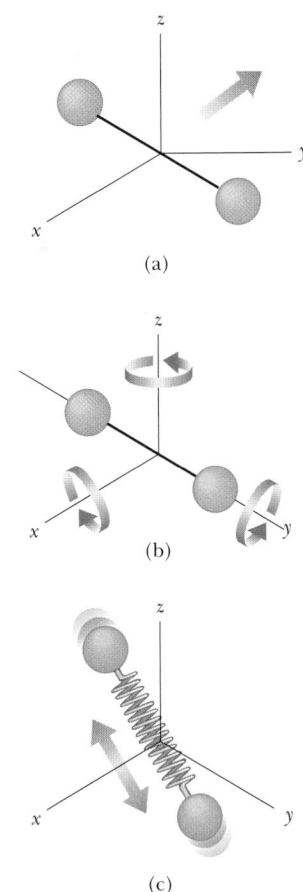

Figure 21.6   Possible motions of a diatomic molecule: (a) translational motion of the center of mass, (b) rotational motion about the various axes, and (c) vibrational motion along the molecular axis.

From Equations 21.16 and 21.17, we find that

$$C_P = C_V + R = \tfrac{7}{2}R$$

$$\gamma = \frac{C_P}{C_V} = \frac{\tfrac{7}{2}R}{\tfrac{5}{2}R} = \frac{7}{5} = 1.40$$

These results agree quite well with most of the data for diatomic molecules given in Table 21.2. That is rather surprising because we have not yet accounted for the possible vibrations of the molecule.

In the model for vibration, the two atoms are joined by an imaginary spring (see Fig. 21.6c). The vibrational motion adds two more degrees of freedom, which correspond to the kinetic energy and the potential energy associated with vibrations along the length of the molecule. Hence, a model that includes all three types of motion predicts a total internal energy of

$$E_{int} = 3N(\tfrac{1}{2}k_B T) + 2N(\tfrac{1}{2}k_B T) + 2N(\tfrac{1}{2}k_B T) = \tfrac{7}{2}Nk_B T = \tfrac{7}{2}nRT$$

and a molar specific heat at constant volume of

$$C_V = \frac{1}{n}\frac{dE_{int}}{dT} = \frac{1}{n}\frac{d}{dT}(\tfrac{7}{2}nRT) = \tfrac{7}{2}R \qquad (21.22)$$

This value is inconsistent with experimental data for molecules such as H_2 and N_2 (see Table 21.2) and suggests a breakdown of our model based on classical physics.

It might seem that our model is a failure for predicting molar specific heats for diatomic gases. We can claim some success for our model, however, if measurements of molar specific heat are made over a wide temperature range rather than at the single temperature that gives us the values in Table 21.2. Figure 21.7 shows the molar specific heat of hydrogen as a function of temperature. The remarkable feature about the three plateaus in the graph's curve is that they are at the values of the molar specific heat predicted by Equations 21.14, 21.21, and 21.22! For low temperatures, the diatomic hydrogen gas behaves like a monatomic gas. As the temperature rises to room temperature, its molar specific heat rises to a value for a diatomic gas, consistent with the inclusion of rotation but not vibration. For high temperatures, the molar specific heat is consistent with a model including all types of motion.

Before addressing the reason for this mysterious behavior, let's make some brief remarks about polyatomic gases. For molecules with more than two atoms, the vibrations are more complex than for diatomic molecules and the number of degrees of freedom is even larger. The result is an even higher predicted molar specific heat, which is in qualitative agreement with experiment. The molar specific heats for the polyatomic gases in Table 21.2 are higher than those for

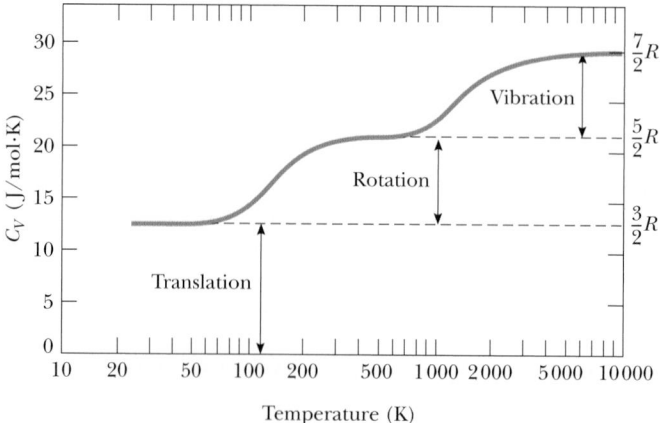

Figure 21.7   The molar specific heat of hydrogen as a function of temperature. The horizontal scale is logarithmic. Notice that hydrogen liquefies at 20 K.

diatomic gases. The more degrees of freedom available to a molecule, the more "ways" there are to store energy, resulting in a higher molar specific heat.

A Hint of Energy Quantization

Our model for molar specific heats has been based so far on purely classical notions. It predicts a value of the specific heat for a diatomic gas that, according to Figure 21.7, only agrees with experimental measurements made at high temperatures. To explain why this value is only true at high temperatures and why the plateaus in Figure 21.7 exist, we must go beyond classical physics and introduce some quantum physics into the model. In Chapter 18, we discussed quantization of frequency for vibrating strings and air columns; only certain frequencies of standing waves can exist. That is a natural result whenever waves are subject to boundary conditions.

Quantum physics (Chapters 40 through 43) shows that atoms and molecules can be described by the physics of waves under boundary conditions. Consequently, these waves have quantized frequencies. Furthermore, in quantum physics, the energy of a system is proportional to the frequency of the wave representing the system. Hence, **the energies of atoms and molecules are quantized**.

For a molecule, quantum physics tells us that the rotational and vibrational energies are quantized. Figure 21.8 shows an **energy-level diagram** for the rotational and vibrational quantum states of a diatomic molecule. The lowest allowed state is called the **ground state**. Notice that vibrational states are separated by larger energy gaps than are rotational states.

At low temperatures, the energy a molecule gains in collisions with its neighbors is generally not large enough to raise it to the first excited state of either rotation or vibration. Therefore, even though rotation and vibration are allowed according to classical physics, they do not occur in reality at low temperatures. All molecules are in the ground state for rotation and vibration. The only contribution to the molecules' average energy is from translation, and the specific heat is that predicted by Equation 21.14.

As the temperature is raised, the average energy of the molecules increases. In some collisions, a molecule may have enough energy transferred to it from another molecule to excite the first rotational state. As the temperature is raised further, more molecules can be excited to this state. The result is that rotation begins to contribute to the internal energy and the molar specific heat rises. At about room temperature in Figure 21.7, the second plateau has been reached and rotation contributes fully to the molar specific heat. The molar specific heat is now equal to the value predicted by Equation 21.21.

There is no contribution at room temperature from vibration because the molecules are still in the ground vibrational state. The temperature must be raised even further to excite the first vibrational state, which happens in Figure 21.7 between 1 000 K and 10 000 K. At 10 000 K on the right side of the figure, vibration is contributing fully to the internal energy and the molar specific heat has the value predicted by Equation 21.22.

The predictions of this model are supportive of the theorem of equipartition of energy. In addition, the inclusion in the model of energy quantization from quantum physics allows a full understanding of Figure 21.7.

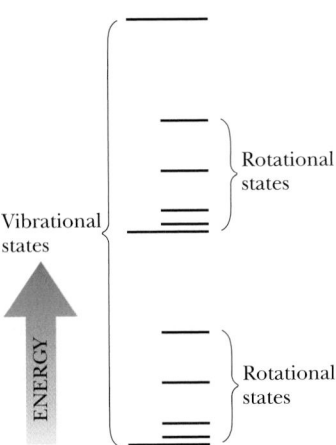

Figure 21.8 An energy-level diagram for vibrational and rotational states of a diatomic molecule. Notice that the rotational states lie closer together in energy than do the vibrational states.

Quick Quiz 21.3 The molar specific heat of a diatomic gas is measured at constant volume and found to be 29.1 J/mol · K. What are the types of energy that are contributing to the molar specific heat? (a) translation only   (b) translation and rotation only   (c) translation and vibration only   (d) translation, rotation, and vibration

---

Quick Quiz 21.4 The molar specific heat of a gas is measured at constant volume and found to be $11R/2$. Is the gas most likely to be (a) monatomic, (b) diatomic, or (c) polyatomic?

21.5 Distribution of Molecular Speeds

Thus far, we have considered only average values of the energies of molecules in a gas and have not addressed the distribution of energies among molecules. In reality, the motion of the molecules is extremely chaotic. Any individual molecule collides with others at an enormous rate, typically a billion times per second. Each collision results in a change in the speed and direction of motion of each of the participant molecules. Equation 21.7 shows that rms molecular speeds increase with increasing temperature. What is the relative number of molecules that possess some characteristic such as energy within a certain range?

We shall address this question by considering the **number density** $n_V(E)$. This quantity, called a *distribution function*, is defined so that $n_V(E)\, dE$ is the number of molecules per unit volume with energy between E and $E + dE$. (The ratio of the number of molecules that have the desired characteristic to the total number of molecules is the probability that a particular molecule has that characteristic.) In general, the number density is found from statistical mechanics to be

Boltzmann distribution law ▶

$$n_V(E) = n_0 e^{-E/k_B T} \tag{21.23}$$

where n_0 is defined such that $n_0\, dE$ is the number of molecules per unit volume having energy between $E = 0$ and $E = dE$. This equation, known as the **Boltzmann distribution law**, is important in describing the statistical mechanics of a large number of molecules. It states that **the probability of finding the molecules in a particular energy state varies exponentially as the negative of the energy divided by $k_B T$.** All the molecules would fall into the lowest energy level if the thermal agitation at a temperature T did not excite the molecules to higher energy levels.

EXAMPLE 21.4   **Thermal Excitation of Atomic Energy Levels**

As discussed in Section 21.4, atoms can occupy only certain discrete energy levels. Consider a gas at a temperature of 2 500 K whose atoms can occupy only two energy levels separated by 1.50 eV, where 1 eV (electron volt) is an energy unit equal to 1.60×10^{-19} J (Fig. 21.9). Determine the ratio of the number of atoms in the higher energy level to the number in the lower energy level.

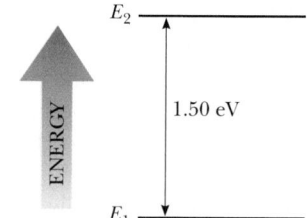

Figure 21.9 (Example 21.4) Energy-level diagram for a gas whose atoms can occupy two energy states.

SOLUTION

Conceptualize In your mental representation of this example, remember that only two possible states are allowed for the system of the atom. Figure 21.9 helps you visualize the two states on an energy-level diagram. In this case, the atom has two possible energies, E_1 and E_2, where $E_1 < E_2$.

Categorize We categorize this example as one in which we apply the Boltzmann distribution law to a quantized system.

Analyze Set up the ratio of the number of atoms in the higher energy level to the number in the lower energy level and use Equation 21.23 to express each number:

$$(1) \quad \frac{n_V(E_2)}{n_V(E_1)} = \frac{n_0 e^{-E_2/k_B T}}{n_0 e^{-E_1/k_B T}} = e^{-(E_2 - E_1)/k_B T}$$

Evaluate $k_B T$ in the exponent:

$$k_B T = (1.38 \times 10^{-23}\, \text{J/K})(2\,500\, \text{K})\left(\frac{1\, \text{eV}}{1.60 \times 10^{-19}\, \text{J}}\right) = 0.216\, \text{eV}$$

Substitute this value into Equation (1):

$$\frac{n_V(E_2)}{n_V(E_1)} = e^{-1.50\, \text{eV}/0.216\, \text{eV}} = e^{-6.96} = \boxed{9.52 \times 10^{-4}}$$

Finalize   This result indicates that at $T = 2\,500$ K, only a small fraction of the atoms are in the higher energy level. In fact, for every atom in the higher energy level, there are about 1 000 atoms in the lower level. The number of atoms in the higher level increases at even higher temperatures, but the distribution law specifies that at equilibrium there are always more atoms in the lower level than in the higher level.

What If?   What if the energy levels in Figure 21.9 were closer together in energy? Would that increase or decrease the fraction of the atoms in the upper energy level?

Answer   If the excited level is lower in energy than that in Figure 21.9, it would be easier for thermal agitation to excite atoms to this level and the fraction of atoms in this energy level would be larger. Let us see this mathematically by expressing Equation (1) as

$$r_2 = e^{-(E_2 - E_1)/k_B T}$$

where r_2 is the ratio of atoms having energy E_2 to those with energy E_1. Differentiating with respect to E_2, we find

$$\frac{dr_2}{dE_2} = \frac{d}{dE_2}\left(e^{-(E_2 - E_1)/k_B T}\right) = -\frac{E_2}{k_B T}e^{-(E_2 - E_1)/k_B T} < 0$$

Because the derivative has a negative value, as E_2 decreases, r_2 increases.

Now that we have discussed the distribution of energies, let's think about the distribution of molecular speeds. In 1860, James Clerk Maxwell (1831–1879) derived an expression that describes the distribution of molecular speeds in a very definite manner. His work and subsequent developments by other scientists were highly controversial because direct detection of molecules could not be achieved experimentally at that time. About 60 years later, however, experiments were devised that confirmed Maxwell's predictions.

Let's consider a container of gas whose molecules have some distribution of speeds. Suppose we want to determine how many gas molecules have a speed in the range from, for example, 400 to 401 m/s. Intuitively, we expect the speed distribution to depend on temperature. Furthermore, we expect the distribution to peak in the vicinity of v_{rms}. That is, few molecules are expected to have speeds much less than or much greater than v_{rms} because these extreme speeds result only from an unlikely chain of collisions.

The observed speed distribution of gas molecules in thermal equilibrium is shown in Active Figure 21.10 (page 602). The quantity N_v, called the **Maxwell–Boltzmann speed distribution function**, is defined as follows. If N is the total number of molecules, the number of molecules with speeds between v and $v + dv$ is $dN = N_v\,dv$. This number is also equal to the area of the shaded rectangle in Active Figure 21.10. Furthermore, the fraction of molecules with speeds between v and $v + dv$ is $(N_v\,dv)/N$. This fraction is also equal to the probability that a molecule has a speed in the range v to $v + dv$.

The fundamental expression that describes the distribution of speeds of N gas molecules is

$$N_v = 4\pi N\left(\frac{m_0}{2\pi k_B T}\right)^{3/2} v^2 e^{-m_0 v^2/2k_B T} \tag{21.24}$$

where m_0 is the mass of a gas molecule, k_B is Boltzmann's constant, and T is the absolute temperature.[3] Observe the appearance of the Boltzmann factor $e^{-E/k_B T}$ with $E = \frac{1}{2}m_0 v^2$.

LUDWIG BOLTZMANN
Austrian physicist (1844–1906)
Boltzmann made many important contributions to the development of the kinetic theory of gases, electromagnetism, and thermodynamics. His pioneering work in the field of kinetic theory led to the branch of physics known as statistical mechanics.

---

[3] For the derivation of this expression, see an advanced textbook on thermodynamics.

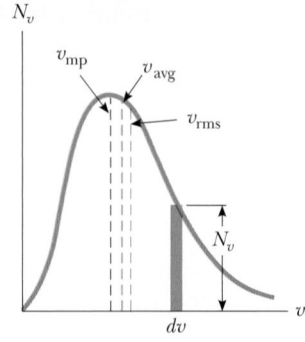

ACTIVE FIGURE 21.10

The speed distribution of gas molecules at some temperature. The number of molecules having speeds in the range v to $v + dv$ is equal to the area of the shaded rectangle, $N_v\, dv$. The function N_v approaches zero as v approaches infinity.

Sign in at www.thomsonedu.com and go to ThomsonNOW to move the blue rectangle and measure the number of molecules with speeds within a small range.

As indicated in Active Figure 21.10, the average speed is somewhat lower than the rms speed. The *most probable speed* v_{mp} is the speed at which the distribution curve reaches a peak. Using Equation 21.24, we find that

$$v_{rms} = \sqrt{\overline{v^2}} = \sqrt{\frac{3k_B T}{m_0}} = 1.73\sqrt{\frac{k_B T}{m_0}} \tag{21.25}$$

$$v_{avg} = \sqrt{\frac{8k_B T}{\pi m_0}} = 1.60\sqrt{\frac{k_B T}{m_0}} \tag{21.26}$$

$$v_{mp} = \sqrt{\frac{2k_B T}{m_0}} = 1.41\sqrt{\frac{k_B T}{m_0}} \tag{21.27}$$

Equation 21.25 has previously appeared as Equation 21.7. The details of the derivations of these equations from Equation 21.24 are left for the student (see Problems 33 and 57). From these equations, we see that

$$v_{rms} > v_{avg} > v_{mp}$$

Active Figure 21.11 represents speed distribution curves for nitrogen, N_2. The curves were obtained by using Equation 21.24 to evaluate the distribution function at various speeds and at two temperatures. Notice that the peak in each curve shifts to the right as T increases, indicating that the average speed increases with increasing temperature, as expected. Because the lowest speed possible is zero and the upper classical limit of the speed is infinity, the curves are asymmetrical. (In Chapter 39, we show that the actual upper limit is the speed of light.)

Equation 21.24 shows that the distribution of molecular speeds in a gas depends both on mass and on temperature. At a given temperature, the fraction of molecules with speeds exceeding a fixed value increases as the mass decreases. Hence, lighter molecules such as H_2 and He escape more readily from the Earth's atmosphere than do heavier molecules such as N_2 and O_2. (See the discussion of escape speed in Chapter 13. Gas molecules escape even more readily from the Moon's surface than from the Earth's because the escape speed on the Moon is lower than that on the Earth.)

The speed distribution curves for molecules in a liquid are similar to those shown in Active Figure 21.11. We can understand the phenomenon of evaporation of a liquid from this distribution in speeds, given that some molecules in the liquid are more energetic than others. Some of the faster-moving molecules in the liquid penetrate the surface and even leave the liquid at temperatures well below

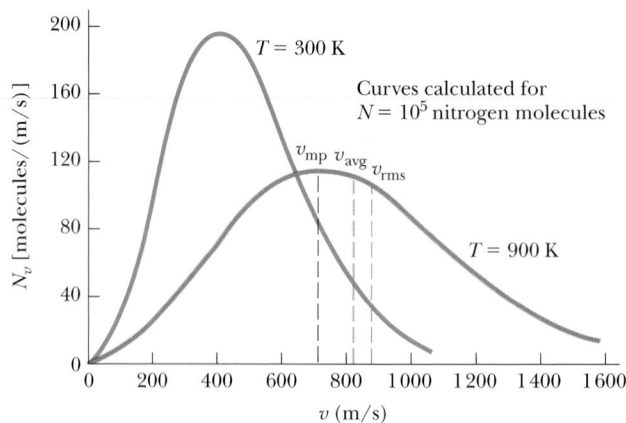

ACTIVE FIGURE 21.11

The speed distribution function for 10^5 nitrogen molecules at 300 K and 900 K. The total area under either curve is equal to the total number of molecules, which in this case equals 10^5. Notice that $v_{rms} > v_{avg} > v_{mp}$.

Sign in at www.thomsonedu.com and go to ThomsonNOW to set the desired temperature and see the effect on the distribution curve.

the boiling point. The molecules that escape the liquid by evaporation are those that have sufficient energy to overcome the attractive forces of the molecules in the liquid phase. Consequently, the molecules left behind in the liquid phase have a lower average kinetic energy; as a result, the temperature of the liquid decreases. Hence, evaporation is a cooling process. For example, an alcohol-soaked cloth can be placed on a feverish head to cool and comfort a patient.

EXAMPLE 21.5 | **A System of Nine Particles**

Nine particles have speeds of 5.00, 8.00, 12.0, 12.0, 12.0, 14.0, 14.0, 17.0, and 20.0 m/s.

(A) Find the particles' average speed.

SOLUTION

Conceptualize Imagine a small number of particles moving in random directions with the few speeds listed.

Categorize Because we are dealing with a small number of particles, we can calculate the average speed directly.

Analyze Find the average speed of the particles by dividing the sum of the speeds by the total number of particles:

$$v_{avg} = \frac{(5.00 + 8.00 + 12.0 + 12.0 + 12.0 + 14.0 + 14.0 + 17.0 + 20.0)\ \text{m/s}}{9}$$

$$= \boxed{12.7\ \text{m/s}}$$

(B) What is the rms speed of the particles?

SOLUTION

Find the average speed squared of the particles by dividing the sum of the speeds squared by the total number of particles:

$$\overline{v^2} = \frac{(5.00^2 + 8.00^2 + 12.0^2 + 12.0^2 + 12.0^2 + 14.0^2 + 14.0^2 + 17.0^2 + 20.0^2)\ \text{m}^2/\text{s}^2}{9}$$

$$= 178\ \text{m}^2/\text{s}^2$$

Find the rms speed of the particles by taking the square root:

$$v_{rms} = \sqrt{\overline{v^2}} = \sqrt{178\ \text{m}^2/\text{s}^2} = \boxed{13.3\ \text{m/s}}$$

(C) What is the most probable speed of the particles?

SOLUTION

Three of the particles have a speed of 12.0 m/s, two have a speed of 14.0 m/s, and the remaining four have different speeds. Hence, the most probable speed v_{mp} is 12.0 m/s.

Finalize Compare this example, in which the number of particles is small and we know the individual particle speeds, with the next example.

EXAMPLE 21.6 | **Molecular Speeds in a Hydrogen Gas**

A 0.500-mol sample of hydrogen gas is at 300 K.

(A) Find the average speed, the rms speed, and the most probable speed of the hydrogen molecules.

SOLUTION

Conceptualize Imagine a huge number of particles in a real gas, all moving in random directions with different speeds.

Categorize   We cannot calculate the averages as was done in Example 21.5 because the individual speeds of the particles are not known. We are dealing with a very large number of particles, however, so we can use the Maxwell-Boltzmann speed distribution function.

Analyze   Use Equation 21.26 to find the average speed:

$$v_{avg} = 1.60 \sqrt{\frac{k_B T}{m_0}} = 1.60 \sqrt{\frac{(1.38 \times 10^{-23} \text{ J/K})(300 \text{ K})}{2(1.67 \times 10^{-27} \text{ kg})}}$$

$$= \boxed{1.78 \times 10^3 \text{ m/s}}$$

Use Equation 21.25 to find the rms speed:

$$v_{rms} = 1.73 \sqrt{\frac{k_B T}{m_0}} = 1.73 \sqrt{\frac{(1.38 \times 10^{-23} \text{ J/K})(300 \text{ K})}{2(1.67 \times 10^{-27} \text{ kg})}}$$

$$= \boxed{1.93 \times 10^3 \text{ m/s}}$$

Use Equation 21.27 to find the most probable speed:

$$v_{mp} = 1.41 \sqrt{\frac{k_B T}{m_0}} = 1.41 \sqrt{\frac{(1.38 \times 10^{-23} \text{ J/K})(300 \text{ K})}{2(1.67 \times 10^{-27} \text{ kg})}}$$

$$= \boxed{1.57 \times 10^3 \text{ m/s}}$$

(B) Find the number of molecules with speeds between 400 m/s and 401 m/s.

SOLUTION

Use Equation 21.24 to evaluate the number of molecules in a narrow speed range between v and $v + dv$:

$$(1) \quad N_v \, dv = 4\pi N \left(\frac{m_0}{2\pi k_B T}\right)^{3/2} v^2 e^{-m_0 v^2 / 2k_B T} \, dv$$

Evaluate the constant in front of v^2:

$$4\pi N \left(\frac{m_0}{2\pi k_B T}\right)^{3/2} = 4\pi n N_A \left(\frac{m_0}{2\pi k_B T}\right)^{3/2}$$

$$= 4\pi (0.500 \text{ mol})(6.02 \times 10^{23} \text{ mol}^{-1}) \left[\frac{2(1.67 \times 10^{-27} \text{ kg})}{2\pi (1.38 \times 10^{-23} \text{ J/K})(300 \text{ K})}\right]^{3/2}$$

$$= 1.74 \times 10^{14} \text{ s}^3/\text{m}^3$$

Evaluate the exponent of e:

$$-\frac{m_0 v^2}{2k_B T} = -\frac{2(1.67 \times 10^{-27} \text{ kg})(400 \text{ m/s})^2}{2(1.38 \times 10^{-23} \text{ J/K})(300 \text{ K})} = -0.064 \, 5$$

Evaluate $N_v \, dv$ using Equation (1):

$$N_v \, dv = (1.74 \times 10^{14} \text{ s}^3/\text{m}^3)(400 \text{ m/s})^2 e^{-0.064 \, 5}(1 \text{ m/s})$$

$$= \boxed{2.61 \times 10^{19} \text{ molecules}}$$

Finalize   In this evaluation, we could calculate the result without integration because $dv = 1$ m/s is much smaller than $v = 400$ m/s. Had we sought the number of particles between, say, 400 m/s and 500 m/s, we would need to integrate Equation (1) between these speed limits.

Summary

ThomsonNOW Sign in at **www.thomsonedu.com** and go to ThomsonNOW to take a practice test for this chapter.

CONCEPTS AND PRINCIPLES

The pressure of N molecules of an ideal gas contained in a volume V is

$$P = \tfrac{2}{3}\left(\frac{N}{V}\right)\left(\tfrac{1}{2}m_0\overline{v^2}\right) \qquad \textbf{(21.2)}$$

The average translational kinetic energy per molecule of a gas, $\tfrac{1}{2}m_0\overline{v^2}$, is related to the temperature T of the gas through the expression

$$\tfrac{1}{2}m_0\overline{v^2} = \tfrac{3}{2}k_B T \qquad \textbf{(21.4)}$$

where k_B is Boltzmann's constant. Each translational degree of freedom (x, y, or z) has $\tfrac{1}{2}k_B T$ of energy associated with it.

The internal energy of N molecules (or n mol) of an ideal monatomic gas is

$$E_{\text{int}} = \tfrac{3}{2}Nk_B T = \tfrac{3}{2}nRT \qquad \textbf{(21.10)}$$

The change in internal energy for n mol of any ideal gas that undergoes a change in temperature ΔT is

$$\Delta E_{\text{int}} = nC_V\,\Delta T \qquad \textbf{(21.12)}$$

where C_V is the **molar specific heat at constant volume**.

The molar specific heat of an ideal monatomic gas at constant volume is $C_V = \tfrac{3}{2}R$; the molar specific heat at constant pressure is $C_P = \tfrac{5}{2}R$. The ratio of specific heats is given by $\gamma = C_P/C_V = \tfrac{5}{3}$.

If an ideal gas undergoes an adiabatic expansion or compression, the first law of thermodynamics, together with the equation of state, shows that

$$PV^{\gamma} = \text{constant} \qquad \textbf{(21.18)}$$

The **Boltzmann distribution law** describes the distribution of particles among available energy states. The relative number of particles having energy between E and $E + dE$ is $n_V(E)\,dE$, where

$$n_V(E) = n_0 e^{-E/k_B T} \qquad \textbf{(21.23)}$$

The **Maxwell–Boltzmann speed distribution function** describes the distribution of speeds of molecules in a gas:

$$N_v = 4\pi N\left(\frac{m_0}{2\pi k_B T}\right)^{3/2} v^2 e^{-m_0 v^2/2k_B T} \qquad \textbf{(21.24)}$$

Equation 21.24 enables us to calculate the **root-mean-square speed**, the **average speed**, and the **most probable speed** of molecules in a gas:

$$v_{\text{rms}} = \sqrt{\overline{v^2}} = \sqrt{\frac{3k_B T}{m_0}} = 1.73\sqrt{\frac{k_B T}{m_0}} \qquad \textbf{(21.25)}$$

$$v_{\text{avg}} = \sqrt{\frac{8k_B T}{\pi m_0}} = 1.60\sqrt{\frac{k_B T}{m_0}} \qquad \textbf{(21.26)}$$

$$v_{\text{mp}} = \sqrt{\frac{2k_B T}{m_0}} = 1.41\sqrt{\frac{k_B T}{m_0}} \qquad \textbf{(21.27)}$$

Questions

☐ denotes answer available in *Student Solutions Manual/Study Guide;* **O** denotes objective question

1. Dalton's law of partial pressures states that the total pressure of a mixture of gases is equal to the sum of the pressures that each gas in the mixture would exert if it were alone in the container. Give a convincing argument for this law based on the kinetic theory of gases.

2. One container is filled with helium gas and another with argon gas. Both containers are at the same temperature. Which molecules have the higher rms speed? Explain.

3. When alcohol is rubbed on your body, it lowers your skin temperature. Explain this effect.

4. **O** A student is asked to give a step-by-step account of what makes the temperature of a sample of gas increase. His

response: When a sample of a gas is held over a hotplate, (a) the molecules speed up. (b) Then the molecules collide with one another more often. (c) Internal friction makes the collisions inelastic. (d) Heat is produced in the collisions. (e) As soon as we put in a thermometer, we see that the temperature has gone up. (f) The same process can take place without the use of a hotplate if you quickly push in the piston in an insulated cylinder containing the gas. **(i)** Which of the parts (a) through (f) of this account are correct statements necessary for a clear and complete explanation? **(ii)** Which are correct statements that are not necessary to account for the higher thermometer reading? **(iii)** Which are incorrect statements?

5. **O** A helium-filled balloon initially at room temperature is placed in a freezer. The rubber remains flexible. **(i)** Does its volume (a) increase, (b) decrease, or (c) remain the same? **(ii)** Does its pressure (a) increase, (b) decrease, or (c) remain the same?

6. **O** A gas is at 200 K. If we wish to double the rms speed of the molecules of the gas, to what must we raise its temperature? (a) 283 K (b) 400 K (c) 566 K (d) 800 K (e) 1 130 K

7. **O** Rank the following from the largest to the smallest, noting any cases of equality. (a) The average speed of molecules in a particular sample of ideal gas. (b) The most probable speed. (c) The root-mean-square speed. (d) The average vector velocity of the molecules. (e) The speed of sound in the gas.

8. **O** Two samples of the same ideal gas have the same pressure and density. Sample B has twice the volume of sample A. What is the rms speed of the molecules in sample B? (a) twice that in sample A (b) equal to that in sample A (c) half that in sample A (d) impossible to determine

9. Which is denser, dry air or air saturated with water vapor? Explain.

10. What happens to a helium-filled balloon released into the air? Does it expand or contract? Does it stop rising at some height?

11. Why does a diatomic gas have a greater energy content per mole than a monatomic gas at the same temperature?

12. **O** An ideal gas is contained in a vessel at 300 K. If the temperature is increased to 900 K, what is the factor of change in **(i)** the average kinetic energy of the molecules? (a) 9 (b) 3 (c) $\sqrt{3}$ (d) 1 (e) $\frac{1}{3}$ **(ii)** What is the factor of change in the rms molecular speed? Choose from the same possibilities. **(iii)** What is the factor of change in the average momentum change that one molecule undergoes in a collision with one particular wall? **(iv)** What is the factor of change in the rate of collisions of molecules with walls? **(v)** What is the factor of change in the pressure of the gas? Choose from the same possibilities (a) through (e).

13. Hot air rises, so why does it generally become cooler as you climb a mountain? *Note:* Air has low thermal conductivity.

14. **O** The brown curve in Active Figure 21.11 shows the speed distribution for 100 000 nitrogen molecules at 900 K. Krypton has very nearly three times the molecular mass of nitrogen. The blue curve, disregarding its label, shows the speed distribution for which of the following? (a) 100 000 krypton molecules at 900 K (b) 100 000 krypton molecules at 520 K (c) 100 000 krypton molecules at 300 K (d) 100 000 krypton molecules at 100 K (e) 33 000 krypton molecules at 900 K (f) 33 000 krypton molecules at 300 K (g) This distribution cannot be attributed to any sample of krypton, which does not exist on Earth.

Problems

WebAssign The Problems from this chapter may be assigned online in WebAssign.

ThomsonNOW‴ Sign in at **www.thomsonedu.com** and go to ThomsonNOW to assess your understanding of this chapter's topics with additional quizzing and conceptual questions.

1, 2, 3 denotes straightforward, intermediate, challenging; ☐ denotes full solution available in *Student Solutions Manual/Study Guide;* ▲ denotes coached solution with hints available at **www.thomsonedu.com;** ▨ denotes developing symbolic reasoning; ● denotes asking for qualitative reasoning; ▪ denotes computer useful in solving problem

Section 21.1 Molecular Model of an Ideal Gas

Note: Problem 25 in Chapter 19 can be assigned with this section.

1. ▲ Calculate the mass of an atom of (a) helium, (b) iron, and (c) lead. Give your answers in grams. The atomic masses of these atoms are 4.00 u, 55.9 u, and 207 u, respectively.

2. ● We use m to represent the mass of a sample, m_0 to represent the mass of one molecule, M for the molar mass, n for the number of moles in a sample, N for the number of molecules, and N_A to represent Avogadro's number. Explain why each of the following equations is true:

$$N = nN_A \qquad m = nM = Nm_0 \qquad M = m_0N_A$$

Are the equations true only for ideal gases? Only for gases? Only for pure chemical elements? Only for pure chemical compounds? For mixtures?

3. In a 30.0-s interval, 500 hailstones strike a glass window of area 0.600 m² at an angle of 45.0° to the window surface. Each hailstone has a mass of 5.00 g and a speed of 8.00 m/s. Assuming the collisions are elastic, find the average force and pressure on the window.

4. In a period of 1.00 s, 5.00×10^{23} nitrogen molecules strike a wall with an area of 8.00 cm². Assume the molecules move with a speed of 300 m/s and strike the wall head-on in elastic collisions. What is the pressure exerted on the wall? (The mass of one N_2 molecule is 4.68×10^{-26} kg.)

5. In an ultrahigh vacuum system, the pressure is measured to be 1.00×10^{-10} torr (where 1 torr = 133 Pa). Assuming the temperature is 300 K, find the number of molecules in a volume of 1.00 m³.

6. A 2.00-mol sample of oxygen gas is confined to a 5.00-L vessel at a pressure of 8.00 atm. Find the average translational kinetic energy of an oxygen molecule under these conditions.

7. A spherical balloon of volume 4 000 cm³ contains helium at an (inside) pressure of 1.20×10^5 Pa. How many moles of helium are in the balloon if the average kinetic energy of each helium atom is 3.60×10^{-22} J?

8. A 5.00-L vessel contains nitrogen gas at 27.0°C and 3.00 atm. (a) Find the total translational kinetic energy of the gas molecules and (b) the average kinetic energy per molecule.

9. (a) How many atoms of helium gas fill a balloon of diameter 30.0 cm at 20.0°C and 1.00 atm? (b) What is the average kinetic energy of the helium atoms? (c) What is the root-mean-square speed of the helium atoms?

10. (a) Show that 1 Pa = 1 J/m³. (b) Show that the density in space of the translational kinetic energy of an ideal gas (the energy per volume) is $3P/2$.

11. ▲ A cylinder contains a mixture of helium and argon gas in equilibrium at 150°C. (a) What is the average kinetic energy for each type of gas molecule? (b) What is the root-mean-square speed of each type of molecule?

Section 21.2 Molar Specific Heat of an Ideal Gas

Note: You may use data in Table 21.2 about particular gases. Here we define a "monatomic ideal gas" to have molar specific heats $C_V = 3R/2$ and $C_P = 5R/2$, and a "diatomic ideal gas" to have $C_V = 5R/2$ and $C_P = 7R/2$.

12. In a constant-volume process, 209 J of energy is transferred by heat to 1.00 mol of an ideal monatomic gas initially at 300 K. Find (a) the increase in internal energy of the gas, (b) the work done on it, and (c) its final temperature.

13. ▲ A 1.00-mol sample of hydrogen gas is heated at constant pressure from 300 K to 420 K. Calculate (a) the energy transferred to the gas by heat, (b) the increase in its internal energy, and (c) the work done on the gas.

14. A house has well-insulated walls. It contains a volume of 100 m³ of air at 300 K. (a) Calculate the energy required to increase the temperature of this diatomic ideal gas by 1.00°C. (b) **What If?** If this energy could be used to lift an object of mass *m* through a height of 2.00 m, what is the value of *m*?

15. A 1-L insulated bottle is full of tea at 90°C. You pour out one cup and immediately screw the stopper back on the bottle. Make an order-of-magnitude estimate of the change in temperature of the tea remaining in the bottle that results from the admission of air at room temperature. State the quantities you take as data and the values you measure or estimate for them.

16. A vertical cylinder with a heavy piston contains air at 300 K. The initial pressure is 200 kPa, and the initial volume is 0.350 m³. Take the molar mass of air as 28.9 g/mol and assume $C_V = 5R/2$. (a) Find the specific heat of air at constant volume in units of J/kg · °C. (b) Calculate the mass of the air in the cylinder. (c) Suppose the piston is held fixed. Find the energy input required to raise the temperature of the air to 700 K. (d) **What If?** Assume again the conditions of the initial state and assume the heavy piston is free to move. Find the energy input required to raise the temperature to 700 K.

17. A 1.00-mol sample of a diatomic ideal gas has pressure *P* and volume *V*. When the gas is warmed, its pressure triples and its volume doubles. This warming process includes two steps, the first at constant pressure and the second at constant volume. Determine the amount of energy transferred to the gas by heat.

Section 21.3 Adiabatic Processes for an Ideal Gas

18. During the compression stroke of a certain gasoline engine, the pressure increases from 1.00 atm to 20.0 atm. If the process is adiabatic and the fuel–air mixture behaves as a diatomic ideal gas, (a) by what factor does the volume change and (b) by what factor does the temperature change? (c) Assuming the compression starts with 0.016 0 mol of gas at 27.0°C, find the values of Q, W, and ΔE_{int} that characterize the process.

19. A 2.00-mol sample of a diatomic ideal gas expands slowly and adiabatically from a pressure of 5.00 atm and a volume of 12.0 L to a final volume of 30.0 L. (a) What is the final pressure of the gas? (b) What are the initial and final temperatures? (c) Find Q, W, and ΔE_{int}.

20. Air (a diatomic ideal gas) at 27.0°C and atmospheric pressure is drawn into a bicycle pump that has a cylinder with an inner diameter of 2.50 cm and length 50.0 cm. The downstroke adiabatically compresses the air, which reaches a gauge pressure of 800 kPa before entering the tire (Fig. P21.20). Determine (a) the volume of the compressed air and (b) the temperature of the compressed air. (c) **What If?** The pump is made of steel and has an inner wall that is 2.00 mm thick. Assume 4.00 cm of the

Figure P21.20

George Semple

cylinder's length is allowed to come to thermal equilibrium with the air. What will be the increase in wall temperature?

21. Air in a thundercloud expands as it rises. If its initial temperature is 300 K and no energy is lost by thermal conduction on expansion, what is its temperature when the initial volume has doubled?

22. During the power stroke in a four-stroke automobile engine, the piston is forced down as the mixture of combustion products and air undergoes an adiabatic expansion. Assume (1) the engine is running at 2 500 cycles/min; (2) the gauge pressure right before the expansion is 20.0 atm; (3) the volumes of the mixture right before and after the expansion are 50.0 and 400 cm³, respectively (Fig. P21.22); (4) the time interval for the expansion is one-fourth that of the total cycle; and (5) the mixture behaves like an ideal gas with specific heat ratio 1.40. Find the average power generated during the expansion stroke.

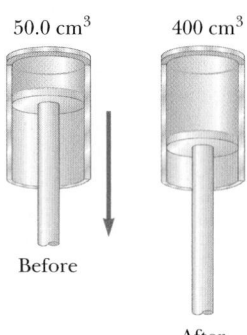

Figure P21.22

23. A 4.00-L sample of a diatomic ideal gas with specific heat ratio 1.40, confined to a cylinder, is carried through a closed cycle. The gas is initially at 1.00 atm and at 300 K. First, its pressure is tripled under constant volume. Then, it expands adiabatically to its original pressure. Finally, the gas is compressed isobarically to its original volume. (a) Draw a PV diagram of this cycle. (b) Determine the volume of the gas at the end of the adiabatic expansion. (c) Find the temperature of the gas at the start of the adiabatic expansion. (d) Find the temperature at the end of the cycle. (e) What was the net work done on the gas for this cycle?

24. A diatomic ideal gas ($\gamma = 1.40$) confined to a cylinder is put through a closed cycle. Initially, the gas is at P_i, V_i, and T_i. First, its pressure is tripled under constant volume. It then expands adiabatically to its original pressure and finally is compressed isobarically to its original volume. (a) Draw a PV diagram of this cycle. (b) Determine the volume at the end of the adiabatic expansion. Find (c) the temperature of the gas at the start of the adiabatic expansion and (d) the temperature at the end of the cycle. (e) What was the net work done on the gas for this cycle?

25. How much work is required to compress 5.00 mol of air at 20.0°C and 1.00 atm to one-tenth of the original volume (a) by an isothermal process? (b) **What If?** How much work is required to produce the same compression in an adiabatic process? (c) What is the final pressure in each of these two cases?

Section 21.4 The Equipartition of Energy

26. A certain molecule has f degrees of freedom. Show that an ideal gas consisting of such molecules has the following properties: (1) its total internal energy is $fnRT/2$, (2) its molar specific heat at constant volume is $fR/2$, (3) its molar specific heat at constant pressure is $(f + 2)R/2$, and (4) its specific heat ratio is $\gamma = C_P/C_V = (f + 2)/f$.

27. ▲ Consider 2.00 mol of an ideal diatomic gas. (a) Find the total heat capacity as defined by Equation 20.2 at constant volume and the total heat capacity at constant pressure, assuming the molecules rotate but do not vibrate. (b) **What If?** Repeat part (a), assuming the molecules both rotate and vibrate.

28. In a crude model (Fig. P21.28) of a rotating diatomic molecule of chlorine (Cl_2), the two Cl atoms are 2.00×10^{-10} m apart and rotate about their center of mass with angular speed $\omega = 2.00 \times 10^{12}$ rad/s. What is the rotational kinetic energy of one molecule of Cl_2, which has a molar mass of 70.0 g/mol?

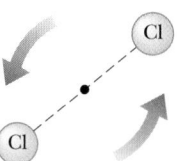

Figure P21.28

29. ● Examine the data for polyatomic gases in Table 21.2 and give a reason why sulfur dioxide has a higher specific heat at constant volume than the other polyatomic gases at 300 K.

30. ● A triatomic molecule can have the three atoms lying along one line, as does CO_2, or it can be nonlinear, like H_2O. Suppose the temperature of a gas of triatomic molecules is sufficiently low that vibrational motion is negligible. What is the molar heat capacity at constant volume, expressed as a multiple of the universal gas constant, (a) if the molecules are linear and (b) if the molecules are nonlinear? At high temperatures, a triatomic molecule has two modes of vibration, and each contributes $\frac{1}{2}R$ to the molar heat capacity for its kinetic energy and another $\frac{1}{2}R$ for its potential energy. Identify the high-temperature molar heat capacity at constant volume for a triatomic ideal gas of (c) linear molecules and of (d) nonlinear molecules. (e) Explain how specific heat data can be used to determine whether a triatomic molecule is linear or nonlinear. Are the data in Table 21.2 sufficient to make this determination?

Section 21.5 Distribution of Molecular Speeds

31. Fifteen identical particles have various speeds: one has a speed of 2.00 m/s, two have speeds of 3.00 m/s, three have speeds of 5.00 m/s, four have speeds of 7.00 m/s, three have speeds of 9.00 m/s, and two have speeds of 12.0 m/s. Find (a) the average speed, (b) the rms speed, and (c) the most probable speed of these particles.

32. One cubic meter of atomic hydrogen at 0°C at atmospheric pressure contains approximately 2.70×10^{25} atoms. The first excited state of the hydrogen atom has an energy of 10.2 eV above the lowest energy level, called the ground

state. Use the Boltzmann factor to find the number of atoms in the first excited state at 0°C and at 10 000°C.

33. From the Maxwell–Boltzmann speed distribution, show that the most probable speed of a gas molecule is given by Equation 21.27. Notice that the most probable speed corresponds to the point at which the slope of the speed distribution curve dN_v/dv is zero.

34. Two gases in a mixture diffuse through a filter at rates proportional to the gases' rms speeds. (a) Find the ratio of speeds for the two isotopes of chlorine, ^{35}Cl and ^{37}Cl, as they diffuse through the air. (b) Which isotope moves faster?

35. **Review problem.** At what temperature would the average speed of helium atoms equal (a) the escape speed from the Earth, 1.12×10^4 m/s and (b) the escape speed from the Moon, 2.37×10^3 m/s? (See Chapter 13 for a discussion of escape speed.) *Note:* The mass of a helium atom is 6.64×10^{-27} kg.

36. ● Calculate (a) the most probable speed, (b) the average speed, and (c) the rms speed for nitrogen gas molecules at 900 K. (d) State how your results compare with the values displayed in Active Figure 21.11.

37. Assume the Earth's atmosphere has a uniform temperature of 20°C and uniform composition, with an effective molar mass of 28.9 g/mol. (a) Show that the number density of molecules depends on height y above sea level according to

$$n_V(y) = n_0 e^{-m_0 g y/k_B T}$$

where n_0 is the number density at sea level (where $y = 0$). This result is called the *law of atmospheres*. (b) Commercial jetliners typically cruise at an altitude of 11.0 km. Find the ratio of the atmospheric density there to the density at sea level.

38. *If you can't walk to outer space, can you at least walk halfway?* Use the law of atmospheres from Problem 37. The average height of a molecule in the Earth's atmosphere is given by

$$\bar{y} = \frac{\int_0^\infty y n_V(y)\, dy}{\int_0^\infty n_V(y)\, dy} = \frac{\int_0^\infty y e^{-m_0 g y/k_B T}\, dy}{\int_0^\infty e^{-m_0 g y/k_B T}\, dy}$$

(a) Prove that this average height is equal to $k_B T/m_0 g$. (b) Evaluate the average height, assuming the temperature is 10°C and the molecular mass is 28.9 u, both uniform throughout the atmosphere.

Additional Problems

39. The function $E_{int} = 3.50nRT$ describes the internal energy of a certain ideal gas. A 2.00-mol sample of the gas always starts at pressure 100 kPa and temperature 300 K. For each of the following processes, determine the final pressure, volume, and temperature; the change in internal energy of the gas; the energy added to the gas by heat; and the work done on the gas. (a) The gas is heated at constant pressure to 400 K. (b) The gas is heated at constant volume to 400 K. (c) The gas is compressed at constant temperature to 120 kPa. (d) The gas is compressed adiabatically to 120 kPa.

40. ● The dimensions of a classroom are 4.20 m × 3.00 m × 2.50 m. (a) Find the number of molecules of air in it at atmospheric pressure and 20.0°C. (b) Find the mass of

this air, assuming the air consists of diatomic molecules with molar mass 28.9 g/mol. (c) Find the average kinetic energy of one molecule. (d) Find the root-mean-square molecular speed. (e) On the assumption that the molar specific heat is a constant independent of temperature, $E_{int} = 5nRT/2$. Find the internal energy in the air. (f) **What If?** Find the internal energy of the air in the room at 25.0°C. Explain how it compares with the result at 20.0°C and how it happens that way.

41. ● In a sample of a solid metal, each atom is free to vibrate about some equilibrium position. The atom's energy consists of kinetic energy for motion in the *x*, *y*, and *z* directions plus elastic potential energy associated with the Hooke's law forces exerted by neighboring atoms on it in the *x*, *y*, and *z* directions. According to the theorem of equipartition of energy, assume the average energy of each atom is $\frac{1}{2}k_B T$ for each degree of freedom. (a) Prove that the molar specific heat of the solid is $3R$. The *Dulong–Petit law* states that this result generally describes pure solids at sufficiently high temperatures. (You may ignore the difference between the specific heat at constant pressure and the specific heat at constant volume.) (b) Evaluate the specific heat c of iron. Explain how it compares with the value listed in Table 20.1. (c) Repeat the evaluation and comparison for gold.

42. Twenty particles, each of mass m_0 and confined to a volume V, have various speeds: two have speed v, three have speed $2v$, five have speed $3v$, four have speed $4v$, three have speed $5v$, two have speed $6v$, and one has speed $7v$. Find (a) the average speed, (b) the rms speed, (c) the most probable speed, (d) the pressure they exert on the walls of the vessel, and (e) the average kinetic energy per particle.

43. ● ▲ A cylinder containing n mol of an ideal gas undergoes an adiabatic process. (a) Starting with the expression $W = -\int P\, dV$ and using the condition $PV^\gamma = $ constant, show that the work done on the gas is

$$W = \left(\frac{1}{\gamma - 1}\right)(P_f V_f - P_i V_i)$$

(b) Starting with the first law of thermodynamics in differential form, show that the work done on the gas is equal to $nC_V(T_f - T_i)$. Explain whether these two results are consistent with each other.

44. As a 1.00-mol sample of a monatomic ideal gas expands adiabatically, the work done on it is –2 500 J. The initial temperature and pressure of the gas are 500 K and 3.60 atm. Calculate (a) the final temperature and (b) the final pressure. You may use the result of Problem 43.

45. A cylinder is closed at both ends and has insulating walls. It is divided into two compartments by an adiabatic partition that is perpendicular to the axis of the cylinder. Each compartment contains 1.00 mol of oxygen that behaves as an ideal gas with $\gamma = \frac{7}{5}$. Initially, the two compartments have equal volumes and their temperatures are 550 K and 250 K. The partition is then allowed to move slowly until the pressures on its two sides are equal. Find the final temperatures in the two compartments. You may use the result of Problem 43.

46. An air rifle shoots a lead pellet by allowing high-pressure air to expand, propelling the pellet down the rifle barrel. Because this process happens very quickly, no appreciable

thermal conduction occurs and the expansion is essentially adiabatic. Suppose the rifle starts with 12.0 cm³ of compressed air, which behaves as an ideal gas with $\gamma = 1.40$. The expanding air pushes a 1.10-g pellet as a piston with cross-sectional area 0.030 0 cm² along the gun barrel, 50.0 cm long. The pellet emerges with a muzzle speed of 120 m/s. Use the result of Problem 43 to find the initial pressure required.

47. **Review problem**. Oxygen at pressures much greater than 1 atm is toxic to lung cells. Assume a deep-sea diver breathes a mixture of oxygen (O_2) and helium (He). By weight, what ratio of helium to oxygen must be used if the diver is at an ocean depth of 50.0 m?

48. A vessel contains 1.00×10^4 oxygen molecules at 500 K. (a) Make an accurate graph of the Maxwell speed distribution function versus speed with points at speed intervals of 100 m/s. (b) Determine the most probable speed from this graph. (c) Calculate the average and rms speeds for the molecules and label these points on your graph. (d) From the graph, estimate the fraction of molecules with speeds in the range 300 m/s to 600 m/s.

49. ▲ The compressibility κ of a substance is defined as the fractional change in volume of that substance for a given change in pressure:

$$\kappa = -\frac{1}{V}\frac{dV}{dP}$$

(a) Explain why the negative sign in this expression ensures κ is always positive. (b) Show that if an ideal gas is compressed isothermally, its compressibility is given by $\kappa_1 = 1/P$. (c) **What If?** Show that if an ideal gas is compressed adiabatically, its compressibility is given by $\kappa_2 = 1/\gamma P$. (d) Determine values for κ_1 and κ_2 for a monatomic ideal gas at a pressure of 2.00 atm.

50. ● **Review problem**. (a) Show that the speed of sound in an ideal gas is

$$v = \sqrt{\frac{\gamma RT}{M}}$$

where M is the molar mass. Use the general expression for the speed of sound in a fluid from Section 17.1; the definition of the bulk modulus from Section 12.4; and the result of Problem 49 above. As a sound wave passes through a gas, the compressions are either so rapid or so far apart that thermal conduction is prevented by a negligible time interval or by effective thickness of insulation. The compressions and rarefactions are adiabatic. (b) Compute the theoretical speed of sound in air at 20°C and state how it compares with the value in Table 17.1. Take $M = 28.9$ g/mol. (c) Show that the speed of sound in an ideal gas is

$$v = \sqrt{\frac{\gamma k_B T}{m_0}}$$

where m_0 is the mass of one molecule. State how it compares with the most probable, average, and rms molecular speeds.

51. ● The latent heat of vaporization for water at room temperature is 2 430 J/g. Consider one particular molecule at the surface of a glass of liquid water, moving upward with sufficiently high speed that it will be the next molecule to join the vapor. (a) Find its translational kinetic energy.

(b) Find its speed. (c) Now consider a thin gas made just of molecules like that one. What is its temperature? Why are you not burned by evaporating water?

52. ● *Brownian motion*. Molecular motion is invisible in itself. When a small particle is suspended in a fluid, bombardment by molecules makes the particle jitter about at random. Robert Brown discovered this motion in 1827 while studying plant fertilization. Albert Einstein analyzed it in 1905, and Jean Perrin used it for an early measurement of Avogadro's number. The visible particle's average kinetic energy can be taken as $\frac{3}{2}k_B T$, the same as that of a molecule in an ideal gas. Consider a spherical particle of density 1 000 kg/m³ in water at 20°C. (a) For a particle of diameter d, evaluate the rms speed. (b) The particle's actual motion is a random walk, but imagine that it moves with constant velocity equal in magnitude to its rms speed. In what time interval would it move by a distance equal to its own diameter? (c) Evaluate the rms speed and the time interval for a particle of diameter 3.00 μm. (d) Evaluate the rms speed and the time interval for a sphere of mass 70.0 kg, modeling your own body. (e) Find the diameter of a particle whose rms speed is equal to its own diameter divided by 1 s. (f) Explain whether your results suggest that there is an optimum particle size for observation of Brownian motion.

53. Model air as a diatomic ideal gas with $M = 28.9$ g/mol. A cylinder with a piston contains 1.20 kg of air at 25.0°C and 200 kPa. Energy is transferred by heat into the system as it is permitted to expand, with the pressure rising to 400 kPa. Throughout the expansion, the relationship between pressure and volume is given by

$$P = CV^{1/2}$$

where C is a constant. (a) Find the initial volume. (b) Find the final volume. (c) Find the final temperature. (d) Find the work done on the air. (e) Find the energy transferred by heat.

54. *Smokin'!* A pitcher throws a 0.142-kg baseball at 47.2 m/s. As it travels 19.4 m to home plate, the ball slows down to 42.5 m/s because of air resistance. Find the change in temperature of the air through which it passes. To find the greatest possible temperature change, you may make the following assumptions. Air has a molar specific heat of $C_P = 7R/2$ and an equivalent molar mass of 28.9 g/mol. The process is so rapid that the cover of the baseball acts as thermal insulation, and the temperature of the ball itself does not change. A change in temperature happens initially only for the air in a cylinder 19.4 m in length and 3.70 cm in radius. This air is initially at 20.0°C.

55. ▦ For a Maxwellian gas, use a computer or programmable calculator to find the numerical value of the ratio $N_v(v)/N_v(v_{mp})$ for the following values of v: $v = (v_{mp}/50)$, $(v_{mp}/10)$, $(v_{mp}/2)$, v_{mp}, $2v_{mp}$, $10v_{mp}$, $50v_{mp}$. Give your results to three significant figures.

56. Consider the particles in a gas centrifuge, a device used to separate particles of different mass by whirling them in a circular path of radius r at angular speed ω. The centripetal force acting on a particle is $m_0\omega^2 r$. (a) Discuss how a gas centrifuge can be used to separate particles of different mass. (b) Show that the density of the particles as a function of r is

$$n(r) = n_0 e^{m_0 r^2 \omega^2 / 2k_B T}$$

2 = intermediate;   3 = challenging;   □ = SSM/SG;   ▲ = ThomsonNOW;   ▦ = symbolic reasoning;   ● = qualitative reasoning

57. Verify Equations 21.25 and 21.26 for the rms and average speed of the molecules of a gas at a temperature T. The average value of v^n is

$$\overline{v^n} = \frac{1}{N} \int\limits_0^\infty v^n N_v \, dv$$

Use the table of integrals B.6 in Appendix B.

58. On the PV diagram for an ideal gas, one isothermal curve and one adiabatic curve pass through each point. Prove that the slope of the adiabatic curve is steeper than the slope of the isotherm by the factor γ.

59. ● A sample of monatomic ideal gas occupies 5.00 L at atmospheric pressure and 300 K (point A in Fig. P21.59). It is warmed at constant volume to 3.00 atm (point B). Then it is allowed to expand isothermally to 1.00 atm (point C) and at last compressed isobarically to its original state. (a) Find the number of moles in the sample. (b) Find the temperature at points B and C and the volume at point C. (c) Assume the molar specific heat does not depend on temperature so that $E_{int} = 3nRT/2$. Find the internal energy at points A, B, and C. (d) Tabulate P, V, T, and E_{int} at the states at points A, B, and C. (e) Now consider the processes $A \rightarrow B$, $B \rightarrow C$, and $C \rightarrow A$. Describe how to carry out each process experimentally. (f) Find Q, W, and ΔE_{int} for each of the processes. (g) For the whole cycle $A \rightarrow B \rightarrow C \rightarrow A$, find Q, W, and ΔE_{int}.

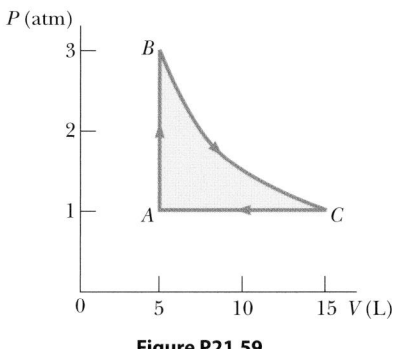

Figure P21.59

60. This problem can help you to think about the size of molecules. In Beijing, a restaurant keeps a pot of chicken broth simmering continuously. Every morning it is topped up to contain 10.0 L of water, along with a fresh chicken, vegetables, and spices. The soup is thoroughly stirred. The molar mass of water is 18.0 g/mol. (a) Find the number of molecules of water in the pot. (b) During a certain month, 90.0% of the broth was served each day to people who then emigrated immediately. Of the water molecules in the pot on the first day of the month, when was the last one likely to have been ladled out of the pot? (c) The broth has been simmering for centuries, through wars, earthquakes, and stove repairs. Suppose the water that was in the pot long ago has thoroughly mixed into the Earth's hydrosphere, of mass 1.32×10^{21} kg. How many of the water molecules originally in the pot are likely to be present in it again today?

61. **Review problem**. (a) If it has enough kinetic energy, a molecule at the surface of the Earth can "escape the Earth's gravitation" in the sense that it can continue to move away from the Earth forever as discussed in Section 13.6. Using the principle of conservation of energy, show that the minimum kinetic energy needed for "escape" is $m_0 g R_E$, where m_0 is the mass of the molecule, g is the free-fall acceleration at the surface, and R_E is the radius of the Earth. (b) Calculate the temperature for which the minimum escape kinetic energy is ten times the average kinetic energy of an oxygen molecule.

62. Using multiple laser beams, physicists have been able to cool and trap sodium atoms in a small region. In one experiment, the temperature of the atoms was reduced to 0.240 mK. (a) Determine the rms speed of the sodium atoms at this temperature. The atoms can be trapped for about 1.00 s. The trap has a linear dimension of roughly 1.00 cm. (b) Over what approximate time interval would an atom wander out of the trap region if there were no trapping action?

Answers to Quick Quizzes

21.1 **(i)**, (b). The average translational kinetic energy per molecule is a function only of temperature. **(ii)**, (a). Because there are twice as many molecules and the temperature of both containers is the same, the total energy in B is twice that in A.

21.2 **(i)**, (a). According to Equation 21.10, E_{int} is a function of temperature only. Because the temperature increases, the internal energy increases. **(ii)**, (c). Along an isotherm, T is constant by definition. Therefore, the internal energy of the gas does not change.

21.3 (d). The value of 29.1 J/mol · K is $7R/2$. According to Figure 21.7, this result suggests that all three types of motion are occurring.

21.4 (c). The highest possible value of C_V for a diatomic gas is $7R/2$, so the gas must be polyatomic.

This computer artwork shows the interior of an automobile engine cylinder at the moment the spark plug (upper left) fires and ignites the air-fuel mixture. The expanding gases push downward on the piston (lower right), ultimately resulting in energy provided to the drive wheels of the automobile. An automobile engine is one example of a heat engine, which we study in this chapter. (Roger Harris/Science Photo Library)

22 Heat Engines, Entropy, and the Second Law of Thermodynamics

J.-L. Charmet/SPL/Photo Researchers, Inc.

LORD KELVIN
British physicist and mathematician
(1824–1907)
Born William Thomson in Belfast, Kelvin was the first to propose the use of an absolute scale of temperature. The Kelvin temperature scale is named in his honor. Kelvin's work in thermodynamics led to the idea that energy cannot pass spontaneously from a colder object to a hotter object.

The first law of thermodynamics, which we studied in Chapter 20, is a statement of conservation of energy. This law states that a change in internal energy in a system can occur as a result of energy transfer by heat, by work, or by both. Although the first law of thermodynamics is very important, it makes no distinction between processes that occur spontaneously and those that do not. Only certain types of energy-conversion and energy-transfer processes actually take place in nature, however. The *second law of thermodynamics,* the major topic in this chapter, establishes which processes do and do not occur. The following are examples of processes that do not violate the first law of thermodynamics if they proceed in either direction, but are observed in reality to proceed in only one direction:

■ When two objects at different temperatures are placed in thermal contact with each other, the net transfer of energy by heat is always from the warmer object to the cooler object, never from the cooler to the warmer.

■ A rubber ball dropped to the ground bounces several times and eventually comes to rest, but a ball lying on the ground never gathers internal energy from the ground and begins bouncing on its own.

■ An oscillating pendulum eventually comes to rest because of collisions with air molecules and friction at the point of suspension. The mechanical energy of the system is converted to internal energy in the air, the pendulum, and the suspension; the reverse conversion of energy never occurs.

All these processes are *irreversible*; that is, they are processes that occur naturally in one direction only. No irreversible process has ever been observed to run backward. If it were to do so, it would violate the second law of thermodynamics.[1]

22.1   Heat Engines and the Second Law of Thermodynamics

A **heat engine** is a device that takes in energy by heat[2] and, operating in a cyclic process, expels a fraction of that energy by means of work. For instance, in a typical process by which a power plant produces electricity, a fuel such as coal is burned and the high-temperature gases produced are used to convert liquid water to steam. This steam is directed at the blades of a turbine, setting it into rotation. The mechanical energy associated with this rotation is used to drive an electric generator. Another device that can be modeled as a heat engine is the internal combustion engine in an automobile. This device uses energy from a burning fuel to perform work on pistons that results in the motion of the automobile.

A heat engine carries some working substance through a cyclic process during which (1) the working substance absorbs energy by heat from a high-temperature energy reservoir, (2) work is done by the engine, and (3) energy is expelled by heat to a lower-temperature reservoir. As an example, consider the operation of a steam engine (Fig. 22.1), which uses water as the working substance. The water in a boiler absorbs energy from burning fuel and evaporates to steam, which then does work by expanding against a piston. After the steam cools and condenses, the liquid water produced returns to the boiler and the cycle repeats.

It is useful to represent a heat engine schematically as in Active Figure 22.2. The engine absorbs a quantity of energy $|Q_h|$ from the hot reservoir. For the mathematical discussion of heat engines, we use absolute values to make all energy transfers positive and the direction of transfer is indicated with an explicit positive or negative sign. The engine does work W_{eng} (so that *negative* work $W = -W_{eng}$ is done *on* the engine) and then gives up a quantity of energy $|Q_c|$ to the cold reservoir. Because the working substance goes through a cycle, its initial and final internal energies are equal: $\Delta E_{int} = 0$. Hence, from the first law of thermodynamics, $\Delta E_{int} = Q + W = Q - W_{eng} = 0$, and **the net work W_{eng} done by a heat engine is**

Figure 22.1   This steam-driven locomotive runs from Durango to Silverton, Colorado. It obtains its energy by burning wood or coal. The generated energy vaporizes water into steam, which powers the locomotive. (This locomotive must take on water from tanks located along the route to replace steam lost through the funnel.) Modern locomotives use diesel fuel instead of wood or coal. Whether old-fashioned or modern, such locomotives can be modeled as heat engines, which extract energy from a burning fuel and convert a fraction of it to mechanical energy.

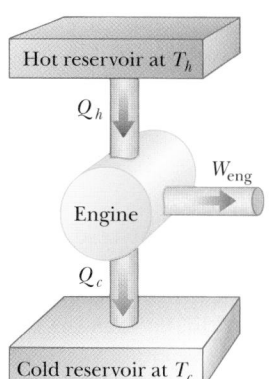

ACTIVE FIGURE 22.2

Schematic representation of a heat engine. The engine does work W_{eng}. The arrow at the top represents energy $Q_h > 0$ entering the engine. At the bottom, $Q_c < 0$ represents energy leaving the engine.

Sign in at www.thomsonedu.com and go to ThomsonNOW to select the efficiency of the engine and observe the transfer of energy.

PITFALL PREVENTION 22.1
The First and Second Laws

Notice the distinction between the first and second laws of thermodynamics. If a gas undergoes a *one-time isothermal process*, then $\Delta E_{int} = Q + W = 0$ and $W = -Q$. Therefore, the first law allows *all* energy input by heat to be expelled by work. In a heat engine, however, in which a substance undergoes a *cyclic* process, only a *portion* of the energy input by heat can be expelled by work according to the second law.

---

[1] Although a process occurring in the time-reversed sense has never been *observed*, it is *possible* for it to occur. As we shall see later in this chapter, however, the probability of such a process occurring is infinitesimally small. From this viewpoint, processes occur with a vastly greater probability in one direction than in the opposite direction.

[2] We use heat as our model for energy transfer into a heat engine. Other methods of energy transfer are possible in the model of a heat engine, however. For example, the Earth's atmosphere can be modeled as a heat engine in which the input energy transfer is by means of electromagnetic radiation from the Sun. The output of the atmospheric heat engine causes the wind structure in the atmosphere.

equal to the net energy Q_{net} transferred to it. As you can see from Active Figure 22.2, $Q_{net} = |Q_h| - |Q_c|$; therefore,

$$W_{eng} = |Q_h| - |Q_c| \qquad (22.1)$$

The **thermal efficiency** e of a heat engine is defined as the ratio of the net work done by the engine during one cycle to the energy input at the higher temperature during the cycle:

Thermal efficiency of ▶
a heat engine

$$e \equiv \frac{W_{eng}}{|Q_h|} = \frac{|Q_h| - |Q_c|}{|Q_h|} = 1 - \frac{|Q_c|}{|Q_h|} \qquad (22.2)$$

You can think of the efficiency as the ratio of what you gain (work) to what you give (energy transfer at the higher temperature). In practice, all heat engines expel only a fraction of the input energy Q_h by mechanical work; consequently, their efficiency is always less than 100%. For example, a good automobile engine has an efficiency of about 20%, and diesel engines have efficiencies ranging from 35% to 40%.

Equation 22.2 shows that a heat engine has 100% efficiency ($e = 1$) only if $|Q_c| = 0$, that is, if no energy is expelled to the cold reservoir. In other words, a heat engine with perfect efficiency would have to expel all the input energy by work. Because efficiencies of real engines are well below 100%, the **Kelvin–Planck form of the second law of thermodynamics** states the following:

> It is impossible to construct a heat engine that, operating in a cycle, produces no effect other than the input of energy by heat from a reservoir and the performance of an equal amount of work.

This statement of the second law means that during the operation of a heat engine, W_{eng} can never be equal to $|Q_h|$ or, alternatively, that some energy $|Q_c|$ must be rejected to the environment. Figure 22.3 is a schematic diagram of the impossible "perfect" heat engine.

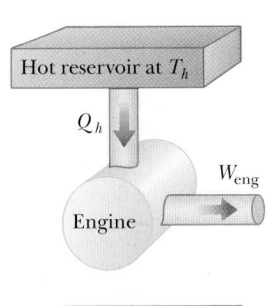

The impossible engine

Figure 22.3 Schematic diagram of a heat engine that takes in energy from a hot reservoir and does an equivalent amount of work. It is impossible to construct such a perfect engine.

Quick Quiz 22.1 The energy input to an engine is 3.00 times greater than the work it performs. **(i)** What is its thermal efficiency? (a) 3.00 (b) 1.00 (c) 0.333 (d) impossible to determine **(ii)** What fraction of the energy input is expelled to the cold reservoir? (a) 0.333 (b) 0.667 (c) 1.00 (d) impossible to determine

---

EXAMPLE 22.1 | **The Efficiency of an Engine**

An engine transfers 2.00×10^3 J of energy from a hot reservoir during a cycle and transfers 1.50×10^3 J as exhaust to a cold reservoir.

(A) Find the efficiency of the engine.

SOLUTION

Conceptualize Review Active Figure 22.2; think about energy going into the engine from the hot reservoir and splitting, with part coming out by work and part by heat into the cold reservoir.

Categorize This example involves evaluation of quantities from the equations introduced in this section, so we categorize it as a substitution problem.

Find the efficiency of the engine from Equation 22.2:

$$e = 1 - \frac{|Q_c|}{|Q_h|} = 1 - \frac{1.50 \times 10^3 \, J}{2.00 \times 10^3 \, J} = \boxed{0.250, \text{ or } 25.0\%}$$

(B) How much work does this engine do in one cycle?

SOLUTION

Find the work done by the engine by taking the difference between the input and output energies:

$$W_{eng} = |Q_h| - |Q_c| = 2.00 \times 10^3 \, J - 1.50 \times 10^3 \, J$$
$$= \boxed{5.0 \times 10^2 \, J}$$

What If? Suppose you were asked for the power output of this engine. Do you have sufficient information to answer this question?

Answer No, you do not have enough information. The power of an engine is the *rate* at which work is done by the engine. You know how much work is done per cycle, but you have no information about the time interval associated with one cycle. If you were told that the engine operates at 2 000 rpm (revolutions per minute), however, you could relate this rate to the period of rotation T of the mechanism of the engine. Assuming there is one thermodynamic cycle per revolution, the power is

$$\mathcal{P} = \frac{W_{\text{eng}}}{T} = \frac{5.0 \times 10^2 \, \text{J}}{\left(\frac{1}{2\,000}\,\text{min}\right)}\left(\frac{1\,\text{min}}{60\,\text{s}}\right) = 1.7 \times 10^4\,\text{W}$$

22.2 Heat Pumps and Refrigerators

In a heat engine, the direction of energy transfer is from the hot reservoir to the cold reservoir, which is the natural direction. The role of the heat engine is to process the energy from the hot reservoir so as to do useful work. What if we wanted to transfer energy from the cold reservoir to the hot reservoir? Because that is not the natural direction of energy transfer, we must put some energy into a device to be successful. Devices that perform this task are called **heat pumps** and **refrigerators**. For example, homes in summer are cooled using heat pumps called *air conditioners*. The air conditioner transfers energy from the cool room in the home to the warm air outside.

In a refrigerator or a heat pump, the engine takes in energy $|Q_c|$ from a cold reservoir and expels energy $|Q_h|$ to a hot reservoir (Active Fig. 22.4), which can be accomplished only if work is done *on* the engine. From the first law, we know that the energy given up to the hot reservoir must equal the sum of the work done and the energy taken in from the cold reservoir. Therefore, the refrigerator or heat pump transfers energy from a colder body (for example, the contents of a kitchen refrigerator or the winter air outside a building) to a hotter body (the air in the kitchen or a room in the building). In practice, it is desirable to carry out this process with a minimum of work. If the process could be accomplished without doing any work, the refrigerator or heat pump would be "perfect" (Fig. 22.5). Again, the existence of such a device would be in violation of the second law of thermodynamics, which in the form of the **Clausius statement**[3] states:

> It is impossible to construct a cyclical machine whose sole effect is to transfer energy continuously by heat from one object to another object at a higher temperature without the input of energy by work.

In simpler terms, **energy does not transfer spontaneously by heat from a cold object to a hot object**.

The Clausius and Kelvin–Planck statements of the second law of thermodynamics appear at first sight to be unrelated, but in fact they are equivalent in all respects. Although we do not prove so here, if either statement is false, so is the other.[4]

In practice, a heat pump includes a circulating fluid that passes through two sets of metal coils that can exchange energy with the surroundings. The fluid is cold and at low pressure when it is in the coils located in a cool environment, where it absorbs energy by heat. The resulting warm fluid is then compressed and enters the other coils as a hot, high-pressure fluid. There it releases its stored energy to the warm surroundings. In an air conditioner, energy is absorbed into the fluid in coils located in a building's interior; after the fluid is compressed, energy leaves the fluid through coils located outdoors. In a refrigerator, the external coils are behind or

[3] First expressed by Rudolf Clausius (1822–1888).

[4] See an advanced textbook on thermodynamics for this proof.

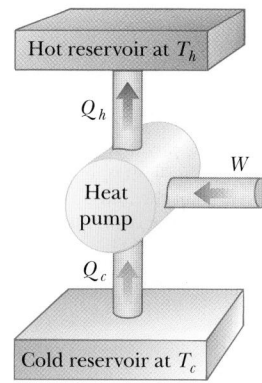

ACTIVE FIGURE 22.4

Schematic diagram of a heat pump, which takes in energy $Q_c > 0$ from a cold reservoir and expels energy $Q_h < 0$ to a hot reservoir. Work W is done *on* the heat pump. A refrigerator works the same way.

Sign in at www.thomsonedu.com and go to ThomsonNOW to select the COP of the heat pump and observe the transfer of energy.

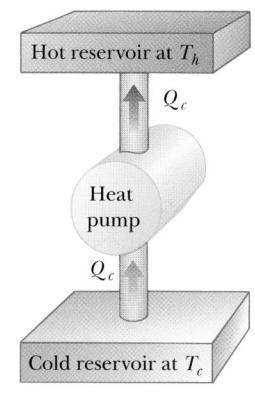

Impossible heat pump

Figure 22.5 Schematic diagram of an impossible heat pump or refrigerator, that is, one that takes in energy from a cold reservoir and expels an equivalent amount of energy to a hot reservoir without the input of energy by work.

Figure 22.6 The coils on the back of a refrigerator transfer energy by heat to the air. Due to the input of energy by work, this amount of energy must be greater than the amount of energy removed from the contents of the refrigerator.

underneath the unit (Fig. 22.6). The internal coils are in the walls of the refrigerator and absorb energy from the food.

The effectiveness of a heat pump is described in terms of a number called the **coefficient of performance** (COP). The COP is similar to the thermal efficiency for a heat engine in that it is a ratio of what you gain (energy transferred to or from a reservoir) to what you give (work input). For a heat pump operating in the cooling mode, "what you gain" is energy removed from the cold reservoir. The most effective refrigerator or air conditioner is one that removes the greatest amount of energy from the cold reservoir in exchange for the least amount of work. Therefore, for these devices operating in the cooling mode, we define the COP in terms of $|Q_c|$:

$$\text{COP (cooling mode)} = \frac{|Q_c|}{W} \qquad \textbf{(22.3)}$$

A good refrigerator should have a high COP, typically 5 or 6.

In addition to cooling applications, heat pumps are becoming increasingly popular for heating purposes. The energy-absorbing coils for a heat pump are located outside a building, in contact with the air or buried in the ground. The other set of coils are in the building's interior. The circulating fluid flowing through the coils absorbs energy from the outside and releases it to the interior of the building from the interior coils.

In the heating mode, the COP of a heat pump is defined as the ratio of the energy transferred to the hot reservoir to the work required to transfer that energy:

$$\text{COP (heating mode)} = \frac{\text{energy transferred at high temperature}}{\text{work done on heat pump}} = \frac{|Q_h|}{W} \qquad \textbf{(22.4)}$$

If the outside temperature is 25°F (−4°C) or higher, a typical value of the COP for a heat pump is about 4. That is, the amount of energy transferred to the building is about four times greater than the work done by the motor in the heat pump. As the outside temperature decreases, however, it becomes more difficult for the heat pump to extract sufficient energy from the air and so the COP decreases. Therefore, the use of heat pumps that extract energy from the air, although satisfactory in moderate climates, is not appropriate in areas where winter temperatures are very low. It is possible to use heat pumps in colder areas by burying the external coils deep in the ground. In that case, the energy is extracted from the ground, which tends to be warmer than the air in the winter.

Quick Quiz 22.2 The energy entering an electric heater by electrical transmission can be converted to internal energy with an efficiency of 100%. By what factor does the cost of heating your home change when you replace your electric heating system with an electric heat pump that has a COP of 4.00? Assume the motor running the heat pump is 100% efficient. (a) 4.00 (b) 2.00 (c) 0.500 (d) 0.250

EXAMPLE 22.2 | **Freezing Water**

A certain refrigerator has a COP of 5.00. When the refrigerator is running, its power input is 500 W. A sample of water of mass 500 g and temperature 20.0°C is placed in the freezer compartment. How long does it take to freeze the water to ice at 0°C? Assume all other parts of the refrigerator stay at the same temperature and there is no leakage of energy from the exterior, so the operation of the refrigerator results only in energy being extracted from the water.

SOLUTION

Conceptualize Energy leaves the water, reducing its temperature and then freezing it into ice. The time interval required for this entire process is related to the rate at which energy is withdrawn from the water, which, in turn, is related to the power input of the refrigerator.

Categorize We categorize this example as one that combines our understanding of temperature changes and phase changes from Chapter 20 and our understanding of heat pumps from this chapter.

Analyze Using Equations 20.4 and 20.7, find the amount of energy that must be extracted from 500 g of water at 20°C to turn it into ice at 0°C:

$$|Q_c| = |mc\,\Delta T - mL_f| = m|c\,\Delta T - L_f|$$

$$= |(0.500 \text{ kg})[(4\,186 \text{ J/kg} \cdot {}^{\circ}\text{C})(-20.0{}^{\circ}\text{C}) - 3.33 \times 10^5 \text{ J/kg}]|$$

$$= 2.08 \times 10^5 \text{ J}$$

Use Equation 22.3 to find how much energy must be provided to the refrigerator to extract this much energy from the water:

$$\text{COP} = \frac{|Q_c|}{W} \quad \rightarrow \quad W = \frac{|Q_c|}{\text{COP}} = \frac{2.08 \times 10^5 \text{ J}}{5.00}$$

$$W = 4.17 \times 10^4 \text{ J}$$

Use the power rating of the refrigerator to find the time interval required for the freezing process to occur:

$$\mathcal{P} = \frac{W}{\Delta t} \quad \rightarrow \quad \Delta t = \frac{W}{\mathcal{P}} = \frac{4.17 \times 10^4 \text{ J}}{500 \text{ W}} = \boxed{83.3 \text{ s}}$$

Finalize In reality, the time interval for the water to freeze in a refrigerator is much longer than 83.3 s, which suggests that the assumptions of our model are not valid. Only a small part of the energy extracted from the refrigerator interior in a given time interval comes from the water. Energy must also be extracted from the container in which the water is placed, and energy that continuously leaks into the interior from the exterior must be extracted.

22.3 Reversible and Irreversible Processes

In the next section, we will discuss a theoretical heat engine that is the most efficient possible. To understand its nature, we must first examine the meaning of reversible and irreversible processes. In a **reversible** process, the system undergoing the process can be returned to its initial conditions along the same path on a *PV* diagram, and every point along this path is an equilibrium state. A process that does not satisfy these requirements is **irreversible.**

All natural processes are known to be irreversible. Let's examine the adiabatic free expansion of a gas, which was already discussed in Section 20.6, and show that it cannot be reversible. Consider a gas in a thermally insulated container as shown in Figure 22.7. A membrane separates the gas from a vacuum. When the membrane is punctured, the gas expands freely into the vacuum. As a result of the puncture, the system has changed because it occupies a greater volume after the expansion. Because the gas does not exert a force through a displacement, it does no work on the surroundings as it expands. In addition, no energy is transferred to or from the gas by heat because the container is insulated from its surroundings. Therefore, in this adiabatic process, the system has changed but the surroundings have not.

For this process to be reversible, we must return the gas to its original volume and temperature without changing the surroundings. Imagine trying to reverse the process by compressing the gas to its original volume. To do so, we fit the container with a piston and use an engine to force the piston inward. During this process, the surroundings change because work is being done by an outside agent on the system. In addition, the system changes because the compression increases the temperature of the gas. The temperature of the gas can be lowered by allowing it to come into contact with an external energy reservoir. Although this step returns the gas to its original conditions, the surroundings are again affected because energy is being added to the surroundings from the gas. If this energy could be used to drive the engine that compressed the gas, the net energy transfer to the surroundings would be zero. In this way, the system and its surroundings could be returned to their initial conditions and we could identify the process as reversible. The Kelvin–Planck statement of the second law, however, specifies that the energy removed from the gas to return the temperature to its original value cannot be completely converted to mechanical energy in the form of the work done by the engine in compressing the gas. Therefore, we must conclude that the process is irreversible.

We could also argue that the adiabatic free expansion is irreversible by relying on the portion of the definition of a reversible process that refers to equilibrium

PITFALL PREVENTION 22.2
All Real Processes Are Irreversible

The reversible process is an idealization; all real processes on the Earth are irreversible.

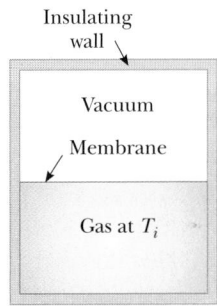

Figure 22.7 Adiabatic free expansion of a gas.

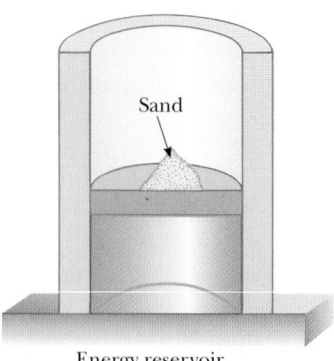

Figure 22.8 A gas in thermal contact with an energy reservoir is compressed slowly as individual grains of sand drop onto the piston. The compression is isothermal and reversible.

states. For example, during the sudden expansion, significant variations in pressure occur throughout the gas. Therefore, there is no well-defined value of the pressure for the entire system at any time between the initial and final states. In fact, the process cannot even be represented as a path on a *PV* diagram. The *PV* diagram for an adiabatic free expansion would show the initial and final conditions as points, but these points would not be connected by a path. Therefore, because the intermediate conditions between the initial and final states are not equilibrium states, the process is irreversible.

Although all real processes are irreversible, some are almost reversible. If a real process occurs very slowly such that the system is always very nearly in an equilibrium state, the process can be approximated as being reversible. Suppose a gas is compressed isothermally in a piston-cylinder arrangement in which the gas is in thermal contact with an energy reservoir and we continuously transfer just enough energy from the gas to the reservoir to keep the temperature constant. For example, imagine that the gas is compressed very slowly by dropping grains of sand onto a frictionless piston as shown in Figure 22.8. As each grain lands on the piston and compresses the gas a small amount, the system deviates from an equilibrium state, but it is so close to one that it achieves a new equilibrium state in a relatively short time interval. Each grain added represents a change to a new equilibrium state, but the differences between states are so small that the entire process can be approximated as occurring through continuous equilibrium states. The process can be reversed by slowly removing grains from the piston.

A general characteristic of a reversible process is that no dissipative effects (such as turbulence or friction) that convert mechanical energy to internal energy can be present. Such effects can be impossible to eliminate completely. Hence, it is not surprising that real processes in nature are irreversible.

22.4 The Carnot Engine

In 1824, a French engineer named Sadi Carnot described a theoretical engine, now called a **Carnot engine**, that is of great importance from both practical and theoretical viewpoints. He showed that a heat engine operating in an ideal, reversible cycle—called a **Carnot cycle**—between two energy reservoirs is the most efficient engine possible. Such an ideal engine establishes an upper limit on the efficiencies of all other engines. That is, the net work done by a working substance taken through the Carnot cycle is the greatest amount of work possible for a given amount of energy supplied to the substance at the higher temperature. **Carnot's theorem** can be stated as follows:

> No real heat engine operating between two energy reservoirs can be more efficient than a Carnot engine operating between the same two reservoirs.

To prove the validity of this theorem, imagine two heat engines operating between the *same* energy reservoirs. One is a Carnot engine with efficiency e_C, and the other is an engine with efficiency e, where we assume $e > e_C$. Because the cycle in the Carnot engine is reversible, the engine can operate in reverse as a refrigerator. The more efficient engine is used to drive the Carnot engine as a Carnot refrigerator. The output by work of the more efficient engine is matched to the input by work of the Carnot refrigerator. For the *combination* of the engine and refrigerator, no exchange by work with the surroundings occurs. Because we have assumed the engine is more efficient than the refrigerator, the net result of the combination is a transfer of energy from the cold to the hot reservoir without work being done on the combination. According to the Clausius statement of the second law, this process is impossible. Hence, the assumption that $e > e_C$ must be false. **All real engines are less efficient than the Carnot engine because they do not operate through a reversible cycle.** The efficiency of a real engine is further reduced by such practical difficulties as friction and energy losses by conduction.

SADI CARNOT
French engineer (1796–1832)
Carnot was the first to show the quantitative relationship between work and heat. In 1824, he published his only work, *Reflections on the Motive Power of Heat*, which reviewed the industrial, political, and economic importance of the steam engine. In it, he defined work as "weight lifted through a height."

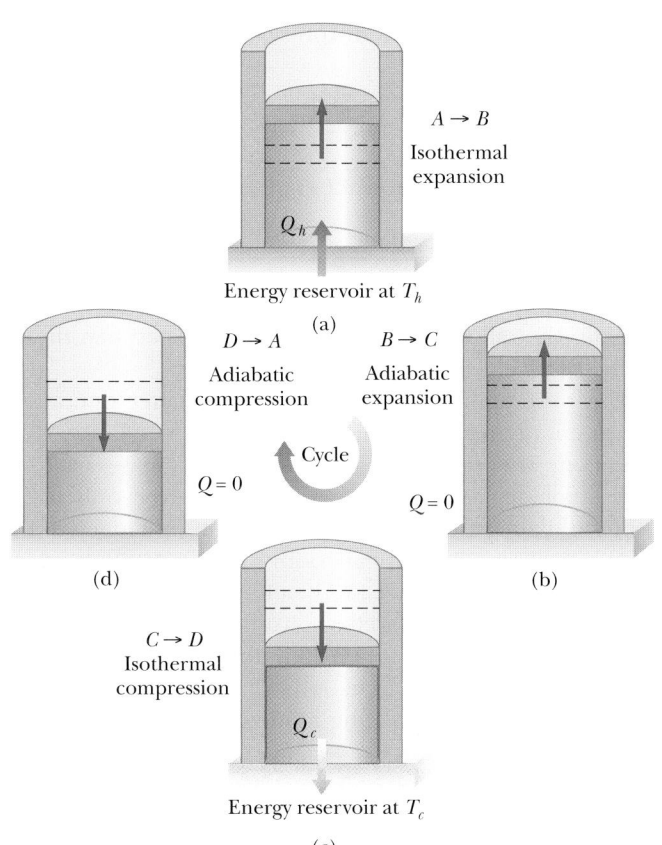

(a)

$A \rightarrow B$
Isothermal
expansion

Q_h

Energy reservoir at T_h

(d)

$D \rightarrow A$
Adiabatic
compression

$Q = 0$

Cycle

(b)

$B \rightarrow C$
Adiabatic
expansion

$Q = 0$

(c)

$C \rightarrow D$
Isothermal
compression

Q_c

Energy reservoir at T_c

ACTIVE FIGURE 22.9

The Carnot cycle. (a) In process $A \rightarrow B$, the gas expands isothermally while in contact with a reservoir at T_h. (b) In process $B \rightarrow C$, the gas expands adiabatically ($Q = 0$). (c) In process $C \rightarrow D$, the gas is compressed isothermally while in contact with a reservoir at $T_c < T_h$. (d) In process $D \rightarrow A$, the gas is compressed adiabatically. The arrows on the piston indicate the direction of its motion during each process.

Sign in at www.thomsonedu.com and go to ThomsonNOW to observe the motion of the piston in the Carnot cycle while you also observe the cycle on the PV diagram of Active Figure 22.10.

PITFALL PREVENTION 22.3
Don't Shop for a Carnot Engine

The Carnot engine is an idealization; do not expect a Carnot engine to be developed for commercial use. We explore the Carnot engine only for theoretical considerations.

To describe the Carnot cycle taking place between temperatures T_c and T_h, let's assume the working substance is an ideal gas contained in a cylinder fitted with a movable piston at one end. The cylinder's walls and the piston are thermally nonconducting. Four stages of the Carnot cycle are shown in Active Figure 22.9, and the PV diagram for the cycle is shown in Active Figure 22.10. The Carnot cycle consists of two adiabatic processes and two isothermal processes, all reversible:

1. Process $A \rightarrow B$ (Active Fig. 22.9a) is an isothermal expansion at temperature T_h. The gas is placed in thermal contact with an energy reservoir at temperature T_h. During the expansion, the gas absorbs energy $|Q_h|$ from the reservoir through the base of the cylinder and does work W_{AB} in raising the piston.
2. In process $B \rightarrow C$ (Active Fig. 22.9b), the base of the cylinder is replaced by a thermally nonconducting wall and the gas expands adiabatically; that is, no energy enters or leaves the system by heat. During the expansion, the temperature of the gas decreases from T_h to T_c and the gas does work W_{BC} in raising the piston.
3. In process $C \rightarrow D$ (Active Fig. 22.9c), the gas is placed in thermal contact with an energy reservoir at temperature T_c and is compressed isothermally at temperature T_c. During this time, the gas expels energy $|Q_c|$ to the reservoir and the work done by the piston on the gas is W_{CD}.
4. In the final process $D \rightarrow A$ (Active Fig. 22.9d), the base of the cylinder is replaced by a nonconducting wall and the gas is compressed adiabatically. The temperature of the gas increases to T_h, and the work done by the piston on the gas is W_{DA}.

The thermal efficiency of the engine is given by Equation 22.2:

$$e = \frac{W_{\text{eng}}}{|Q_h|} = \frac{|Q_h| - |Q_c|}{|Q_h|} = 1 - \frac{|Q_c|}{|Q_h|}$$

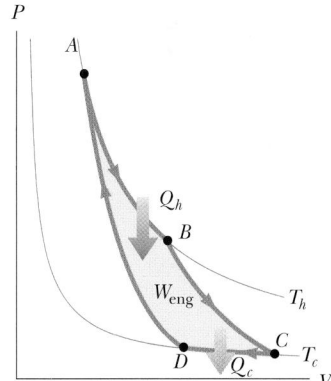

ACTIVE FIGURE 22.10

PV diagram for the Carnot cycle. The net work done W_{eng} equals the net energy transferred into the Carnot engine in one cycle, $|Q_h| - |Q_c|$. As with any cycle, the work done during the cycle is the area enclosed by the path on the PV diagram. Notice that $\Delta E_{\text{int}} = 0$ for the cycle.

Sign in at www.thomsonedu.com and go to ThomsonNOW to observe the Carnot cycle on the PV diagram while you also observe the motion of the piston in Active Figure 22.9.

In Example 22.3, we show that for a Carnot cycle,

$$\frac{|Q_c|}{|Q_h|} = \frac{T_c}{T_h} \tag{22.5}$$

Hence, the thermal efficiency of a Carnot engine is

Efficiency of a Carnot ▶
engine

$$e_C = 1 - \frac{T_c}{T_h} \tag{22.6}$$

This result indicates that **all Carnot engines operating between the same two temperatures have the same efficiency.**[5]

Equation 22.6 can be applied to any working substance operating in a Carnot cycle between two energy reservoirs. According to this equation, the efficiency is zero if $T_c = T_h$, as one would expect. The efficiency increases as T_c is lowered and T_h is raised. The efficiency can be unity (100%), however, only if $T_c = 0$ K. Such reservoirs are not available; therefore, the maximum efficiency is always less than 100%. In most practical cases, T_c is near room temperature, which is about 300 K. Therefore, one usually strives to increase the efficiency by raising T_h. Theoretically, a Carnot-cycle heat engine run in reverse constitutes the most effective heat pump possible, and it determines the maximum COP for a given combination of hot and cold reservoir temperatures. Using Equations 22.1 and 22.4, we see that the maximum COP for a heat pump in its heating mode is

$$\text{COP}_C \text{ (heating mode)} = \frac{|Q_h|}{W}$$

$$= \frac{|Q_h|}{|Q_h| - |Q_c|} = \frac{1}{1 - \frac{|Q_c|}{|Q_h|}} = \frac{1}{1 - \frac{T_c}{T_h}} = \frac{T_h}{T_h - T_c}$$

The Carnot COP for a heat pump in the cooling mode is

$$\text{COP}_C \text{ (cooling mode)} = \frac{T_c}{T_h - T_c}$$

As the difference between the temperatures of the two reservoirs approaches zero in this expression, the theoretical COP approaches infinity. In practice, the low temperature of the cooling coils and the high temperature at the compressor limit the COP to values below 10.

Quick Quiz 22.3   Three engines operate between reservoirs separated in temperature by 300 K. The reservoir temperatures are as follows: Engine A: $T_h = 1\,000$ K, $T_c = 700$ K; Engine B: $T_h = 800$ K, $T_c = 500$ K; Engine C: $T_h = 600$ K, $T_c = 300$ K. Rank the engines in order of theoretically possible efficiency from highest to lowest.

---

[5] For the processes in the Carnot cycle to be reversible, they must be carried out infinitesimally slowly. Therefore, although the Carnot engine is the most efficient engine possible, it has zero power output because it takes an infinite time interval to complete one cycle! For a real engine, the short time interval for each cycle results in the working substance reaching a high temperature lower than that of the hot reservoir and a low temperature higher than that of the cold reservoir. An engine undergoing a Carnot cycle between this narrower temperature range was analyzed by F. L. Curzon and B. Ahlborn (*Am. J. Phys.* **43**(1), 22, 1975), who found that the efficiency at maximum power output depends only on the reservoir temperatures T_c and T_h and is given by $e_{C\text{-}A} = 1 - (T_c/T_h)^{1/2}$. The Curzon–Ahlborn efficiency $e_{C\text{-}A}$ provides a closer approximation to the efficiencies of real engines than does the Carnot efficiency.

EXAMPLE 22.3 **Efficiency of the Carnot Engine**

Show that the ratio of energy transfers by heat in a Carnot engine is equal to the ratio of reservoir temperatures, as given by Equation 22.5.

SOLUTION

Conceptualize   Make use of Active Figures 22.9 and 22.10 to help you visualize the processes in the Carnot cycle.

Categorize   Because of our understanding of the Carnot cycle, we can categorize the processes in the cycle as isothermal and adiabatic.

Analyze   For the isothermal expansion (process $A \rightarrow B$ in Active Fig. 22.9), find the energy transfer by heat from the hot reservoir using Equation 20.14 and the first law of thermodynamics:

$$|Q_h| = |\Delta E_{int} - W_{AB}| = |0 - W_{AB}| = W_{AB} = nRT_h \ln \frac{V_B}{V_A}$$

In a similar manner, find the energy transfer to the cold reservoir during the isothermal compression $C \rightarrow D$:

$$|Q_c| = |\Delta E_{int} - W_{CD}| = |0 - W_{CD}| = W_{CD} = nRT_c \ln \frac{V_C}{V_D}$$

Divide the second expression by the first:

$$(1) \quad \frac{|Q_c|}{|Q_h|} = \frac{T_c}{T_h} \frac{\ln (V_C/V_D)}{\ln (V_B/V_A)}$$

Apply Equation 21.20 to the adiabatic processes $B \rightarrow C$ and $D \rightarrow A$:

$$T_h V_B{}^{\gamma-1} = T_c V_C{}^{\gamma-1}$$
$$T_h V_A{}^{\gamma-1} = T_c V_D{}^{\gamma-1}$$

Divide the first equation by the second:

$$\left(\frac{V_B}{V_A}\right)^{\gamma-1} = \left(\frac{V_C}{V_D}\right)^{\gamma-1}$$

$$(2) \quad \frac{V_B}{V_A} = \frac{V_C}{V_D}$$

Substitute Equation (2) into Equation (1):

$$\frac{|Q_c|}{|Q_h|} = \frac{T_c}{T_h} \frac{\ln (V_C/V_D)}{\ln (V_B/V_A)} = \frac{T_c}{T_h} \frac{\ln (V_C/V_D)}{\ln (V_C/V_D)} = \frac{T_c}{T_h}$$

Finalize   This last equation is Equation 22.5, the one we set out to prove.

EXAMPLE 22.4 **The Steam Engine**

A steam engine has a boiler that operates at 500 K. The energy from the burning fuel changes water to steam, and this steam then drives a piston. The cold reservoir's temperature is that of the outside air, approximately 300 K. What is the maximum thermal efficiency of this steam engine?

SOLUTION

Conceptualize   In a steam engine, the gas pushing on the piston in Active Figure 22.9 is steam. A real steam engine does not operate in a Carnot cycle, but, to find the maximum possible efficiency, imagine a Carnot steam engine.

Categorize   We calculate an efficiency using Equation 22.6, so we categorize this example as a substitution problem.

Substitute the reservoir temperatures into Equation 22.6:

$$e_C = 1 - \frac{T_c}{T_h} = 1 - \frac{300 \text{ K}}{500 \text{ K}} = \boxed{0.400} \quad \text{or} \quad \boxed{40.0\%}$$

This result is the highest *theoretical* efficiency of the engine. In practice, the efficiency is considerably lower.

What If?   Suppose we wished to increase the theoretical efficiency of this engine. This increase can be achieved by raising T_h by ΔT or by decreasing T_c by the same ΔT. Which would be more effective?

Answer   A given ΔT would have a larger fractional effect on a smaller temperature, so you would expect a larger change in efficiency if you alter T_c by ΔT. Let's test that numerically. Raising T_h by 50 K, corresponding to $T_h = 550$ K, would give a maximum efficiency of

$$e_C = 1 - \frac{T_c}{T_h} = 1 - \frac{300 \text{ K}}{550 \text{ K}} = 0.455$$

Decreasing T_c by 50 K, corresponding to $T_c = 250$ K, would give a maximum efficiency of

$$e_C = 1 - \frac{T_c}{T_h} = 1 - \frac{250 \text{ K}}{500 \text{ K}} = 0.500$$

Although changing T_c is *mathematically* more effective, often changing T_h is *practically* more feasible.

22.5   Gasoline and Diesel Engines

In a gasoline engine, six processes occur in each cycle; five of them are illustrated in Active Figure 22.11. In this discussion, let's consider the interior of the cylinder above the piston to be the system that is taken through repeated cycles in the engine's operation. For a given cycle, the piston moves up and down twice, which represents a four-stroke cycle consisting of two upstrokes and two downstrokes. The processes in the cycle can be approximated by the **Otto cycle** shown in the *PV* diagram in Active Figure 22.12. In the following discussion, refer to Active Figure 22.11 for the pictorial representation of the strokes and Active Figure 22.12 for the significance on the *PV* diagram of the letter designations below:

1. During the *intake stroke* $O \rightarrow A$ (Active Fig. 22.11a), the piston moves downward and a gaseous mixture of air and fuel is drawn into the cylinder at atmospheric pressure. In this process, the volume increases from V_2 to V_1. That is the energy input part of the cycle: energy enters the system (the interior of the cylinder) by matter transfer as potential energy stored in the fuel.

2. During the *compression stroke* $A \rightarrow B$ (Active Fig. 22.11b), the piston moves upward, the air-fuel mixture is compressed adiabatically from volume V_1 to volume V_2, and the temperature increases from T_A to T_B. The work done on the gas is positive, and its value is equal to the negative of the area under the curve AB in Active Figure 22.12.

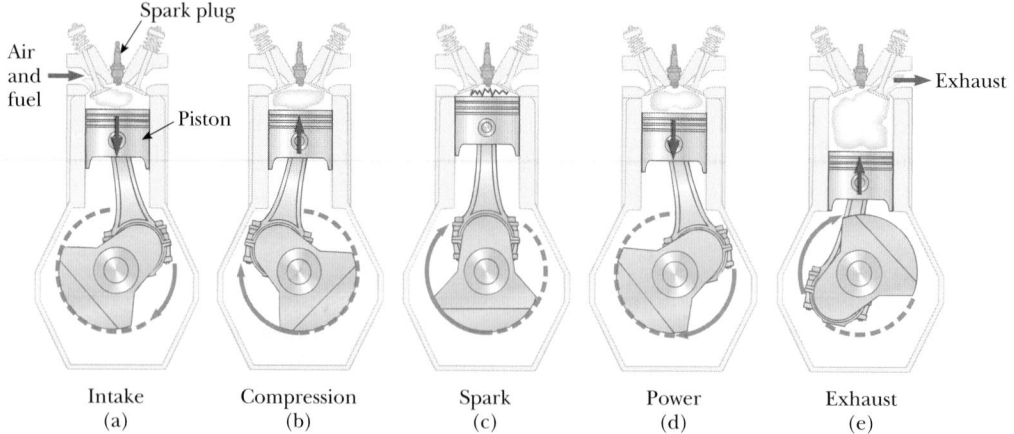

Intake   Compression   Spark   Power   Exhaust
(a)   (b)   (c)   (d)   (e)

ACTIVE FIGURE 22.11

The four-stroke cycle of a conventional gasoline engine. The arrows on the piston indicate the direction of its motion during each process. (a) In the intake stroke, air and fuel enter the cylinder. (b) The intake valve is then closed, and the air–fuel mixture is compressed by the piston. (c) The mixture is ignited by the spark plug, with the result that the temperature of the mixture increases at essentially constant volume. (d) In the power stroke, the gas expands against the piston. (e) Finally, the residual gases are expelled and the cycle repeats.

Sign in at www.thomsonedu.com and go to ThomsonNOW to observe the motion of the piston and crankshaft while you also observe the cycle on the *PV* diagram of Active Figure 22.12.

3. In process $B \to C$, combustion occurs when the spark plug fires (Active Fig. 22.11c). That is not one of the strokes of the cycle because it occurs in a very short time interval while the piston is at its highest position. The combustion represents a rapid transformation from potential energy stored in chemical bonds in the fuel to internal energy associated with molecular motion, which is related to temperature. During this time interval, the mixture's pressure and temperature increase rapidly, with the temperature rising from T_B to T_C. The volume, however, remains approximately constant because of the short time interval. As a result, approximately no work is done on or by the gas. We can model this process in the PV diagram (Active Fig. 22.12) as that process in which the energy $|Q_h|$ enters the system. (In reality, however, this process is a *conversion* of energy already in the cylinder from process $O \to A$.)

4. In the *power stroke* $C \to D$ (Active Fig. 22.11d), the gas expands adiabatically from V_2 to V_1. This expansion causes the temperature to drop from T_C to T_D. Work is done by the gas in pushing the piston downward, and the value of this work is equal to the area under the curve CD.

5. In the process $D \to A$ (not shown in Active Fig. 22.11), an exhaust valve is opened as the piston reaches the bottom of its travel and the pressure suddenly drops for a short time interval. During this time interval, the piston is almost stationary and the volume is approximately constant. Energy is expelled from the interior of the cylinder and continues to be expelled during the next process.

6. In the final process, the *exhaust stroke* $A \to O$ (Active Fig. 22.11e), the piston moves upward while the exhaust valve remains open. Residual gases are exhausted at atmospheric pressure, and the volume decreases from V_1 to V_2. The cycle then repeats.

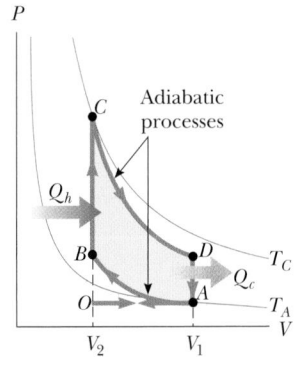

ACTIVE FIGURE 22.12

PV diagram for the Otto cycle, which approximately represents the processes occurring in an internal combustion engine.

Sign in at www.thomsonedu.com and go to ThomsonNOW to observe the Otto cycle on the *PV* diagram while you observe the motion of the piston and crankshaft in Active Figure 22.11.

If the air–fuel mixture is assumed to be an ideal gas, the efficiency of the Otto cycle is

$$e = 1 - \frac{1}{(V_1/V_2)^{\gamma-1}} \quad \text{(Otto cycle)} \tag{22.7}$$

where V_1/V_2 is the **compression ratio** and γ is the ratio of the molar specific heats C_P/C_V for the fuel–air mixture. Equation 22.7, which is derived in Example 22.5, shows that the efficiency increases as the compression ratio increases. For a typical compression ratio of 8 and with $\gamma = 1.4$, Equation 22.7 predicts a theoretical efficiency of 56% for an engine operating in the idealized Otto cycle. This value is much greater than that achieved in real engines (15% to 20%) because of such effects as friction, energy transfer by conduction through the cylinder walls, and incomplete combustion of the air–fuel mixture.

Diesel engines operate on a cycle similar to the Otto cycle, but they do not employ a spark plug. The compression ratio for a diesel engine is much greater than that for a gasoline engine. Air in the cylinder is compressed to a very small volume, and, as a consequence, the cylinder temperature at the end of the compression stroke is very high. At this point, fuel is injected into the cylinder. The temperature is high enough for the fuel–air mixture to ignite without the assistance of a spark plug. Diesel engines are more efficient than gasoline engines because of their greater compression ratios and resulting higher combustion temperatures.

EXAMPLE 22.5   **Efficiency of the Otto Cycle**

Show that the thermal efficiency of an engine operating in an idealized Otto cycle (see Active Figs. 22.11 and 22.12) is given by Equation 22.7. Treat the working substance as an ideal gas.

SOLUTION

Conceptualize   Study Active Figures 22.11 and 22.12 to make sure you understand the working of the Otto cycle.

Categorize As seen in Active Figure 22.12, we categorize the processes in the Otto cycle as isovolumetric and adiabatic.

Analyze Model the energy input and output as occurring by heat in processes $B \rightarrow C$ and $D \rightarrow A$. (In reality, most of the energy enters and leaves by matter transfer as the fuel–air mixture enters and leaves the cylinder.) Use Equation 21.8 to find the energy transfers by heat for these processes, which take place at constant volume:

$$B \rightarrow C \quad |Q_h| = nC_V (T_C - T_B)$$

$$D \rightarrow A \quad |Q_c| = nC_V (T_D - T_A)$$

Substitute these expressions into Equation 22.2:

$$(1) \quad e = \frac{W_{\text{eng}}}{|Q_h|} = 1 - \frac{|Q_c|}{|Q_h|} = 1 - \frac{T_D - T_A}{T_C - T_B}$$

Apply Equation 21.20 to the adiabatic processes $A \rightarrow B$ and $C \rightarrow D$:

$$A \rightarrow B \quad T_A V_A^{\gamma-1} = T_B V_B^{\gamma-1}$$

$$C \rightarrow D \quad T_C V_C^{\gamma-1} = T_D V_D^{\gamma-1}$$

Solve these equations for the temperatures T_A and T_D, noting that $V_A = V_D = V_1$ and $V_B = V_C = V_2$:

$$(2) \quad T_A = T_B \left(\frac{V_B}{V_A}\right)^{\gamma-1} = T_B \left(\frac{V_2}{V_1}\right)^{\gamma-1}$$

$$(3) \quad T_D = T_C \left(\frac{V_C}{V_D}\right)^{\gamma-1} = T_C \left(\frac{V_2}{V_1}\right)^{\gamma-1}$$

Subtract Equation (2) from Equation (3) and rearrange:

$$(4) \quad \frac{T_D - T_A}{T_C - T_B} = \left(\frac{V_2}{V_1}\right)^{\gamma-1}$$

Substitute Equation (4) into Equation (1):

$$e = 1 - \frac{1}{(V_1/V_2)^{\gamma-1}}$$

Finalize This final expression is Equation 22.7.

PITFALL PREVENTION 22.4
Entropy Is Abstract

Entropy is one of the most abstract notions in physics, so follow the discussion in this and the subsequent sections very carefully. Do not confuse energy with entropy. Even though the names sound similar, they are very different concepts.

22.6 Entropy

The zeroth law of thermodynamics involves the concept of temperature, and the first law involves the concept of internal energy. Temperature and internal energy are both state variables; that is, the value of each depends only on the thermodynamic state of a system, not on the process that brought it to that state. Another state variable—this one related to the second law of thermodynamics—is **entropy** S. In this section, we define entropy on a macroscopic scale as it was first expressed by Clausius in 1865.

Entropy was originally formulated as a useful concept in thermodynamics. Its importance grew, however, as the field of statistical mechanics developed because the analytical techniques of statistical mechanics provide an alternative means of interpreting entropy and a more global significance to the concept. In statistical mechanics, the behavior of a substance is described in terms of the statistical behavior of its atoms and molecules. An important finding in these studies is that **isolated systems tend toward disorder and entropy is a measure of this disorder**. For example, consider the molecules of a gas in the air in your room. If half the gas molecules had velocity vectors of equal magnitude directed toward the left and the other half had velocity vectors of the same magnitude directed toward the right, the situation would be very ordered. Such a situation is extremely unlikely, however. If you could view the molecules, you would see that they move haphazardly in all directions, bumping into one another, changing speed upon collision, some going fast and others going slowly. This situation is highly disordered.

The cause of the tendency of an isolated system toward disorder is easily explained. To do so, let's distinguish between *microstates* and *macrostates* of a system. A **microstate** is a particular configuration of the individual constituents of the system. For example, the description of the ordered velocity vectors of the air molecules in your room refers to a particular microstate, and the more likely haphazard motion is another microstate, one that represents disorder. A **macrostate** is a description of the system's conditions from a macroscopic point of view and makes use of macroscopic variables such as pressure, density, and temperature for gases.

For any given macrostate of the system, a number of microstates are possible. For example, the macrostate of a 4 on a pair of dice can be formed from the possible microstates 1–3, 2–2, and 3–1. It is assumed that all microstates are equally probable. When all possible macrostates are examined, however, it is found that macrostates associated with disorder have far more possible microstates than those associated with order. For example, there is only one microstate associated with the macrostate of a royal flush in a poker hand of five spades, laid out in order from ten to ace (Fig. 22.13a). This combination of cards is a highly ordered hand. Many microstates (the set of five individual cards in a poker hand), however, are associated with a worthless hand in poker (Fig. 22.13b).

The probability of being dealt the royal flush in spades is exactly the same as the probability of being dealt any *particular* worthless hand. Because there are so many worthless hands, however, the probability of a macrostate of a worthless hand is far larger than the probability of a macrostate of the royal flush in spades.

Quick Quiz 22.4   (a) Suppose you select four cards at random from a standard deck of playing cards and end up with a macrostate of four deuces. How many microstates are associated with this macrostate? (b) Suppose you pick up two cards and end up with a macrostate of two aces. How many microstates are associated with this macrostate?

We can also imagine ordered macrostates and disordered macrostates in physical processes, not just in games of dice and poker. The probability of a system moving in time from an ordered macrostate to a disordered macrostate is far greater than the probability of the reverse because there are more microstates in a disordered macrostate.

If we consider a system and its surroundings to include the entire Universe, the Universe is always moving toward a macrostate corresponding to greater disorder. Because entropy is a measure of disorder, an alternative way of stating this law is that **the entropy of the Universe increases in all real processes**. This statement is yet another wording of the second law of thermodynamics that can be shown to be equivalent to the Kelvin–Planck and Clausius statements.

The original formulation of entropy in thermodynamics involves the transfer of energy by heat during a reversible process. Consider any infinitesimal process in which a system changes from one equilibrium state to another. If dQ_r is the amount of energy transferred by heat when the system follows a reversible path between the states, the change in entropy dS is equal to this amount of energy for the reversible process divided by the absolute temperature of the system:

$$dS = \frac{dQ_r}{T} \tag{22.8}$$

We have assumed the temperature is constant because the process is infinitesimal. Because entropy is a state variable, **the change in entropy during a process depends only on the endpoints and therefore is independent of the actual path followed. Consequently, the entropy change for an irreversible process can be determined by calculating the entropy change for a reversible process that connects the same initial and final states**.

The subscript r on the quantity dQ_r is a reminder that the transferred energy is to be measured along a reversible path even though the system may actually have

(a)

(b)

Figure 22.13   (a) A royal flush is a highly ordered poker hand with low probability of occurring. (b) A disordered and worthless poker hand. The probability of this *particular* hand occurring is the same as that of the royal flush in spades. There are so many worthless hands, however, that the probability of being dealt a worthless hand is much higher than that of being dealt a royal flush in spades.

◄   Entropy statement of the second law of thermodynamics

followed some irreversible path. When energy is absorbed by the system, dQ_r is positive and the entropy of the system increases. When energy is expelled by the system, dQ_r is negative and the entropy of the system decreases. Notice that Equation 22.8 does not define entropy but, rather, the *change* in entropy. Hence, the meaningful quantity in describing a process is the *change* in entropy.

To calculate the change in entropy for a *finite* process, first recognize that T is generally not constant. Therefore, we must integrate Equation 22.8:

◄ Change in entropy for a finite process

$$\Delta S = \int_i^f dS = \int_i^f \frac{dQ_r}{T} \qquad (22.9)$$

As with an infinitesimal process, the change in entropy ΔS of a system going from one state to another has the same value for *all* paths connecting the two states. That is, the finite change in entropy ΔS of a system depends only on the properties of the initial and final equilibrium states. Therefore, we are free to choose a particular reversible path over which to evaluate the entropy in place of the actual path as long as the initial and final states are the same for both paths. This point is explored further in Section 22.7.

Quick Quiz 22.5 An ideal gas is taken from an initial temperature T_i to a higher final temperature T_f along two different reversible paths. Path A is at constant pressure and path B is at constant volume. What is the relation between the entropy changes of the gas for these paths? (a) $\Delta S_A > \Delta S_B$ (b) $\Delta S_A = \Delta S_B$ (c) $\Delta S_A < \Delta S_B$

EXAMPLE 22.6 | **Change in Entropy: Melting**

A solid that has a latent heat of fusion L_f melts at a temperature T_m. Calculate the change in entropy of this substance when a mass m of the substance melts.

SOLUTION

Conceptualize Imagine placing the substance in a warm environment so that energy enters the substance by heat. The process can be reversed by placing the substance in a cool environment so that energy leaves the substance by heat.

Categorize Because the melting takes place at a fixed temperature, we categorize the process as isothermal.

Analyze Use Equation 20.7 in Equation 22.9, noting that the temperature remains fixed:

$$\Delta S = \int \frac{dQ_r}{T} = \frac{1}{T_m} \int dQ_r = \frac{Q_r}{T_m} = \boxed{\frac{mL_f}{T_m}}$$

Finalize Notice that ΔS is positive, representing that energy is added to the ice cube.

What If? Suppose you did not have Equation 22.9 available to calculate an entropy change. How could you argue from the statistical description of entropy that the changes in entropy should be positive?

Answer When a solid melts, its entropy increases because the molecules are much more disordered in the liquid state than they are in the solid state. The positive value for ΔS also means that the substance in its liquid state does not spontaneously transfer energy from itself to the warm surroundings and freeze because to do so would involve a spontaneous increase in order and a decrease in entropy.

Let's consider the changes in entropy that occur in a Carnot heat engine that operates between the temperatures T_c and T_h. In one cycle, the engine takes in energy $|Q_h|$ from the hot reservoir and expels energy $|Q_c|$ to the cold reservoir. These energy transfers occur only during the isothermal portions of the Carnot cycle; therefore, the constant temperature can be brought out in front of the integral sign in Equation 22.9. The integral then simply has the value of the total amount of energy transferred by heat. Therefore, the total change in entropy for one cycle is

$$\Delta S = \frac{|Q_h|}{T_h} - \frac{|Q_c|}{T_c}$$

where the minus sign represents that energy is leaving the engine. In Example 22.3, we showed that for a Carnot engine,

$$\frac{|Q_c|}{|Q_h|} = \frac{T_c}{T_h}$$

Using this result in the previous expression for ΔS, we find that the total change in entropy for a Carnot engine operating in a cycle is *zero*:

$$\Delta S = 0$$

Now consider a system taken through an arbitrary (non-Carnot) reversible cycle. Because entropy is a state variable—and hence depends only on the properties of a given equilibrium state—we conclude that $\Delta S = 0$ for *any* reversible cycle. In general, we can write this condition as

$$\oint \frac{dQ_r}{T} = 0 \quad \text{(reversible cycle)} \tag{22.10}$$

where the symbol $\oint$ indicates that the integration is over a closed path.

22.7 Entropy Changes in Irreversible Processes

By definition, a calculation of the change in entropy for a system requires information about a reversible path connecting the initial and final equilibrium states. To calculate changes in entropy for real (irreversible) processes, remember that entropy (like internal energy) depends only on the *state* of the system. That is, entropy is a state variable, and the change in entropy depends only on the initial and final states.

You can calculate the entropy change in some irreversible process between two equilibrium states by devising a reversible process (or series of reversible processes) between the same two states and computing $\Delta S = \int dQ_r/T$ for the reversible process. In irreversible processes, it is important to distinguish between Q, the actual energy transfer in the process, and Q_r, the energy that would have been transferred by heat along a reversible path. Only Q_r is the correct value to be used in calculating the entropy change.

The change in entropy for a system and its surroundings is always positive for an irreversible process. In general, the total entropy—and therefore the disorder—always increases in an irreversible process. Keeping these considerations in mind, we can state the second law of thermodynamics as follows:

> The total entropy of an isolated system that undergoes a change cannot decrease.

Furthermore, **if the process is irreversible, the total entropy of an isolated system always increases. In a reversible process, the total entropy of an isolated system remains constant**.

When dealing with a system that is not isolated from its surroundings, remember that the increase in entropy described in the second law is that of the system *and* its surroundings. When a system and its surroundings interact in an irreversible process, the increase in entropy of one is greater than the decrease in entropy of the other. Hence, **the change in entropy of the Universe must be greater than zero for an irreversible process and equal to zero for a reversible process**. Ultimately, the entropy of the Universe should reach a maximum value. At this value, the Universe will be in a state of uniform temperature and density. All physical, chemical, and biological processes will cease because a state of perfect disorder implies that no energy is available for doing work. This gloomy state of affairs is sometimes referred to as the heat death of the Universe.

Quick Quiz 22.6 True or False: The entropy change in an adiabatic process must be zero because $Q = 0$.

Entropy Change in Thermal Conduction

Let's now consider a system consisting of a hot reservoir and a cold reservoir that are in thermal contact with each other and isolated from the rest of the Universe. A process occurs during which energy Q is transferred by heat from the hot reservoir at temperature T_h to the cold reservoir at temperature T_c. The process as described is irreversible, so we must find an equivalent reversible process. Because the temperature of a reservoir does not change during the process, we can replace the real process for each reservoir with a reversible, isothermal process in which the same amount of energy is transferred by heat. Consequently, for a reservoir, the entropy change does not depend on whether the process is reversible or irreversible.

Because the cold reservoir absorbs energy Q, its entropy increases by Q/T_c. At the same time, the hot reservoir loses energy Q, so its entropy change is $-Q/T_h$. Because $T_h > T_c$, the increase in entropy of the cold reservoir is greater than the decrease in entropy of the hot reservoir. Therefore, the change in entropy of the system (and of the Universe) is greater than zero:

$$\Delta S_U = \frac{Q}{T_c} + \frac{-Q}{T_h} > 0$$

Suppose energy were to transfer spontaneously from a cold object to a hot object, in violation of the second law. This impossible energy transfer can be described in terms of disorder. Before the transfer, a certain degree of order is associated with the different temperatures of the objects. The hot object's molecules have a higher average energy than the cold object's molecules. If energy spontaneously transfers from the cold object to the hot object, the cold object becomes colder over a time interval and the hot object becomes hotter. The difference in average molecular energy becomes even greater, which would represent an increase in order for the system and a violation of the second law.

In comparison, the process that does occur naturally is the transfer of energy from the hot object to the cold object. In this process, the difference in average molecular energy decreases, which represents a more random distribution of energy and an increase in disorder.

Entropy Change in a Free Expansion

Let's again consider the adiabatic free expansion of a gas occupying an initial volume V_i (Fig. 22.14). In this situation, a membrane separating the gas from an evacuated region is broken and the gas expands (irreversibly) to a volume V_f. What are the changes in entropy of the gas and of the Universe during this process? The process is neither reversible nor quasi-static. As shown in Section 20.6, the initial and final temperatures of the gas are the same.

To apply Equation 22.9, we cannot take $Q = 0$, the value for the irreversible process, but must instead find Q_r; that is, we must find an equivalent reversible path that shares the same initial and final states. A simple choice is an isothermal, reversible expansion in which the gas pushes slowly against a piston while energy enters the gas by heat from a reservoir to hold the temperature constant. Because T is constant in this process, Equation 22.9 gives

$$\Delta S = \int_i^f \frac{dQ_r}{T} = \frac{1}{T} \int_i^f dQ_r$$

For an isothermal process, the first law of thermodynamics specifies that $\int_i^f dQ_r$ is equal to the negative of the work done on the gas during the expansion from V_i to

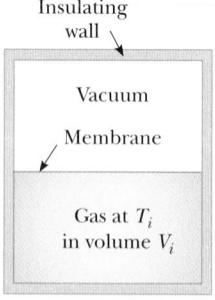

Figure 22.14 Adiabatic free expansion of a gas. When the membrane separating the gas from the evacuated region is ruptured, the gas expands freely and irreversibly. As a result, it occupies a greater final volume. The container is thermally insulated from its surroundings; therefore, $Q = 0$.

Insulating wall

Vacuum

Membrane

Gas at T_i in volume V_i

V_f, which is given by Equation 20.14. Using this result, we find that the entropy change for the gas is

$$\Delta S = nR \ln \left(\frac{V_f}{V_i} \right) \qquad \textbf{(22.11)}$$

Because $V_f > V_i$, we conclude that ΔS is positive. This positive result indicates that both the entropy and the disorder of the gas *increase* as a result of the irreversible, adiabatic expansion.

It is easy to see that the gas is more disordered after the expansion. Instead of being concentrated in a relatively small space, the molecules are scattered over a larger region.

Because the free expansion takes place in an insulated container, no energy is transferred by heat from the surroundings. (Remember that the isothermal, reversible expansion is only a *replacement* process used to calculate the entropy change for the gas; it is not the *actual* process.) Therefore, the free expansion has no effect on the surroundings, and the entropy change of the surroundings is zero.

22.8   Entropy on a Microscopic Scale

As we have seen, entropy can be approached by relying on macroscopic concepts. Entropy can also be treated from a microscopic viewpoint through statistical analysis of molecular motions. Let's use a microscopic model to investigate once again the free expansion of an ideal gas, which was discussed from a macroscopic point of view in Section 22.7.

In the kinetic theory of gases, gas molecules are represented as particles moving randomly. Suppose the gas is initially confined to the volume V_i shown in Figure 22.14. When the membrane is removed, the molecules eventually are distributed throughout the greater volume V_f of the entire container. For a given uniform distribution of gas in the volume, there are a large number of equivalent microstates, and the entropy of the gas can be related to the number of microstates corresponding to a given macrostate.

Let's count the number of microstates by considering the variety of molecular locations available to the molecules. At the instant after the partition is removed (and before the molecules have had a chance to rush into the other half of the container), all the molecules are in the initial volume. Let's assume each molecule occupies some microscopic volume V_m. The total number of possible locations of a single molecule in a macroscopic initial volume V_i is the ratio $w_i = V_i / V_m$, which is a huge number. We use w_i here to represent either the number of *ways* the molecule can be placed in the initial volume or the number of microstates, which is equivalent to the number of available locations. We assume the probabilities of a molecule occupying any of these locations are equal.

As more molecules are added to the system, the number of possible ways the molecules can be positioned in the volume multiplies. For example, if you consider two molecules, for every possible placement of the first, all possible placements of the second are available. Therefore, there are w_i ways of locating the first molecule, and for each way, there are w_i ways of locating the second molecule. The total number of ways of locating the two molecules is $w_i w_i = w_i^2$.

Neglecting the very small probability of having two molecules occupy the same location, each molecule may go into any of the V_i / V_m locations, and so the number of ways of locating N molecules in the volume becomes $W_i = w_i^N = (V_i / V_m)^N$. ($W_i$ is not to be confused with work.) Similarly, when the volume is increased to V_f, the number of ways of locating N molecules increases to $W_f = w_f^N = (V_f / V_m)^N$. The ratio of the number of ways of placing the molecules in the volume for the initial and final configurations is

$$\frac{W_f}{W_i} = \frac{(V_f / V_m)^N}{(V_i / V_m)^N} = \left(\frac{V_f}{V_i} \right)^N$$

Taking the natural logarithm of this equation and multiplying by Boltzmann's constant gives

$$k_\text{B} \ln \left(\frac{W_f}{W_i} \right) = k_\text{B} \ln \left(\frac{V_f}{V_i} \right)^N = n N_\text{A} k_\text{B} \ln \left(\frac{V_f}{V_i} \right)$$

where we have used the equality $N = n N_\text{A}$. We know from Equation 19.11 that $N_\text{A} k_\text{B}$ is the universal gas constant R; therefore, we can write this equation as

$$k_\text{B} \ln W_f - k_\text{B} \ln W_i = nR \ln \left(\frac{V_f}{V_i} \right) \qquad (22.12)$$

From Equation 22.11, we know that when a gas undergoes a free expansion from V_i to V_f, the change in entropy is

$$S_f - S_i = nR \ln \left(\frac{V_f}{V_i} \right) \qquad (22.13)$$

Notice that the right sides of Equations 22.12 and 22.13 are identical. Therefore, from the left sides, we make the following important connection between entropy and the number of microstates for a given macrostate:

Entropy (microscopic definition) ▶

$$S \equiv k_\text{B} \ln W \qquad (22.14)$$

The more microstates there are that correspond to a given macrostate, the greater the entropy of that macrostate. As discussed previously, there are many more microstates associated with disordered macrostates than with ordered macrostates. Therefore, Equation 22.14 indicates mathematically that **entropy is a measure of disorder**. Although our discussion used the specific example of the free expansion of an ideal gas, a more rigorous development of the statistical interpretation of entropy would lead us to the same conclusion.

We have stated that individual microstates are equally probable. Because there are far more microstates associated with a disordered macrostate than with an ordered macrostate, however, a disordered macrostate is much more probable than an ordered one.

Let's explore this concept by considering 100 molecules in a container. At any given moment, the probability of one molecule being in the left part of the container shown in Active Figure 22.15a as a result of random motion is $\frac{1}{2}$. If there are two molecules as shown in Active Figure 22.15b, the probability of both being in the left part is $\left(\frac{1}{2} \right)^2$, or 1 in 4. If there are three molecules (Active Fig. 22.15c), the probability of them all being in the left portion at the same moment is $\left(\frac{1}{2} \right)^3$, or 1 in 8. For 100 independently moving molecules, the probability that the 50 fastest ones will be found in the left part at any moment is $\left(\frac{1}{2} \right)^{50}$. Likewise, the probability that the remaining 50 slower molecules will be found in the right part at any moment is $\left(\frac{1}{2} \right)^{50}$. Therefore, the probability of finding this fast-slow separation as a result of random motion is the product $\left(\frac{1}{2} \right)^{50} \left(\frac{1}{2} \right)^{50} = \left(\frac{1}{2} \right)^{100}$, which corresponds to about 1 in 10^{30}. When this calculation is extrapolated from 100 molecules to the number in 1 mol of gas (6.02×10^{23}), the ordered arrangement is found to be *extremely* improbable!

ACTIVE FIGURE 22.15

(a) One molecule in a container has a 1-in-2 chance of being on the left side. (b) Two molecules have a 1-in-4 chance of being on the left side at the same time. (c) Three molecules have a 1-in-8 chance of being on the left side at the same time.

Sign in at www.thomsonedu.com and go to ThomsonNOW to choose the number of molecules to put in the container and measure the probability of them all being on the left side.

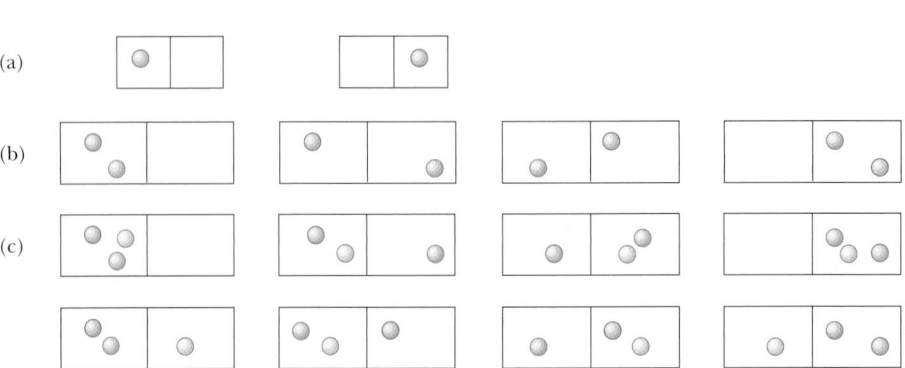

CONCEPTUAL EXAMPLE 22.7   **Let's Play Marbles!**

Suppose you have a bag of 100 marbles of which 50 are red and 50 are green. You are allowed to draw four marbles from the bag according to the following rules. Draw one marble, record its color, and return it to the bag. Shake the bag and then draw another marble. Continue this process until you have drawn and returned four marbles. What are the possible macrostates for this set of events? What is the most likely macrostate? What is the least likely macrostate?

SOLUTION

Because each marble is returned to the bag before the next one is drawn and the bag is then shaken, the probability of drawing a red marble is always the same as the probability of drawing a green one. All the possible microstates and macrostates are shown in Table 22.1. As this table indicates, there is only one way to draw a macrostate of four red marbles, so there is only one microstate for that macrostate. There are, however, four possible microstates that correspond to the macrostate of one green marble and three red marbles, six microstates that correspond to two green marbles and two red marbles, four microstates that correspond to three green marbles and one red marble, and one microstate that corresponds to four green marbles. The most likely, and most disordered, macrostate—two red marbles and two green marbles—corresponds to the largest number of microstates. The least likely, most ordered macrostates—four red marbles or four green marbles—correspond to the smallest number of microstates.

TABLE 22.1

Possible Results of Drawing Four Marbles from a Bag

Macrostate	Possible Microstates	Total Number of Microstates
All R	RRRR	1
1G, 3R	RRRG, RRGR, RGRR, GRRR	4
2G, 2R	RRGG, RGRG, GRRG, RGGR, GRGR, GGRR	6
3G, 1R	GGGR, GGRG, GRGG, RGGG	4
All G	GGGG	1

EXAMPLE 22.8   **Adiabatic Free Expansion: One Last Time**

Let's verify that the macroscopic and microscopic approaches to the calculation of entropy lead to the same conclusion for the adiabatic free expansion of an ideal gas. Suppose an ideal gas expands to four times its initial volume. As we have seen for this process, the initial and final temperatures are the same.

(A) Using a macroscopic approach, calculate the entropy change for the gas.

SOLUTION

Conceptualize   Look back at Figure 22.14, which is a diagram of the system before the adiabatic free expansion. Imagine breaking the membrane so that the gas moves into the evacuated area. The expansion is irreversible.

Categorize   We can replace the irreversible process with a reversible isothermal process between the same initial and final states. This approach is macroscopic, so we use thermodynamics state variables such as P, V, and T.

Analyze   Use Equation 22.11 to evaluate the entropy change:

$$\Delta S = nR \ln \left(\frac{V_f}{V_i} \right) = nR \ln \left(\frac{4V_i}{V_i} \right) = \boxed{nR \ln 4}$$

(B) Using statistical considerations, calculate the change in entropy for the gas and show that it agrees with the answer you obtained in part (A).

SOLUTION

Categorize   This approach is microscopic, so we use variables related to the individual molecules.

Analyze   The number of microstates available to a single molecule in the initial volume V_i is $w_i = V_i/V_m$. Use this number to find the number of available microstates for N molecules:

$$W_i = w_i{}^N = \left(\frac{V_i}{V_m} \right)^N$$

Find the number of available microstates for N molecules in the final volume $V_f = 4V_i$:

$$W_f = \left(\frac{V_f}{V_m} \right)^N = \left(\frac{4V_i}{V_m} \right)^N$$

Use Equation 22.14 to find the entropy change:

$$\Delta S = k_B \ln W_f - k_B \ln W_i = k_B \ln \left(\frac{W_f}{W_i}\right)$$

$$= k_B \ln \left(\frac{4V_i}{V_i}\right)^N = k_B \ln (4^N) = N k_B \ln 4 = \boxed{nR \ln 4}$$

Finalize The answer is the same as that for part (A), which dealt with macroscopic parameters.

What If? In part (A), we used Equation 22.11, which was based on a reversible isothermal process connecting the initial and final states. Would you arrive at the same result if you chose a different reversible process?

Answer You *must* arrive at the same result because entropy is a state variable. For example, consider the two-step process in Figure 22.16: a reversible adiabatic expansion from V_i to $4V_i$, ($A \rightarrow B$) during which the temperature drops from T_1 to T_2 and a reversible isovolumetric process ($B \rightarrow C$) that takes the gas back to the initial temperature T_1. During the reversible adiabatic process, $\Delta S = 0$ because $Q_r = 0$.

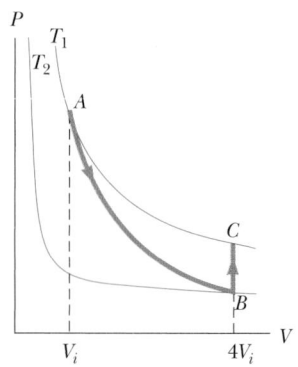

Figure 22.16 (Example 22.8) A gas expands to four times its initial volume and back to the initial temperature by means of a two-step process.

For the reversible isovolumetric process ($B \rightarrow C$), use Equation 22.9:

$$\Delta S = \int_i^f \frac{dQ_r}{T} = \int_{T_2}^{T_1} \frac{nC_V dT}{T} = nC_V \ln \left(\frac{T_1}{T_2}\right)$$

Find the ratio of temperature T_2 to T_1 from Equation 21.20 for the adiabatic process:

$$\frac{T_1}{T_2} = \left(\frac{4V_i}{V_i}\right)^{\gamma-1} = (4)^{\gamma-1}$$

Substitute to find ΔS:

$$\Delta S = nC_V \ln (4)^{\gamma-1} = nC_V (\gamma - 1) \ln 4$$

$$= nC_V \left(\frac{C_P}{C_V} - 1\right) \ln 4 = n(C_P - C_V) \ln 4 = nR \ln 4$$

and you do indeed obtain the exact same result for the entropy change.

Summary

ThomsonNOW™ Sign in at **www.thomsonedu.com** and go to ThomsonNOW to take a practice test for this chapter.

DEFINITIONS

The **thermal efficiency** e of a heat engine is $$e \equiv \frac{W_{eng}}{|Q_h|} = \frac{|Q_h| - |Q_c|}{|Q_h|} = 1 - \frac{|Q_c|}{|Q_h|} \quad (22.2)$$	From a microscopic viewpoint, the entropy of a given macrostate is defined as $$S \equiv k_B \ln W \quad (22.14)$$ where k_B is Boltzmann's constant and W is the number of microstates of the system corresponding to the macrostate.

In a **reversible** process, the system can be returned to its initial conditions along the same path on a PV diagram, and every point along this path is an equilibrium state. A process that does not satisfy these requirements is **irreversible**.

(continued)

CONCEPTS AND PRINCIPLES

A **heat engine** is a device that takes in energy by heat and, operating in a cyclic process, expels a fraction of that energy by means of work. The net work done by a heat engine in carrying a working substance through a cyclic process ($\Delta E_{int} = 0$) is

$$W_{eng} = |Q_h| - |Q_c| \quad \textbf{(22.1)}$$

where $|Q_h|$ is the energy taken in from a hot reservoir and $|Q_c|$ is the energy expelled to a cold reservoir.

Two ways the **second law of thermodynamics** can be stated are as follows:

- It is impossible to construct a heat engine that, operating in a cycle, produces no effect other than the input of energy by heat from a reservoir and the performance of an equal amount of work (the Kelvin–Planck statement).
- It is impossible to construct a cyclical machine whose sole effect is to transfer energy continuously by heat from one object to another object at a higher temperature without the input of energy by work (the Clausius statement).

Carnot's theorem states that no real heat engine operating (irreversibly) between the temperatures T_c and T_h can be more efficient than an engine operating reversibly in a Carnot cycle between the same two temperatures.

The thermal efficiency of a heat engine operating in the Carnot cycle is

$$e_C = 1 - \frac{T_c}{T_h} \quad \textbf{(22.6)}$$

The second law of thermodynamics states that when real (irreversible) processes occur, the degree of disorder in the system plus the surroundings increases. When a process occurs in an isolated system, the state of the system becomes more disordered. The measure of disorder in a system is called **entropy** S. Therefore, yet another way the second law can be stated is as follows:

- The entropy of the Universe increases in all real processes.

The **change in entropy** dS of a system during a process between two infinitesimally separated equilibrium states is

$$dS = \frac{dQ_r}{T} \quad \textbf{(22.8)}$$

where dQ_r is the energy transfer by heat for the system for a reversible process that connects the initial and final states.

The change in entropy of a system during an arbitrary process between an initial state and a final state is

$$\Delta S = \int_i^f \frac{dQ_r}{T} \quad \textbf{(22.9)}$$

The value of ΔS for the system is the same for all paths connecting the initial and final states. The change in entropy for a system undergoing any reversible, cyclic process is zero, and when such a process occurs, the entropy of the Universe remains constant.

Questions

☐ denotes answer available in *Student Solutions Manual/Study Guide;* **O** denotes objective question

1. What are some factors that affect the efficiency of automobile engines?

2. O Consider cyclic processes completely characterized by each of the following net energy inputs and outputs. In each case, the energy transfers listed are the *only* ones occurring. Classify each process as (a) possible, (b) impossible according to the first law of thermodynamics, (c) impossible according to the second law of thermodynamics, or (d) impossible according to both the first and second laws. **(i)** Input is 5 J of work and output is 4 J of work. **(ii)** Input is 5 J of work and output is 5 J of energy transferred by heat. **(iii)** Input is 5 J of energy transferred by electrical transmission and output is 6 J of work. **(iv)** Input is 5 J of energy transferred by heat and output is 5 J of energy transferred by heat. **(v)** Input is 5 J of energy transferred by heat and output is 5 J of work. **(vi)** Input is 5 J of energy transferred by heat and output is 3 J of work plus 2 J of energy transferred by heat. **(vii)** Input is 5 J of energy transferred by heat and output is 3 J of work plus 2 J of energy transferred by mechanical waves. **(viii)** Input is 5 J of energy transferred by heat and output is 3 J of work plus 1 J of energy transferred by electromagnetic radiation.

3. A steam-driven turbine is one major component of an electric power plant. Why is it advantageous to have the temperature of the steam as high as possible?

4. Does the second law of thermodynamics contradict or correct the first law? Argue for your answer.

5. "The first law of thermodynamics says you can't really win, and the second law says you can't even break even." Explain how this statement applies to a particular device or process; alternatively, argue against the statement.

6. **O** The arrow *OA* in the *PV* diagram shown in Figure Q22.6 represents a reversible adiabatic expansion of an ideal gas. The same sample of gas, starting from the same state *O*, now undergoes an adiabatic free expansion to the same final volume. What point on the diagram could represent the final state of the gas? (a) the same point *A* as for the reversible expansion   (b) point *B*   (c) point *C*   (d) any of these choices   (e) none of these choices

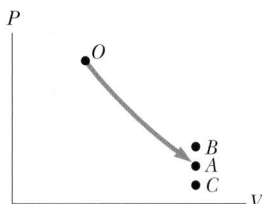

Figure Q22.6

7. Give various examples of irreversible processes that occur in nature. Give an example of a process in nature that is nearly reversible.

8. The device shown in Figure Q22.8, called a thermoelectric converter, uses a series of semiconductor cells to transform internal energy to electric potential energy, which we will study in Chapter 25. In the photograph at the left, both legs of the device are at the same temperature and no electric potential energy is produced. When one leg is at a higher temperature than the other as shown in the photograph on the right, however, electric potential energy is produced as the device extracts energy from the hot reservoir and drives a small electric motor. (a) Why is the difference in temperature necessary to produce electric potential energy in this demonstration? (b) In what sense does this intriguing experiment demonstrate the second law of thermodynamics?

Figure Q22.8

9. **O** Suppose you come home to a small, hot apartment in a well-insulated building on a summer afternoon. The appliance store has just delivered your new air conditioner, but you are too tired to install it properly. Until the sun sets, it will be hotter outside than inside, so you do not open a window. **(i)** You take the air conditioner out of its box, set it on the dining room table, plug it in, and turn it on. What happens to the temperature of the apartment? (a) It increases. (b) It decreases. (c) It remains constant. **(ii)** Suppose instead you quickly take all the ice cubes and frozen vegetables from the refrigerator's freezing compartment, put them into a bowl on the table, and close the refrigerator. What happens to the apartment temperature now? Choose from the same possibilities.

10. **O (i)** The second law of thermodynamics implies that the coefficient of performance of a refrigerator must be (a) less than 1, (b) less than or equal to 1, (c) greater than or equal to 1, (d) less than infinity, or (e) greater than 0. **(ii)** What does the second law of thermodynamics imply that the coefficient of performance of a heat pump must be? Choose from the same possibilities.

11. Discuss three different common examples of natural processes that involve an increase in entropy. Be sure to account for all parts of each system under consideration.

12. Discuss the change in entropy of a gas that expands (a) at constant temperature and (b) adiabatically.

13. **O** A thermodynamic process occurs in which the entropy of a system changes by -8 J/K. According to the second law of thermodynamics, what can you conclude about the entropy change of the environment? (a) It must be -8 J/K or less. (b) It must be equal to -8 J/K. (c) It must be between -8 J/K and 0. (d) It must be 0. (e) It must be between 0 and $+8$ J/K. (e) It must be equal to $+8$ J/K (f) It must be $+8$ J/K or more. (g) We would need to know the nature of the process to reach a conclusion. (h) It is impossible for the system to have a negative entropy change.

14. **O** A sample of a monatomic ideal gas is contained in a cylinder with a piston. Its state is represented by the dot in the *PV* diagram shown in Figure Q22.14. Arrows *A* through *H* represent isothermal, isobaric, isovolumetric, and adiabatic processes that the sample can undergo. In each compression and expansion, the volume changes by a factor of 2. (a) Rank these processes according to the work $W_{eng} = +\int P\,dV$ done by the gas from the largest positive value to the largest-magnitude negative value. In your ranking, display any cases of equality. (b) Rank the same processes according to the change in internal energy of the gas from the largest positive value to the largest-magnitude negative value. (c) Rank the same processes according to the energy transferred to the sample by heat.

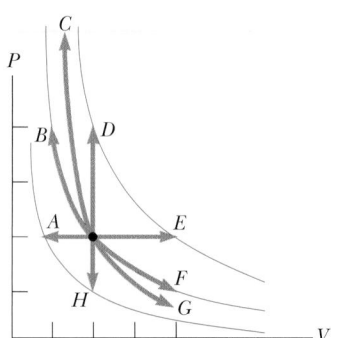

Figure Q22.14

15. **O** Consider the processes shown in Figure Q22.14 and described in Question 14. Rank the processes *A* through *H* according to the change in entropy of the monatomic ideal gas sample from the largest positive value to the largest-magnitude negative value.

16. The energy exhaust from a certain coal-fired electric generating station is carried by "cooling water" into Lake Ontario. The water is warm from the viewpoint of living things in the lake. Some of them congregate around the outlet port and can impede the water flow. (a) Use the theory of heat engines to explain why this action can reduce the electric power output of the station. (b) An engineer says that the electric output is reduced because of "higher back pressure on the turbine blades." Comment on the accuracy of this statement.

17. O Assume a sample of an ideal gas is at room temperature. What action will necessarily make the entropy of the sample increase? (a) transfer energy into it by heat (b) transfer energy into it irreversibly by heat (c) do work on it (d) increase either its temperature or its volume, without letting the other variable decrease (e) none of these choices

18. Suppose your roommate is "Mr. Clean" and tidies up your messy room after a big party. Because your roommate is creating more order, does this process represent a violation of the second law of thermodynamics?

19. "Energy is the mistress of the Universe and entropy is her shadow." Writing for an audience of general readers, argue for this statement with examples. Alternatively, argue for the view that entropy is like a decisive hands-on executive instantly determining what will happen, whereas energy is like a wretched back-office bookkeeper telling us how little we can afford. (Arnold Sommerfeld suggested the idea for this question.)

20. If you shake a jar full of jelly beans of different sizes, the larger jelly beans tend to appear near the top and the smaller ones tend to fall to the bottom. Why? Does this process violate the second law of thermodynamics?

Problems

WebAssign The Problems from this chapter may be assigned online in WebAssign.

ThomsonNOW Sign in at **www.thomsonedu.com** and go to ThomsonNOW to assess your understanding of this chapter's topics with additional quizzing and conceptual questions.

1, 2, 3 denotes straightforward, intermediate, challenging; ☐ denotes full solution available in *Student Solutions Manual/Study Guide;* ▲ denotes coached solution with hints available at **www.thomsonedu.com;** denotes developing symbolic reasoning; ● denotes asking for qualitative reasoning; ⌘ denotes computer useful in solving problem

Section 22.1 Heat Engines and the Second Law of Thermodynamics

1. A heat engine takes in 360 J of energy from a hot reservoir and performs 25.0 J of work in each cycle. Find (a) the efficiency of the engine and (b) the energy expelled to the cold reservoir in each cycle.

2. A gun is a heat engine. In particular, it is an internal combustion piston engine that does not operate in a cycle, but comes apart during its adiabatic expansion process. A certain gun consists of 1.80 kg of iron. It fires one 2.40-g bullet at 320 m/s with an energy efficiency of 1.10%. Assume the body of the gun absorbs all the energy exhaust—the other 98.9%—and increases uniformly in temperature for a short time interval before it loses any energy by heat into the environment. Find its temperature increase.

3. A particular heat engine has a mechanical power output of 5.00 kW and an efficiency of 25.0%. The engine expels 8 000 J of exhaust energy in each cycle. Find (a) the energy taken in during each cycle and (b) the time interval for each cycle.

4. A multicylinder gasoline engine in an airplane, operating at 2 500 rev/min, takes in energy 7.89×10^3 J and exhausts 4.58×10^3 J for each revolution of the crankshaft. (a) How many liters of fuel does it consume in 1.00 h of operation if the heat of combustion is 4.03×10^7 J/L? (b) What is the mechanical power output of the engine? Ignore friction and express the answer in horsepower. (c) What is the torque exerted by the crankshaft on the load? (d) What power must the exhaust and cooling system transfer out of the engine?

5. Suppose a heat engine is connected to two energy reservoirs, one a pool of molten aluminum (660°C) and the other a block of solid mercury (−38.9°C). The engine runs by freezing 1.00 g of aluminum and melting 15.0 g of mercury during each cycle. The heat of fusion of aluminum is 3.97×10^5 J/kg; the heat of fusion of mercury is 1.18×10^4 J/kg. What is the efficiency of this engine?

Section 22.2 Heat Pumps and Refrigerators

6. A refrigerator has a coefficient of performance equal to 5.00. The refrigerator takes in 120 J of energy from a cold reservoir in each cycle. Find (a) the work required in each cycle and (b) the energy expelled to the hot reservoir.

7. A refrigerator has a coefficient of performance of 3.00. The ice tray compartment is at −20.0°C, and the room temperature is 22.0°C. The refrigerator can convert 30.0 g of water at 22.0°C to 30.0 g of ice at −20.0°C each minute. What input power is required? Give your answer in watts.

8. ● In 1993, the U.S. government instituted a requirement that all room air conditioners sold in the United States must have an energy efficiency ratio (EER) of 10 or higher. The EER is defined as the ratio of the cooling capacity of the air conditioner, measured in British thermal units per hour, or Btu/h, to its electrical power requirement in watts. (a) Convert the EER of 10.0 to dimensionless form, using the conversion 1 Btu = 1 055 J. (b) What is the appropriate name for this dimensionless quantity? (c) In the 1970s, it was common to find room air conditioners with EERs of 5 or lower. State how the operating costs compare for 10 000-Btu/h air conditioners with EERs of 5.00 and 10.0. Assume each air conditioner operates for 1 500 h during the summer in a city where electricity costs 10.0¢ per kWh.

Section 22.3 Reversible and Irreversible Processes
Section 22.4 The Carnot Engine

9. One of the most efficient heat engines ever built is a steam turbine in the Ohio River valley, operating between

430°C and 1 870°C on energy from West Virginia coal to produce electricity for the Midwest. (a) What is its maximum theoretical efficiency? (b) The actual efficiency of the engine is 42.0%. How much mechanical power does the engine deliver if it takes in 1.40×10^5 J of energy each second from its hot reservoir?

10. A Carnot engine has a power output of 150 kW. The engine operates between two reservoirs at 20.0°C and 500°C. (a) How much energy does it take in per hour? (b) How much energy is lost per hour in its exhaust?

11. ● An engine operates in a cycle, taking in energy by heat at 180°C and putting out exhaust at 100°C. In each cycle, the exhaust energy is 2.00×10^4 J and the engine does 1.50×10^3 J of work. Explain how the actual efficiency of the engine compares with the efficiency of a reversible engine operating between the same temperatures.

12. A Carnot heat engine operates between temperatures T_h and T_c. (a) If $T_h = 500$ K and $T_c = 350$ K, what is the efficiency of the engine? (b) What is the change in its efficiency for each degree of increase in T_h above 500 K? (c) What is the change in its efficiency for each degree of decrease in T_c below 350 K?

13. ▲ An ideal gas is taken through a Carnot cycle. The isothermal expansion occurs at 250°C, and the isothermal compression takes place at 50.0°C. The gas takes in 1 200 J of energy from the hot reservoir during the isothermal expansion. Find (a) the energy expelled to the cold reservoir in each cycle and (b) the net work done by the gas in each cycle.

14. A power plant operates at a 32.0% efficiency during the summer when the seawater used for cooling is at 20.0°C. The plant uses 350°C steam to drive turbines. If the plant's efficiency changes in the same proportion as the ideal efficiency, what is the plant's efficiency in the winter, when the seawater is 10.0°C?

15. Argon enters a turbine at a rate of 80.0 kg/min, a temperature of 800°C, and a pressure of 1.50 MPa. It expands adiabatically as it pushes on the turbine blades and exits at pressure 300 kPa. (a) Calculate its temperature at exit. (b) Calculate the (maximum) power output of the turning turbine. (c) The turbine is one component of a model closed-cycle gas turbine engine. Calculate the maximum efficiency of the engine.

16. ● An electric power plant that would make use of the temperature gradient in the ocean has been proposed. The system is to operate between 20.0°C (surface-water temperature) and 5.00°C (water temperature at a depth of about 1 km). (a) What is the maximum efficiency of such a system? (b) If the electric power output of the plant is 75.0 MW, how much energy is taken in from the warm reservoir per hour? (c) In view of your answer to part (a), explain whether you think such a system is worthwhile. Note that the "fuel" is free.

17. ● Suppose you build a two-engine device with the exhaust energy output from one heat engine supplying the input energy for a second heat engine. We say that the two engines are running *in series*. Let e_1 and e_2 represent the efficiencies of the two engines. (a) The overall efficiency of the two-engine device is defined as the total work output divided by the energy put into the first engine by heat. Show that the overall efficiency is given by

$$e = e_1 + e_2 - e_1 e_2$$

(b) **What If?** Assume the two engines are Carnot engines. Engine 1 operates between temperatures T_h and T_i. The gas in engine 2 varies in temperature between T_i and T_c. In terms of the temperatures, what is the efficiency of the combination engine? Does an improvement in net efficiency result from the use of two engines instead of one? (c) What value of the intermediate temperature T_i results in equal work being done by each of the two engines in series? (d) What value of T_i results in each of the two engines in series having the same efficiency?

18. ● An electric generating station is designed to have an electric output power 1.40 MW using a turbine with two-thirds the efficiency of a Carnot engine. The exhaust energy is transferred by heat into a cooling tower at 110°C. (a) Find the rate at which the station exhausts energy by heat, as a function of the fuel combustion temperature T_h. If the firebox is modified to run hotter by using more advanced combustion technology, how does the amount of energy exhaust change? (b) Find the exhaust power for $T_h = 800$°C. (c) Find the value of T_h for which the exhaust power would be only half as large as in part (b). (d) Find the value of T_h for which the exhaust power would be one quarter as large as in part (b).

19. What is the coefficient of performance of a refrigerator that operates with Carnot efficiency between temperatures −3.00°C and +27.0°C?

20. At point A in a Carnot cycle, 2.34 mol of a monatomic ideal gas has a pressure of 1 400 kPa, a volume of 10.0 L, and a temperature of 720 K. The gas expands isothermally to point B and then expands adiabatically to point C, where its volume is 24.0 L. An isothermal compression brings it to point D, where its volume is 15.0 L. An adiabatic process returns the gas to point A. (a) Determine all the unknown pressures, volumes, and temperatures as you fill in the following table:

	P	V	T
A	1 400 kPa	10.0 L	720 K
B			
C		24.0 L	
D		15.0 L	

(b) Find the energy added by heat, the work done by the engine, and the change in internal energy for each of the steps $A \rightarrow B$, $B \rightarrow C$, $C \rightarrow D$, and $D \rightarrow A$. (c) Calculate the efficiency $W_{net}/|Q_h|$. Show that it is equal to $1 - T_C/T_A$, the Carnot efficiency.

21. An ideal refrigerator or ideal heat pump is equivalent to a Carnot engine running in reverse. That is, energy $|Q_c|$ is taken in from a cold reservoir and energy $|Q_h|$ is rejected to a hot reservoir. (a) Show that the work that must be supplied to run the refrigerator or heat pump is

$$W = \frac{T_h - T_c}{T_c} |Q_c|$$

(b) Show that the coefficient of performance of the ideal refrigerator is

$$\text{COP} = \frac{T_c}{T_h - T_c}$$

22. What is the maximum possible coefficient of performance of a heat pump that brings energy from outdoors at

−3.00°C into a 22.0°C house? *Note:* The work done to run the heat pump is also available to warm up the house.

23. ▲ How much work does an ideal Carnot refrigerator require to remove 1.00 J of energy from liquid helium at 4.00 K and reject this energy to a room-temperature (293 K) environment?

24. A heat pump used for heating shown in Figure P22.24 is essentially an air conditioner installed backward. It extracts energy from colder air outside and deposits it in a warmer room. Suppose the ratio of the actual energy entering the room to the work done by the device's motor is 10.0% of the theoretical maximum ratio. Determine the energy entering the room per joule of work done by the motor, given that the inside temperature is 20.0°C and the outside temperature is −5.00°C.

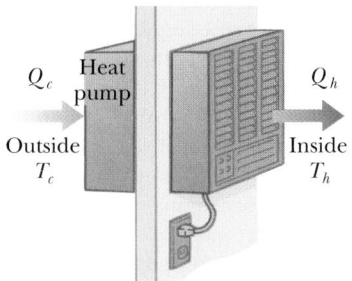

Figure P22.24

25. An ideal (Carnot) freezer in a kitchen has a constant temperature of 260 K, whereas the air in the kitchen has a constant temperature of 300 K. Suppose the insulation for the freezer is not perfect and conducts energy into the freezer at a rate of 0.150 W. Determine the average power required for the freezer's motor to maintain the constant temperature in the freezer.

26. If a 35.0%-efficient Carnot heat engine (Active Fig. 22.2) is run in reverse so as to form a refrigerator (Active Fig. 22.4), what would be this refrigerator's coefficient of performance?

Section 22.5 Gasoline and Diesel Engines

27. In a cylinder of an automobile engine, immediately after combustion, the gas is confined to a volume of 50.0 cm³ and has an initial pressure of 3.00×10^6 Pa. The piston moves outward to a final volume of 300 cm³, and the gas expands without energy loss by heat. (a) If $\gamma = 1.40$ for the gas, what is the final pressure? (b) How much work is done by the gas in expanding?

28. The compression ratio of an Otto cycle as shown in Active Figure 22.12 is $V_A/V_B = 8.00$. At the beginning A of the compression process, 500 cm³ of gas is at 100 kPa and 20.0°C. At the beginning of the adiabatic expansion, the temperature is $T_C = 750°C$. Model the working fluid as an ideal gas with $E_{int} = nC_VT = 2.50\ nRT$ and $\gamma = 1.40$. (a) Fill in this table to follow the states of the gas:

	T (K)	P (kPa)	V (cm³)	E_{int} (J)
A	293	100	500	
B				
C	1 023			
D				
A				

(b) Fill in this table to follow the processes:

	Q (input)	W (output)	ΔE_{int}
$A \rightarrow B$			
$B \rightarrow C$			
$C \rightarrow D$			
$D \rightarrow A$			
$ABCDA$			

(c) Identify the energy input $|Q_h|$, the energy exhaust $|Q_c|$, and the net output work W_{eng}. (d) Calculate the thermal efficiency. (e) Find the number of crankshaft revolutions per minute required for a one-cylinder engine to have an output power of 1.00 kW = 1.34 hp. *Note:* The thermodynamic cycle involves four piston strokes.

29. A gasoline engine has a compression ratio of 6.00 and uses a gas for which $\gamma = 1.40$. (a) What is the efficiency of the engine if it operates in an idealized Otto cycle? (b) **What If?** If the actual efficiency is 15.0%, what fraction of the fuel is wasted as a result of friction and energy losses by heat that could by avoided in a reversible engine? Assume complete combustion of the air-fuel mixture.

Section 22.6 Entropy

30. An ice tray contains 500 g of liquid water at 0°C. Calculate the change in entropy of the water as it freezes slowly and completely at 0°C.

31. A sample consisting of a mass m of a substance with specific heat c is warmed from temperature T_i to temperature T_f. Imagine that it absorbs energy by heat successively from reservoirs at incrementally higher temperatures $T_i + \delta$, $T_i + 2\delta$, $T_i + 3\delta$, ..., T_f. Prove that the change in entropy of the sample is given by $mc \ln (T_f/T_i)$.

32. ● In making raspberry jelly, 900 g of raspberry juice is combined with 930 g of sugar. The mixture starts at room temperature, 23.0°C, and is slowly warmed on a stove until it reaches 220°F. It is then poured into hot jars and allowed to cool. Assume the juice has the same specific heat as water. The specific heat of sucrose is 0.299 cal/g · °C. Consider the warming process. (a) Which of the following terms describe(s) this process: adiabatic, isobaric, isothermal, isovolumetric, cyclic, reversible, isentropic? Explain your answer. (b) How much energy does the mixture absorb? (c) What is the minimum change in entropy of the jelly while it is warmed? You may use the result of Problem 31.

33. Calculate the change in entropy of 250 g of water warmed slowly from 20.0°C to 80.0°C. You may use the result of Problem 31.

Section 22.7 Entropy Changes in Irreversible Processes

34. The temperature at the surface of the Sun is approximately 5 700 K, and the temperature at the surface of the Earth is approximately 290 K. What entropy change occurs when 1 000 J of energy is transferred by radiation from the Sun to the Earth?

35. ▲ A 1 500-kg car is moving at 20.0 m/s. The driver brakes to a stop. The brakes cool to the temperature of the surrounding air, which is nearly constant at 20.0°C. What is the total entropy change? You may use the result of Problem 31.

36. Calculate the increase in entropy of the Universe when you add 20.0 g of 5.00°C cream to 200 g of 60.0°C coffee.

Assume the specific heats of cream and coffee are both 4.20 J/g · °C. You may use the result of Problem 31.

37. How fast are you personally making the entropy of the Universe increase right now? Compute an order-of-magnitude estimate, stating what quantities you take as data and the values you measure or estimate for them.

38. A 1.00-kg iron horseshoe is taken from a forge at 900°C and dropped into 4.00 kg of water at 10.0°C. Assuming no energy is lost by heat to the surroundings, determine the total entropy change of the horseshoe-plus-water system. You may use the result of Problem 31.

39. A 1.00-mol sample of H_2 gas is contained in the left side of the container shown in Figure P22.39, which has equal volumes left and right. The right side is evacuated. When the valve is opened, the gas streams into the right side. What is the final entropy change of the gas? Does the temperature of the gas change? Assume the container is so large that the hydrogen behaves as an ideal gas.

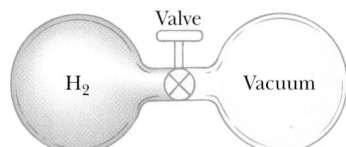

Figure P22.39

40. A 2.00-L container has a center partition that divides it into two equal parts as shown in Figure P22.40. The left side contains H_2 gas, and the right side contains O_2 gas. Both gases are at room temperature and at atmospheric pressure. The partition is removed and the gases are allowed to mix. What is the entropy increase of the system?

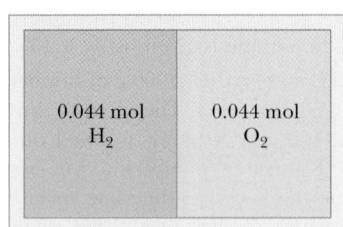

Figure P22.40

Section 22.8 Entropy on a Microscopic Scale

41. If you roll two dice, what is the total number of ways in which you can obtain (a) a 12? (b) a 7?

42. Prepare a table like Table 22.1 for the following occurrence. You toss four coins into the air simultaneously and then record the results of your tosses in terms of the numbers of heads and tails that result. For example, HHTH and HTHH are two possible ways in which three heads and one tail can be achieved. (a) On the basis of your table, what is the most probable result recorded for a toss? In terms of entropy, (b) what is the most ordered macrostate, and (c) what is the most disordered?

43. Repeat the procedure used to construct Table 22.1 (a) for the case in which you draw three marbles from your bag rather than four and (b) for the case in which you draw five rather than four.

Additional Problems

44. Every second at Niagara Falls, some 5 000 m³ of water falls a distance of 50.0 m. What is the increase in entropy per

second due to the falling water? Assume the mass of the surroundings is so great that its temperature and that of the water stay nearly constant at 20.0°C. Also assume a negligible amount of water evaporates.

45. ● A firebox is at 750 K, and the ambient temperature is 300 K. The efficiency of a Carnot engine doing 150 J of work as it transports energy between these constant-temperature baths is 60.0%. The Carnot engine must take in energy 150 J/0.600 = 250 J from the hot reservoir and must put out 100 J of energy by heat into the environment. To follow Carnot's reasoning, suppose some other heat engine S could have an efficiency of 70.0%. (a) Find the energy input and wasted energy output of engine S as it does 150 J of work. (b) Let engine S operate as in part (a) and run the Carnot engine in reverse. Find the total energy the firebox puts out as both engines operate together and the total energy transferred to the environment. Explain how the results show that the Clausius statement of the second law of thermodynamics is violated. (c) Find the energy input and work output of engine S as it puts out exhaust energy of 100 J. (d) Let engine S operate as in part (c) and contribute 150 J of its work output to running the Carnot engine in reverse. Find the total energy the firebox puts out as both engines operate together, the total work output, and the total energy transferred to the environment. Explain how the results show that the Kelvin–Planck statement of the second law is violated. Therefore, our assumption about the efficiency of engine S must be false. (e) Let the engines operate together through one cycle as in part (d). Find the change in entropy of the Universe. Explain how the result shows that the entropy statement of the second law is violated.

46. **Review problem.** This problem complements Problem 24 in Chapter 10. In the operation of a single-cylinder internal combustion piston engine, one charge of fuel explodes to drive the piston outward in the so-called power stroke. Part of its energy output is stored in a turning flywheel. This energy is then used to push the piston inward to compress the next charge of fuel and air. In this compression process, assume an original volume of 0.120 L of a diatomic ideal gas at atmospheric pressure is compressed adiabatically to one-eighth of its original volume. (a) Find the work input required to compress the gas. (b) Assume the flywheel is a solid disk of mass 5.10 kg and radius 8.50 cm, turning freely without friction between the power stroke and the compression stroke. How fast must the flywheel turn immediately after the power stroke? This situation represents the minimum angular speed at which the engine can operate; it is on the point of stalling. (c) When the engine's operation is well above the point of stalling, assume the flywheel puts 5.00% of its maximum energy into compressing the next charge of fuel and air. Find its maximum angular speed in this case.

47. ▲ A house loses energy through the exterior walls and roof at a rate of 5 000 J/s = 5.00 kW when the interior temperature is 22.0°C and the outside temperature is −5.00°C. (a) Calculate the electric power required to maintain the interior temperature at 22.0°C if the electric power is used in electric resistance heaters that convert all the energy transferred in by electrical transmission into internal energy. (b) **What If?** Calculate the electric power required to maintain the interior temperature at 22.0°C if the elec-

tric power is used to drive an electric motor that operates the compressor of a heat pump that has a coefficient of performance equal to 60.0% of the Carnot-cycle value.

48. A heat engine operates between two reservoirs at $T_2 = 600$ K and $T_1 = 350$ K. It takes in 1 000 J of energy from the higher-temperature reservoir and performs 250 J of work. Find (a) the entropy change of the Universe ΔS_U for this process and (b) the work W that could have been done by an ideal Carnot engine operating between these two reservoirs. (c) Show that the difference between the amounts of work done in parts (a) and (b) is $T_1 \Delta S_U$.

49. ▲ In 1816, Robert Stirling, a Scottish clergyman, patented the *Stirling engine*, which has found a wide variety of applications ever since. Fuel is burned externally to warm one of the engine's two cylinders. A fixed quantity of inert gas moves cyclically between the cylinders, expanding in the hot one and contracting in the cold one. Figure P22.49 represents a model for its thermodynamic cycle. Consider n mol of an ideal monatomic gas being taken once through the cycle, consisting of two isothermal processes at temperatures $3T_i$ and T_i and two constant-volume processes. Determine in terms of n, R, and T_i (a) the net energy transferred by heat to the gas and (b) the efficiency of the engine. A Stirling engine is easier to manufacture than an internal combustion engine or a turbine. It can run on burning garbage. It can run on the energy of sunlight and produce no material exhaust.

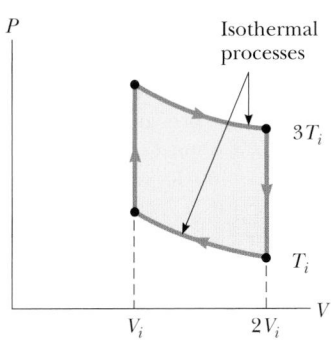

Figure P22.49

50. ● An athlete whose mass is 70.0 kg drinks 16 ounces (453.6 g) of refrigerated water. The water is at a temperature of 35.0°F. (a) Ignoring the temperature change of the body that results from the water intake (so that the body is regarded as a reservoir always at 98.6°F), find the entropy increase of the entire system. (b) **What If?** Assume the entire body is cooled by the drink and the average specific heat of a person is equal to the specific heat of liquid water. Ignoring any other energy transfers by heat and any metabolic energy release, find the athlete's temperature after she drinks the cold water, given an initial body temperature of 98.6°F. Under these assumptions, what is the entropy increase of the entire system? State how this result compares with the one you obtained in part (a).

51. A power plant, having a Carnot efficiency, produces 1 000 MW of electrical power from turbines that take in steam at 500 K and reject water at 300 K into a flowing river. The water downstream is 6.00 K warmer due to the output of the power plant. Determine the flow rate of the river.

52. A power plant, having a Carnot efficiency, produces electric power $\mathscr{P}$ from turbines that take in energy from steam at temperature T_h and discharge energy at temperature T_c through a heat exchanger into a flowing river. The water downstream is warmer by ΔT due to the output of the power plant. Determine the flow rate of the river.

53. A biology laboratory is maintained at a constant temperature of 7.00°C by an air conditioner, which is vented to the air outside. On a typical hot summer day, the outside temperature is 27.0°C and the air-conditioning unit emits energy to the outside at a rate of 10.0 kW. Model the unit as having a coefficient of performance equal to 40.0% of the coefficient of performance of an ideal Carnot device. (a) At what rate does the air conditioner remove energy from the laboratory? (b) Calculate the power required for the work input. (c) Find the change in entropy produced by the air conditioner in 1.00 h. (d) **What If?** The outside temperature increases to 32.0°C. Find the fractional change in the coefficient of performance of the air conditioner.

54. ● A 1.00-mol sample of an ideal monatomic gas is taken through the cycle shown in Figure P22.54. The process $A \rightarrow B$ is a reversible isothermal expansion. Calculate (a) the net work done by the gas, (b) the energy added to the gas by heat, (c) the energy exhausted from the gas by heat, and (d) the efficiency of the cycle. (e) Explain how the efficiency compares with that of a Carnot engine operating between the same temperature extremes.

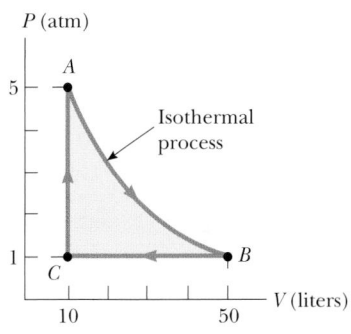

Figure P22.54

55. ● A 1.00-mol sample of a monatomic ideal gas is taken through the cycle shown in Figure P22.55. At point A, the pressure, volume, and temperature are P_i, V_i, and T_i, respectively. In terms of R and T_i, find (a) the total energy entering the system by heat per cycle, (b) the total energy leaving the system by heat per cycle, and (c) the efficiency of an engine operating in this cycle. (d) Explain how the efficiency compares with that of an engine operating in a Carnot cycle between the same temperature extremes.

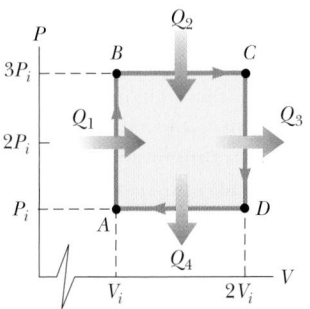

Figure P22.55

2 = intermediate; 3 = challenging; □ = SSM/SG; ▲ = ThomsonNOW; ▊ = symbolic reasoning; ● = qualitative reasoning

56. A sample consisting of n mol of an ideal gas undergoes a reversible isobaric expansion from volume V_i to volume $3V_i$. Find the change in entropy of the gas by calculating $\int_i^f dQ/T$, where $dQ = nC_P\, dT$.

57. ● A system consisting of n mol of an ideal gas undergoes two reversible processes. It starts with pressure P_i and volume V_i, expands isothermally, and then contracts adiabatically to reach a final state with pressure P_i and volume $3V_i$. (a) Find its change in entropy in the isothermal process. (The entropy does not change in the adiabatic process.) (b) **What If?** Explain why the answer to part (a) must be the same as the answer to Problem 56.

58. ● A 1.00-mol sample of an ideal gas expands isothermally, doubling in volume. (a) Show that the work it does in expanding is $W_{eng} = RT \ln 2$. (b) Because the internal energy E_{int} of an ideal gas depends solely on its temperature, the change in internal energy is zero during the expansion. It follows from the first law that the energy input to the gas by heat during the expansion is equal to the energy output by work. Does this process have 100% efficiency in converting energy input by heat into work output? Does this conversion violate the second law? Explain your answers.

59. An idealized diesel engine operates in a cycle known as the *air-standard diesel cycle* shown in Figure P22.59. Fuel is

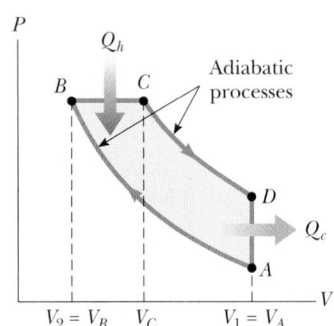

Figure P22.59

sprayed into the cylinder at the point of maximum compression, B. Combustion occurs during the expansion $B \rightarrow C$, which is modeled as an isobaric process. Show that the efficiency of an engine operating in this idealized diesel cycle is

$$e = 1 - \frac{1}{\gamma}\left(\frac{T_D - T_A}{T_C - T_B}\right)$$

60. ● Suppose you are working in a patent office and an inventor comes to you with the claim that her heat engine, which employs water as a working substance, has a thermodynamic efficiency of 0.61. She explains that it operates between energy reservoirs at 4°C and 0°C. It is a very complicated device, with many pistons, gears, and pulleys, and the cycle involves freezing and melting. Does her claim that $e = 0.61$ warrant serious consideration? Explain your answer.

61. ● Suppose 1.00 kg of water at 10.0°C is mixed with 1.00 kg of water at 30.0°C at constant pressure. When the mixture has reached equilibrium, (a) what is the final temperature? (b) Take $c_P = 4.19$ kJ/kg · K for water and show that the entropy of the system increases by

$$\Delta S = 4.19 \ln\left[\left(\frac{293}{283}\right)\left(\frac{293}{303}\right)\right] \text{ kJ/K}$$

You may use the result of Problem 31. (c) Verify numerically that $\Delta S > 0$. (d) Is the mixing an irreversible process? Explain how you know.

62. A 1.00-mol sample of an ideal gas ($\gamma = 1.40$) is carried through the Carnot cycle described in Active Figure 22.10. At point A, the pressure is 25.0 atm and the temperature is 600 K. At point C, the pressure is 1.00 atm and the temperature is 400 K. (a) Determine the pressures and volumes at points A, B, C, and D. (b) Calculate the net work done per cycle. (c) Determine the efficiency of an engine operating in this cycle.

Answers to Quick Quizzes

22.1 (i), (c). Equation 22.2 gives this result directly. (ii), (b). The work represents one third of the input energy. The remaining two thirds must be expelled to the cold reservoir.

22.2 (d). The COP of 4.00 for the heat pump means that you are receiving four times as much energy as that entering by electrical transmission. With four times as much energy per unit of energy from electricity, you need only one-fourth as much electricity.

22.3 C, B, A. Although all three engines operate over a 300-K temperature difference, the efficiency depends on the ratio of temperatures, not the difference.

22.4 (a) One microstate: all four deuces. (b) Six microstates: club–diamond, club–heart, club–spade, diamond–heart, diamond–spade, heart–spade. The macrostate of two aces is more probable than that of four deuces in part (a) because there are six times as many microstates for this particular macrostate compared with the macrostate

of four deuces. Therefore, in a hand of poker, two of a kind is less valuable than four of a kind.

22.5 (a). From the first law of thermodynamics, for these two reversible processes, $Q_r = \Delta E_{int} - W$. During the constant-volume process, $W = 0$, while the work W is nonzero and negative during the constant-pressure expansion. Therefore, Q_r is larger for the constant-pressure process, leading to a larger value for the change in entropy. In terms of entropy as disorder, during the constant-pressure process the gas must expand. The increase in volume results in more ways of locating the molecules of the gas in a container, resulting in a larger increase in entropy.

22.6 False. The determining factor for the entropy change is Q_r, not Q. If the adiabatic process is not reversible, the entropy change is not necessarily zero because a reversible path between the same initial and final states may involve energy transfer by heat.

TABLE A.1

Conversion Factors

Length

	m	cm	km	in.	ft	mi
1 meter	1	10^2	10^{-3}	39.37	3.281	6.214×10^{-4}
1 centimeter	10^{-2}	1	10^{-5}	0.393 7	3.281×10^{-2}	6.214×10^{-6}
1 kilometer	10^3	10^5	1	3.937×10^4	3.281×10^3	0.621 4
1 inch	2.540×10^{-2}	2.540	2.540×10^{-5}	1	8.333×10^{-2}	1.578×10^{-5}
1 foot	0.304 8	30.48	3.048×10^{-4}	12	1	1.894×10^{-4}
1 mile	1 609	1.609×10^5	1.609	6.336×10^4	5 280	1

Mass

	kg	g	slug	u
1 kilogram	1	10^3	6.852×10^{-2}	6.024×10^{26}
1 gram	10^{-3}	1	6.852×10^{-5}	6.024×10^{23}
1 slug	14.59	1.459×10^4	1	8.789×10^{27}
1 atomic mass unit	1.660×10^{-27}	1.660×10^{-24}	1.137×10^{-28}	1

Note: 1 metric ton = 1 000 kg.

Time

	s	min	h	day	yr
1 second	1	1.667×10^{-2}	2.778×10^{-4}	1.157×10^{-5}	3.169×10^{-8}
1 minute	60	1	1.667×10^{-2}	6.994×10^{-4}	1.901×10^{-6}
1 hour	3 600	60	1	4.167×10^{-2}	1.141×10^{-4}
1 day	8.640×10^4	1 440	24	1	2.738×10^{-5}
1 year	3.156×10^7	5.259×10^5	8.766×10^3	365.2	1

Speed

	m/s	cm/s	ft/s	mi/h
1 meter per second	1	10^2	3.281	2.237
1 centimeter per second	10^{-2}	1	3.281×10^{-2}	2.237×10^{-2}
1 foot per second	0.304 8	30.48	1	0.681 8
1 mile per hour	0.447 0	44.70	1.467	1

Note: 1 mi/min = 60 mi/h = 88 ft/s.

Force

	N	lb
1 newton	1	0.224 8
1 pound	4.448	1

(Continued)

TABLE A.1

Conversion Factors (*Continued*)

Energy, Energy Transfer

	J	ft · lb	eV
1 joule	1	0.737 6	6.242×10^{18}
1 foot-pound	1.356	1	8.464×10^{18}
1 electron volt	1.602×10^{-19}	1.182×10^{-19}	1
1 calorie	4.186	3.087	2.613×10^{19}
1 British thermal unit	1.055×10^3	7.779×10^2	6.585×10^{21}
1 kilowatt-hour	3.600×10^6	2.655×10^6	2.247×10^{25}

	cal	Btu	kWh
1 joule	0.238 9	9.481×10^{-4}	2.778×10^{-7}
1 foot-pound	0.323 9	1.285×10^{-3}	3.766×10^{-7}
1 electron volt	3.827×10^{-20}	1.519×10^{-22}	4.450×10^{-26}
1 calorie	1	3.968×10^{-3}	1.163×10^{-6}
1 British thermal unit	2.520×10^2	1	2.930×10^{-4}
1 kilowatt-hour	8.601×10^5	3.413×10^2	1

Pressure

	Pa	atm
1 pascal	1	9.869×10^{-6}
1 atmosphere	1.013×10^5	1
1 centimeter mercury[a]	1.333×10^3	1.316×10^{-2}
1 pound per square inch	6.895×10^3	6.805×10^{-2}
1 pound per square foot	47.88	4.725×10^{-4}

	cm Hg	lb/in.^{2}	lb/ft^2
1 pascal	7.501×10^{-4}	1.450×10^{-4}	2.089×10^{-2}
1 atmosphere	76	14.70	2.116×10^3
1 centimeter mercury[a]	1	0.194 3	27.85
1 pound per square inch	5.171	1	144
1 pound per square foot	3.591×10^{-2}	6.944×10^{-3}	1

[a]At 0°C and at a location where the free-fall acceleration has its "standard" value, 9.806 65 m/s^2.

TABLE A.2

Symbols, Dimensions, and Units of Physical Quantities

Quantity	Common Symbol	Unit[a]	Dimensions[b]	Unit in Terms of Base SI Units
Acceleration	$\vec{a}$	m/s^2	L/T^2	m/s^2
Amount of substance	n	MOLE		mol
Angle	θ, ϕ	radian (rad)	1	
Angular acceleration	$\vec{\alpha}$	rad/s^2	T^{-2}	s^{-2}
Angular frequency	ω	rad/s	T^{-1}	s^{-1}
Angular momentum	$\vec{L}$	kg · m^2/s	ML^2/T	kg · m^2/s
Angular velocity	$\vec{\omega}$	rad/s	T^{-1}	s^{-1}
Area	A	m^2	L^2	m^2
Atomic number	Z			
Capacitance	C	farad (F)	Q^{2}T^2/ML^2	A^2 · s^4/kg · m^2
Charge	q, Q, e	coulomb (C)	Q	A · s

(*Continued*)

TABLE A.2

Symbols, Dimensions, and Units of Physical Quantities *(Continued)*

Charge density				
Line	λ	C/m	Q/L	A·s/m
Surface	σ	C/m^2	Q/L^2	A·s/m^2
Volume	ρ	C/m^3	Q/L^3	A·s/m^3
Conductivity	σ	1/Ω·m	Q^{2}T/ML^3	A^2·s^3/kg·m^3
Current	I	AMPERE	Q/T	A
Current density	J	A/m^2	Q/TL^2	A/m^2
Density	ρ	kg/m^3	M/L^3	kg/m^3
Dielectric constant	κ			
Electric dipole moment	$\vec{\mathbf{p}}$	C·m	QL	A·s·m
Electric field	$\vec{\mathbf{E}}$	V/m	ML/QT^2	kg·m/A·s^3
Electric flux	Φ_E	V·m	ML^3/QT^2	kg·m^3/A·s^3
Electromotive force	$\boldsymbol{\varepsilon}$	volt (V)	ML^2/QT^2	kg·m^2/A·s^3
Energy	E, U, K	joule (J)	ML^2/T^2	kg·m^2/s^2
Entropy	S	J/K	ML^2/T^{2}K	kg·m^2/s^2·K
Force	$\vec{\mathbf{F}}$	newton (N)	ML/T^2	kg·m/s^2
Frequency	f	hertz (Hz)	T^{-1}	s^{-1}
Heat	Q	joule (J)	ML^2/T^2	kg·m^2/s^2
Inductance	L	henry (H)	ML^2/Q^2	kg·m^2/A^2·s^2
Length	ℓ, L	METER	L	m
Displacement	$\Delta x, \Delta\vec{\mathbf{r}}$			
Distance	d, h			
Position	$x, y, z, \vec{\mathbf{r}}$			
Magnetic dipole moment	$\vec{\boldsymbol{\mu}}$	N·m/T	QL^2/T	A·m^2
Magnetic field	$\vec{\mathbf{B}}$	tesla (T) (= Wb/m^2)	M/QT	kg/A·s^2
Magnetic flux	Φ_B	weber (Wb)	ML^2/QT	kg·m^2/A·s^2
Mass	m, M	KILOGRAM	M	kg
Molar specific heat	C	J/mol·K		kg·m^2/s^2·mol·K
Moment of inertia	I	kg·m^2	ML^2	kg·m^2
Momentum	$\vec{\mathbf{p}}$	kg·m/s	ML/T	kg·m/s
Period	T	s	T	s
Permeability of free space	μ_0	N/A^2 (= H/m)	ML/Q^2	kg·m/A^2·s^2
Permittivity of free space	ϵ_0	C^2/N·m^2 (= F/m)	Q^{2}T^2/ML^3	A^2·s^4/kg·m^3
Potential	V	volt (V) (= J/C)	ML^2/QT^2	kg·m^2/A·s^3
Power	$\mathscr{P}$	watt (W) (= J/s)	ML^2/T^3	kg·m^2/s^3
Pressure	P	pascal (Pa) (= N/m^2)	M/LT^2	kg/m·s^2
Resistance	R	ohm (Ω) (= V/A)	ML^2/Q^{2}T	kg·m^2/A^2·s^3
Specific heat	c	J/kg·K	L^2/T^{2}K	m^2/s^2·K
Speed	v	m/s	L/T	m/s
Temperature	T	KELVIN	K	K
Time	t	SECOND	T	s
Torque	$\vec{\boldsymbol{\tau}}$	N·m	ML^2/T^2	kg·m^2/s^2
Velocity	$\vec{\mathbf{v}}$	m/s	L/T	m/s
Volume	V	m^3	L^3	m^3
Wavelength	λ	m	L	m
Work	W	joule (J) (= N·m)	ML^2/T^2	kg·m^2/s^2

[a]The base SI units are given in uppercase letters.

[b]The symbols M, L, T, K, and Q denote mass, length, time, temperature, and charge, respectively.

This appendix in mathematics is intended as a brief review of operations and methods. Early in this course, you should be totally familiar with basic algebraic techniques, analytic geometry, and trigonometry. The sections on differential and integral calculus are more detailed and are intended for students who have difficulty applying calculus concepts to physical situations.

B.1   Scientific Notation

Many quantities used by scientists often have very large or very small values. The speed of light, for example, is about 300 000 000 m/s, and the ink required to make the dot over an *i* in this textbook has a mass of about 0.000 000 001 kg. Obviously, it is very cumbersome to read, write, and keep track of such numbers. We avoid this problem by using a method incorporating powers of the number 10:

$$10^0 = 1$$

$$10^1 = 10$$

$$10^2 = 10 \times 10 = 100$$

$$10^3 = 10 \times 10 \times 10 = 1\ 000$$

$$10^4 = 10 \times 10 \times 10 \times 10 = 10\ 000$$

$$10^5 = 10 \times 10 \times 10 \times 10 \times 10 = 100\ 000$$

and so on. The number of zeros corresponds to the power to which ten is raised, called the **exponent** of ten. For example, the speed of light, 300 000 000 m/s, can be expressed as 3.00×10^8 m/s.

In this method, some representative numbers smaller than unity are the following:

$$10^{-1} = \frac{1}{10} = 0.1$$

$$10^{-2} = \frac{1}{10 \times 10} = 0.01$$

$$10^{-3} = \frac{1}{10 \times 10 \times 10} = 0.001$$

$$10^{-4} = \frac{1}{10 \times 10 \times 10 \times 10} = 0.000\ 1$$

$$10^{-5} = \frac{1}{10 \times 10 \times 10 \times 10 \times 10} = 0.000\ 01$$

In these cases, the number of places the decimal point is to the left of the digit 1 equals the value of the (negative) exponent. Numbers expressed as some power of ten multiplied by another number between one and ten are said to be in **scientific notation.** For example, the scientific notation for 5 943 000 000 is 5.943×10^9 and that for 0.000 083 2 is 8.32×10^{-5}.

When numbers expressed in scientific notation are being multiplied, the following general rule is very useful:

$$10^n \times 10^m = 10^{n+m} \tag{B.1}$$

where *n* and *m* can be *any* numbers (not necessarily integers). For example, $10^2 \times 10^5 = 10^7$. The rule also applies if one of the exponents is negative: $10^3 \times 10^{-8} = 10^{-5}$.

When dividing numbers expressed in scientific notation, note that

$$\frac{10^n}{10^m} = 10^n \times 10^{-m} = 10^{n-m} \qquad \textbf{(B.2)}$$

Exercises

With help from the preceding rules, verify the answers to the following equations:

1. $86\,400 = 8.64 \times 10^4$
2. $9\,816\,762.5 = 9.816\,762\,5 \times 10^6$
3. $0.000\,000\,039\,8 = 3.98 \times 10^{-8}$
4. $(4.0 \times 10^8)(9.0 \times 10^9) = 3.6 \times 10^{18}$
5. $(3.0 \times 10^7)(6.0 \times 10^{-12}) = 1.8 \times 10^{-4}$
6. $\dfrac{75 \times 10^{-11}}{5.0 \times 10^{-3}} = 1.5 \times 10^{-7}$
7. $\dfrac{(3 \times 10^6)(8 \times 10^{-2})}{(2 \times 10^{17})(6 \times 10^5)} = 2 \times 10^{-18}$

B.2   Algebra

Some Basic Rules

When algebraic operations are performed, the laws of arithmetic apply. Symbols such as x, y, and z are usually used to represent unspecified quantities, called the **unknowns.**

First, consider the equation

$$8x = 32$$

If we wish to solve for x, we can divide (or multiply) each side of the equation by the same factor without destroying the equality. In this case, if we divide both sides by 8, we have

$$\frac{8x}{8} = \frac{32}{8}$$

$$x = 4$$

Next consider the equation

$$x + 2 = 8$$

In this type of expression, we can add or subtract the same quantity from each side. If we subtract 2 from each side, we have

$$x + 2 - 2 = 8 - 2$$

$$x = 6$$

In general, if $x + a = b$, then $x = b - a$.

Now consider the equation

$$\frac{x}{5} = 9$$

If we multiply each side by 5, we are left with x on the left by itself and 45 on the right:

$$\left(\frac{x}{5}\right)(5) = 9 \times 5$$

$$x = 45$$

In all cases, *whatever operation is performed on the left side of the equality must also be performed on the right side.*

The following rules for multiplying, dividing, adding, and subtracting fractions should be recalled, where a, b, c, and d are four numbers:

	Rule	Example
Multiplying	$\left(\dfrac{a}{b}\right)\left(\dfrac{c}{d}\right) = \dfrac{ac}{bd}$	$\left(\dfrac{2}{3}\right)\left(\dfrac{4}{5}\right) = \dfrac{8}{15}$
Dividing	$\dfrac{(a/b)}{(c/d)} = \dfrac{ad}{bc}$	$\dfrac{2/3}{4/5} = \dfrac{(2)(5)}{(4)(3)} = \dfrac{10}{12}$
Adding	$\dfrac{a}{b} \pm \dfrac{c}{d} = \dfrac{ad \pm bc}{bd}$	$\dfrac{2}{3} - \dfrac{4}{5} = \dfrac{(2)(5) - (4)(3)}{(3)(5)} = -\dfrac{2}{15}$

Exercises

In the following exercises, solve for x.

Answers

1. $a = \dfrac{1}{1 + x}$ $\qquad x = \dfrac{1 - a}{a}$

2. $3x - 5 = 13$ $\qquad x = 6$

3. $ax - 5 = bx + 2$ $\qquad x = \dfrac{7}{a - b}$

4. $\dfrac{5}{2x + 6} = \dfrac{3}{4x + 8}$ $\qquad x = -\dfrac{11}{7}$

Powers

When powers of a given quantity x are multiplied, the following rule applies:

$$x^n x^m = x^{n+m} \tag{B.3}$$

For example, $x^2 x^4 = x^{2+4} = x^6$.

When dividing the powers of a given quantity, the rule is

$$\frac{x^n}{x^m} = x^{n-m} \tag{B.4}$$

For example, $x^8/x^2 = x^{8-2} = x^6$.

A power that is a fraction, such as $\frac{1}{3}$, corresponds to a root as follows:

$$x^{1/n} = \sqrt[n]{x} \tag{B.5}$$

For example, $4^{1/3} = \sqrt[3]{4} = 1.587\,4$. (A scientific calculator is useful for such calculations.)

Finally, any quantity x^n raised to the mth power is

$$\left(x^n\right)^m = x^{nm} \tag{B.6}$$

Table B.1 summarizes the rules of exponents.

TABLE B.1

Rules of Exponents

$$x^0 = 1$$
$$x^1 = x$$
$$x^n x^m = x^{n+m}$$
$$x^n/x^m = x^{n-m}$$
$$x^{1/n} = \sqrt[n]{x}$$
$$\left(x^n\right)^m = x^{nm}$$

Exercises

Verify the following equations:

1. $3^2 \times 3^3 = 243$

2. $x^5 x^{-8} = x^{-3}$

3. $x^{10}/x^{-5} = x^{15}$

4. $5^{1/3} = 1.709\,976$ (Use your calculator.)

5. $60^{1/4} = 2.783\,158$ (Use your calculator.)

6. $\left(x^4\right)^3 = x^{12}$

Factoring

Some useful formulas for factoring an equation are the following:

$$ax + ay + az = a(x + y + z) \quad \text{common factor}$$

$$a^2 + 2ab + b^2 = (a + b)^2 \quad \text{perfect square}$$

$$a^2 - b^2 = (a + b)(a - b) \quad \text{differences of squares}$$

Quadratic Equations

The general form of a quadratic equation is

$$ax^2 + bx + c = 0 \tag{B.7}$$

where x is the unknown quantity and a, b, and c are numerical factors referred to as **coefficients** of the equation. This equation has two roots, given by

$$x = \frac{-b \pm \sqrt{b^2 - 4ac}}{2a} \tag{B.8}$$

If $b^2 \geq 4ac$, the roots are real.

EXAMPLE **B.1**

The equation $x^2 + 5x + 4 = 0$ has the following roots corresponding to the two signs of the square-root term:

$$x = \frac{-5 \pm \sqrt{5^2 - (4)(1)(4)}}{2(1)} = \frac{-5 \pm \sqrt{9}}{2} = \frac{-5 \pm 3}{2}$$

$$x_+ = \frac{-5 + 3}{2} = \boxed{-1} \quad x_- = \frac{-5 - 3}{2} = \boxed{-4}$$

where x_+ refers to the root corresponding to the positive sign and x_- refers to the root corresponding to the negative sign.

Exercises

Solve the following quadratic equations:

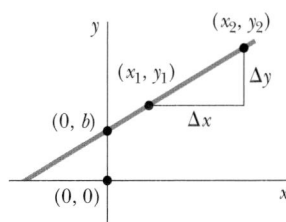

Figure B.1 A straight line graphed on an xy coordinate system. The slope of the line is the ratio of Δy to Δx.

	Answers	
1. $x^2 + 2x - 3 = 0$	$x_+ = 1$	$x_- = -3$
2. $2x^2 - 5x + 2 = 0$	$x_+ = 2$	$x_- = \frac{1}{2}$
3. $2x^2 - 4x - 9 = 0$	$x_+ = 1 + \sqrt{22}/2$	$x_- = 1 - \sqrt{22}/2$

Linear Equations

A linear equation has the general form

$$y = mx + b \tag{B.9}$$

where m and b are constants. This equation is referred to as linear because the graph of y versus x is a straight line as shown in Figure B.1. The constant b, called the **y-intercept,** represents the value of y at which the straight line intersects the y axis. The constant m is equal to the **slope** of the straight line. If any two points on the straight line are specified by the coordinates (x_1, y_1) and (x_2, y_2) as in Figure B.1, the slope of the straight line can be expressed as

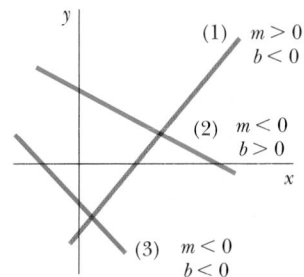

Figure B.2 The brown line has a positive slope and a negative y-intercept. The blue line has a negative slope and a positive y-intercept. The green line has a negative slope and a negative y-intercept.

$$\text{Slope} = \frac{y_2 - y_1}{x_2 - x_1} = \frac{\Delta y}{\Delta x} \tag{B.10}$$

Note that m and b can have either positive or negative values. If $m > 0$, the straight line has a *positive* slope as in Figure B.1. If $m < 0$, the straight line has a *negative* slope. In Figure B.1, both m and b are positive. Three other possible situations are shown in Figure B.2.

Exercises

1. Draw graphs of the following straight lines: (a) $y = 5x + 3$ (b) $y = -2x + 4$
   (c) $y = -3x - 6$

2. Find the slopes of the straight lines described in Exercise 1.

   Answers   (a) 5   (b) -2 (c) -3

3. Find the slopes of the straight lines that pass through the following sets of points:
   (a) $(0, -4)$ and $(4, 2)$ (b) $(0, 0)$ and $(2, -5)$ (c) $(-5, 2)$ and $(4, -2)$

   Answers   (a) $\frac{3}{2}$ (b) $-\frac{5}{2}$ (c) $-\frac{4}{9}$

Solving Simultaneous Linear Equations

Consider the equation $3x + 5y = 15$, which has two unknowns, x and y. Such an equation does not have a unique solution. For example, $(x = 0, y = 3)$, $(x = 5, y = 0)$, and $(x = 2, y = \frac{9}{5})$ are all solutions to this equation.

If a problem has two unknowns, a unique solution is possible only if we have *two* equations. In general, if a problem has n unknowns, its solution requires n equations. To solve two simultaneous equations involving two unknowns, x and y, we solve one of the equations for x in terms of y and substitute this expression into the other equation.

EXAMPLE B.2

Solve the two simultaneous equations

$$(1) \quad 5x + y = -8$$

$$(2) \quad 2x - 2y = 4$$

Solution   From Equation (2), $x = y + 2$. Substitution of this equation into Equation (1) gives

$$5(y + 2) + y = -8$$

$$6y = -18$$

$$y = \boxed{-3}$$

$$x = y + 2 = \boxed{-1}$$

Alternative Solution   Multiply each term in Equation (1) by the factor 2 and add the result to Equation (2):

$$10x + 2y = -16$$

$$\underline{2x - 2y = 4}$$

$$12x \qquad = -12$$

$$x = \boxed{-1}$$

$$y = x - 2 = \boxed{-3}$$

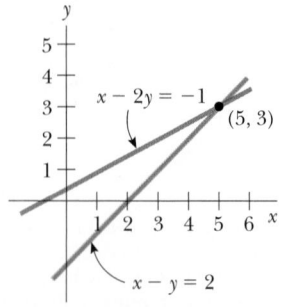

Figure B.3   A graphical solution for two linear equations.

Two linear equations containing two unknowns can also be solved by a graphical method. If the straight lines corresponding to the two equations are plotted in a conventional coordinate system, the intersection of the two lines represents the solution. For example, consider the two equations

$$x - y = 2$$

$$x - 2y = -1$$

These equations are plotted in Figure B.3. The intersection of the two lines has the coordinates $x = 5$ and $y = 3$, which represents the solution to the equations. You should check this solution by the analytical technique discussed earlier.

Exercises

Solve the following pairs of simultaneous equations involving two unknowns:

	Answers
1. $x + y = 8$	$x = 5, y = 3$
$\ x - y = 2$	
2. $98 - T = 10a$	$T = 65, a = 3.27$
$\ T - 49 = 5a$	
3. $6x + 2y = 6$	$x = 2, y = -3$
$\ 8x - 4y = 28$	

Logarithms

Suppose a quantity x is expressed as a power of some quantity a:

$$x = a^y \tag{B.11}$$

The number a is called the **base** number. The **logarithm** of x with respect to the base a is equal to the exponent to which the base must be raised to satisfy the expression $x = a^y$:

$$y = \log_a x \tag{B.12}$$

Conversely, the **antilogarithm** of y is the number x:

$$x = \operatorname{antilog}_a y \tag{B.13}$$

In practice, the two bases most often used are base 10, called the *common* logarithm base, and base $e = 2.718\ 282$, called Euler's constant or the *natural* logarithm base. When common logarithms are used,

$$y = \log_{10} x \quad (\text{or } x = 10^y) \tag{B.14}$$

When natural logarithms are used,

$$y = \ln x \quad (\text{or } x = e^y) \tag{B.15}$$

For example, $\log_{10} 52 = 1.716$, so antilog$_{10}$ $1.716 = 10^{1.716} = 52$. Likewise, $\ln 52 = 3.951$, so antiln $3.951 = e^{3.951} = 52$.

In general, note you can convert between base 10 and base e with the equality

$$\ln x = (2.302\ 585) \log_{10} x \tag{B.16}$$

Finally, some useful properties of logarithms are the following:

$$
\left.
\begin{aligned}
\log(ab) &= \log a + \log b \\
\log(a/b) &= \log a - \log b \\
\log(a^n) &= n \log a
\end{aligned}
\right\} \text{ any base}
$$

$$\ln e = 1$$

$$\ln e^a = a$$

$$\ln\left(\frac{1}{a}\right) = -\ln a$$

B.3   Geometry

The **distance** d between two points having coordinates (x_1, y_1) and (x_2, y_2) is

$$d = \sqrt{(x_2 - x_1)^2 + (y_2 - y_1)^2} \tag{B.17}$$

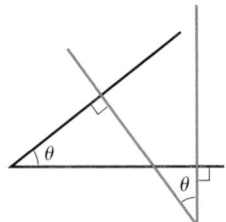

Figure B.4 The angles are equal because their sides are perpendicular.

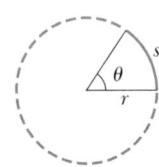

Figure B.5 The angle θ in radians is the ratio of the arc length s to the radius r of the circle.

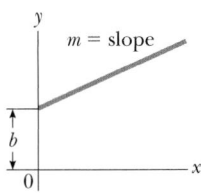

Figure B.6 A straight line with a slope of m and a y-intercept of b.

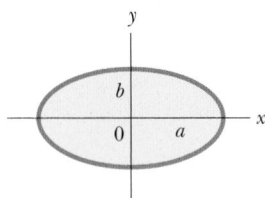

Figure B.7 An ellipse with semimajor axis a and semiminor axis b.

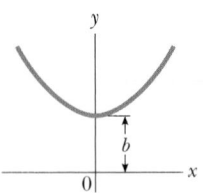

Figure B.8 A parabola with its vertex at $y = b$.

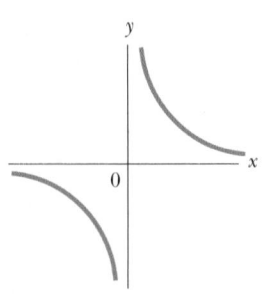

Figure B.9 A hyperbola.

TABLE B.2

Useful Information for Geometry

Shape	Area or Volume	Shape	Area or Volume
Rectangle	Area $= \ell w$	Sphere	Surface area $= 4\pi r^2$ Volume $= \dfrac{4\pi r^3}{3}$
Circle	Area $= \pi r^2$ Circumference $= 2\pi r$	Cylinder	Lateral surface area $= 2\pi r\ell$ Volume $= \pi r^2 \ell$
Triangle	Area $= \frac{1}{2}bh$	Rectangular box	Surface area $= 2(\ell h + \ell w + hw)$ Volume $= \ell wh$

Two angles are equal if their sides are perpendicular, right side to right side and left side to left side. For example, the two angles marked θ in Figure B.4 are the same because of the perpendicularity of the sides of the angles. To distinguish the left and right sides of an angle, imagine standing at the angle's apex and facing into the angle.

Radian measure: The arc length s of a circular arc (Fig. B.5) is proportional to the radius r for a fixed value of θ (in radians):

$$s = r\theta$$

$$\theta = \frac{s}{r}$$

(B.18)

Table B.2 gives the **areas** and **volumes** for several geometric shapes used throughout this text.

The equation of a **straight line** (Fig. B.6) is

$$y = mx + b$$

(B.19)

where b is the y-intercept and m is the slope of the line.

The equation of a **circle** of radius R centered at the origin is

$$x^2 + y^2 = R^2$$

(B.20)

The equation of an **ellipse** having the origin at its center (Fig. B.7) is

$$\frac{x^2}{a^2} + \frac{y^2}{b^2} = 1$$

(B.21)

where a is the length of the semimajor axis (the longer one) and b is the length of the semiminor axis (the shorter one).

The equation of a **parabola** the vertex of which is at $y = b$ (Fig. B.8) is

$$y = ax^2 + b$$

(B.22)

The equation of a **rectangular hyperbola** (Fig. B.9) is

$$xy = \text{constant}$$

(B.23)

B.4 Trigonometry

That portion of mathematics based on the special properties of the right triangle is called trigonometry. By definition, a right triangle is a triangle containing a 90° angle. Consider the right triangle shown in Figure B.10, where side a is opposite the angle θ, side b is adjacent to the angle θ, and side c is the hypotenuse of the triangle. The three basic trigonometric functions defined by such a triangle are the sine (sin), cosine (cos), and tangent (tan). In terms of the angle θ, these functions are defined as follows:

$$\sin \theta = \frac{\text{side opposite } \theta}{\text{hypotenuse}} = \frac{a}{c} \qquad \textbf{(B.24)}$$

$$\cos \theta = \frac{\text{side adjacent to } \theta}{\text{hypotenuse}} = \frac{b}{c} \qquad \textbf{(B.25)}$$

$$\tan \theta = \frac{\text{side opposite } \theta}{\text{side adjacent to } \theta} = \frac{a}{b} \qquad \textbf{(B.26)}$$

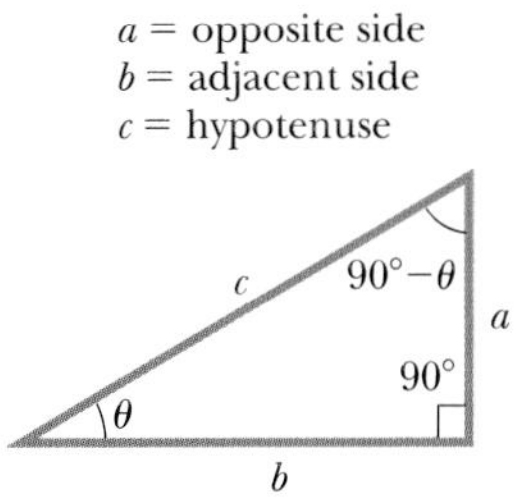

a = opposite side
b = adjacent side
c = hypotenuse

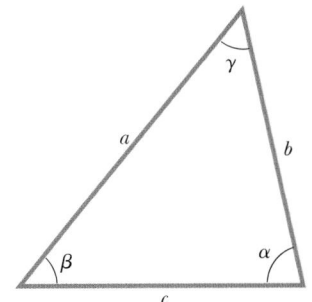

Figure B.10   A right triangle, used to define the basic functions of trigonometry.

The Pythagorean theorem provides the following relationship among the sides of a right triangle:

$$c^2 = a^2 + b^2 \qquad \textbf{(B.27)}$$

From the preceding definitions and the Pythagorean theorem, it follows that

$$\sin^2 \theta + \cos^2 \theta = 1$$

$$\tan \theta = \frac{\sin \theta}{\cos \theta}$$

The cosecant, secant, and cotangent functions are defined by

$$\csc \theta = \frac{1}{\sin \theta} \qquad \sec \theta = \frac{1}{\cos \theta} \qquad \cot \theta = \frac{1}{\tan \theta}$$

The following relationships are derived directly from the right triangle shown in Figure B.10:

$$\sin \theta = \cos (90° - \theta)$$

$$\cos \theta = \sin (90° - \theta)$$

$$\cot \theta = \tan (90° - \theta)$$

Some properties of trigonometric functions are the following:

$$\sin (-\theta) = -\sin \theta$$

$$\cos (-\theta) = \cos \theta$$

$$\tan (-\theta) = -\tan \theta$$

The following relationships apply to *any* triangle as shown in Figure B.11:

$$\alpha + \beta + \gamma = 180°$$

Law of cosines $\begin{cases} a^2 = b^2 + c^2 - 2bc \cos \alpha \\ b^2 = a^2 + c^2 - 2ac \cos \beta \\ c^2 = a^2 + b^2 - 2ab \cos \gamma \end{cases}$

Law of sines $\qquad \dfrac{a}{\sin \alpha} = \dfrac{b}{\sin \beta} = \dfrac{c}{\sin \gamma}$

Table B.3 (page A-12) lists a number of useful trigonometric identities.

Figure B.11   An arbitrary, nonright triangle.

EXAMPLE B.3

Consider the right triangle in Figure B.12 in which $a = 2.00$, $b = 5.00$, and c is unknown. From the Pythagorean theorem, we have

$$c^2 = a^2 + b^2 = 2.00^2 + 5.00^2 = 4.00 + 25.0 = 29.0$$

$$c = \sqrt{29.0} = \boxed{5.39}$$

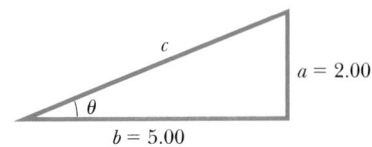

Figure B.12   (Example B.3)

To find the angle θ, note that

$$\tan \theta = \frac{a}{b} = \frac{2.00}{5.00} = 0.400$$

Using a calculator, we find that

$$\theta = \tan^{-1}(0.400) = \boxed{21.8°}$$

where $\tan^{-1}(0.400)$ is the notation for "angle whose tangent is 0.400," sometimes written as arctan (0.400).

TABLE B.3

Some Trigonometric Identities

$\sin^2 \theta + \cos^2 \theta = 1$	$\csc^2 \theta = 1 + \cot^2 \theta$
$\sec^2 \theta = 1 + \tan^2 \theta$	$\sin^2 \dfrac{\theta}{2} = \tfrac{1}{2}(1 - \cos \theta)$
$\sin 2\theta = 2 \sin \theta \cos \theta$	$\cos^2 \dfrac{\theta}{2} = \tfrac{1}{2}(1 + \cos \theta)$
$\cos 2\theta = \cos^2 \theta - \sin^2 \theta$	$1 - \cos \theta = 2 \sin^2 \dfrac{\theta}{2}$
$\tan 2\theta = \dfrac{2 \tan \theta}{1 - \tan^2 \theta}$	$\tan \dfrac{\theta}{2} = \sqrt{\dfrac{1 - \cos \theta}{1 + \cos \theta}}$

$\sin (A \pm B) = \sin A \cos B \pm \cos A \sin B$

$\cos (A \pm B) = \cos A \cos B \mp \sin A \sin B$

$\sin A \pm \sin B = 2 \sin \left[\tfrac{1}{2}(A \pm B)\right] \cos \left[\tfrac{1}{2}(A \mp B)\right]$

$\cos A + \cos B = 2 \cos \left[\tfrac{1}{2}(A + B)\right] \cos \left[\tfrac{1}{2}(A - B)\right]$

$\cos A - \cos B = 2 \sin \left[\tfrac{1}{2}(A + B)\right] \sin \left[\tfrac{1}{2}(B - A)\right]$

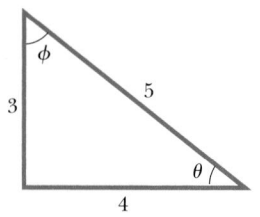

Figure B.13   (Exercise 1)

Exercises

1. In Figure B.13, identify (a) the side opposite θ (b) the side adjacent to ϕ and then find (c) $\cos \theta$, (d) $\sin \phi$, and (e) $\tan \phi$.

Answers   (a) 3   (b) 3   (c) $\tfrac{4}{5}$ (d) $\tfrac{4}{5}$ (e) $\tfrac{4}{3}$

2. In a certain right triangle, the two sides that are perpendicular to each other are 5.00 m and 7.00 m long. What is the length of the third side?

Answer   8.60 m

3. A right triangle has a hypotenuse of length 3.0 m, and one of its angles is 30°. (a) What is the length of the side opposite the 30° angle? (b) What is the side adjacent to the 30° angle?

Answers   (a) 1.5 m   (b) 2.6 m

B.5   Series Expansions

$$(a + b)^n = a^n + \frac{n}{1!} a^{n-1}b + \frac{n(n - 1)}{2!} a^{n-2}b^2 + \cdots$$

$$(1 + x)^n = 1 + nx + \frac{n(n - 1)}{2!} x^2 + \cdots$$

$$e^x = 1 + x + \frac{x^2}{2!} + \frac{x^3}{3!} + \cdots$$

$$\ln(1 \pm x) = \pm x - \tfrac{1}{2}x^2 \pm \tfrac{1}{3}x^3 - \cdots$$

$$\left.\begin{array}{l} \sin x = x - \dfrac{x^3}{3!} + \dfrac{x^5}{5!} - \cdots \\[2mm] \cos x = 1 - \dfrac{x^2}{2!} + \dfrac{x^4}{4!} - \cdots \\[2mm] \tan x = x + \dfrac{x^3}{3} + \dfrac{2x^5}{15} + \cdots \quad |x| < \dfrac{\pi}{2} \end{array}\right\} \quad x \text{ in radians}$$

For $x \ll 1$, the following approximations can be used:[1]

$$(1 + x)^n \approx 1 + nx \qquad \sin x \approx x$$

$$e^x \approx 1 + x \qquad\qquad \cos x \approx 1$$

$$\ln(1 \pm x) \approx \pm x \qquad \tan x \approx x$$

B.6   Differential Calculus

In various branches of science, it is sometimes necessary to use the basic tools of calculus, invented by Newton, to describe physical phenomena. The use of calculus is fundamental in the treatment of various problems in Newtonian mechanics, electricity, and magnetism. In this section, we simply state some basic properties and "rules of thumb" that should be a useful review to the student.

First, a **function** must be specified that relates one variable to another (e.g., a coordinate as a function of time). Suppose one of the variables is called y (the dependent variable), and the other x (the independent variable). We might have a function relationship such as

$$y(x) = ax^3 + bx^2 + cx + d$$

If a, b, c, and d are specified constants, y can be calculated for any value of x. We usually deal with continuous functions, that is, those for which y varies "smoothly" with x.

The **derivative** of y with respect to x is defined as the limit as Δx approaches zero of the slopes of chords drawn between two points on the y versus x curve. Mathematically, we write this definition as

$$\frac{dy}{dx} = \lim_{\Delta x \to 0} \frac{\Delta y}{\Delta x} = \lim_{\Delta x \to 0} \frac{y(x + \Delta x) - y(x)}{\Delta x} \tag{B.28}$$

where Δy and Δx are defined as $\Delta x = x_2 - x_1$ and $\Delta y = y_2 - y_1$ (Fig. B.14). Note that dy/dx *does not* mean dy divided by dx, but rather is simply a notation of the limiting process of the derivative as defined by Equation B.28.

A useful expression to remember when $y(x) = ax^n$, where a is a *constant* and n is *any* positive or negative number (integer or fraction), is

$$\frac{dy}{dx} = nax^{n-1} \tag{B.29}$$

If $y(x)$ is a polynomial or algebraic function of x, we apply Equation B.29 to *each* term in the polynomial and take $d[\text{constant}]/dx = 0$. In Examples B.4 through B.7, we evaluate the derivatives of several functions.

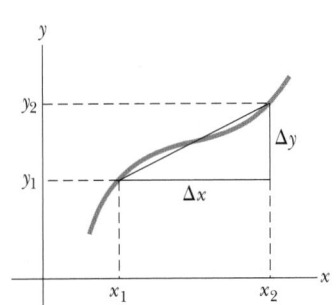

Figure B.14 The lengths Δx and Δy are used to define the derivative of this function at a point.

---

[1] The approximations for the functions $\sin x$, $\cos x$, and $\tan x$ are for $x \le 0.1$ rad.

TABLE B.4

Derivative for Several Functions

$$\frac{d}{dx}(a) = 0$$

$$\frac{d}{dx}(ax^n) = nax^{n-1}$$

$$\frac{d}{dx}(e^{ax}) = ae^{ax}$$

$$\frac{d}{dx}(\sin ax) = a\cos ax$$

$$\frac{d}{dx}(\cos ax) = -a\sin ax$$

$$\frac{d}{dx}(\tan ax) = a\sec^2 ax$$

$$\frac{d}{dx}(\cot ax) = -a\csc^2 ax$$

$$\frac{d}{dx}(\sec x) = \tan x\sec x$$

$$\frac{d}{dx}(\csc x) = -\cot x\csc x$$

$$\frac{d}{dx}(\ln ax) = \frac{1}{x}$$

$$\frac{d}{dx}(\sin^{-1} ax) = \frac{a}{\sqrt{1 - a^2x^2}}$$

$$\frac{d}{dx}(\cos^{-1} ax) = \frac{-a}{\sqrt{1 - a^2x^2}}$$

$$\frac{d}{dx}(\tan^{-1} ax) = \frac{a}{1 + a^2x^2}$$

Note: The symbols a and n represent constants.

Special Properties of the Derivative

A. Derivative of the product of two functions If a function $f(x)$ is given by the product of two functions—say, $g(x)$ and $h(x)$—the derivative of $f(x)$ is defined as

$$\frac{d}{dx}f(x) = \frac{d}{dx}[g(x)h(x)] = g\frac{dh}{dx} + h\frac{dg}{dx} \tag{B.30}$$

B. Derivative of the sum of two functions If a function $f(x)$ is equal to the sum of two functions, the derivative of the sum is equal to the sum of the derivatives:

$$\frac{d}{dx}f(x) = \frac{d}{dx}[g(x) + h(x)] = \frac{dg}{dx} + \frac{dh}{dx} \tag{B.31}$$

C. Chain rule of differential calculus If $y = f(x)$ and $x = g(z)$, then dy/dz can be written as the product of two derivatives:

$$\frac{dy}{dz} = \frac{dy}{dx}\frac{dx}{dz} \tag{B.32}$$

D. The second derivative The second derivative of y with respect to x is defined as the derivative of the function dy/dx (the derivative of the derivative). It is usually written as

$$\frac{d^2y}{dx^2} = \frac{d}{dx}\left(\frac{dy}{dx}\right) \tag{B.33}$$

Some of the more commonly used derivatives of functions are listed in Table B.4.

EXAMPLE B.4

Suppose $y(x)$ (that is, y as a function of x) is given by

$$y(x) = ax^3 + bx + c$$

where a and b are constants. It follows that

$$y(x + \Delta x) = a(x + \Delta x)^3 + b(x + \Delta x) + c$$

$$= a(x^3 + 3x^2\,\Delta x + 3x\,\Delta x^2 + \Delta x^3) + b(x + \Delta x) + c$$

so

$$\Delta y = y(x + \Delta x) - y(x) = a(3x^2\,\Delta x + 3x\,\Delta x^2 + \Delta x^3) + b\,\Delta x$$

Substituting this into Equation B.28 gives

$$\frac{dy}{dx} = \lim_{\Delta x \to 0}\frac{\Delta y}{\Delta x} = \lim_{\Delta x \to 0}[3ax^2 + 3ax\,\Delta x + a\,\Delta x^2] + b$$

$$\frac{dy}{dx} = 3ax^2 + b$$

EXAMPLE B.5

Find the derivative of

$$y(x) = 8x^5 + 4x^3 + 2x + 7$$

Solution Applying Equation B.29 to each term independently and remembering that d/dx (constant) $= 0$, we have

$$\frac{dy}{dx} = 8(5)x^4 + 4(3)x^2 + 2(1)x^0 + 0$$

$$\frac{dy}{dx} = \boxed{40x^4 + 12x^2 + 2}$$

EXAMPLE B.6

Find the derivative of $y(x) = x^3/(x+1)^2$ with respect to x.

Solution We can rewrite this function as $y(x) = x^3(x+1)^{-2}$ and apply Equation B.30:

$$\frac{dy}{dx} = (x+1)^{-2}\frac{d}{dx}(x^3) + x^3\frac{d}{dx}(x+1)^{-2}$$

$$= (x+1)^{-2}3x^2 + x^3(-2)(x+1)^{-3}$$

$$\frac{dy}{dx} = \boxed{\frac{3x^2}{(x+1)^2} - \frac{2x^3}{(x+1)^3}}$$

EXAMPLE B.7

A useful formula that follows from Equation B.30 is the derivative of the quotient of two functions. Show that

$$\frac{d}{dx}\left[\frac{g(x)}{h(x)}\right] = \frac{h\dfrac{dg}{dx} - g\dfrac{dh}{dx}}{h^2}$$

Solution We can write the quotient as gh^{-1} and then apply Equations B.29 and B.30:

$$\frac{d}{dx}\left(\frac{g}{h}\right) = \frac{d}{dx}(gh^{-1}) = g\frac{d}{dx}(h^{-1}) + h^{-1}\frac{d}{dx}(g)$$

$$= -gh^{-2}\frac{dh}{dx} + h^{-1}\frac{dg}{dx}$$

$$= \frac{h\dfrac{dg}{dx} - g\dfrac{dh}{dx}}{h^2}$$

B.7 Integral Calculus

We think of integration as the inverse of differentiation. As an example, consider the expression

$$f(x) = \frac{dy}{dx} = 3ax^2 + b \tag{B.34}$$

which was the result of differentiating the function

$$y(x) = ax^3 + bx + c$$

in Example B.4. We can write Equation B.34 as $dy = f(x)\, dx = (3ax^2 + b)\, dx$ and obtain $y(x)$ by "summing" over all values of x. Mathematically, we write this inverse operation as

$$y(x) = \int f(x)\, dx$$

For the function $f(x)$ given by Equation B.34, we have

$$y(x) = \int (3ax^2 + b)\, dx = ax^3 + bx + c$$

where c is a constant of the integration. This type of integral is called an *indefinite integral* because its value depends on the choice of c.

A general **indefinite integral** $I(x)$ is defined as

$$I(x) = \int f(x)\, dx \tag{B.35}$$

where $f(x)$ is called the *integrand* and $f(x) = dI(x)/dx$.

For a *general continuous* function $f(x)$, the integral can be described as the area under the curve bounded by $f(x)$ and the x axis, between two specified values of x, say, x_1 and x_2, as in Figure B.15.

The area of the blue element in Figure B.15 is approximately $f(x_i)\, \Delta x_i$. If we sum all these area elements between x_1 and x_2 and take the limit of this sum as $\Delta x_i \to 0$, we obtain the *true* area under the curve bounded by $f(x)$ and the x axis, between the limits x_1 and x_2:

$$\text{Area} = \lim_{\Delta x_i \to 0} \sum_i f(x_i)\Delta x_i = \int_{x_1}^{x_2} f(x)\, dx \tag{B.36}$$

Integrals of the type defined by Equation B.36 are called **definite integrals.**

Figure B.15 The definite integral of a function is the area under the curve of the function between the limits x_1 and x_2.

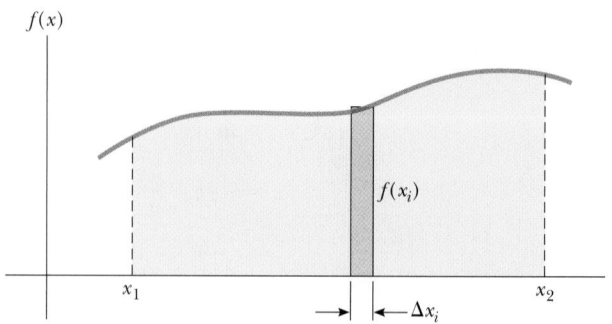

One common integral that arises in practical situations has the form

$$\int x^n \, dx = \frac{x^{n+1}}{n+1} + c \quad (n \neq -1) \tag{B.37}$$

This result is obvious, being that differentiation of the right-hand side with respect to x gives $f(x) = x^n$ directly. If the limits of the integration are known, this integral becomes a *definite integral* and is written

$$\int_{x_1}^{x_2} x^n \, dx = \frac{x^{n+1}}{n+1}\Big|_{x_1}^{x_2} = \frac{x_2^{n+1} - x_1^{n+1}}{n+1} \quad (n \neq -1) \tag{B.38}$$

EXAMPLES

1. $\displaystyle\int_0^a x^2 \, dx = \frac{x^3}{3}\Big]_0^a = \frac{a^3}{3}$

2. $\displaystyle\int_0^b x^{3/2} \, dx = \frac{x^{5/2}}{5/2}\Big]_0^b = \tfrac{2}{5}b^{5/2}$

3. $\displaystyle\int_3^5 x \, dx = \frac{x^2}{2}\Big]_3^5 = \frac{5^2 - 3^2}{2} = 8$

Partial Integration

Sometimes it is useful to apply the method of *partial integration* (also called "integrating by parts") to evaluate certain integrals. This method uses the property

$$\int u \, dv = uv - \int v \, du \tag{B.39}$$

where u and v are *carefully* chosen so as to reduce a complex integral to a simpler one. In many cases, several reductions have to be made. Consider the function

$$I(x) = \int x^2 e^x \, dx$$

which can be evaluated by integrating by parts twice. First, if we choose $u = x^2$, $v = e^x$, we obtain

$$\int x^2 e^x \, dx = \int x^2 \, d(e^x) = x^2 e^x - 2\int e^x x \, dx + c_1$$

Now, in the second term, choose $u = x$, $v = e^x$, which gives

$$\int x^2 e^x \, dx = x^2 e^x - 2x e^x + 2\int e^x \, dx + c_1$$

or

$$\int x^2 e^x \, dx = x^2 e^x - 2xe^x + 2e^x + c_2$$

TABLE B.5

Some Indefinite Integrals (An arbitrary constant should be added to each of these integrals.)

$$\int x^n \, dx = \frac{x^{n+1}}{n+1} \quad \text{(provided } n \neq 1\text{)}$$

$$\int \frac{dx}{x} = \int x^{-1} \, dx = \ln x$$

$$\int \frac{dx}{a+bx} = \frac{1}{b} \ln (a+bx)$$

$$\int \frac{x \, dx}{a+bx} = \frac{x}{b} - \frac{a}{b^2} \ln (a+bx)$$

$$\int \frac{dx}{x(x+a)} = -\frac{1}{a} \ln \frac{x+a}{x}$$

$$\int \frac{dx}{(a+bx)^2} = -\frac{1}{b(a+bx)}$$

$$\int \frac{dx}{a^2+x^2} = \frac{1}{a} \tan^{-1} \frac{x}{a}$$

$$\int \frac{dx}{a^2-x^2} = \frac{1}{2a} \ln \frac{a+x}{a-x} \quad (a^2-x^2>0)$$

$$\int \frac{dx}{x^2-a^2} = \frac{1}{2a} \ln \frac{x-a}{x+a} \quad (x^2-a^2>0)$$

$$\int \frac{x \, dx}{a^2 \pm x^2} = \pm \tfrac{1}{2} \ln (a^2 \pm x^2)$$

$$\int \frac{dx}{\sqrt{a^2-x^2}} = \sin^{-1} \frac{x}{a} = -\cos^{-1} \frac{x}{a} \quad (a^2-x^2>0)$$

$$\int \frac{dx}{\sqrt{x^2+a^2}} = \ln (x + \sqrt{x^2 \pm a^2})$$

$$\int \frac{x \, dx}{\sqrt{a^2-x^2}} = -\sqrt{a^2-x^2}$$

$$\int \frac{x \, dx}{\sqrt{x^2 \pm a^2}} = \sqrt{x^2 \pm a^2}$$

$$\int \sqrt{a^2-x^2} \, dx = \tfrac{1}{2} \left(x\sqrt{a^2-x^2} + a^2 \sin^{-1} \frac{x}{a} \right)$$

$$\int x\sqrt{a^2-x^2} \, dx = -\tfrac{1}{3}(a^2-x^2)^{3/2}$$

$$\int \sqrt{x^2 \pm a^2} \, dx = \tfrac{1}{2}\left[x\sqrt{x^2 \pm a^2} \pm a^2 \ln (x+\sqrt{x^2 \pm a^2}) \right]$$

$$\int x(\sqrt{x^2 \pm a^2}) \, dx = \tfrac{1}{3}(x^2 \pm a^2)^{3/2}$$

$$\int e^{ax} \, dx = \frac{1}{a} e^{ax}$$

$$\int \ln ax \, dx = (x \ln ax) - x$$

$$\int xe^{ax} \, dx = \frac{e^{ax}}{a^2} \, (ax-1)$$

$$\int \frac{dx}{a+be^{cx}} = \frac{x}{a} - \frac{1}{ac} \ln (a+be^{cx})$$

$$\int \sin ax \, dx = -\frac{1}{a} \cos ax$$

$$\int \cos ax \, dx = \frac{1}{a} \sin ax$$

$$\int \tan ax \, dx = -\frac{1}{a} \ln (\cos ax) = \frac{1}{a} \ln (\sec ax)$$

$$\int \cot ax \, dx = \frac{1}{a} \ln (\sin ax)$$

$$\int \sec ax \, dx = \frac{1}{a} \ln (\sec ax + \tan ax) = \frac{1}{a} \ln \left[\tan \left(\frac{ax}{2} + \frac{\pi}{4} \right) \right]$$

$$\int \csc ax \, dx = \frac{1}{a} \ln (\csc ax - \cot ax) = \frac{1}{a} \ln \left(\tan \frac{ax}{2} \right).$$

$$\int \sin^2 ax \, dx = \frac{x}{2} + \frac{\sin 2ax}{4a}$$

$$\int \cos^2 ax \, dx = \frac{x}{2} + \frac{\sin 2ax}{4a}$$

$$\int \frac{dx}{\sin^2 ax} = -\frac{1}{a} \cot ax$$

$$\int \frac{dx}{\cos^2 ax} = \frac{1}{a} \tan ax$$

$$\int \tan^2 ax \, dx = \frac{1}{a} (\tan ax) - x$$

$$\int \cot^2 ax \, dx = -\frac{1}{a} (\cot ax) - x$$

$$\int \sin^{-1} ax \, dx = x(\sin^{-1} ax) + \frac{\sqrt{1-a^2x^2}}{a}$$

$$\int \cos^{-1} ax \, dx = x(\cos^{-1} ax) - \frac{\sqrt{1-a^2x^2}}{a}$$

$$\int \frac{dx}{(x^2+a^2)^{3/2}} = \frac{x}{a^2\sqrt{x^2+a^2}}$$

$$\int \frac{x \, dx}{(x^2+a^2)^{3/2}} = -\frac{1}{\sqrt{x^2+a^2}}$$

TABLE B.6

Gauss's Probability Integral and Other Definite Integrals

$$\int_0^\infty x^n e^{-ax}\, dx = \frac{n!}{a^{n+1}}$$

$$I_0 = \int_0^\infty e^{-ax^2}\, dx = \frac{1}{2}\sqrt{\frac{\pi}{a}} \qquad \text{(Gauss's probability integral)}$$

$$I_1 = \int_0^\infty x e^{-ax^2}\, dx = \frac{1}{2a}$$

$$I_2 = \int_0^\infty x^2 e^{-ax^2}\, dx = -\frac{dI_0}{da} = \frac{1}{4}\sqrt{\frac{\pi}{a^3}}$$

$$I_3 = \int_0^\infty x^3 e^{-ax^2}\, dx = -\frac{dI_1}{da} = \frac{1}{2a^2}$$

$$I_4 = \int_0^\infty x^4 e^{-ax^2}\, dx = \frac{d^2 I_0}{da^2} = \frac{3}{8}\sqrt{\frac{\pi}{a^5}}$$

$$I_5 = \int_0^\infty x^5 e^{-ax^2}\, dx = \frac{d^2 I_1}{da^2} = \frac{1}{a^3}$$

$$\vdots$$

$$I_{2n} = (-1)^n \frac{d^n}{da^n} I_0$$

$$I_{2n+1} = (-1)^n \frac{d^n}{da^n} I_1$$

The Perfect Differential

Another useful method to remember is that of the *perfect differential,* in which we look for a change of variable such that the differential of the function is the differential of the independent variable appearing in the integrand. For example, consider the integral

$$I(x) = \int \cos^2 x \, \sin x \, dx$$

This integral becomes easy to evaluate if we rewrite the differential as $d(\cos x) = -\sin x\, dx$. The integral then becomes

$$\int \cos^2 x \, \sin x \, dx = -\int \cos^2 x \, d(\cos x)$$

If we now change variables, letting $y = \cos x$, we obtain

$$\int \cos^2 x \, \sin x \, dx = -\int y^2\, dy = -\frac{y^3}{3} + c = -\frac{\cos^3 x}{3} + c$$

Table B.5 (page A-18) lists some useful indefinite integrals. Table B.6 gives Gauss's probability integral and other definite integrals. A more complete list can be found in various handbooks, such as *The Handbook of Chemistry and Physics* (Boca Raton, FL: CRC Press, published annually).

B.8   Propagation of Uncertainty

In laboratory experiments, a common activity is to take measurements that act as raw data. These measurements are of several types—length, time interval, temperature, voltage, and so on—and are taken by a variety of instruments. Regardless of the measurement and the quality of the instrumentation, **there is always uncertainty associated with a physical measurement.** This uncertainty is a combination of that associated with the instrument and that related to the system being measured. An example of the former is the inability to exactly determine the position of a length measurement between the lines on a meterstick. An example of uncertainty related to the system being measured is the variation of temperature within a sample of water so that a single temperature for the sample is difficult to determine.

Uncertainties can be expressed in two ways. **Absolute uncertainty** refers to an uncertainty expressed in the same units as the measurement. Therefore, the length of a computer disk label might be expressed as (5.5 ± 0.1) cm. The uncertainty of ± 0.1 cm by itself is not descriptive enough for some purposes, however. This uncertainty is large if the measurement is 1.0 cm, but it is small if the measurement is 100 m. To give a more descriptive account of the uncertainty, **fractional uncertainty** or **percent uncertainty** is used. In this type of description, the uncertainty is divided by the actual measurement. Therefore, the length of the computer disk label could be expressed as

$$\ell = 5.5 \text{ cm } \pm \frac{0.1 \text{ cm}}{5.5 \text{ cm}} = 5.5 \text{ cm } \pm 0.018 \quad \text{(fractional uncertainty)}$$

or as

$$\ell = 5.5 \text{ cm } \pm 1.8\% \quad \text{(percent uncertainty)}$$

When combining measurements in a calculation, the percent uncertainty in the final result is generally larger than the uncertainty in the individual measurements. This is called **propagation of uncertainty** and is one of the challenges of experimental physics.

Some simple rules can provide a reasonable estimate of the uncertainty in a calculated result:

Multiplication and division: When measurements with uncertainties are multiplied or divided, add the *percent uncertainties* to obtain the percent uncertainty in the result.

Example: The Area of a Rectangular Plate

$$A = \ell w = (5.5 \text{ cm } \pm 1.8\%) \times (6.4 \text{ cm } \pm 1.6\%) = 35 \text{ cm}^2 \pm 3.4\%$$

$$= (35 \pm 1) \text{ cm}^2$$

Addition and subtraction: When measurements with uncertainties are added or subtracted, add the *absolute uncertainties* to obtain the absolute uncertainty in the result.

Example: A Change in Temperature

$$\Delta T = T_2 - T_1 = (99.2 \pm 1.5)°\text{C} - (27.6 \pm 1.5)°\text{C} = (71.6 \pm 3.0)°\text{C}$$

$$= 71.6°\text{C} \pm 4.2\%$$

Powers: If a measurement is taken to a power, the percent uncertainty is multiplied by that power to obtain the percent uncertainty in the result.

Example: The Volume of a Sphere

$$V = \tfrac{4}{3}\pi r^3 = \tfrac{4}{3}\pi (6.20 \text{ cm } \pm 2.0\%)^3 = 998 \text{ cm}^3 \pm 6.0\%$$

$$= (998 \pm 60) \text{ cm}^3$$

For complicated calculations, many uncertainties are added together, which can cause the uncertainty in the final result to be undesirably large. Experiments should be designed such that calculations are as simple as possible.

Notice that uncertainties in a calculation always add. As a result, an experiment involving a subtraction should be avoided if possible, especially if the measurements being subtracted are close together. The result of such a calculation is a small difference in the measurements and uncertainties that add together. It is possible that the uncertainty in the result could be larger than the result itself!

Symbol — Ca 20 — Atomic number
Atomic mass† — 40.078
$4s^2$ — Electron configuration

Group I	Group II	Transition elements						
H 1 1.007 9 $1s$								
Li 3 6.941 $2s^1$	Be 4 9.0122 $2s^2$							
Na 11 22.990 $3s^1$	Mg 12 24.305 $3s^2$							
K 19 39.098 $4s^1$	Ca 20 40.078 $4s^2$	Sc 21 44.956 $3d^14s^2$	Ti 22 47.867 $3d^24s^2$	V 23 50.942 $3d^34s^2$	Cr 24 51.996 $3d^54s^1$	Mn 25 54.938 $3d^54s^2$	Fe 26 55.845 $3d^64s^2$	Co 27 58.933 $3d^74s^2$
Rb 37 85.468 $5s^1$	Sr 38 87.62 $5s^2$	Y 39 88.906 $4d^15s^2$	Zr 40 91.224 $4d^25s^2$	Nb 41 92.906 $4d^45s^1$	Mo 42 95.94 $4d^55s^1$	Tc 43 (98) $4d^55s^2$	Ru 44 101.07 $4d^75s^1$	Rh 45 102.91 $4d^85s^1$
Cs 55 132.91 $6s^1$	Ba 56 137.33 $6s^2$	57–71*	Hf 72 178.49 $5d^26s^2$	Ta 73 180.95 $5d^36s^2$	W 74 183.84 $5d^46s^2$	Re 75 186.21 $5d^56s^2$	Os 76 190.23 $5d^66s^2$	Ir 77 192.2 $5d^76s^2$
Fr 87 (223) $7s^1$	Ra 88 (226) $7s^2$	89–103**	Rf 104 (261) $6d^27s^2$	Db 105 (262) $6d^37s^2$	Sg 106 (266)	Bh 107 (264)	Hs 108 (277)	Mt 109 (268)

*Lanthanide series	La 57 138.91 $5d^16s^2$	Ce 58 140.12 $5d^14f^16s^2$	Pr 59 140.91 $4f^36s^2$	Nd 60 144.24 $4f^46s^2$	Pm 61 (145) $4f^56s^2$	Sm 62 150.36 $4f^66s^2$
**Actinide series	Ac 89 (227) $6d^17s^2$	Th 90 232.04 $6d^27s^2$	Pa 91 231.04 $5f^26d^17s^2$	U 92 238.03 $5f^36d^17s^2$	Np 93 (237) $5f^46d^17s^2$	Pu 94 (244) $5f^66d^07s^2$

Note: Atomic mass values given are averaged over isotopes in the percentages in which they exist in nature.
†For an unstable element, mass number of the most stable known isotope is given in parentheses.
††Elements 112 and 114 have not yet been named.
†††For a description of the atomic data, visit *physics.nist.gov/PhysRefData/Elements/per_text.html*

	Group III	Group IV	Group V	Group VI	Group VII	Group 0
					H 1 1.007 9 $1s^1$	**He** 2 4.002 6 $1s^2$
	B 5 10.811 $2p^1$	**C** 6 12.011 $2p^2$	**N** 7 14.007 $2p^3$	**O** 8 15.999 $2p^4$	**F** 9 18.998 $2p^5$	**Ne** 10 20.180 $2p^6$
	Al 13 26.982 $3p^1$	**Si** 14 28.086 $3p^2$	**P** 15 30.974 $3p^3$	**S** 16 32.066 $3p^4$	**Cl** 17 35.453 $3p^5$	**Ar** 18 39.948 $3p^6$
Ni 28 58.693 $3d^84s^2$ · **Cu** 29 63.546 $3d^{10}4s^1$ · **Zn** 30 65.41 $3d^{10}4s^2$	**Ga** 31 69.723 $4p^1$	**Ge** 32 72.64 $4p^2$	**As** 33 74.922 $4p^3$	**Se** 34 78.96 $4p^4$	**Br** 35 79.904 $4p^5$	**Kr** 36 83.80 $4p^6$
Pd 46 106.42 $4d^{10}$ · **Ag** 47 107.87 $4d^{10}5s^1$ · **Cd** 48 112.41 $4d^{10}5s^2$	**In** 49 114.82 $5p^1$	**Sn** 50 118.71 $5p^2$	**Sb** 51 121.76 $5p^3$	**Te** 52 127.60 $5p^4$	**I** 53 126.90 $5p^5$	**Xe** 54 131.29 $5p^6$
Pt 78 195.08 $5d^96s^1$ · **Au** 79 196.97 $5d^{10}6s^1$ · **Hg** 80 200.59 $5d^{10}6s^2$	**Tl** 81 204.38 $6p^1$	**Pb** 82 207.2 $6p^2$	**Bi** 83 208.98 $6p^3$	**Po** 84 (209) $6p^4$	**At** 85 (210) $6p^5$	**Rn** 86 (222) $6p^6$
Ds 110 (271) · **Rg** 111 (272) · 112†† (285)		114†† (289)				

Eu 63 151.96 $4f^76s^2$	**Gd** 64 157.25 $4f^75d^16s^2$	**Tb** 65 158.93 $4f^85d^16s^2$	**Dy** 66 162.50 $4f^{10}6s^2$	**Ho** 67 164.93 $4f^{11}6s^2$	**Er** 68 167.26 $4f^{12}6s^2$	**Tm** 69 168.93 $4f^{13}6s^2$	**Yb** 70 173.04 $4f^{14}6s^2$	**Lu** 71 174.97 $4f^{14}5d^16s^2$
Am 95 (243) $5f^77s^2$	**Cm** 96 (247) $5f^76d^17s^2$	**Bk** 97 (247) $5f^86d^17s^2$	**Cf** 98 (251) $5f^{10}7s^2$	**Es** 99 (252) $5f^{11}7s^2$	**Fm** 100 (257) $5f^{12}7s^2$	**Md** 101 (258) $5f^{13}7s^2$	**No** 102 (259) $5f^{14}7s^2$	**Lr** 103 (262) $6d^15f^{14}7s^2$

TABLE D.1

SI Units

| | SI Base Unit | |
Base Quantity	Name	Symbol
Length	meter	m
Mass	kilogram	kg
Time	second	s
Electric current	ampere	A
Temperature	kelvin	K
Amount of substance	mole	mol
Luminous intensity	candela	cd

TABLE D.2

Some Derived SI Units

Quantity	Name	Symbol	Expression in Terms of Base Units	Expression in Terms of Other SI Units
Plane angle	radian	rad	m/m	
Frequency	hertz	Hz	s^{-1}	
Force	newton	N	$kg \cdot m/s^2$	J/m
Pressure	pascal	Pa	$kg/m \cdot s^2$	N/m^2
Energy	joule	J	$kg \cdot m^2/s^2$	$N \cdot m$
Power	watt	W	$kg \cdot m^2/s^3$	J/s
Electric charge	coulomb	C	$A \cdot s$	
Electric potential	volt	V	$kg \cdot m^2/A \cdot s^3$	W/A
Capacitance	farad	F	$A^2 \cdot s^4/kg \cdot m^2$	C/V
Electric resistance	ohm	Ω	$kg \cdot m^2/A^2 \cdot s^3$	V/A
Magnetic flux	weber	Wb	$kg \cdot m^2/A \cdot s^2$	$V \cdot s$
Magnetic field	tesla	T	$kg/A \cdot s^2$	
Inductance	henry	H	$kg \cdot m^2/A^2 \cdot s^2$	$T \cdot m^2/A$

CHAPTER 1

1. 5.52×10^3 kg/m³, between the density of aluminum and iron and greater than the densities of typical surface rocks

3. 23.0 kg

5. 7.69 cm

7. (b) only

9. The units of G are m³/kg · s².

11. 1.39×10^3 m²

13. Not with the pages from Volume 1, but yes with the pages from the full version. Each page has area 0.059 m². The room has wall area 37 m², requiring 630 sheets, which would be counted as 1 260 pages.

15. 11.4×10^3 kg/m³

17. (a) 250 yr (b) 3.09×10^4 times

19. 1.00×10^{10} lb

21. 151 μm

23. 2.86 cm

25. ~10^6 balls

27. ~10^2 kg; ~10^3 kg

29. ~10^2 tuners

31. (a) 3 (b) 4 (c) 3 (d) 2

33. (a) 797 (b) 1.1 (c) 17.66

35. 8.80%

37. 9

39. 63

41. 108° and 288°

43. 48.6 kg

45. (a) smaller by nine times (b) Δt is inversely proportional to d^2. (c) Plot Δt on the vertical axis and $1/d^2$ on the horizontal axis. (d) $4QL/[k\pi(T_h - T_c)]$

47. (a) $m = 346$ g $- (14.5$ g/cm³$)a^3$ (b) $a = 0$ (c) 346 g (d) yes (e) $a = 2.60$ cm (f) 90.6 g (g) yes (h) 218 g (i) No; 218 g is not equal to 314 g. (j) Parts (b), (c), and (d) describe a uniform solid sphere with $\rho = 4.70$ g/cm³ as a approaches zero. Parts (e), (f), and (g) describe a uniform liquid drop with $\rho = 1.23$ g/cm³ as a approaches 2.60 cm. The function $m(a)$ is not a linear function, so a halfway between 0 and 2.60 cm does not give a value for m halfway between the minimum and maximum values. The graph of m versus a starts at $a = 0$ with a horizontal tangent. Then it curves down more and more steeply as a increases. The liquid drop of radius 1.30 cm has only one eighth the volume of the whole sphere, so its presence brings down the mass by only a small amount, from 346 g to 314 g. (k) The answer would not change as long as the wall of the shell is unbroken.

49. 5.0 m

51. $0.579t$ ft³/s $+ (1.19 \times 10^{-9})t^2$ ft³/s²

53. 3.41 m

55. 0.449%

57. (a) 0.529 cm/s (b) 11.5 cm/s

59. 1×10^{10} gal/yr

CHAPTER 2

1. (a) 5 m/s (b) 1.2 m/s (c) -2.5 m/s (d) -3.3 m/s (e) 0

3. (a) 3.75 m/s (b) 0

5. (a) -2.4 m/s (b) -3.8 m/s (c) 4.0 s

7. (a) and (c)

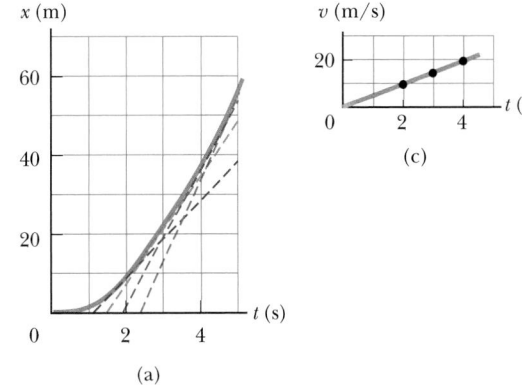

(a)

(b) $v_{t=5.0\,s} = 23$ m/s, $v_{t=4.0\,s} = 18$ m/s, $v_{t=3.0\,s} = 14$ m/s, $v_{t=2.0\,s} = 9.0$ m/s (c) 4.6 m/s² (d) 0

9. 5.00 m

11. (a) 20.0 m/s, 5.00 m/s (b) 262 m

13. (a) 2.00 m (b) -3.00 m/s (c) -2.00 m/s²

15. (a) 13.0 m/s (b) 10.0 m/s, 16.0 m/s (c) 6.00 m/s² (d) 6.00 m/s²

17.

(a)

19. (a) 9.00 m/s (b) 5.00 m/s (c) 3.00 m/s (d) -3.00 m/s (e) 17.0 m/s (f) The graph of velocity versus time is a straight line passing through 13 m/s at 10:05 a.m. and sloping downward, decreasing by 4 m/s for each second thereafter. (g) If and only if we know the object's velocity at one instant of time, knowing its acceleration tells us its velocity at every other moment, as long as the acceleration is constant.

21. -16.0 cm/s²

23. (a) 20.0 s (b) It cannot; it would need a longer runway.

25. 3.10 m/s

27. (a) -202 m/s² (b) 198 m

29. (a) 4.98×10^{-9} s (b) 1.20×10^{15} m/s²

31. (a) False unless the acceleration is zero. We define constant acceleration to mean that the velocity is changing steadily in time. Then the velocity cannot be changing steadily in space. (b) True. Because the velocity is changing steadily in time, the velocity halfway through an interval is equal to the average of its initial and final values.

33. (a) 3.45 s (b) 10.0 ft

35. (a) 19.7 cm/s (b) 4.70 cm/s² (c) The time interval required for the speed to change between Ⓐ and Ⓑ is sufficient to find the acceleration, more directly than we could find it from the distance between the points.

37. We ignore air resistance. We assume the worker's flight time, "a mile," and "a dollar" were measured to three-digit precision. We have interpreted "up in the sky" as referring to free-fall time, not to the launch and landing times. Therefore, the wage was $99.3/h.

39. (a) 10.0 m/s up   (b) 4.68 m/s down

41. (a) 29.4 m/s   (b) 44.1 m

43. (a) 7.82 m   (b) 0.782 s

45. 38.2 m

47. (a) $a_x(t) = a_{xi} + Jt$, $v_x(t) = v_{xi} + a_{xi}t + \frac{1}{2}Jt^2$,
$x(t) = x_i + v_{xi}t + \frac{1}{2}a_{xi}t^2 + \frac{1}{6}Jt^3$

49. (a) 0   (b) 6.0 m/s²   (c) -3.6 m/s²   (d) 6 s and 18 s
(e) 18 s   (f) 84 m   (g) 204 m

51. (a) 41.0 s   (b) 1.73 km   (c) -184 m/s

53. (a) 5.43 m/s² and 3.83 m/s²   (b) 10.9 m/s and 11.5 m/s
(c) Maggie by 2.62 m

55. 155 s, 129 s

57. (a) 3.00 s   (b) -15.3 m/s   (c) 31.4 m/s down and 34.8 m/s down

59. (a) 5.46 s   (b) 73.0 m   (c) $v_{Stan} = 22.6$ m/s, $v_{Kathy} = 26.7$ m/s

61. (a) yes, to two significant digits   (b) 0.742 s   (c) Yes; the braking distance is proportional to the square of the original speed.   (d) -19.7 ft/s² $= -6.01$ m/s²

63. $0.577v$

CHAPTER 3

1. $(-2.75, -4.76)$ m

3. (a) 2.24 m   (b) 2.24 m at 26.6°

5. (a) r, $180° - \theta$ (b) $2r$, $180° + \theta$ (c) $3r$, $-\theta$

7. 70.0 m

9. (a) 10.0 m   (b) 15.7 m   (c) 0

11. (a) 5.2 m at 60°   (b) 3.0 m at 330°   (c) 3.0 m at 150°
(d) 5.2 m at 300°

13. approximately 420 ft at $-3°$

15. 47.2 units at 122°

17. Yes. The speed of the camper should be 28.3 m/s or greater.

19. (a) $(-11.1\hat{i} + 6.40\hat{j})$ m   (b) $(1.65\hat{i} + 2.86\hat{j})$ cm
(c) $(-18.0\hat{i} - 12.6\hat{j})$ in.

21. 358 m at 2.00° S of E

23. 196 cm at 345°

25. (a) $2.00\hat{i} - 6.00\hat{j}$ (b) $4.00\hat{i} + 2.00\hat{j}$ (c) 6.32
(d) 4.47   (e) 288°, 26.6°

27. 9.48 m at 166°

29. 4.64 m at 78.6° N of E

31. (a) 185 N at 77.8° from the $+x$ axis
(b) $(-39.3\hat{i} - 181\hat{j})$ N

33. $|\vec{B}| = 7.81$, $\theta_x = 59.2°$, $\theta_y = 39.8°$, $\theta_z = 67.4°$

35. (a) 5.92 m is the magnitude of
$(5.00\hat{i} - 1.00\hat{j} - 3.00\hat{k})$ m. (b) 19.0 m is the magnitude of $(4.00\hat{i} - 11.0\hat{j} - 15.0\hat{k})$ m.

37. (a) $8.00\hat{i} + 12.0\hat{j} - 4.00\hat{k}$ (b) $2.00\hat{i} + 3.00\hat{j} - 1.00\hat{k}$
(c) $-24.0\hat{i} - 36.0\hat{j} + 12.0\hat{k}$

39. (a) $(3.12\hat{i} + 5.02\hat{j} - 2.20\hat{k})$ km   (b) 6.31 km

41. (a) $-3.00\hat{i} + 2.00\hat{j}$ (b) 3.61 at 146°
(c) $3.00\hat{i} - 6.00\hat{j}$

43. (a) $49.5\hat{i} + 27.1\hat{j}$ (b) 56.4 units at 28.7°

45. (a) $[(5 + 11f)\hat{i} + (3 + 9f)\hat{j}]$ m   (b) $(5\hat{i} + 3\hat{j})$ m is reasonable because it is the starting point.   (c) $(16\hat{i} + 12\hat{j})$ m is reasonable because it is the endpoint.

47. 1.15°

49. 2.29 km

51. (a) 7.17 km   (b) 6.15 km

53. 390 mi/h at 7.37° N of E

55. $(0.456\hat{i} - 0.708\hat{j})$ m

57. 240 m at 237°

59. (a) (10.0 m, 16.0 m)   (b) You will arrive at the treasure if you take the trees in any order. The directions take you to the average position of the trees.

61. 106°

CHAPTER 4

1. (a) 4.87 km at 209° from E   (b) 23.3 m/s
(c) 13.5 m/s at 209°

3. 2.50 m/s

5. (a) $(0.800\hat{i} - 0.300\hat{j})$ m/s²   (b) 339°
(c) $(360\hat{i} - 72.7\hat{j})$ m, $-15.2°$

7. (a) $\vec{v} = 5\hat{i} + 4t^{3/2}\hat{j}$ (b) $\vec{r} = 5t\hat{i} + 1.6t^{5/2}\hat{j}$

9. (a) 3.34$\hat{i}$ m/s   (b) $-50.9°$

11. $(7.23 \times 10^3$ m, 1.68×10^3 m$)$

13. 53.1°

15. (a) 22.6 m   (b) 52.3 m   (c) 1.18 s

17. (a) The ball clears by 0.889 m. (b) while descending

19. (a) 18.1 m/s   (b) 1.13 m   (c) 2.79 m

21. 9.91 m/s

23. $\tan^{-1}[(2gh)^{1/2}/v]$

25. 377 m/s²

27. (a) 6.00 rev/s   (b) 1.52 km/s²   (c) 1.28 km/s²

29. 1.48 m/s² inward and 29.9° backward

31. (a) 13.0 m/s²   (b) 5.70 m/s   (c) 7.50 m/s²

33. (a) 57.7 km/h at 60.0° W of vertical
(b) 28.9 km/h downward

35. 2.02×10^3 s; 21.0% longer

37. $t_{Alan} = \dfrac{2L/c}{1 - v^2/c^2}$, $t_{Beth} = \dfrac{2L/c}{\sqrt{1 - v^2/c^2}}$. Beth returns first.

39. 15.3 m

41. 27.7° E of N

43. (a) 9.80 m/s² down   (b) 3.72 m

45. (a) 41.7 m/s   (b) 3.81 s
(c) $(34.1\hat{i} - 13.4\hat{j})$ m/s; 36.7 m/s

47. (a) 25.0 m/s²; 9.80 m/s²
(b)

(c) 26.8 m/s² inward at 21.4° below the horizontal

49. (a)

t (s)	0	1	2	3	4	5
r (m)	0	45.7	82.0	109	127	136

t (s)	6	7	8	9	10
r (m)	138	133	124	117	120

(b) The vector $\vec{\mathbf{v}}$ tells how $\vec{\mathbf{r}}$ is changing. If $\vec{\mathbf{v}}$ at a particular point has a component along $\vec{\mathbf{r}}$, then $\vec{\mathbf{r}}$ will be increasing in magnitude (if $\vec{\mathbf{v}}$ is at an angle less than 90° from $\vec{\mathbf{r}}$) or decreasing (if the angle between $\vec{\mathbf{v}}$ and $\vec{\mathbf{r}}$ is more than 90°). To be at a maximum, the distance from the origin must be momentarily staying constant, and the only way that can happen is if the angle between velocity and position is a right angle. Then $\vec{\mathbf{r}}$ will be changing in direction at that point, but not in magnitude.   (c) The requirement for perpendicularity can be defined as equality between the tangent of the angle between $\vec{\mathbf{v}}$ and the x direction and the tangent of the angle between $\vec{\mathbf{r}}$ and the y direction. In symbols, this equality can be written $(9.8t - 49)/12 = 12t/(49t - 4.9t^2)$, which has the solution $t = 5.70$ s, giving, in turn, $r = 138$ m. Alternatively, we can require $dr^2/dt = 0 = (d/dt)[(12t)^2 + (49t - 4.9t^2)^2]$, which results in the same equation with the same solution.

51. (a) 26.6°   (b) 0.949
53. (a) 6.80 km   (b) 3.00 km vertically above the impact point   (c) 66.2°
55. (a) 46.5 m/s   (b) −77.6°   (c) 6.34 s
57. (a) 20.0 m/s, 5.00 s   (b) $(16.0\hat{\mathbf{i}} - 27.1\hat{\mathbf{j}})$ m/s
  (c) 6.53 s   (d) $24.5\hat{\mathbf{i}}$ m
59. (a) 43.2 m   (b) $(9.66\hat{\mathbf{i}} - 25.5\hat{\mathbf{j}})$ m/s. Air resistance would ordinarily make the jump distance smaller and the final horizontal and vertical velocity components both somewhat smaller. When the skilled jumper makes his body into an airfoil, he deflects downward the air through which he passes so that it deflects him upward, giving him more time in the air and a longer jump.
61. Safe distances are less than 270 m or greater than 3.48×10^3 m from the western shore.

CHAPTER 5

1. $(6.00\hat{\mathbf{i}} + 15.0\hat{\mathbf{j}})$ N; 16.2 N
3. (a) $(2.50\hat{\mathbf{i}} + 5.00\hat{\mathbf{j}})$ N (b) 5.59 N
5. (a) 3.64×10^{-18} N   (b) 8.93×10^{-30} N is 408 billion times smaller
7. 2.55 N for an 88.7-kg person
9. (a) 5.00 m/s² at 36.9°   (b) 6.08 m/s² at 25.3°
11. (a) $\sim 10^{-22}$ m/s²   (b) $\sim 10^{-23}$ m
13. (a) 15.0 lb up   (b) 5.00 lb up   (c) 0
15. (a) 3.43 kN   (b) 0.967 m/s horizontally forward
17.

613 N
19. (a) $P\cos 40° - n = 0$ and $P\sin 40° - 220$ N $= 0$; $P = 342$ N and $n = 262$ N   (b) $P - n\cos 40° - (220$ N$)\sin 40° = 0$ and $n\sin 40 - (220$ N$)\cos 40° = 0$; $n = 262$ N and $P = 342$ N   (c) The results agree. The methods have a similar level of difficulty. Each involves one equation in one unknown and one equation in two unknowns. If we are interested in finding n without finding P, method (b) is simpler.
23. (a) 49.0 N   (b) 49.0 N   (c) 98.0 N   (d) 24.5 N
25. 8.66 N east
27. (a) 646 N up   (b) 646 N up   (c) 627 N up
  (d) 589 N up

29. 3.73 m
31. (a) $F_x > 19.6$ N   (b) $F_x \le -78.4$ N
  (c)

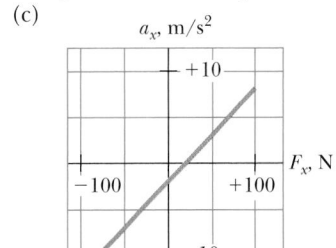

33. (a) 706 N   (b) 814 N   (c) 706 N   (d) 648 N
35. (a) 256 m   (b) 42.7 m
37. (a) no   (b) 16.9 N backwards + 37.2 N upward = 40.9 N upward and backward at 65.6° with the horizontal
39. (a) 1.78 m/s²   (b) 0.368   (c) 9.37 N   (d) 2.67 m/s
41. 37.8 N
43. (a)

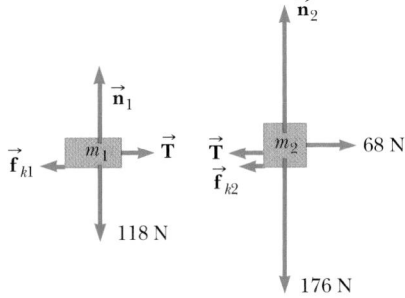

(b) 27.2 N, 1.29 m/s²
45. (a) $a = 0$ if $P < 8.11$ N; $a = -3.33$ m/s² $+ (1.41/$kg$)\,P$ to the right if $P > 8.11$ N   (b) $a = 0$; 3.99 N horizontally backward   (c) 10.8 m/s² to the right; 3.45 N to the left   (d) The acceleration is zero for all values of P less than 8.11 N. When P passes this threshold, the acceleration jumps to its minimum nonzero value of 8.14 m/s². From there it increases linearly with P toward arbitrarily high values.
47. 72.0 N
49. (a) 2.94 m/s² forward (b) 2.45 m/s² forward (c) 1.19 m/s² up the incline   (d) 0.711 m/s² up the incline   (e) 16.7° (f) The mass makes no difference. Mathematically, the mass divides out in determinations of acceleration. If several packages of dishes were placed in the truck, they would all slide together, whether they were tied to one another or not.
51. (a)

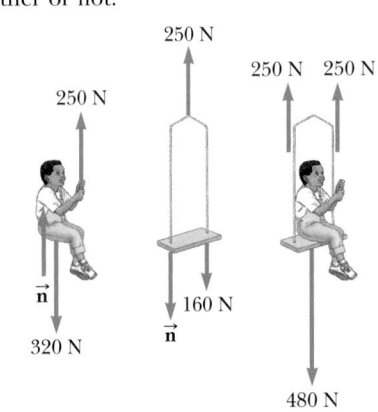

(b) 0.408 m/s²   (c) 83.3 N
53. (a) 3.00 s   (b) 20.1 m   (c) $(18.0\hat{\mathbf{i}} - 9.00\hat{\mathbf{j}})$ m

55. (a) $a = 12 \text{ N}/(4 \text{ kg} + m_1)$ forward   (b) $12 \text{ N}/(1 + m_1/4 \text{ kg})$ forward   (c) 2.50 m/s^2 forward and 10.0 N forward   (d) The force approaches zero   (e) The force approaches 12.0 N   (f) The tension in a cord of negligible mass is constant along its length.

57. (a) $Mg/2$, $Mg/2$, $Mg/2$, $3Mg/2$, Mg (b) $Mg/2$

59. (a) Both are equal respectively.   (b) 1.61×10^4 N   (c) 2.95×10^4 N   (d) 0 N; 3.51 m/s upward. The first 3.50 m/s of the speed of 3.51 m/s needs no dynamic cause; the motion of the cable continues on its own, as described by the law of "inertia" or "pigheadedness." The increase from 3.50 m/s to 3.51 m/s must be caused by some total upward force on the section of cable. Because its mass is very small compared to a thousand kilograms, however, the force is very small compared to 1.61×10^4 N, the nearly uniform tension of this section of cable.

61. (b)

θ	0	15°	30°	45°	60°
P (N)	40.0	46.4	60.1	94.3	260

63. (a) The net force on the cushion is in a fixed direction, downward and forward making angle $\tan^{-1}(F/mg)$ with the vertical. Starting from rest, it will move along this line with (b) increasing speed. Its velocity changes in magnitude. (c) 1.63 m   (d) It will move along a parabola. The axis of the parabola is parallel to the dashed line in the problem figure. If the cushion is thrown in a direction above the dashed line, its path will be concave downward, making its velocity become more and more nearly parallel to the dashed line over time. If the cushion is thrown down more steeply, its path will be concave upward, again making its velocity turn toward the fixed direction of its acceleration.

65. (a) $19.3°$ (b) 4.21 N

67. $(M + m_1 + m_2)(m_2 g/m_1)$

69. (a) $30.7°$ (b) 0.843 N

71. (a) $T_1 = \dfrac{2mg}{\sin \theta_1}$, $T_2 = \dfrac{mg}{\sin \theta_2} = \dfrac{mg}{\sin\left[\tan^{-1}\left(\frac{1}{2}\tan \theta_1\right)\right]}$,

$T_3 = \dfrac{2\,mg}{\tan \theta_1}$

(b) $\theta_2 = \tan^{-1}\left(\dfrac{\tan \theta_1}{2}\right)$

CHAPTER 6

1. Any speed up to 8.08 m/s

3. (a) 8.32×10^{-8} N toward the nucleus   (b) 9.13×10^{22} m/s^2 inward

5. (a) static friction   (b) $0.085\ 0$

7. 2.14 rev/min

9. $v \leq 14.3$ m/s

11. (a) 108 N   (b) 56.2 N

13. (a) 4.81 m/s   (b) 700 N up

15. No. Tarzan needs a vine of tensile strength 1.38 kN.

17. 3.13 m/s

19. (a) 3.60 m/s^2 (b) zero   (c) An observer in the car (a noninertial frame) claims an 18.0-N force toward the left and an 18.0-N force toward the right. An inertial observer (outside the car) claims only an 18.0-N force toward the right.

21. (a) $17.0°$ (b) 5.12 N

23. (a) 491 N   (b) 50.1 kg   (c) 2.00 m/s

25. $0.092\ 8°$

27. (a) 32.7 s^{-1} (b) 9.80 m/s^2 down   (c) 4.90 m/s^2 down

29. 3.01 N up

31. (a) 1.47 N·s/m   (b) 2.04×10^{-3} s   (c) 2.94×10^{-2} N

33. (a) 78.3 m/s   (b) 11.1 s   (c) 121 m

35. (a) $x = k^{-1} \ln (1 + kv_0\, t)$ (b) $v = v_0 e^{-kx}$

37. (a) $0.034\ 7$ s^{-1} (b) 2.50 m/s   (c) $a = -cv$

39. $v = v_0 e^{-bt/m}$

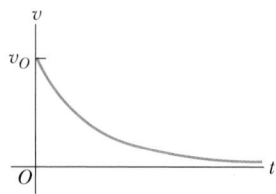

In this model, the object keeps moving forever. It travels a finite distance in an infinite time interval.

41. (a) 106 N up the incline   (b) 0.396

43. (a) 11.5 kN   (b) 14.1 m/s

45. (a) $0.016\ 2$ kg/m   (b) $\frac{1}{2}D\rho A$ (c) 0.778 (d) 1.5% (e) For stacked coffee filters falling in air at terminal speed, the graph of air resistance force as a function of the square of speed demonstrates that the force is proportional to the speed squared, within the experimental uncertainty estimated as 2%. This proportionality agrees with the theoretical model of air resistance at high speeds. The drag coefficient of a coffee filter is $D = 0.78 \pm 2\%$.

47. $g(\cos \phi \tan \theta - \sin \phi)$

49. (b) 732 N down at the equator and 735 N down at the poles

51. (a) The only horizontal force on the car is the force of friction, with a maximum value determined by the surface roughness (described by the coefficient of static friction) and the normal force (here equal to the gravitational force on the car). (b) 34.3 m   (c) 68.6 m   (d) Braking is better. You should not turn the wheel. If you used any of the available friction force to change the direction of the car, it would be unavailable to slow the car and the stopping distance would be longer.   (e) The conclusion is true in general. The radius of the curve you can barely make is twice your minimum stopping distance.

53. (a) 5.19 m/s   (b) $T = 555$ N

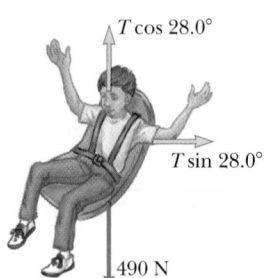

55. (b) 2.54 s; 23.6 rev/min   (c) The gravitational and friction forces remain constant. The normal force increases. The person remains in motion with the wall. (d) The gravitational force remains constant. The normal and friction forces decrease. The person slides relative to the wall and downward into the pit.

57. (a) $v_{\min} = \sqrt{\dfrac{Rg\,(\tan \theta - \mu_s)}{1 + \mu_s \tan \theta}}$, $v_{\max} = \sqrt{\dfrac{Rg\,(\tan \theta + \mu_s)}{1 - \mu_s \tan \theta}}$

(b) $\mu_s = \tan \theta$ (c) 8.57 m/s $\leq v \leq 16.6$ m/s

59. (a) $0.013\ 2$ m/s   (b) 1.03 m/s   (c) 6.87 m/s

61. 12.8 N

CHAPTER 7

1. (a) 31.9 J   (b) 0   (c) 0   (d) 31.9 J
3. −4.70 kJ
7. (a) 16.0 J   (b) 36.9°
9. (a) 11.3°   (b) 156°   (c) 82.3°
11. $\vec{\mathbf{A}}$ = 7.05 m at 28.4°
13. (a) 24.0 J   (b) −3.00 J   (c) 21.0 J
15. (a) 7.50 J   (b) 15.0 J   (c) 7.50 J   (d) 30.0 J
17. (a) 0.938 cm   (b) 1.25 J
19. 7.37 N/m
21. 0.299 m/s
23. (a) 0.020 4 m   (b) 720 N/m
25. (b) mgR
27. (a) 0.600 J   (b) −0.600 J   (c) 1.50 J
29. (a) 1.20 J   (b) 5.00 m/s   (c) 6.30 J
31. (a) 60.0 J   (b) 60.0 J
33. 878 kN up
35. (a) 4.56 kJ   (b) 6.34 kN   (c) 422 km/s² (d) 6.34 kN
    (e) The forces are the same. The two theories agree.
37. (a) 259 kJ, 0, −259 kJ   (b) 0, −259 kJ, −259 kJ
39. (a) −196 J   (b) −196 J   (c) −196 J. The force is
    conservative.
41. (a) 125 J   (b) 50.0 J   (c) 66.7 J   (d) The force is
    nonconservative. The results differ.
43. (a) 40.0 J   (b) −40.0 J   (c) 62.5 J
45. (A/r^2) away from the other particle
47. (a) + at Ⓑ, − at Ⓓ, 0 at Ⓐ, Ⓒ, and Ⓔ
    (b) Ⓒ stable; Ⓐ and Ⓔ unstable
    (c)

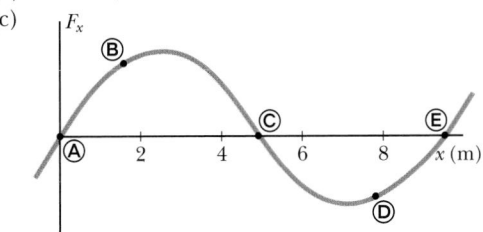

49. (c)   Equilibrium at $x = 0$

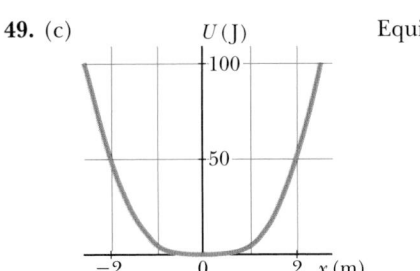

    (d) 0.823 m/s
51. 90.0 J
53. (a) $x = (3.62\ m)/(4.30 − 23.4m)$ where x is in meters and
    m is in kilograms   (b) 0.095 1 m (c) 0.492 m   (d) 6.85 m
    (e) The situation is impossible.   (f) The extension is
    directly proportional to m when m is only a few grams.
    Then it grows faster and faster, diverging to infinity for
    $m = 0.184$ kg.
55. $U(x) = 1 + 4e^{−2x}$. The force must be conservative because
    the work the force does on the object on which it acts
    depends only on the original and final positions of the
    object, not on the path between them.
57. 1.68 m/s
59. 0.799 J

CHAPTER 8

1. (a) $\Delta E_{\text{int}} = Q + T_{\text{ET}} + T_{\text{ER}}$ (b) $\Delta K + \Delta U + \Delta E_{\text{int}} =$
    $W + Q + T_{\text{MW}} + T_{\text{MT}}$ (c) $\Delta U = Q + T_{\text{MT}}$
    (d) $0 = Q + T_{\text{MT}} + T_{\text{ET}} + T_{\text{ER}}$
3. (a) $v = (3gR)^{1/2}$ (b) 0.098 0 N down
5. 10.2 m
7. (a) 4.43 m/s   (b) 5.00 m
9. 5.49 m/s
11. (a) 25.8 m   (b) 27.1 m/s²
13. (a) 650 J   (b) 588 J   (c) 0   (d) 0   (e) 62.0 J
    (f) 1.76 m/s
15. (a) −168 J   (b) 184 J   (c) 500 J   (d) 148 J   (e) 5.65 m/s
17. 2.04 m
19. 3.74 m/s
21. (a) −160 J   (b) 73.5 J   (c) 28.8 N   (d) 0.679
23. (a) 1.40 m/s   (b) 4.60 cm after release   (c) 1.79 m/s
25. (a) 0.381 m   (b) 0.143 m   (c) 0.371 m
27. (a) $a_x = −\mu_k gx/L$ (b) $v = (\mu_k gL)^{1/2}$
29. 875 W
31. ~ 10^4 W
33. \$46.2
35. (a) 10.2 kW   (b) 10.6 kW   (c) 5.82 MJ
37. (a) 11.1 m/s   (b) 19.6 m/s² upward   (c) 2.23 × 10³ N
    upward   (d) 1.01 × 10³ J   (e) 5.14 m/s   (f) 1.35 m
    (g) 1.39 s
39. (a) $(2 + 24t^2 + 72t^4)$ J   (b) $12t$ m/s²; $48t$ N
    (c) $(48t + 288t^3)$ W   (d) 1 250 J
41. (a) 1.38 × 10⁴ J   (b) 3.02 × 10⁴ W
43. (a) 4.12 m   (b) 3.35 m
45. (a) 2.17 kW   (b) 58.6 kW
47. (a) $x = −4.0$ mm   (b) −1.0 cm
49. 33.4 kW
51. (a) 0.225 J   (b) $\Delta E_{\text{mech}} = −0.363$ J   (c) No. The normal
    force changes in a complicated way.
53. (a) 100 J   (b) 0.410 m   (c) 2.84 m/s   (d) −9.80 mm
    (e) 2.85 m/s
55. 0.328
57. 1.24 m/s
59. (a) 0.400 m   (b) 4.10 m/s   (c) The block stays on the
    track.
61. $2m$
65. (a) 14.1 m/s   (b) −7.90 kJ   (c) 800 N   (d) 771 N
    (e) 1.57 kN up

CHAPTER 9

1. (a) $(9.00\hat{\mathbf{i}} − 12.0\hat{\mathbf{j}})$ kg · m/s   (b) 15.0 kg · m/s at 307°
3. ~ $10^{−23}$ m/s
5. (b) $p = \sqrt{2mK}$
7. (a) 13.5 N · s   (b) 9.00 kN   (c) 18.0 kN
9. 260 N normal to the wall
11. (a) $12.0\hat{\mathbf{i}}$ N · s   (b) $4.80\hat{\mathbf{i}}$ m/s   (c) $2.80\hat{\mathbf{i}}$ m/s
    (d) $2.40\hat{\mathbf{i}}$ N
13. (b) small   (d) large   (e) no difference
15. 301 m/s
17. (a) 2.50 m/s   (b) 37.5 kJ   (c) Each process is the time-
    reversal of the other. The same momentum conservation
    equation describes both.
19. 0.556 m
21. (a) $\vec{\mathbf{v}}_g = 1.15\hat{\mathbf{i}}$ m/s   (b) $\vec{\mathbf{v}}_p = −0.346\hat{\mathbf{i}}$ m/s
23. (a) 0.284   (b) 115 fJ and 45.4 fJ

25. 91.2 m/s

27. 2.50 m/s at $-60.0°$

29. $v_{orange} = 3.99$ m/s, $v_{yellow} = 3.01$ m/s

31. $(3.00\hat{i} - 1.20\hat{j})$ m/s

33. (a) $(-9.33\hat{i} - 8.33\hat{j})$ Mm/s   (b) 439 fJ

35. $\vec{r}_{CM} = (0\hat{i} + 1.00\hat{j})$ m

37. $\vec{r}_{CM} = (11.7\hat{i} + 13.3\hat{j})$ cm

39. (a) 15.9 g   (b) 0.153 m

41. (a) $(1.40\hat{i} + 2.40\hat{j})$ m/s   (b) $(7.00\hat{i} + 12.0\hat{j})$ kg·m/s

43. 0.700 m

45. (a) Yes. $18.0\hat{i}$ kg·m/s.   (b) No. The floor does zero work.   (c) Yes. We could say that the final momentum of the cart came from the floor or from the Earth through the floor.   (d) No. The kinetic energy came from the original gravitational energy of the elevated load, in amount 27.0 J.   (e) Yes. The acceleration is caused by the static friction force exerted by the floor that prevents the caterpillar tracks from slipping backward.

47. (b) 2.06 m/s   (c) Yes. The bumper continues to exert a force to the left until the particle has swung down to its lowest point.

49. (a) 3.75 kg·m/s² to the right   (b) 3.75 N to the right   (c) 3.75 N   (d) 2.81 J   (e) 1.41 J   (f) Friction between sand and belt converts half of the input work into extra internal energy.

51. (a) 39.0 MN   (b) 3.20 m/s² up

53. (a) 442 metric tons   (b) 19.2 metric tons. This amount is much less than the value suggested. Mathematically, the logarithm in the rocket propulsion equation is not a linear function. Physically, a higher exhaust speed has an extra-large cumulative effect on the rocket frame's final speed, by counting again and again in the speed the frame attains second after second during its burn.

55. 240 s

57. $\left(\dfrac{M + m}{m}\right)\sqrt{\dfrac{gd^2}{2h}}$

59. (a) 0; inelastic
(b) $(-0.250\hat{i} + 0.750\hat{j} - 2.00\hat{k})$ m/s; perfectly inelastic
(c) either $a = -6.74$ with $\vec{v} = -0.419\ \hat{k}$ m/s or $a = 2.74$ with $\vec{v} = -3.58\ \hat{k}$ m/s

61. (a) $m/M = 0.403$ (b) no changes; no difference

63. (b) 0.042 9   (c) 1.00   (d) Energy is an entirely different thing from momentum. A comparison: When children eat their soup, they do not eat the tablecloth. Another comparison: When a photographer's single-use flashbulb flashes, a magnesium filament oxidizes. Chemical energy disappears. (Internal energy appears and light carries some energy away.) The measured mass of the flashbulb is the same before and after. It can be the same despite the 100% energy conversion because energy and mass are totally different things in classical physics. In the ballistic pendulum, conversion of energy from mechanical into internal does not upset conservation of mass or conservation of momentum.

65. (a) $-0.256\hat{i}$ m/s and $0.128\hat{i}$ m/s
(b) $-0.064\ 2\hat{i}$ m/s and 0   (c) 0 and 0

67. (a) 100 m/s   (b) 374 J

69. $(3Mgx/L)\hat{j}$

CHAPTER 10

1. (a) 5.00 rad, 10.0 rad/s, 4.00 rad/s²   (b) 53.0 rad, 22.0 rad/s, 4.00 rad/s²

3. (a) 4.00 rad/s²   (b) 18.0 rad

5. (a) 5.24 s   (b) 27.4 rad

7. (a) 7.27×10^{-5} rad/s   (b) 2.57×10^4 s = 428 min

9. 50.0 rev

11. $\sim 10^7$ rev

13. (a) 8.00 rad/s   (b) 8.00 m/s, $a_r = -64.0$ m/s², $a_t = 4.00$ m/s²   (c) 9.00 rad

15. (a) $(-2.73\hat{i} + 1.24\hat{j})$ m   (b) in the second quadrant, at 156°   (c) $(-1.85\hat{i} - 4.10\hat{j})$ m/s   (d) toward the third quadrant, at 246°

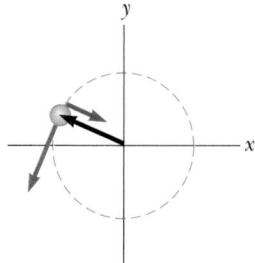

(e) $(6.15\hat{i} - 2.78\hat{j})$ m/s²   (f) $(24.6\hat{i} - 11.1\hat{j})$ N

17. (a) 126 rad/s   (b) 3.77 m/s   (c) 1.26 km/s²   (d) 20.1 m

19. 0.572

21. (a) 143 kg·m²   (b) 2.57 kJ

25. (a) 24.5 m/s   (b) no; no; no; no; yes

27. 1.28 kg·m²

29. $\sim 10^0$ kg·m²

33. -3.55 N·m

35. (a) 24.0 N·m   (b) 0.035 6 rad/s²   (c) 1.07 m/s²

37. (a) 0.309 m/s²   (b) 7.67 N and 9.22 N

39. 21.5 N

41. 24.5 km

43. 149 rad/s

45. (a) 1.59 m/s   (b) 53.1 rad/s

47. (a) 11.4 N, 7.57 m/s², 9.53 m/s down   (b) 9.53 m/s

51. (a) $2(Rg/3)^{1/2}$ (b) $4(Rg/3)^{1/2}$ (c) $(Rg)^{1/2}$

53. (a) 500 J   (b) 250 J   (c) 750 J

55. (a) $\frac{2}{3}g \sin \theta$ for the disk, larger than $\frac{1}{2}g \sin \theta$ for the hoop   (b) $\frac{1}{3} \tan \theta$

57. 1.21×10^{-4} kg·m²; height is unnecessary

59. $\frac{1}{3}\ell$

61. (a) 4.00 J   (b) 1.60 s   (c) yes

63. (a) $\omega = 3F\ell/b$ (b) $\alpha = 3F\ell/mL^2$ (c) and (d) Both larger. A component of the thrust force, exerted by the water about to spray from the ends of the arms, causes a forward torque on the rotor. Notice also that the rotor with bent arms has a slightly smaller moment of inertia than it would if the same metal tubes were straight.

65. (a) $(3g/L)^{1/2}$ (b) $3g/2L$ (c) $-\frac{3}{2}g\hat{i} - \frac{3}{4}g\hat{j}$
(d) $-\frac{3}{2}Mg\hat{i} + \frac{1}{4}Mg\hat{j}$

67. -0.322 rad/s²

71. (a) 118 N and 156 N   (b) 1.17 kg·m²

73. (a) $\alpha = -0.176$ rad/s²   (b) 1.29 rev   (c) 9.26 rev

75. (a) $\omega(2h^3/g)^{1/2}$ (b) 0.011 6 m   (c) Yes; the deflection is only 0.02% of the original height.

79. (a) 2.70R   (b) $\Sigma F_x = -20mg/7$, $\Sigma F_y = -5mg/7$

81. (a) $(3gh/4)^{1/2}$ (b) $(3gh/4)^{1/2}$

83. (c) $(8Fd/3M)^{1/2}$

85. to the left

CHAPTER 11

1. $-7.00\hat{\mathbf{i}} + 16.0\hat{\mathbf{j}} - 10.0\hat{\mathbf{k}}$
3. (a) $-17.0\hat{\mathbf{k}}$ (b) $70.6°$
5. 0.343 N $\cdot$ m horizontally north
7. $45.0°$
9. $F_3 = F_1 + F_2$; no
11. $17.5\hat{\mathbf{k}}$ kg $\cdot$ m^2/s
13. $(60.0\hat{\mathbf{k}})$ kg $\cdot$ m^2/s
15. $mvR[\cos (vt/R) + 1]\hat{\mathbf{k}}$
17. (a) zero   (b) $(-mv_i^3 \sin^2 \theta \cos \theta/2g)\hat{\mathbf{k}}$
    (c) $(-2mv_i^3 \sin^2 \theta \cos \theta/g)\hat{\mathbf{k}}$ (d) The downward gravitational force exerts a torque in the $-z$ direction.
19. (a) $-m\ell gt \cos \theta\hat{\mathbf{k}}$ (b) The planet exerts a gravitational torque on the ball.   (c) $-mg\ell \cos \theta\hat{\mathbf{k}}$
23. (a) 0.360 kg $\cdot$ m^2/s   (b) 0.540 kg $\cdot$ m^2/s
25. (a) 0.433 kg $\cdot$ m^2/s   (b) 1.73 kg $\cdot$ m^2/s
27. (a) 1.57×10^8 kg $\cdot$ m^2/s   (b) 6.26×10^3 s $= 1.74$ h
29. (a) $\omega_f = \omega_i I_1/(I_1 + I_2)$ (b) $I_1/(I_1 + I_2)$
31. (a) 11.1 rad/s counterclockwise   (b) No. 507 J is transformed into internal energy.   (c) No. The turntable bearing promptly imparts impulse 44.9 kg $\cdot$ m/s north into the turntable-clay system and thereafter keeps changing the system momentum.
33. 7.14 rev/min
35. (a) Mechanical energy is not conserved; some chemical energy is converted into mechanical energy. Momentum is not conserved. The turntable bearing exerts an external northward force on the axle. Angular momentum is conserved.   (b) 0.360 rad/s counterclockwise   (c) 99.9 J
37. (a) $mv\ell$ down   (b) $M/(M + m)$
39. (a) $\omega = 2mv_i d/[M + 2m]R^2$ (b) No; some mechanical energy changes into internal energy.   (c) Momentum is not conserved. The axle exerts a backward force on the cylinder.
41. $\sim 10^{-13}$ rad/s
43. 5.45×10^{22} N $\cdot$ m
45. (a) $1.67\hat{\mathbf{i}}$ m/s   (b) $0.033\ 5 = 3.35\%$ (c) $1.67\hat{\mathbf{i}}$ m/s
    (d) 15.8 rad/s   (e) $1.00 = 100\%$
47. (a) $7md^2/3$ (b) $mgd\hat{\mathbf{k}}$ (c) $3g/7d$ counterclockwise
    (d) $2g/7$ upward   (e) mgd (f) $\sqrt{6g/7d}$ (g) $m\sqrt{14gd^3}/3$
    (h) $\sqrt{2gd/21}$
49. 0.910 km/s
51. (a) $v_i r_i/r$ (b) $T = (mv_i^2 r_i^2) r^{-3}$ (c) $\frac{1}{2}mv_i^2 (r_i^2/r^2 - 1)$
    (d) 4.50 m/s, 10.1 N, 0.450 J
53. (a) $3\ 750$ kg $\cdot$ m^2/s   (b) 1.88 kJ   (c) $3\ 750$ kg $\cdot$ m^2/s
    (d) 10.0 m/s   (e) 7.50 kJ   (f) 5.62 kJ
55. (a) $2mv_0$ (b) $2v_0/3$ (c) $4m\ell v_0/3$ (d) $4v_0/9\ell$ (e) mv_0^2
    (f) $26mv_0^2/27$ (g) No horizontal forces act on the bola from outside after release, so the horizontal momentum stays constant. Its center of mass moves steadily with the horizontal velocity it had at release. No torques about its axis of rotation act on the bola, so its spin angular momentum stays constant. Internal forces cannot affect momentum conservation and angular momentum conservation, but they can affect mechanical energy. Energy $mv_0^2/27$ changes from mechanical energy into internal energy as the bola takes its stable configuration.
57. An increase of 0.550 s. It is not a significant change.

CHAPTER 12

1. $[(m_1 + m_b)d + m_1\ell/2]/m_2$
3. $(3.85$ cm, 6.85 cm$)$

5. $(-1.50$ m, -1.50 m$)$
7. $(2.54$ m, 4.75 m$)$
9. 177 kg
11. (a) $f_s = 268$ N, $n = 1\ 300$ N   (b) 0.324
13. 2.94 kN on each rear wheel and 4.41 kN on each front wheel
15. (a) 29.9 N   (b) 22.2 N
17. (a) 1.73 rad/s^2 (b) 1.56 rad/s
    (c) $(-4.72\hat{\mathbf{i}} + 6.62\hat{\mathbf{j}})$ kN   (d) $38.9\hat{\mathbf{j}}$ kN
19. 2.82 m
21. 88.2 N and 58.8 N
23. 4.90 mm
25. 23.8 μm
27. (a) 3.14×10^4 N   (b) 6.28×10^4 N
29. 1.65×10^8 N/m^2
31. 0.860 mm
33. $n_A = 5.98 \times 10^5$ N, $n_B = 4.80 \times 10^5$ N
35. 9.00 ft
37. (a)

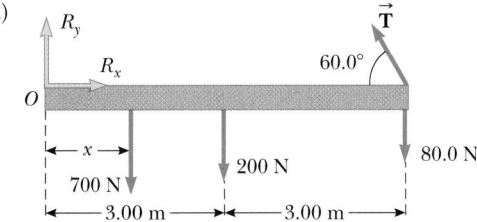

(b) $T = 343$ N, $R_x = 171$ N to the right, $R_y = 683$ N up
    (c) 5.13 m
39. (a) $T = F_g(L + d)/[\sin \theta (2L + d)]$
    (b) $R_x = F_g(L + d)\cot \theta/(2L + d)$, $R_y = F_gL/(2L + d)$
41. $\vec{\mathbf{F}}_A = (-6.47 \times 10^5\hat{\mathbf{i}} + 1.27 \times 10^5\hat{\mathbf{j}})$ N,
    $\vec{\mathbf{F}}_B = 6.47 \times 10^5\hat{\mathbf{i}}$ N
43. 5.08 kN, $R_x = 4.77$ kN, $R_y = 8.26$ kN
45. (a) 20.1 cm to the left of the front edge; $\mu_k = 0.571$
    (b) 0.501 m
47. (a) $M = (m/2) (2\mu_s \sin \theta - \cos \theta)(\cos \theta - \mu_s \sin \theta)^{-1}$
    (b) $R = (m + M)g(1 + \mu_s^2)^{1/2}$
    $F = g[M^2 + \mu_s^2(m + M)^2]^{1/2}$
49. (b) AB compression 732 N, AC tension 634 N, BC compression 897 N
51. (a) 133 N   (b) $n_A = 429$ N and $n_B = 257$ N
    (c) $R_x = 133$ N and $R_y = -257$ N
55. 1.09 m
57. (a) $4\ 500$ N   (b) 4.50×10^6 N/m^2 (c) The board will break.
59. (a) $P_y = (F_g/L) (d - ah/g)$ (b) 0.306 m
    (c) $(-306\hat{\mathbf{i}} + 553\hat{\mathbf{j}})$ N

CHAPTER 13

1. $\sim 10^{-7}$ N toward you
3. (a) 2.50×10^{-5} N toward the 500-kg object   (b) between the objects and 0.245 m from the 500-kg object
5. $(-100\hat{\mathbf{i}} + 59.3\hat{\mathbf{j}})$ pN
7. 7.41×10^{-10} N
9. 0.613 m/s^2 toward the Earth
11. $\rho_{Moon}/\rho_{Earth} = \frac{2}{3}$
13. 1.26×10^{32} kg
15. 1.90×10^{27} kg
17. 8.92×10^7 m
19. After 3.93 yr, Mercury would be farther from the Sun than Pluto.

21. $\vec{\mathbf{g}} = \dfrac{Gm}{\ell^2}\left(\tfrac{1}{2} + \sqrt{2}\right)$ toward the opposite corner

23. (a) $\vec{\mathbf{g}} = 2MGr(r^2 + a^2)^{-3/2}$ toward the center of mass (b) At $r = 0$, the fields of the two objects are equal in magnitude and opposite in direction, to add to zero. (d) When r is much greater than a, the fact that the two masses are separate is unimportant. They create a total field like that of a single object of mass $2M$.

25. (a) 1.84×10^9 kg/m^3 (b) 3.27×10^6 m/s^2
(c) -2.08×10^{13} J

27. (a) -1.67×10^{-14} J   (b) Each object will slowly accelerate toward the center of the triangle, where the three will simultaneously collide.

29. (b) 340 s

31. 1.66×10^4 m/s

35. (a) 5.30×10^3 s   (b) 7.79 km/s   (c) 6.43×10^9 J

37. (b) 1.00×10^7 m   (c) 1.00×10^4 m/s

39. (a) 0.980   (b) 127 yr   (c) -2.13×10^{17} J

43. (b) $2[Gm^3(1/2r - 1/R)]^{1/2}$

45. (a) -7.04×10^4 J   (b) -1.57×10^5 J   (c) 13.2 m/s

47. 7.79×10^{14} kg

49. $\omega = 0.057\ 2$ rad/s or 1 rev in 110 s

51. (a) $m_2(2G/d)^{1/2}(m_1 + m_2)^{-1/2}$ and
$m_1(2G/d)^{1/2}(m_1 + m_2)^{-1/2}$; relative speed
$(2G/d)^{1/2}(m_1 + m_2)^{1/2}$ (b) 1.07×10^{32} J and 2.67×10^{31} J

53. (a) 200 Myr   (b) $\sim 10^{41}$ kg; $\sim 10^{11}$ stars

55. $(GM_E/4R_E)^{1/2}$

59. $(800 + 1.73 \times 10^{-4})\hat{\mathbf{i}}$ m/s and $(800 - 1.73 \times 10^{-4})\hat{\mathbf{i}}$ m/s

61. 18.2 ms

CHAPTER 14

1. 0.111 kg

3. 6.24 MPa

5. 1.62 m

7. 7.74×10^{-3} m^2

9. 271 kN horizontally backward

11. 5.88×10^6 N down; 196 kN outward; 588 kN outward

13. 0.722 mm

15. 10.5 m; no because some alcohol and water evaporate

17. 98.6 kPa

19. (a) 1.57 Pa, 1.55×10^{-2} atm, 11.8 mm Hg   (b) The fluid level in the tap should rise.   (c) blockage of flow of the cerebrospinal fluid

21. 0.258 N down

23. (a) $1.017\ 9 \times 10^3$ N down, $1.029\ 7 \times 10^3$ N up   (b) 86.2 N (c) By either method of evaluation, the buoyant force is 11.8 N up.

25. (a) 1.20×10^3 N/s   (b) 0

27. (a) 7.00 cm   (b) 2.80 kg

31. 1 430 m^3

33. 1 250 kg/m^3 and 500 kg/m^3

35. (a) 17.7 m/s   (b) 1.73 mm

37. 31.6 m/s

39. 0.247 cm

41. (a) 2.28 N toward Holland   (b) 1.74×10^6 s

43. (a) 1 atm + 15.0 MPa   (b) 2.95 m/s   (c) 4.34 kPa

45. 2.51×10^{-3} m^3/s

47. (a) 4.43 m/s   (b) The siphon can be no higher than 10.3 m.

49. 12.6 m/s

51. 1.91 m

55. 0.604 m

57. If the helicopter could create the air it expels downward, the mass flow rate of the air would have to be at least 233 kg/s. In reality, the rotor takes in air from above, which is moving over a larger area with lower speed, and blows it downward at higher speed. The amount of this air has to be at least a few times larger than 233 kg every second.

61. 17.3 N and 31.7 N

63. 90.04%

65. 758 Pa

67. 4.43 m/s

69. (a) 1.25 cm   (b) 13.8 m/s

71. (c) 1.70 m^2

CHAPTER 15

1. (a) The motion repeats precisely.   (b) 1.81 s   (c) No, the force is not in the form of Hooke's law.

3. (a) 1.50 Hz, 0.667 s   (b) 4.00 m   (c) π rad   (d) 2.83 m

5. (b) 18.8 cm/s, 0.333 s   (c) 178 cm/s^2, 0.500 s
(d) 12.0 cm

7. 40.9 N/m

9. 18.8 m/s, 7.11 km/s^2

11. (a) 40.0 cm/s, 160 cm/s^2 (b) 32.0 cm/s, -96.0 cm/s^2
(c) 0.232 s

13. 0.628 m/s

15. 2.23 m/s

17. (a) 28.0 mJ   (b) 1.02 m/s   (c) 12.2 mJ   (d) 15.8 mJ

19. 2.60 cm and -2.60 cm

21. (a) at 0.218 s and at 1.09 s   (b) 0.014 6 W

23. (b) 0.628 s

25. Assuming simple harmonic motion, (a) 0.820 m/s, (b) 2.57 rad/s^2, and (c) 0.641 N. More precisely, (a) 0.817 m/s, (b) 2.54 rad/s^2, and (c) 0.634 N. The answers agree to two digits. The answers computed from conservation of energy and from Newton's second law are more precisely correct. With this amplitude, the motion of the pendulum is approximately simple harmonic.

29. 0.944 kg $\cdot$ m^2

33. (a) 5.00×10^{-7} kg $\cdot$ m^2 (b) 3.16×10^{-4} N $\cdot$ m/rad

35. 1.00×10^{-3} s^{-1}

37. (a) 7.00 Hz   (b) 2.00%   (c) 10.6 s

39. (a) 1.00 s   (b) 5.09 cm

41. 318 N

43. 1.74 Hz

45. (a) 2.09 s   (b) 0.477 Hz   (c) 36.0 cm/s
(d) $(0.064\ 8\ \text{m}^2/\text{s}^2)\,m$ (e) $(9.00/\text{s}^2)\,m$
(f) Period, frequency, and maximum speed are all independent of mass in this situation. The energy and the force constant are directly proportional to mass.

47. (a) $2Mg$, $Mg(1 + y/L)$ (b) $T = (4\pi/3)(2L/g)^{1/2}$, 2.68 s

49. 6.62 cm

51. 9.19×10^{13} Hz

53. (a)

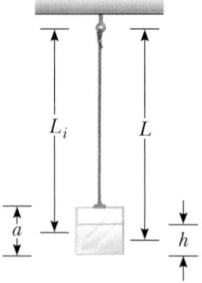

(b) $\dfrac{dT}{dt} = \dfrac{\pi\, dM/dt}{2\rho a^2 g^{1/2}[L_i + (dM/dt)t/2\rho a^2]^{1/2}}$

(c) $T = 2\pi g^{-1/2}\left[L_i + \left(\dfrac{dM}{dt}\right)\left(\dfrac{t}{2\rho a^2}\right)\right]^{1/2}$

55. $f = (2\pi L)^{-1}\left(gL + \dfrac{kh^2}{M}\right)^{1/2}$

57. (b) 1.23 Hz

59. (a) 3.00 s   (b) 14.3 J   (c) 25.5°

61. If the cyclist goes over washboard bumps at one certain speed, they can excite a resonance vibration of the bike, so large in amplitude as to make the rider lose control. $\sim 10^1$ m

69. (b) after 42.2 minutes

CHAPTER 16

1. $y = 6\,[(x - 4.5t)^2 + 3]^{-1}$

3. (a) the P wave   (b) 665 s

5. (a) $(3.33\hat{\mathbf{i}})$ m/s   (b) −5.48 cm   (c) 0.667 m, 5.00 Hz   (d) 11.0 m/s

7. 0.319 m

9. 2.00 cm, 2.98 m, 0.576 Hz, 1.72 m/s

11. (a) 31.4 rad/s   (b) 1.57 rad/m   (c) $y = (0.120\text{ m})\sin(1.57x - 31.4t)$ where x is in meters and t is in seconds   (d) 3.77 m/s   (e) 118 m/s²

13. (a) 0.250 m   (b) 40.0 rad/s   (c) 0.300 rad/m   (d) 20.9 m   (e) 133 m/s   (f) $+x$

15. (a) $y = (8.00\text{ cm})\sin(7.85x + 6\pi t)$ (b) $y = (8.00\text{ cm})\sin(7.85x + 6\pi t - 0.785)$

17. (a) −1.51 m/s, 0   (b) 16.0 m, 0.500 s, 32.0 m/s

19. (a) 0.500 Hz, 3.14 rad/s   (b) 3.14 rad/m   (c) $(0.100\text{ m})\sin(3.14\,x/\text{m} - 3.14\,t/\text{s})$ (d) $(0.100\text{ m})\sin(-3.14\,t/\text{s})$ (e) $(0.100\text{ m})\sin(4.71\text{ rad} - 3.14\,t/\text{s})$ (f) 0.314 m/s

21. 80.0 N

23. 520 m/s

25. 1.64 m/s²

27. 13.5 N

29. 185 m/s

31. 0.329 s

35. 55.1 Hz

37. (a) 62.5 m/s   (b) 7.85 m   (c) 7.96 Hz   (d) 21.1 W

39. $\sqrt{2}\,\mathcal{P}_0$

41. (a) $A = 40$ (b) $A = 7.00$, $B = 0$, $C = 3.00$. One can take the dot product of the given equation with each one of $\hat{\mathbf{i}}, \hat{\mathbf{j}}$, and $\hat{\mathbf{k}}$.   (c) $A = 0$, $B = 7.00$ mm, $C = 3.00$/m, $D = 4.00$/s, $E = 2.00$. Consider the average value of both sides of the given equation to find A. Then consider the maximum value of both sides to find B. You can evaluate the partial derivative of both sides of the given equation with respect to x and separately with respect to t to obtain equations yielding C and D upon chosen substitutions for x and t. Then substitute $x = 0$ and $t = 0$ to obtain E.

45. ~ 1 min

47. 0.456 m/s

49. (a) 39.2 N   (b) 0.892 m   (c) 83.6 m/s

51. (a) The energy a wave crest carries is constant in the absence of absorption. Then the rate at which energy moves beyond a fixed distance from the source, which is the power of the wave, is constant. The power is proportional to the square of the amplitude and to the wave

speed. The speed decreases as the wave moves into shallower water near shore, so the amplitude must increase. (b) 8.31 m   (c) As the water depth goes to zero, our model would predict zero speed and infinite amplitude. The amplitude must be finite as the wave comes ashore. As the speed decreases, the wavelength also decreases. When it becomes comparable to the water depth, or smaller, the expression $v = \sqrt{gd}$ no longer applies.

53. (a) $\mathcal{P} = (0.050\ 0\text{ kg/s})v_{y,\text{max}}^2$ (b) The power is proportional to the square of the maximum element speed.   (c) $(7.5 \times 10^{-4}\text{ kg})v_{y,\text{max}}^2 = \frac12 m_3 v_{y,\text{max}}^2$ (d) $(0.300\text{ kg})v_{y,\text{max}}^2$

55. 0.084 3 rad

59. (a) $(0.707)2(L/g)^{1/2}$ (b) $L/4$

61. 3.86×10^{-4}

63. (a) $\dfrac{\mu\omega^3}{2k}A_0^2 e^{-2bx}$ (b) $\dfrac{\mu\omega^3}{2k}A_0^2$ (c) e^{-2bx}

65. (a) $\mu_0 + (\mu_L - \mu_0)x/L$

CHAPTER 17

1. 5.56 km. As long as the speed of light is much greater than the speed of sound, its actual value does not matter.

3. 0.196 s

5. 7.82 m

7. (a) 826 m   (b) 1.47 s

9. (a) 0.625 mm   (b) 1.50 mm to 75.0 μm

11. (a) 2.00 μm, 40.0 cm, 54.6 m/s   (b) −0.433 μm   (c) 1.72 mm/s

13. $\Delta P = (0.200\text{ N/m}^2)\sin(62.8x/\text{m} - 2.16 \times 10^4 t/\text{s})$

15. 5.81 m

17. 66.0 dB

19. (a) 3.75 W/m²   (b) 0.600 W/m²

21. (a) 2.34 m and 0.390 m   (b) 0.161 N/m² for both notes   (c) 4.25×10^{-7} m and 7.09×10^{-8} m   (d) The wavelengths and displacement amplitudes would be larger by a factor of 1.09. The answer to part (b) would be unchanged.

23. (a) 1.32×10^{-4} W/m²   (b) 81.2 dB

25. (a) 0.691 m   (b) 691 km

27. 65.6 dB

29. (a) 30.0 m   (b) 9.49×10^5 m

31. (a) 332 J   (b) 46.4 dB

33. (a) 3.04 kHz   (b) 2.08 kHz   (c) 2.62 kHz, 2.40 kHz

35. 26.4 m/s

37. 19.3 m

39. (a) 56.3 s   (b) 56.6 km farther along

41. 2.82×10^8 m/s

43. It is unreasonable, implying a sound level of 123 dB. Nearly all the missing mechanical energy becomes internal energy in the latch.

45. (a) f is a few hundred hertz. $\lambda \sim 1$ m, duration ~ 0.1 s.   (b) Yes. The frequency can be close to 1 000 Hz. If the person clapping his or her hands is at the base of the pyramid, the echo can drop somewhat in frequency and in loudness as sound returns, with the later cycles coming from the smaller and more distant upper risers. The sound could imitate some particular bird and could in fact be a recording of the call.

49. (a) 0.515/min   (b) 0.614/min

51. (a) 55.8 m/s   (b) 2 500 Hz

53. 1 204.2 Hz

55. (a) 0.642 W   (b) 0.004 28 = 0.428%

57. (a) The sound through the metal arrives first.
(b) $(365 \text{ m/s}) \Delta t$ (c) 46.3 m   (d) The answer becomes

$$\ell = \frac{\Delta t}{\dfrac{1}{331 \text{ m/s}} - \dfrac{1}{v_r}}$$

where v_r is the speed of sound in the rod. As v_r goes to infinity, the travel time in the rod becomes negligible. The answer approaches $(331 \text{ m/s}) \Delta t$, which is the distance the sound travels in air during the delay time.
59. (a) $0.948°$ (b) $4.40°$
61. 1.34×10^4 N
63. (a) 6.45   (b) 0

CHAPTER 18

1. (a) -1.65 cm   (b) -6.02 cm   (c) 1.15 cm
3. (a) $+x, -x$ (b) 0.750 s   (c) 1.00 m
5. (a) 9.24 m   (b) 600 Hz
7. (a) 2   (b) 9.28 m and 1.99 m
9. (a) $156°$ (b) 0.058 4 cm
11. 15.7 m, 31.8 Hz, 500 m/s
13. At 0.089 1 m, 0.303 m, 0.518 m, 0.732 m, 0.947 m, 1.16 m from one speaker
15. (a) 4.24 cm   (b) 6.00 cm   (c) 6.00 cm
(d) 0.500 cm, 1.50 cm, 2.50 cm
17. 0.786 Hz, 1.57 Hz, 2.36 Hz, 3.14 Hz
19. (a) 350 Hz   (b) 400 kg
21. (a) 163 N   (b) 660 Hz
23. $\dfrac{Mg}{4Lf^2 \tan \theta}$
25. (a) 3 loops   (b) 16.7 Hz   (c) 1 loop
27. (a) 3.66 m/s   (b) 0.200 Hz
29. (a) 0.357 m   (b) 0.715 m
31. 0.656 m and 1.64 m
33. $n(206 \text{ Hz})$ for $n = 1$ to 9 and $n(84.5 \text{ Hz})$ for $n = 2$ to 23
35. 50.0 Hz, 1.70 m
37. (a) 350 m/s   (b) 1.14 m
39. (21.5 ± 0.1) m. The data suggest 0.6-Hz uncertainty in the frequency measurements, which is only a little more than 1%.
41. (a) 1.59 kHz   (b) odd-numbered harmonics   (c) 1.11 kHz
43. 5.64 beats/s
45. (a) 1.99 beats/s   (b) 3.38 m/s
47. The second harmonic of E is close to the third harmonic of A, and the fourth harmonic of C# is close to the fifth harmonic of A.
49. (a) The yo-yo's downward speed is $dL/dt = (0.8 \text{ m/s}^2)(1.2 \text{ s}) = 0.960 \text{ m/s}$. The instantaneous wavelength of the fundamental string wave is given by $d_{NN} = \lambda/2 = L$, so $\lambda = 2L$ and $d\lambda/dt = 2 \, dL/dt = 2(0.96 \text{ m/s}) = 1.92 \text{ m/s}$. (b) For the second harmonic, the wavelength is equal to the length of the string. Then the rate of change of wavelength is equal to $dL/dt = 0.960 \text{ m/s}$, half as much as for the first harmonic.   (c) A yo-yo of different mass will hold the string under different tension to make each string wave vibrate with a different frequency, but the geometrical argument given in parts (a) and (b) still applies to the wavelength. The answers are unchanged: $d\lambda_1/dt = 1.92 \text{ m/s}$ and $d\lambda_2/dt = 0.960 \text{ m/s}$.
51. (a) 34.8 m/s   (b) 0.977 m
53. 3.85 m/s away from the station or 3.77 m/s toward the station

55. (a) 59.9 Hz   (b) 20.0 cm
57. (a) $\frac{1}{2}$ (b) $[n/(n+1)]^2 T$ (c) $\frac{9}{16}$
59. $y_1 + y_2 = 11.2 \sin (2.00x - 10.0t + 63.4°)$
61. (a) 78.9 N   (b) 211 Hz

CHAPTER 19

1. (a) $-274°C$ (b) 1.27 atm   (c) 1.74 atm
3. (a) $-320°F$ (b) 77.3 K
5. 3.27 cm
7. (a) 0.176 mm   (b) 8.78 μm   (c) 0.093 0 cm^3
9. (a) $-179°C$ is attainable.   (b) $-376°C$ is below 0 K and unattainable.
11. (a) 99.8 mL   (b) about 6% of the volume change of the acetone
13. (a) 99.4 cm^3 (b) 0.943 cm
15. 5 336 images
17. (a) 400 kPa   (b) 449 kPa
19. 1.50×10^{29} molecules
21. 472 K
23. (a) 41.6 mol   (b) 1.20 kg, nearly in agreement with the tabulated density
25. (a) 1.17 g   (b) 11.5 mN   (c) 1.01 kN
(d) The molecules must be moving very fast.
27. 4.39 kg
29. (a) 7.13 m   (b) The open end of the tube should be at the bottom after the bird surfaces so that the water can drain out. There is no other requirement. Air does not tend to bubble out of a narrow tube.
31. (a) 94.97 cm   (b) 95.03 cm
33. 3.55 cm
35. It falls by 0.094 3 Hz.
37. (a) Expansion makes density drop.   (b) $5 \times 10^{-5}(°C)^{-1}$
39. (a) $h = nRT/(mg + P_0 A)$ (b) 0.661 m
41. We assume $\alpha \, \Delta T$ is much less than 1.
43. Yes, as long as the coefficients of expansion remain constant. The lengths L_C and L_S at 0°C need to satisfy $17L_C = 11L_S$. Then the steel rod must be longer. With $L_S - L_C = 5.00$ cm, the only possibility is $L_S = 14.2$ cm and $L_C = 9.17$ cm.
45. (a) 0.340%   (b) 0.480%
47. 2.74 m
49. (b) 1.33 kg/m^3
53. No. Steel would need to be 2.30 times stronger.
55. (a) $L_f = L_i e^{\alpha \Delta T}$ (b) $2.00 \times 10^{-4}\%; 59.4\%$
57. (a) 6.17×10^{-3} kg/m   (b) 632 N   (c) 580 N; 192 Hz
59. 4.54 m

CHAPTER 20

1. $(10.0 + 0.117)°C$
3. 0.234 kJ/kg $\cdot$ °C
5. 1.78×10^4 kg
7. 29.6°C
9. (a) 0.435 cal/g $\cdot$ °C   (b) We cannot make a definite identification. The material might be an unknown alloy or a material not listed in the table. It might be beryllium.
11. 23.6°C
13. 1.22×10^5 J
15. 0.294 g
17. 0.414 kg
19. (a) 0°C   (b) 114 g
21. -1.18 MJ

23. -466 J

25. (a) $-4P_iV_i$ (b) It is proportional to the square of the volume, according to $T = (P_i/nRV_i)V^2$.

27. $Q = -720$ J

29.

	Q	W	ΔE_{int}
BC	$-$	0	$-$
CA	$-$	$+$	$-$
AB	$+$	$-$	$+$

31. (a) 7.50 kJ   (b) 900 K

33. -3.10 kJ, 37.6 kJ

35. (a) $0.041\,0$ m^3 (b) $+5.48$ kJ   (c) -5.48 kJ

37. 10.0 kW

39. 51.2°C

41. 74.8 kJ

43. (a) 0.964 kg or more   (b) The test samples and the inner surface of the insulation can be prewarmed to 37.0°C as the box is assembled. Then nothing changes in temperature during the test period, and the masses of the test samples and insulation make no difference.

45. 3.49×10^3 K

47. Intensity is defined as power per area perpendicular to the direction of energy flow. The direction of sunlight is along the line from the Sun to the object. The perpendicular area is the projected flat, circular area enclosed by the *terminator*, the line that separates day and night on the object. The object radiates infrared light outward in all directions. The area perpendicular to this energy flow is its spherical surface area. The steady-state surface temperature is 279 K = 6°C. We find this temperature to be chilly, well below comfortable room temperatures.

49. 2.27 km

51. (a) 16.8 L   (b) 0.351 L/s

53. $c = \mathscr{P}/\rho R\,\Delta T$

55. 5.87×10^{4}°C

57. 5.31 h

59. 1.44 kg

61. 38.6 m^3/d

63. 9.32 kW

65. (a) The equation $dT/dr = \mathscr{P}/4\pi kr^2$ represents the law of thermal conduction, incorporating the definition of thermal conductivity, applied to a spherical surface within the shell. The rate of energy transfer $\mathscr{P}$ must be the same for all radii so that each bit of material stays at a temperature that is constant in time.   (b) We separate the variables T and r in the thermal conduction equation and integrate the equation between points on the interior and exterior surfaces.   (c) 18.5 W   (d) With $\mathscr{P}$ now known, we separate the variables again and integrate between a point on the interior surface and any point within the shell.   (e) $T = 5°C + 184$ cm $\cdot$ °C $[1/(3$ cm$) - 1/r]$ (f) 29.5°C

CHAPTER 21

1. (a) 4.00 u $= 6.64 \times 10^{-24}$ g   (b) 55.9 u $= 9.28 \times 10^{-23}$ g   (c) 207 u $= 3.44 \times 10^{-22}$ g

3. 0.943 N, 1.57 Pa

5. 3.21×10^{12} molecules

7. 3.32 mol

9. (a) 3.54×10^{23} atoms   (b) 6.07×10^{-21} J   (c) 1.35 km/s

11. (a) 8.76×10^{-21} J for both   (b) 1.62 km/s for helium and 514 m/s for argon

13. (a) 3.46 kJ   (b) 2.45 kJ   (c) -1.01 kJ

15. Between 10^{-2}°C and 10^{-3}°C

17. $13.5PV$

19. (a) 1.39 atm   (b) 366 K, 253 K   (c) 0, -4.66 kJ, -4.66 kJ

21. 227 K

23. (a)

   (b) 8.77 L   (c) 900 K   (d) 300 K   (e) -336 J

25. (a) 28.0 kJ   (b) 46.0 kJ   (c) isothermal process: $P_f = 10.0$ atm; adiabatic process: $P_f = 25.1$ atm

27. (a) 9.95 cal/K, 13.9 cal/K   (b) 13.9 cal/K, 17.9 cal/K

29. Sulfur dioxide is the gas in Table 21.2 with the greatest molecular mass. If the effective spring constants for various chemical bonds are comparable, SO$_2$ can then be expected to have low frequencies of atomic vibration. Vibration can be excited at lower temperature for sulfur dioxide than for the other gases. Some vibration may be going on at 300 K.

31. (a) 6.80 m/s   (b) 7.41 m/s   (c) 7.00 m/s

35. (a) 2.37×10^4 K   (b) 1.06×10^3 K

37. (b) 0.278

39. (a) 100 kPa, 66.5 L, 400 K, 5.82 kJ, 7.48 kJ, -1.66 kJ
   (b) 133 kPa, 49.9 L, 400 K, 5.82 kJ, 5.82 kJ, 0
   (c) 120 kPa, 41.6 L, 300 K, 0, -909 J, $+909$ J
   (d) 120 kPa, 43.3 L, 312 K, 722 J, 0, $+722$ J

41. (b) 447 J/kg·°C agrees with the tabulated value within 0.3%.   (c) 127 J/kg·°C agrees with the tabulated value within 2%.

43. (b) The expressions are equal because $PV = nRT$ and $\gamma = (C_V + R)/C_V = 1 + R/C_V$ give $R = (\gamma - 1)C_V$, so $PV = n(\gamma - 1)C_VT$ and $PV/(\gamma - 1) = nC_VT$

45. 510 K and 290 K

47. 0.623

49. (a) Pressure increases as volume decreases.
   (d) 0.500 atm^{-1}, 0.300 atm^{-1}

51. (a) 7.27×10^{-20} J   (b) 2.20 km/s   (c) 3 510 K. The evaporating molecules are exceptional, at the high-speed tail of the distribution of molecular speeds. The average speed of molecules in the liquid and in the vapor is appropriate only to room temperature.

53. (a) 0.514 m^3 (b) 2.06 m^3 (c) 2.38×10^3 K   (d) -480 kJ   (e) 2.28 MJ

55. 1.09×10^{-3}, 2.69×10^{-2}, 0.529, 1.00, 0.199, 1.01×10^{-41}, $1.25 \times 10^{-1\,082}$

59. (a) 0.203 mol   (b) $T_B = T_C = 900$ K, $V_C = 15.0$ L

(c, d)	P, atm	V, L	T, K	E_{int}, kJ
A	1.00	5.00	300	0.760
B	3.00	5.00	900	2.28
C	1.00	15.0	900	2.28
A	1.00	5.00	300	0.760

   (e) Lock the piston in place and put the cylinder into an oven at 900 K. Keep the gas in the oven while gradually letting the gas expand to lift a load on the piston as far as it can. Move the cylinder from the oven back to the 300-K room and let the gas cool and contract.

(f, g)	Q, kJ	W, kJ	ΔE_{int}, kJ
AB	1.52	0	1.52
BC	1.67	−1.67	0
CA	−2.53	+1.01	−1.52
ABCA	0.656	−0.656	0

61. (b) 1.60×10^4 K

CHAPTER 22

1. (a) 6.94% (b) 335 J
3. (a) 10.7 kJ (b) 0.533 s
5. 55.4%
7. 77.8 W
9. (a) 67.2% (b) 58.8 kW
11. The actual efficiency of 0.069 8 is less than four-tenths of the Carnot efficiency of 0.177.
13. (a) 741 J (b) 459 J
15. (a) 564 K (b) 212 kW (c) 47.5%
17. (b) $1 - T_c/T_h$, the same as for a single reversible engine (c) $(T_c + T_h)/2$ (d) $(T_h T_c)^{1/2}$
19. 9.00
23. 72.2 J
25. 23.1 mW
27. (a) 244 kPa (b) 192 J
29. (a) 51.2% (b) 36.2%
33. 195 J/K
35. 1.02 kJ/K
37. $\sim 10^0$ W/K from metabolism; much more if you are using high-power electric appliances or an automobile
39. 5.76 J/K; the temperature is constant if the gas is ideal.
41. (a) 1 (b) 6
43. (a)

Result	Number of ways to draw
All R	1
2 R, 1 G	3
1 R, 2 G	3
All G	1

(b)

Result	Number of ways to draw
All R	1
4R, 1G	5
3R, 2G	10
2R, 3G	10
1R, 4G	5
All G	1

45. (a) 214 J, 64.3 J (b) −35.7 J, −35.7 J. The net effect would be the transport of energy by heat from the cold to the hot reservoir without expenditure of external work. (c) 333 J, 233 J (d) 83.3 J, 83.3 J, 0. The net effect would be converting energy, taken in by heat, entirely into energy output by work in a cyclic process. (e) −0.111 J/K. The entropy of the Universe would have decreased.

47. (a) 5.00 kW (b) 763 W
49. (a) $2nRT_i \ln 2$ (b) 0.273
51. 5.97×10^4 kg/s
53. (a) 8.48 kW (b) 1.52 kW (c) 1.09×10^4 J/K (d) The COP drops by 20.0%.
55. (a) $10.5nRT_i$ (b) $8.50nRT_i$ (c) 0.190 (d) This efficiency is much less than the 0.833 for a Carnot engine operating between the temperatures used here.
57. (a) $nC_P \ln 3$ (b) Both ask for the change in entropy between the same two states of the same system. Entropy is a state variable. The change in entropy does not depend on path, but only on original and final states.
61. (a) 20.0°C (c) $\Delta S = +4.88$ J/K (d) The mixing is irreversible. It is clear that warm water and cool water do not come unmixed, and the entropy change is positive.

CHAPTER 23

1. (a) +160 zC, 1.01 u (b) +160 zC, 23.0 u (c) −160 zC, 35.5 u (d) +320 zC, 40.1 u (e) −480 zC, 14.0 u (f) +640 zC, 14.0 u (g) +1.12 aC, 14.0 u (h) −160 zC, 18.0 u
3. The force is $\sim 10^{26}$ N.
5. (a) 1.59 nN away from the other (b) 1.24×10^{36} times larger (c) 8.61×10^{-11} C/kg
7. 0.872 N at 330°
9. (a) 2.16×10^{-5} N toward the other (b) 8.99×10^{-7} N away from the other
11. (a) 82.2 nN toward the other particle (b) 2.19 Mm/s
13. (a) 55.8 pN/C down (b) 102 nN/C up
15. The field at the origin can be to the right if the unknown charge is $-9Q$, or the field can be to the left if and only if the unknown charge is $+27Q$.
17. (a) $5.91k_e q/a^2$ at 58.8° (b) $5.91 k_e q^2/a^2$ at 58.8°
19. (a) $k_e Qx\hat{\mathbf{i}}/(R^2 + x^2)^{3/2}$ (b) As long as the charge is symmetrically placed, the number of charges does not matter. A continuous ring corresponds to n becoming larger without limit.
21. 1.59×10^6 N/C toward the rod
23. (a) $6.64\hat{\mathbf{i}}$ MN/C (b) $24.1\hat{\mathbf{i}}$ MN/C (c) $6.40\hat{\mathbf{i}}$ MN/C (d) $0.664\hat{\mathbf{i}}$ MN/C, taking the axis of the ring as the x axis
25. (a) 93.6 MN/C; the near-field approximation is 104 MN/C, about 11% high. (b) 0.516 MN/C; the charged-particle approximation is 0.519 MN/C, about 0.6% high.
27. $-21.6\hat{\mathbf{i}}$ MN/C
31. (a) 86.4 pC for each (b) 324 pC, 459 pC, 459 pC, 432 pC (c) 57.6 pC, 106 pC, 154 pC, 96.0 pC
33.

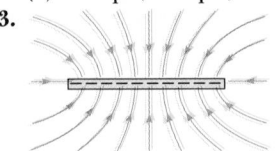

35. (a)

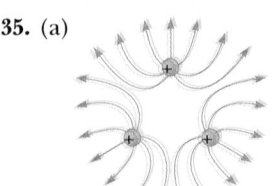

The field is zero at the center of the triangle. (b) $1.73 k_e q\hat{\mathbf{j}}/a^2$

37. (a) 61.3 Gm/s² (b) 19.5 μs (c) 11.7 m (d) 1.20 fJ
39. K/ed in the direction of motion
41. (a) 111 ns (b) 5.68 mm (c) $(450\hat{\mathbf{i}} + 102\hat{\mathbf{j}})$ km/s

43. (a) 21.8 μm (b) 2.43 cm
45. (a) 10.9 nC (b) 5.44 mN
47. 40.9 N at 263°
49. $Q = 2L\sqrt{\dfrac{k(L - L_i)}{k_e}}$
53. $-707\hat{\mathbf{j}}$ mN
55. (a) $\theta_1 = \theta_2$
57. (a) 0.307 s (b) Yes. Ignoring gravity makes a difference of 2.28%.
59. (a) $\vec{\mathbf{F}} = 1.90(k_e q^2/s^2)(\hat{\mathbf{i}} + \hat{\mathbf{j}} + \hat{\mathbf{k}})$ (b) $\vec{\mathbf{F}} = 3.29(k_e q^2/s^2)$ in the direction away from the diagonally opposite vertex
65. $\dfrac{k_e \lambda_0}{2x_0}(-\hat{\mathbf{i}})$

CHAPTER 24

1. 4.14 MN/C
3. (a) aA (b) bA (c) 0
5. 1.87 kN·m²/C
7. (a) -6.89 MN·m²/C (b) The number of lines entering exceeds the number leaving by 2.91 times or more.
9. $-Q/\epsilon_0$ for S_1; 0 for S_2; $-2Q/\epsilon_0$ for S_3; 0 for S_4
11. (a) $+Q/2\epsilon_0$ (b) $-Q/2\epsilon_0$
13. -18.8 kN·m²/C
15. 0 if $R \le d$; $(2\lambda/\epsilon_0)\sqrt{R^2 - d^2}$ if $R > d$
17. (a) 3.20 MN·m²/C (b) 19.2 MN·m²/C (c) The answer to part (a) could change, but the answer to part (b) would stay the same.
19. 2.33×10^{21} N/C
21. 508 kN/C up
23. -2.48 μC/m²
25. 5.94×10^5 m/s
27. $\vec{\mathbf{E}} = \rho r/2\epsilon_0$ away from the axis
29. (a) 0 (b) 7.19 MN/C away from the center
31. (a) 51.4 kN/C outward (b) 646 N·m²/C
33. (a) 0 (b) 5 400 N/C outward (c) 540 N/C outward
35. (a) $+708$ nC/m² and -708 nC/m² (b) $+177$ nC and -177 nC
37. 2.00 N
39. (a) $-\lambda, +3\lambda$ (b) $3\lambda/2\pi\epsilon_0 r$ radially outward·
41. (a) 80.0 nC/m² on each face (b) $9.04\hat{\mathbf{k}}$ kN/C (c) $-9.04\hat{\mathbf{k}}$ kN/C
43. (b) $Q/2\epsilon_0$ (c) Q/ϵ_0
45. (a) The charge on the exterior surface is -55.7 nC distributed uniformly. (b) The charge on the interior surface is $+55.7$ nC. It might have any distribution. (c) The charge within the shell is -55.7 nC. It might have any distribution.
47. (a) $\rho r/3\epsilon_0$, $Q/4\pi\epsilon_0 r^2$, 0, $Q/4\pi\epsilon_0 r^2$, all radially outward (b) $-Q/4\pi b^2$ and $+Q/4\pi c^2$
49. $\theta = \tan^{-1}[qQ/(2\pi\epsilon_0 dmv^2)]$
51. (a) σ/ϵ_0 away from both plates (b) 0 (c) σ/ϵ_0 away from both plates
53. $\sigma/2\epsilon_0$ radially outward
57. $\vec{\mathbf{E}} = a/2\epsilon_0$ radially outward
61. (b) $\vec{\mathbf{g}} = GM_E r/R_E^3$ radially inward
63. (a) -4.00 nC (b) $+9.56$ nC (c) $+4.00$ nC and $+5.56$ nC
65. (a) If the volume charge density is nonzero, the field cannot be uniform in magnitude. (b) The field must be uniform in magnitude along any line in the direction of the field. The field magnitude can vary between points in a plane perpendicular to the field lines.

CHAPTER 25

1. (a) 152 km/s (b) 6.49 Mm/s
3. 1.67 MN/C
5. 38.9 V; the origin
7. (a) $2QE/k$ (b) QE/k (c) $2\pi\sqrt{m/k}$ (d) $2(QE - \mu_k mg)/k$
9. (a) 0.400 m/s (b) It is the same. Each bit of the rod feels a force of the same size as before.
11. (a) 1.44×10^{-7} V (b) -7.19×10^{-8} V (c) -1.44×10^{-7} V, $+7.19 \times 10^{-8}$ V
13. (a) 6.00 m (b) -2.00 μC
15. -11.0 MV
17. 8.95 J
21. (a) no point at a finite distance from the particles (b) $2k_e q/a$
23. (a) 10.8 m/s and 1.55 m/s (b) Greater. The conducting spheres will polarize each other, with most of the positive charge of one and of the negative charge of the other on their inside faces. Immediately before they collide, their centers of charge will be closer than their geometric centers, so they will have less electric potential energy and more kinetic energy.
25. $5k_e q^2/9d$
27. $\left[(1 + \sqrt{\tfrac{1}{8}})\dfrac{k_e q^2}{mL}\right]^{1/2}$
29. (a) 10.0 V, -11.0 V, -32.0 V (b) 7.00 N/C in the $+x$ direction
31. $\vec{\mathbf{E}} = (-5 + 6xy)\hat{\mathbf{i}} + (3x^2 - 2z^2)\hat{\mathbf{j}} - 4yz\hat{\mathbf{k}}$; 7.07 N/C
33. $E_y = \dfrac{k_e Q}{y\sqrt{\ell^2 + y^2}}$
35. (a) C/m² (b) $k_e\alpha[L - d\ln(1 + L/d)]$
37. -1.51 MV
39. (a) 0, 1.67 MV (b) 5.84 MN/C away, 1.17 MV (c) 11.9 MN/C away, 1.67 MV
41. (a) 248 nC/m² (b) 496 nC/m²
43. (a) 450 kV (b) 7.51 μC
45. (a) 1.42 mm (b) 9.20 kV/m
47. 253 MeV
49. (a) -27.2 eV (b) -6.80 eV (c) 0
51. (a) Yes. The inverse proportionality of potential to radius is sufficient to show that $200R = 150(R + 10$ cm$)$, so $R = 30.0$ cm. Then $Q = 6.67$ nC. (b) Almost but not quite. Two possibilities exist: $R = 29.1$ cm with $Q = 6.79$ nC and $R = 3.44$ cm with $Q = 804$ pC.
53. 4.00 nC at $(-1.00$ m, 0$)$ and -5.01 nC at $(0, 2.00$ m$)$
55. $k_e Q^2/2R$
57. $V_2 - V_1 = (-\lambda/2\pi\epsilon_0)\ln(r_2/r_1)$
61. (b) $E_r = 2k_e p\cos\theta/r^3$; $E_\theta = k_e p\sin\theta/r^3$; yes; no (c) $V = k_e py(x^2 + y^2)^{-3/2}$; $\vec{\mathbf{E}} = 3k_e pxy(x^2 + y^2)^{-5/2}\hat{\mathbf{i}} + k_e p(2y^2 - x^2)(x^2 + y^2)^{-5/2}\hat{\mathbf{j}}$
63. $V = \pi k_e C\left[R\sqrt{x^2 + R^2} + x^2\ln\left(\dfrac{x}{R + \sqrt{x^2 + R^2}}\right)\right]$
65. (a) 488 V (b) 78.1 aJ (c) 306 km/s (d) 390 Gm/s² toward the negative plate (e) 651 aN toward the negative plate (f) 4.07 kN/C
67. Outside the sphere, $E_x = 3E_0 a^3 xz(x^2 + y^2 + z^2)^{-5/2}$, $E_y = 3E_0 a^3 yz(x^2 + y^2 + z^2)^{-5/2}$, and $E_z = E_0 + E_0 a^3(2z^2 - x^2 - y^2)(x^2 + y^2 + z^2)^{-5/2}$. Inside the sphere, $E_x = E_y = E_z = 0$.

CHAPTER 26

1. (a) 48.0 μC   (b) 6.00 μC
3. (a) 1.33 μC/m^2 (b) 13.3 pF
5. (a) 11.1 kV/m toward the negative plate   (b) 98.3 nC/m^2
   (c) 3.74 pF   (d) 74.7 pC
7. 4.42 μm
9. (a) 2.68 nF   (b) 3.02 kV
11. (a) 15.6 pF   (b) 256 kV
13. (a) 3.53 μF   (b) 6.35 V and 2.65 V   (c) 31.8 μC on each
15. 6.00 pF and 3.00 pF
17. (a) 5.96 μF   (b) 89.5 μC on 20 μF, 63.2 μC on 6 μF, 26.3 μC on 15 μF and on 3 μF
19. 120 μC; 80.0 μC and 40.0 μC
21. ten
23. 6.04 μF
25. 12.9 μF
27. (a) 216 μJ   (b) 54.0 μJ
31. (a) 1.50 μC   (b) 1.83 kV
35. 9.79 kg
37. (a) 81.3 pF   (b) 2.40 kV
39. 1.04 m
41. 22.5 V
43. (b) -8.78×10^6 N/C·m; $-5.53 \times 10^{-2}\hat{\mathbf{i}}$ N
45. 19.0 kV
47. (a) 11.2 pF   (b) 134 pC   (c) 16.7 pF   (d) 66.9 pC
49. (a) 40.0 μJ   (b) 500 V
51. 0.188 m^2
55. Gasoline has 194 times the specific energy content of the battery and 727 000 times that of the capacitor.
57. (a) $Q_0^2 d(\ell - x)/(2\ell^3 \epsilon_0)$ (b) $Q_0^2 d/(2\ell^3 \epsilon_0)$ to the right   (c) $Q_0^2/(2\ell^4 \epsilon_0)$ (d) $Q_0^2/(2\ell^4 \epsilon_0)$; they are precisely the same.
59. 4.29 μF
61. (a) The additional energy comes from work done by the electric field in the wires as it forces more charge onto the already-charged plates.   (b) The charge increases according to $Q/Q_0 = \kappa$.
63. 750 μC on C_1 and 250 μC on C_2
65. $\frac{4}{3}C$

CHAPTER 27

1. 7.50×10^{15} electrons
3. (a) $0.632 I_0 \tau$ (b) $0.999\,95 I_0 \tau$ (c) $I_0 \tau$
5. (a) 17.0 A   (b) 85.0 kA/m^2
7. (a) 2.55 A/m^2 (b) 5.31×10^{10} m^{-3} (c) 1.20×10^{10} s
9. (a) 221 nm   (b) No. The deuterons are so far apart that one does not produce a significant potential at the location of the next.
11. 6.43 A
13. (a) 1.82 m   (b) 280 μm
15. $6.00 \times 10^{-15}/\Omega \cdot$m
17. 0.180 V/m
19. (a) 31.5 n$\Omega \cdot$m   (b) 6.35 MA/m^2 (c) 49.9 mA
   (d) 659 μm/s   (e) 0.400 V
21. 0.125
23. 5.00 A, 24.0 Ω
25. 5.49 Ω
27. 36.1%
29. (a) 3.17 m   (b) 340 W
31. (a) 0.660 kWh   (b) $0.039 6
33. $0.232
35. $0.269/day

37. (a) 184 W   (b) 461°C
39. ~ $1
41. Any diameter d and length ℓ related by $d^2 = (4.77 \times 10^{-8}$ m$)\ell$, such as length 0.900 m and diameter 0.207 mm. Yes.
45. Experimental resistivity $= 1.47\ \mu\Omega \cdot$m $\pm 4\%$, in agreement with 1.50 $\mu\Omega \cdot$m
47. (a) 8.00 V/m in the x direction   (b) 0.637 Ω (c) 6.28 A
   (d) 200 MA/m^2 in the x direction
49. (a) 667 A   (b) 50.0 km
51.

Material	$\alpha' = \alpha/(1 - 20\alpha)$
Silver	$4.1 \times 10^{-3}/$°C
Copper	$4.2 \times 10^{-3}/$°C
Gold	$3.6 \times 10^{-3}/$°C
Aluminum	$4.2 \times 10^{-3}/$°C
Tungsten	$4.9 \times 10^{-3}/$°C
Iron	$5.6 \times 10^{-3}/$°C
Platinum	$4.25 \times 10^{-3}/$°C
Lead	$4.2 \times 10^{-3}/$°C
Nichrome	$0.4 \times 10^{-3}/$°C
Carbon	$-0.5 \times 10^{-3}/$°C
Germanium	$-24 \times 10^{-3}/$°C
Silicon	$-30 \times 10^{-3}/$°C

53. It is exact. The resistance can be written $R = \rho L^2/V$ and the stretched length as $L = L_i(1 + \delta)$. Then the result follows directly.
55. (b) Charge is conducted by current in the direction of decreasing potential. Energy is conducted by heat in the direction of decreasing temperature.
59. Coat the surfaces of entry and exit with a material of much higher conductivity than the bulk material of the object. The electric potential will be essentially uniform over each of these electrodes. Current will be distributed over the whole area where each electrode is in contact with the resistive object.
61. (a) $\dfrac{\epsilon_0 \ell}{2d}(\ell + 2x + \kappa\ell - 2\kappa x)$
   (b) $\dfrac{\epsilon_0 \ell v\, \Delta V(\kappa - 1)}{d}$ clockwise
63. 2.71 MΩ
65. 2 020°C

CHAPTER 28

1. (a) 6.73 Ω (b) 1.97 Ω
3. (a) 12.4 V   (b) 9.65 V
5. (a) 17.1 Ω (b) 1.99 A for 4 Ω and 9 Ω, 1.17 A for 7 Ω, 0.818 A for 10 Ω
7. (a) 227 mA   (b) 5.68 V
9. (a) 75.0 V   (b) 25.0 W, 6.25 W, and 6.25 W; 37.5 W
11. $R_1 = 1.00$ kΩ, $R_2 = 2.00$ kΩ, $R_3 = 3.00$ kΩ
13. It decreases. Closing the switch opens a new path with resistance of only 20 Ω. $R = 14.0\ \Omega$
15. 14.2 W to 2 Ω, 28.4 W to 4 Ω, 1.33 W to 3 Ω, 4.00 W to 1 Ω
17. 846 mA down in the 8-Ω resistor; 462 mA down in the middle branch; 1.31 A up in the right-hand branch
19. (a) -222 J and 1.88 kJ   (b) 687 J, 128 J, 25.6 J, 616 J, 205 J   (c) 1.66 kJ of chemical energy is transformed into internal energy.

21. 0.395 A and 1.50 V

23. 1.00 A up in 200 Ω, 4.00 A up in 70 Ω, 3.00 A up in 80 Ω, 8.00 A down in 20 Ω, 200 V

25. (a) 909 mA   (b) -1.82 V $= V_b - V_a$

27. (a) 5.00 s   (b) 150 μC   (c) 4.06 μA

29. (a) -61.6 mA   (b) 0.235 μC   (c) 1.96 A

31. (a) 6.00 V   (b) 8.29 μs

33. 0.302 Ω

35. 16.6 kΩ

37. (a) 12.5 A, 6.25 A, 8.33 A   (b) No. Together they would require 27.1 A.

39. (a) 1.02 A down   (b) 0.364 A down
(c) 1.38 A up   (d) 0   (e) 66.0 μC

41. 2.22 h

43. a is 4.00 V higher

45. 87.3 %

47. 6.00 Ω, 3.00 Ω

49. (a) $I_1 = \dfrac{IR_2}{R_1 + R_2}$, $I_2 = \dfrac{IR_1}{R_1 + R_2}$

51. (a) $R \le 1\,050$ Ω   (b) $R \ge 10.0$ Ω

53. (a) 9.93 μC   (b) 33.7 nA   (c) 334 nW   (d) 337 nW

55. (a) 40.0 W   (b) 80.0 V, 40.0 V, 40.0 V

57. (a) 9.30 V, 2.51 Ω   (b) 186 V and 3.70 A   (c) 1.09 A
(d) 143 W   (e) 0.162 Ω   (f) 3.00 mW   (g) 2.21 W
(h) The power output of the emf depends on the resistance connected to it. A question about "the rest of the power" is not meaningful when it compares circuits with different currents. The net emf produces more current in the circuit where the copper wire is used. The net emf delivers more power when the copper wire is used, 687 W rather than 203 W without the wire. Nearly all this power results in extra internal energy in the internal resistance of the batteries, which rapidly rise to a high temperature. The circuit with the copper wire is unsafe because the batteries overheat. The circuit without the copper wire is unsafe because it delivers an electric shock to the experimenter.

61. (a) 0 in 3 kΩ and 333 μA in 12 kΩ and 15 kΩ
(b) 50.0 μC   (c) $(278 \text{ μA})e^{-t/180 \text{ ms}}$ (d) 290 ms

63. (a) $R_x = R_2 - R_1/4$ (b) $R_x = 2.75$ Ω. The station is inadequately grounded.

65. (a) $2\Delta t/3$ (b) $3\Delta t$

CHAPTER 29

1. (a) up   (b) toward you, out of the plane of the paper
(c) no deflection   (d) into the plane of the paper

3. $(-20.9\hat{\mathbf{j}})$ mT

5. 48.9° or 131°

7. 2.34 aN

9. (a) 49.6 aN south   (b) 1.29 km

11. $r_\alpha = r_d = \sqrt{2}r_p$

13. (a) 5.00 cm   (b) 8.78×10^6 m/s

15. 7.88 pT

17. 244 kV/m

19. 0.278 m

21. (a) 4.31×10^7 rad/s   (b) 51.7 Mm/s

23. 70.1 mT

25. 0.245 T east

27. (a) 4.73 N   (b) 5.46 N   (c) 4.73 N

29. 1.07 m/s

31. $2\pi rIB \sin\theta$ up

33. 2.98 μN west

35. 9.98 N·m clockwise as seen looking down from above

37. (a) Minimum: pointing north at 48.0° below the horizontal; maximum: pointing south at 48.0° above the horizontal. (b) 1.07 μJ

39. The magnetic moment cannot go to infinity. Its maximum value is 5.37 mA·m² for a single-turn circle. Smaller by 21% and by 40% are the magnetic moments for the single-turn square and triangle. Circular coils with several turns have magnetic moments inversely proportional to the number of turns, approaching zero as the number of turns goes to infinity.

41. 43.1 μT

43. (a) The electric current experiences a magnetic force.
(c) no, no, no

45. 12.5 km. It will not hit the Earth, but it will perform a hairpin turn and go back parallel to its original direction.

47. (a) -8.00×10^{-21} kg·m/s   (b) 8.90°

49. (a) $(3.52\hat{\mathbf{i}} - 1.60\hat{\mathbf{j}})$ aN   (b) 24.4°

51. 128 mT north at an angle of 78.7° below the horizontal

53. 0.588 T

55. 0.713 A counterclockwise as seen from above

57. 2.75 Mrad/s

59. 3.70×10^{-24} N·m

61. (a) 1.33 m/s   (b) Positive ions moving toward you in magnetic field to the right feel upward magnetic force and migrate upward in the blood vessel. Negative ions moving toward you feel downward magnetic force and accumulate at the bottom of this section of vessel. Therefore, both species can participate in the generation of the emf.

63. (a) $v = qBh/m$. If its speed is slightly less than the critical value, the particle moves in a semicircle of radius h and leaves the field with velocity $-v\hat{\mathbf{j}}$. If its speed is incrementally greater, the particle moves in a quarter circle of the same radius and moves along the boundary outside the field with velocity $v\hat{\mathbf{i}}$. (b) The particle moves in a smaller semicircle of radius mv/qB, attaining final velocity $-v\hat{\mathbf{j}}$. (c) The particle moves in a circular arc of radius $r = mv/qB$, leaving the field with velocity $v\sin\theta\hat{\mathbf{i}} + v\cos\theta\hat{\mathbf{j}}$, where $\theta = \sin^{-1}(h/r)$.

65. (a) For small angular displacements, the torque on the dipole is equal to a negative constant times the displacement.
(b) $f = \dfrac{1}{2\pi}\sqrt{\dfrac{\mu B}{I}}$
(c) The equilibrium orientation of the needle shows the direction of the field. In a stronger field, the frequency is higher. The frequency is easy to measure precisely over a wide range of values. 2.04 mT.

CHAPTER 30

1. 12.5 T

3. (a) 28.3 μT into the paper   (b) 24.7 μT into the paper

5. $\dfrac{\mu_0 I}{4\pi x}$ into the paper

7. (a) $2I_1$ out of the page   (b) $6I_1$ into the page

9. (a) along the line $(y = -0.420$ m, $z = 0)$
(b) $(-34.7\hat{\mathbf{j}})$ mN   (c) $(17.3\hat{\mathbf{j}})$ kN/C

11. at A, 53.3 μT toward the bottom of the page; at B, 20.0 μT toward the bottom of the page; at C, zero.

13. (a) $4.5\,\dfrac{\mu_0 I}{\pi L}$

(b) Stronger. Each of the two sides meeting at the nearby vertex contributes more than twice as much to the net field at the new point.

15. $(-13.0\hat{\mathbf{j}})\,\mu\text{T}$

17. $(-27.0\hat{\mathbf{i}})\,\mu\text{N}$

19. parallel to the wires and 0.167 m below the upper wire

21. (a) opposite directions (b) 67.8 A (c) Smaller. A smaller gravitational force would be pulling down on the wires, therefore tending to reduce the angle.

23. 20.0 μT toward the bottom of the page

25. at a, 200 μT toward the top of the page; at b, 133 μT toward the bottom of the page

27. (a) 6.34 mN/m inward (b) Greater. The magnetic field increases toward the outside of the bundle, where more net current lies inside a particular radius. The larger field exerts a stronger force on the strand we choose to monitor.

29. (a) 0

(b) $\dfrac{\mu_0 I}{2\pi R}$ tangent to the wall in a counterclockwise sense

(c) $\dfrac{\mu_0 I^2}{(2\pi R)^2}$ inward

31. (a) $\mu_0 b r_1^2/3$ (b) $\mu_0 b R^3/3 r_2$

35. 31.8 mA

37. 226 μN away from the center of the loop, 0

39. (a) 3.13 mWb (b) 0

41. (a) 7.40 μWb (b) 2.27 μWb

43. 2.02

45. (a) 8.63×10^{45} electrons (b) 4.01×10^{20} kg

47. $\dfrac{\mu_0 I}{2\pi w} \ln\left(1 + \dfrac{w}{b}\right)\hat{\mathbf{k}}$

49. $(-12.0\hat{\mathbf{k}})$ mN

51. 143 pT

57. (a) 2.46 N upward (b) The magnetic field at the center of the loop or on its axis is much weaker than the magnetic field immediately outside the wire. The wire has negligible curvature on the scale of 1 mm, so we model the lower loop as a long, straight wire to find the field it creates at the location of the upper wire. (c) 107 m/s^2 upward

59. (a) 274 μT (b) $(-274\hat{\mathbf{j}})\,\mu\text{T}$ (c) $(1.15\hat{\mathbf{i}})$ mN
(d) $(0.384\hat{\mathbf{i}})$ m/s^2 (e) acceleration is constant
(f) $(0.999\hat{\mathbf{i}})$ m/s

61. $\dfrac{\mu_0 I_1 I_2 L}{\pi R}$ to the right

65. $\frac{1}{3}\rho\mu_0\omega R^2$

67. (a) $\dfrac{\mu_0 I(2r^2 - a^2)}{\pi r(4r^2 - a^2)}$ to the left

(b) $\dfrac{\mu_0 I(2r^2 + a^2)}{\pi r(4r^2 + a^2)}$ toward the top of the page

CHAPTER 31

1. (a) 101 μV tending to produce clockwise current as seen from above (b) It is twice as large in magnitude and in the opposite sense.

3. 9.82 mV

5. (b) 3.79 mV (c) 28.0 mV

7. 160 A

9. (a) 1.60 A counterclockwise (b) 20.1 μT (c) left

11. $-(14.2 \text{ mV})\cos(120t)$

13. 283 μA upward

15. $(68.2 \text{ mV})e^{-1.6t}$, tending to produce counterclockwise current

17. 272 m

19. 13.3 mA counterclockwise in the lower loop and clockwise in the upper loop

21. (a) 1.18 mV. The wingtip on the pilot's left is positive. (b) no change (c) No. If we try to connect the wings into a circuit with the lightbulb, we run an extra insulated wire along the wing. In a uniform field, the total emf generated in the one-turn coil is zero.

23. (a) 3.00 N to the right (b) 6.00 W

25. 24.1 V with the outer contact positive

27. 2.83 mV

29. (a) $F = N^2 B^2 w^2 v/R$ to the left (b) 0
(c) $F = N^2 B^2 w^2 v/R$ to the left

31. 145 μA upward in the picture

33. 1.80 mN/C upward and to the left, perpendicular to r_1

35. (a) 7.54 kV (b) The plane of the loop is parallel to $\vec{\mathbf{B}}$.

37. $(28.6 \text{ mV})\sin(4\pi t)$

39. (a) 110 V (b) 8.53 W (c) 1.22 kW

41. Both are correct. The current in the magnet creates an upward magnetic field , so the N and S poles on the solenoid core are shown correctly. On the rail in front of the brake, the upward magnetic flux increases as the coil approaches, so a current is induced here to create downward magnetic field . This current is clockwise, so the S pole on the rail is shown correctly. On the rail behind the brake, the upward magnetic flux is decreasing. The induced current in the rail will produce upward magnetic field by being counterclockwise as the picture correctly shows.

43. (b) Larger R makes current smaller, so the loop must travel faster to maintain equality of magnetic force and weight. (c) The magnetic force is proportional to the product of field and current, while the current is itself proportional to field. If B becomes two times smaller, the speed must become four times larger to compensate.

45. $-(7.22 \text{ mV})\cos(2\pi\, 523t/\text{s})$

47.

(a) Doubling N doubles amplitude. (b) Doubling ω doubles the amplitude and halves the period. (c) Doubling ω and halving N leaves the amplitude the same and cuts the period in half.

49. (a) 3.50 A up in 2 Ω, and 1.40 A up in 5 Ω (b) 34.3 W
(c) 4.29 N

51. $\sim 10^{-4}$ V, by reversing a 20-turn coil of diameter 3 cm in 0.1 s in a field of 10^{-3} T

53. 1.20 μC

55. (a) 0.900 A from *b* toward *a* (b) 0.108 N (c) *b* (d) No. Instead of decreasing downward magnetic flux to induce clockwise current, the new loop will see increasing downward flux to cause counterclockwise current, but the current in the resistor is still from *b* to *a*.

57. (a) $C\pi a^2 K$ (b) the upper plate (c) The changing magnetic field within the loop induces an electric field around the circumference, which pushes on charged particles in the wire.

59. (a) 36.0 V (b) 600 mWb/s (c) 35.9 V (d) 4.32 N·m

63. 6.00 A

67. $(-87.1 \text{ mV}) \cos(200\pi t + \phi)$

CHAPTER 32

1. 100 V

3. $-(18.8 \text{ V}) \cos(377t)$

5. −0.421 A/s

7. (a) 188 μT (b) 33.3 nT·m² (c) 0.375 mH (d) *B* and Φ_B are proportional to current; *L* is independent of current

9. $\mathcal{E}_0/k^2 L$

11. (a) 0.139 s (b) 0.461 s

13. (a) 2.00 ms (b) 0.176 A (c) 1.50 A (d) 3.22 ms

15. (a) 0.800 (b) 0

17. (a) 6.67 A/s (b) 0.332 A/s

19. (a) 1.00 kΩ (b) 3.00 ms

21. (a) 5.66 ms (b) 1.22 A (c) 58.1 ms

23. 2.44 μJ

25. 44.2 nJ/m³ for the $\vec{\mathbf{E}}$ field and 995 μJ/m³ for the $\vec{\mathbf{B}}$ field

27. (a) 66.0 W (b) 45.0 W (c) 21.0 W (d) At all instants after the connection is made, the battery power is equal to the sum of the power delivered to the resistor and the power delivered to the magnetic field. Immediately after $t = 0$, the resistor power is nearly zero and nearly all the battery power is going into the magnetic field. Long after the connection is made, the magnetic field is absorbing no more power and the battery power is going into the resistor.

29. $\dfrac{2\pi B_0^2 R^3}{\mu_0} = 2.70 \times 10^{18}$ J

31. 1.00 V

33. (a) 18.0 mH (b) 34.3 mH (c) −9.00 mV

35. $M = \dfrac{N_1 N_2 \pi \mu_0 R_1^2 R_2^2}{2(x^2 + R_1^2)^{3/2}}$

37. 400 mA

39. 281 mH

41. 608 pF

43. (a) 6.03 J (b) 0.529 J (c) 6.56 J

45. (a) 4.47 krad/s (b) 4.36 krad/s (c) 2.53%

47. (a) 0.693(2L/R) (b) 0.347(2L/R)

49. (a) −20.0 mV (b) $-(10.0 \text{ MV/s}^2)t^2$ (c) 63.2 μs

51. $(Q/2N)(3L/C)^{1/2}$

53. (a) Immediately after the circuit is connected, the potential difference across the resistor is zero and the emf across the coil is 24.0 V. (b) After several seconds, the potential difference across the resistor is 24.0 V and that across the coil is 0. (c) The two voltages are equal to each other, both being 12.0 V, only once, at 0.578 ms after the circuit is connected. (d) As the current decays, the potential difference across the resistor is always equal to the emf across the coil.

55.

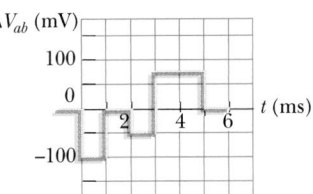

57. (b) 91.2 μH (c) 90.9 μH is only 0.3% smaller

61. (a) 72.0 V; *b*

(b)

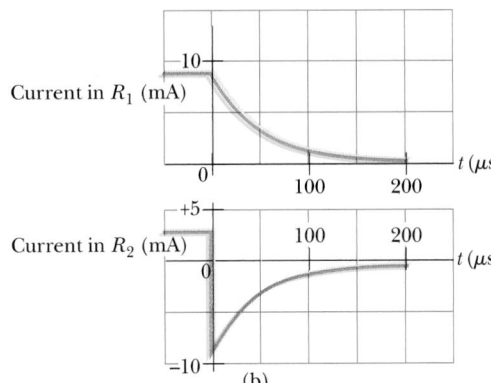

(c) 75.2 μs

63. 300 Ω

65. (a) 62.5 GJ (b) 2 000 N

67. (a) 2.93 mT up (b) 3.42 Pa (c) The supercurrents must be clockwise to produce a downward magnetic field that cancels the upward field of the current in the windings. (d) The field of the windings is upward and radially outward around the top of the solenoid. It exerts a force radially inward and upward on each bit of the clockwise supercurrent. The total force on the supercurrents in the bar is upward. (e) 1.30 mN

CHAPTER 33

1. $\Delta v(t) = (283 \text{ V}) \sin(628t)$

3. 2.95 A, 70.7 V

5. 14.6 Hz

7. (a) 42.4 mH (b) 942 rad/s

9. 5.60 A

11. 0.450 Wb

13. (a) 141 mA (b) 235 mA

15. 100 mA

17. (a) 194 V (b) current leads by 49.9°

19. (a) 78.5 Ω (b) 1.59 kΩ (c) 1.52 kΩ (d) 138 mA (e) −84.3°

21. (a) 17.4° (b) The voltage leads the current.

23. 1.88 V

25.

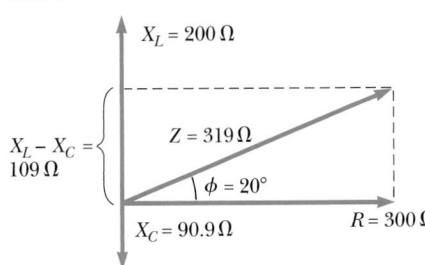

27. 8.00 W

29. (a) 16.0 Ω (b) −12.0 Ω

31. (a) 39.5 V·m/ΔV (b) The diameter is inversely proportional to the potential difference. (c) 26.3 mm (d) 13.2 kV

33. $11(\Delta V_{\text{rms}})^2/14R$

35. 1.82 pF

37. 242 mJ

39. 0.591 and 0.987; the circuit in Problem 21

41. 687 V

43. (a) 29.0 kW (b) 5.80×10^{-3} (c) If the generator were limited to 4 500 V, no more than 17.5 kW could be delivered to the load, never 5 000 kW.

45. (b) 0; 1 (c) $f_h = (10.88RC)^{-1}$

47. (a) 613 μF (b) 0.756

49. (a) 580 μH and 54.6 μF (b) 1 (c) 894 Hz (d) Δv_{out} leads Δv_{in} by 60.0° at 200 Hz. Δv_{out} and Δv_{in} are in phase at 894 Hz. Δv_{out} lags Δv_{in} by 60.0° at 4 000 Hz. (e) 1.56 W, 6.25 W, 1.56 W (f) 0.408

51. (a) X_C could be 53.8 Ω or it could be 1.35 kΩ. (b) X_C must be 53.8 Ω. (c) X_C must be 1.43 kΩ.

53. 56.7 W

55. Tension T and separation d must be related by $T = (274 \text{ N/m}^2)d^2$. One possibility is $T = 10.9$ N and $d = 0.200$ m.

57. (a) 225 mA (b) 450 mA

59. (a) 1.25 A (b) The current lags the voltage by 46.7°.

61. (a) 200 mA; voltage leads by 36.8° (b) 40.0 V; $\phi = 0$° (c) 20.0 V; $\phi = -90.0$° (d) 50.0 V; $\phi = +90.0$°

63. (b) 31.6

67. (a)

f (Hz)	X_L (Ω)	X_C (Ω)	Z (Ω)
300	283	12 600	12 300
600	565	6 280	5 720
800	754	4 710	3 960
1 000	942	3 770	2 830
1 500	1 410	2 510	1 100
2 000	1 880	1 880	40.0
3 000	2 830	1 260	1 570
4 000	3 770	942	2 830
6 000	5 650	628	5 020
10 000	9 420	377	9 040

(b) Impedance (kΩ)

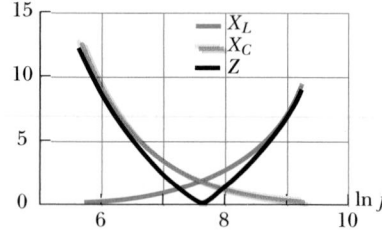

69. (a) and (b) 19.7 cm at 35.0°. The answers are identical. (c) 9.36 cm at 169°

CHAPTER 34

1. (a) 11.3 GV$\cdot$m/s (b) 0.100 A

3. 1.85 aT up

5. $(-2.87\hat{\mathbf{j}} + 5.75\hat{\mathbf{k}})$ Gm/s^2

7. (a) the year 2.69×10^3 (b) 499 s (c) 2.56 s (d) 0.133 s (e) 33.3 μs

9. (a) 6.00 MHz (b) $(-73.3\hat{\mathbf{k}})$ nT (c) $\vec{\mathbf{B}} = [(-73.3\hat{\mathbf{k}})\text{ nT}]\cos(0.126x - 3.77 \times 10^7 t)$

11. (a) 0.333 μT (b) 0.628 μm (c) 477 THz

13. 75.0 MHz

15. 3.33 μJ/m^3

17. 307 μW/m^2

19. 3.33×10^3 m^2

21. (a) 332 kW/m^2 radially inward (b) 1.88 kV/m and 222 μT

23. (a) $\vec{\mathbf{E}} \cdot \vec{\mathbf{B}} = 0$ (b) $(11.5\hat{\mathbf{i}} - 28.6\hat{\mathbf{j}})$ W/m^2

25. (a) 2.33 mT (b) 650 MW/m^2 (c) 510 W

27. (a) 88.8 nW/m^2 (b) 11.3 MW

29. 83.3 nPa

31. (a) 1.90 kN/C (b) 50.0 pJ (c) 1.67×10^{-19} kg $\cdot$ m/s

33. (a) 590 W/m^2 (b) 2.10×10^{16} W (c) 70.1 MN (d) The gravitational force is $\sim 10^{13}$ times stronger and in the opposite direction. (e) On the Earth, the Sun's gravitational force is also $\sim 10^{13}$ times stronger than the light-pressure force and in the opposite direction.

35. (a) 134 m (b) 46.9 m

37. (a) away along the perpendicular bisector of the line segment joining the antennas (b) along the extensions of the line segment joining the antennas

39. (a) $\vec{\mathbf{E}} = \frac{1}{2}\mu_0 c J_{\text{max}}[\cos(kx - \omega t)]\hat{\mathbf{j}}$
(b) $\vec{\mathbf{S}} = \frac{1}{4}\mu_0 c J_{\text{max}}^2[\cos^2(kx - \omega t)]\hat{\mathbf{i}}$
(c) $I = \dfrac{\mu_0 c J_{\text{max}}^2}{8}$ (d) 3.48 A/m

41. (a) 6.00 pm (b) 7.50 cm

43. (a) 4.17 m to 4.55 m (b) 3.41 m to 3.66 m (c) 1.61 m to 1.67 m

45. 1.00 Mm = 621 mi; not very practical

47. (a) 3.85×10^{26} W (b) 1.02 kV/m and 3.39 μT

49. (a)

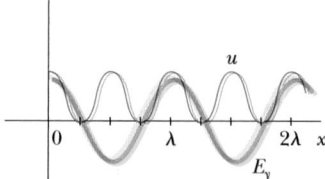

(b), (c) $u_E = u_B = \frac{1}{2}\epsilon_0 E_{\text{max}}^2 \cos^2(kx)$
(d) $u = \epsilon_0 E_{\text{max}}^2 \cos^2(kx)$ (e) $E_\lambda = \frac{1}{2}A\lambda\epsilon_0 E_{\text{max}}^2$

(f) $I = \frac{1}{2}c\epsilon_0 E_{\text{max}}^2 = \frac{1}{2}\sqrt{\dfrac{\epsilon_0}{\mu_0}} E_{\text{max}}^2$. This result agrees with

$I = \dfrac{E_{\text{max}}^2}{2\mu_0 c}$ in Equation 34.24.

51. (a) 6.67×10^{-16} T (b) 5.31×10^{-17} W/m^2 (c) 1.67×10^{-14} W (d) 5.56×10^{-23} N

53. 95.1 mV/m

55. (a) $B_{\text{max}} = 583$ nT, $k = 419$ rad/m, $\omega = 126$ Grad/s; $\vec{\mathbf{B}}$ vibrates in xz plane (b) $\vec{\mathbf{S}}_{\text{avg}} = (40.6\hat{\mathbf{i}})$ W/m^2 (c) 271 nPa (d) $(406\hat{\mathbf{i}})$ nm/s^2

57. (a) 22.6 h (b) 30.6 s

59. (a) 8.32×10^7 W/m^2 (b) 1.05 kW

61. (b) 17.6 Tm/s^2, 1.75×10^{-27} W (c) 1.80×10^{-24} W

63. (a) $2\pi^2 r^2 f B_{\text{max}} \cos\theta$, where θ is the angle between the magnetic field and the normal to the loop (b) The loop